i486™ PROCESSOR PROGRAMMER'S REFERENCE MANUAL

1990

Additional copies of this manual or other Intel literature may be obtained from:

Intel Corporation
Literature Sales
P.O. Box 7641
Mt. Prospect, IL 60056-7641

CUSTOMER SUPPORT

INTEL'S COMPLETE SUPPORT SOLUTION WORLDWIDE

Customer Support is Intel's complete support service that provides Intel customers with hardware support, software support, customer training, consulting services and network management services. For detailed information contact your local sales offices.

After a customer purchases any system hardware or software product, service and support become major factors in determining whether that product will continue to meet a customer's expectations. Such support requires an international support organization and a breadth of programs to meet a variety of customer needs. As you might expect, Intel's customer support is quite extensive. It can start with assistance during your development effort to network management. 100 Intel sales and service offices are located worldwide — in the U.S., Canada, Europe and the Far East. So wherever you're using Intel technology, our professional staff is within close reach.

HARDWARE SUPPORT SERVICES

Intel's hardware maintenance service, starting with complete on-site installation will boost your productivity from the start and keep you running at maximum efficiency. Support for system or board level products can be tailored to match your needs, from complete on-site repair and maintenance support economical carry-in or mail-in factory service.

Intel can provide support service for not only Intel systems and emulators, but also support for equipment in your development lab or provide service on your product to your end-user/customer.

SOFTWARE SUPPORT SERVICES

Software products are supported by our Technical Information Phone Service (TIPS) that has a special toll free number to provide you with direct, ready information on known, documented problems and deficiencies, as well as work-arounds, patches and other solutions.

Intel's software support consists of two levels of contracts. Standard support includes TIPS (Technical Information Phone Service), updates and subscription service (product-specific troubleshooting guides and; *COMMENTS Magazine*). Basic support consists of updates and the subscription service. Contracts are sold in environments which represent product groupings (e.g., iRMX® environment).

CONSULTING SERVICES

Intel provides field system engineering consulting services for any phase of your development or application effort. You can use our system engineers in a variety of ways ranging from assistance in using a new product, developing an application, personalizing training and customizing an Intel product to providing technical and management consulting. Systems Engineers are well versed in technical areas such as microcommunications, real-time applications, embedded microcontrollers, and network services. You know your application needs; we know our products. Working together we can help you get a successful product to market in the least possible time.

CUSTOMER TRAINING

Intel offers a wide range of instructional programs covering various aspects of system design and implementation. In just three to ten days a limited number of individuals learn more in a single workshop than in weeks of self-study. For optimum convenience, workshops are scheduled regularly at Training Centers worldwide or we can take our workshops to you for on-site instruction. Covering a wide variety of topics, Intel's major course categories include: architecture and assembly language, programming and operating systems, BITBUS™ and LAN applications.

NETWORK MANAGEMENT SERVICES

Today's networking products are powerful and extremely flexible. The return they can provide on your investment via increased productivity and reduced costs can be very substantial.

Intel offers complete network support, from definition of your network's physical and functional design, to implementation, installation and maintenance. Whether installing your first network or adding to an existing one, Intel's Networking Specialists can optimize network performance for you.

TABLE OF CONTENTS

PART II – SYSTEM PROGRAMMING

CHAPTER 4
SYSTEM ARCHITECTURE

CHAPTER 5
MEMORY MANAGEMENT

CHAPTER 6
PROTECTION

PART IV – COMPATIBILITY

TABLE OF CONTENTS

APPENDICES

Figures

Figures

Figures

Tables

Tables

1 Introduction to the i486™ Processor

CHAPTER 1
INTRODUCTION TO THE i486™ PROCESSOR

The i486™ processor offers the highest performance for DOS, OS/2, Windows and UNIX System V/386 applications. It is 100% binary compatible with 386™ DX and SX microprocessors. One million transistors integrate cache memory, floating-point hardware and memory management on-chip while retaining binary compatibility with previous members of the 86 architectural family. Frequently-used instructions execute in one cycle, resulting in RISC performance levels. An eight-Kbyte unified code and data cache combined with an 80/106 Mbyte/sec burst bus at 25/33 MHz ensure high system throughput even with inexpensive DRAMs.

New features enhance multiprocessing systems. New instructions speed manipulation of memory-based semaphores. On-chip hardware ensures cache consistency and provides hooks for multi-level caching.

The built-in self-test extensively tests on-chip logic, cache memory and the on-chip paging translation cache. Debug features include breakpoint traps on code execution and data accesses.

Features of the i486 processor include:

- Full binary compatibility with 386 DX CPU, 386 SX CPU, 376™ embedded processor, 80286, 8086, and 8088 processors
- Execution unit designed to execute frequently-used instructions in one clock cycle
- 32-bit integer processor for performing arithmetic and logical operations
- Internal floating-point arithmetic unit for supporting the 32-, 64-, and 80-bit formats specified in IEEE standard 754 (object-code compatible with 387™ DX and 387 SX math coprocessors)
- Internal 8K-byte cache memory, which provides fast access to recently-used instructions and data
- Bus control signals for maintaining cache consistency in multiprocessor systems
- Segmentation, a form of memory management for creating independent, protected address spaces
- Paging, a form of memory management which provides access to data structures larger than the available memory space by keeping them partly in memory and partly on disk
- Restartable instructions that allow a program to be restarted following an exception (necessary for supporting demand-paged virtual memory)
- Pipelined instruction execution overlaps the interpretation of different instructions
- Debugging registers for hardware support of instruction and data breakpoints

The i486 processor is object-code compatible with three other 386 processors:

- 386 DX Processor (32-bit data bus)—A cost-effective form for high-end personal computers and mid-range workstations.

- 386 SX Processor (16-bit data bus) – The 386 processor adapted for mid-range personal computers, which are sensitive to the higher system cost of a 32-bit bus.
- 376 Embedded Processor (16-bit data bus) – A reduced form of the 386 processor optimized for embedded applications, such as process controllers. The 376 processor lacks the paging and 8086-compatibility features provided in the i486 processor. The 376 processor is available in a surface-mount plastic package, which provides the lowest cost and smallest form factor for any implementation of the 386 processor.

The operating mode of the i486 processor determines which instructions and architectural features are accessible. The i486 processor has three modes for running programs:

- Protected mode uses the native 32-bit instruction set of the processor. In this mode all instructions and architectural features are available.
- Real-address mode (also called "real mode") emulates the programming environment of the 8086 processor, with a few extensions (such as the ability to break out of this mode). Reset initialization places the processor into real mode.
- Virtual-8086 mode (also called "V86 mode") is another form of 8086 emulation mode. Unlike real-address mode, virtual-8086 mode is compatible with protection and memory-management. The processor can enter virtual-8086 mode from protected mode to run a program written for the 8086 processor, then leave virtual-8086 mode and re-enter protected mode to continue a program which uses the 32-bit instruction set.

1.1 ORGANIZATION OF THIS MANUAL

This book presents the architecture of the i486 processor in five parts:

- Part I – Application Programming
- Part II – System Programming
- Part III – Numeric Processing
- Part IV – Compatibility
- Part V – Instruction Set
- Appendices

These divisions are determined by the architecture and by the ways programmers use this book. The first three parts are explanatory, showing the purpose of architectural features, developing terminology and concepts, and describing instructions as they relate to specific purposes or to specific architectural features. The remaining parts are reference material for programmers developing software for the i486 processor.

The first four parts cover the operating modes and protection mechanism of the i486 processor. The distinction between application programming and system programming is related to the protection mechanism of the i486 processor. One purpose of protection is to prevent applications from interfering with the operating system. For this reason, certain registers and instructions are inaccessible to application programs. The features discussed in Part I and Part III are those which are accessible to applications; the features in Part II are available only to programs running with special privileges, or programs running on systems where the protection mechanism is not used.

The features available to application programs in protected mode and to all programs in virtual-8086 mode are the same. These features are described in Part I and Part III of this book. The additional features available to system programs in protected mode are described in Part II. Part IV describes real-address mode and virtual-8086 mode, as well as how to run a mix of 16-bit and 32-bit programs.

1.1.1 Part I—Application Programming

This part presents the features used by most application programmers. It does not include features used in numeric applications, which are discussed in Part III.

Chapter 2—Basic Programming Model: Introduces the models of memory organization. Defines the data types. Presents the register set used by applications. Introduces the stack. Explains string operations. Defines the parts of an instruction. Explains address calculations. Introduces interrupts and exceptions as they apply to application programming.

Chapter 3—Application Instruction Set: Surveys the instructions commonly used for application programming. Considers instructions in functionally related groups; for example, string instructions are considered in one section, while control-transfer instructions are considered in another. Explains the concepts behind the instructions. Details of individual instructions are deferred until Part IV, the instruction-set reference.

1.1.2 Part II—System Programming

This part presents the features used by operating systems, device drivers, debuggers, and other software which support application programs. Some additional information relevant to systems programming is presented in Part III.

Chapter 4—System Architecture: Describes the features of the i486 processor used by system programmers. Introduces the registers and data structures of the i486 processor which are not discussed in Part I or Part III. Introduces the system-oriented instructions in the context of the registers and data structures they support. References the chapters in which each register, data structure, and instruction is discussed in more detail.

Chapter 5—Memory Management: Presents details of the data structures, registers, and instructions which support segmentation. Explains how system designers can choose between an unsegmented ("flat") model of memory organization and a model with segmentation.

Chapter 6—Protection: Discusses protection as it applies to segments. Explains the implementation of privilege rules, stack switching, pointer validation, user and supervisor modes. Protection aspects of multitasking are deferred until the following chapter.

Chapter 7 – Multitasking: Explains how the hardware of the i486 processor supports multitasking with context-switching operations and intertask protection.

Chapter 8 – Input/Output: Describes the I/O features of the i486 processor, including I/O instructions, protection as it relates to I/O, and the I/O permission bit map.

Chapter 9 – Exceptions and Interrupts: Explains the basic interrupt mechanisms of the i486 processor. Shows how interrupts and exceptions relate to protection. Discusses all possible exceptions, listing causes and including information needed to handle and recover from each exception.

Chapter 10 – Initialization: Defines the condition of the processor after reset initialization. Explains how to set up registers, flags, and data structures. Shows how to test the on-chip cache and the translation lookaside buffer. Contains an example of an initialization program.

Chapter 11 – Debugging: Tells how to use the debugging registers of the i486 processor.

Chapter 12 – Caching: Explains the general concept of caching and the specific mechanisms used by the internal cache on the i486 processor.

Chapter 13 – Multiprocessing: Explains the instructions and flags which support multiple processors with shared memory.

1.1.3 Part III – Numeric Processing

This part explains the floating-point arithmetic features of the i486 processor. These features are an object-code compatible implementation of the features provided by the 387 DX or SX math coprocessor used with the 386 DX or SX processor.

Chapter 14 – Introduction to Numeric Applications: Gives an overview of the floating-point unit and reviews the concepts of numerical computation.

Chapter 15 – Architecture of the Numeric Unit: Presents the floating-point registers and data types available to both applications and systems programmers.

Chapter 16 – Special Computational Situations: Discusses the special values that can be represented in the real formats of the i486 processor – denormal numbers, zeros, infinities, NaNs (Not a Number) – as well as the numerical exceptions. This chapter should be read thoroughly by systems programmers, but can be skimmed by applications programmers. Many of these special situations may never arise in applications programs.

Chapter 17 – Floating-Point Instructions: Surveys the instructions commonly used for numeric processing. Details of individual instructions are deferred until Part V, the instruction-set reference.

Chapter 18 – Numeric Applications: Describes the i486 processor's floating-point arithmetic facilities. Gives short programming examples in both assembly language and high-level languages.

Chapter 19 – System-Level Considerations: Provides information of interest to systems software writers.

Chapter 20 – Numeric Programming Examples: Provides detailed examples of assembly-language numeric programming with the i486 processor, including conditional branching, conversion between floating-point values and their ASCII representations, and use of trigonometric functions.

1.1.4 Part IV – Compatibility

This part explains the features of the architecture which support programs written for earlier Intel processors. The native mode of execution is an upward-compatible superset of the environment of the 80286 and 386 DX processors. All three execution modes have support for 16-bit programming: 16-bit operations can be performed in protected mode using the operand-size prefix, programs written for the 8086 processor or the real mode of the 80286 processor can run in real mode on the 386 DX processor, and a virtual machine monitor can be used to emulate real mode using virtual-8086 mode, even while multitasking with 32-bit programs.

Chapter 21 – Executing 80286 and 386 DX Processor Programs: Explains the programming differences between the 80286 and i486 processors, and between the 386 DX and i486 processors.

Chapter 22 – Real-Address Mode: Explains the real mode of the i486 processor. In this mode, the i486 processor appears as a fast real-mode 80286 or 386 DX processor or a fast 8086 processor enhanced with additional instructions.

Chapter 23 – Virtual-8086 Mode: Describes how the i486 processor supports execution of one or more 8086, 8088, 80186 or 80188 programs in an i486 processor protected-mode environment.

Chapter 24 – Mixing 16-Bit and 32-Bit Code: Explains how the i486 processor can mix 16-bit and 32-bit modules within the same program or task. Any particular module can use both 16-bit and 32-bit operands and addresses.

Chapter 25 – Compatibility with 8087, 80287, and 387 DX Math Coprocessors: Compares the floating-point arithmetic of the i486 processor with the arithmetic of the numerics coprocessors used with earlier Intel processors.

1.1.5 Part V—Instruction Set

Parts I, II, and III present the general features of the instruction set as they relate to specific aspects of the architecture. Part V presents the instructions in alphabetical order, with the detail needed by assembly language programmers and programmers of debuggers, compilers, operating systems, etc. Instruction descriptions include an algorithmic description of operations, effect of flag settings, effect on flag settings, effect of operand- and address-size attributes, and exceptions which may be generated.

1.1.6 Appendices

The appendices present tables of encodings and other details in a format designed for quick reference by programmers.

1.2 RELATED LITERATURE

The following books contain additional material related to Intel processors:

Introduction to the 80386, Order Number 231252
80386 Processor Hardware Reference Manual, Order Number 231732
80386 Processor System Software Writer's Guide, Order Number 231499
80386 High-Performance 32-Bit CHMOS Microprocessor with Integrated Memory Management, Order Number 231630
376™ Embedded Processor Programmer's Reference Manual, Order Number 240314
386™ DX Processor Programmer's Reference Manual, Order Number 230985
386™ SX Processor Programmer's Reference Manual, Order Number 240331
80387 Programmer's Reference Manual, Order Number 231917
376™ High-Performance 32-Bit Embedded Processor, Order Number 240182
386™ SX Microprocessor, Order Number 240187
Microprocessor and Peripheral Handbook (vol. 1), Order Number 230843

The *i486™ Microprocessor Hardware Reference Manual* is the companion of this book for use by hardware designers. It contains information which may be useful to programmers, especially system programmers. Order Number 240552

The *i486™ Microprocessor Data Sheet* contains the latest information regarding device parameters (voltage levels, bus cycle timing, priority of simultaneous exceptions and interrupts, etc.). Order Number 240440

The *i486™ Microprocessor Product Brief Book* describes many related products commonly used with i486 CPU. Order Number 240459

1.3 NOTATIONAL CONVENTIONS

This manual uses special notation for data-structure formats, for symbolic representation of instructions, and for hexadecimal numbers. A review of this notation makes the manual easier to read.

1.3.1 Bit and Byte Order

In illustrations of data structures in memory, smaller addresses appear toward the bottom of the figure; addresses increase toward the top. Bit positions are numbered from right to left. The numerical value of a set bit is equal to two raised to the power of the bit position. The i486 processor is a "little endian" machine; this means the bytes of a word are numbered starting from the least significant byte. Figure 1-1 illustrates these conventions.

Numbers are usually expressed in decimal notation (base 10). When hexadecimal (base 16) numbers are used, they are indicated by an 'H' suffix.

1.3.2 Undefined Bits and Software Compatibility

In many register and memory layout descriptions, certain bits are marked as *reserved*. When bits are marked as undefined or reserved, it is essential for compatibility with future processors that software treat these bits as having a future, though unknown, effect. Software should follow these guidelines in dealing with reserved bits:

- Do not depend on the states of any reserved bits when testing the values of registers which contain such bits. Mask out the reserved bits before testing.
- Do not depend on the states of any reserved bits when storing to memory or to a register.
- Do not depend on the ability to retain information written into any reserved bits.
- When loading a register, always load the reserved bits with the values indicated in the documentation, if any, or reload them with values previously stored from the same register.

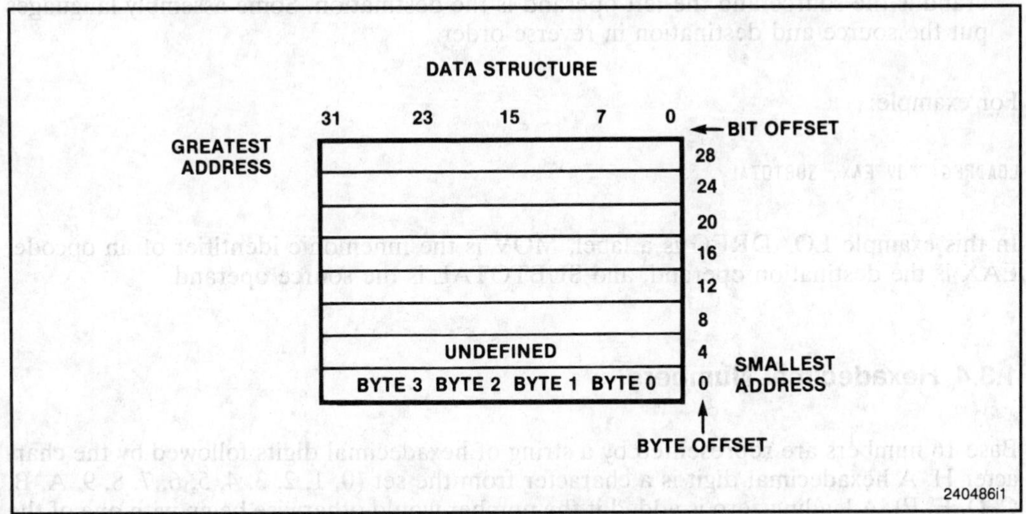

Figure 1-1. Bit and Byte Order

NOTE

Depending upon the values of reserved register bits will make software dependent upon the unspecified manner in which the i486 processor handles these bits. Depending upon reserved values risks incompatibility with future processors. ***AVOID ANY SOFTWARE DEPENDENCE UPON THE STATE OF RESERVED i486 PROCESSOR REGISTER BITS.***

1.3.3 Instruction Operands

When instructions are represented symbolically, a subset of the assembly language for the i486 processor is used. In this subset, an instruction has the following format:

label: mnemonic argument1, argument2, argument3

where:

- A *label* is an identifier which is followed by a colon.
- A *mnemonic* is a reserved name for a class of instruction opcodes which have the same function.
- The operands *argument1*, *argument2*, and *argument3* are optional. There may be from zero to three operands, depending on the opcode. When present, they take the form of either literals or identifiers for data items. Operand identifiers are either reserved names of registers or are assumed to be assigned to data items declared in another part of the program (which may not be shown in the example).

  When two operands are present in an arithmetic or logical instruction, the right operand is the source and the left operand is the destination. Some assembly languages put the source and destination in reverse order.

For example:

```
LOADREG: MOV EAX, SUBTOTAL
```

In this example LOADREG is a label, MOV is the mnemonic identifier of an opcode, EAX is the destination operand, and SUBTOTAL is the source operand.

1.3.4 Hexadecimal Numbers

Base 16 numbers are represented by a string of hexadecimal digits followed by the character H. A hexadecimal digit is a character from the set (0, 1, 2, 3, 4, 5, 6, 7, 8, 9, A, B, C, D, E, F). A leading zero is added if the number would otherwise begin with one of the digits **A-F**. For example, 0FH is equivalent to the decimal number 15.

1.3.5 Segmented Addressing

The i486 processor uses byte addressing. This means memory is organized and accessed as a sequence of bytes. Whether one or more bytes are being accessed, a byte number is used to address memory. The memory which can be addressed with this number is called an *address space*.

The i486 processor also supports segmented addressing. This is a form of addressing where a program may have many independent address spaces, called *segments*. For example, a program can keep its code (instructions) and stack in separate segments. Code addresses would always refer to the code space, and stack addresses would always refer to the stack space. An example of the notation used to show segmented addresses is shown below.

CS:EIP

This example refers to a byte within the code segment. The byte number is held in the EIP register.

1.3.6 Exceptions

An exception is an event which occurs when an instruction causes an error. For example, an attempt to divide by zero generates an exception. There are several different types of exceptions, and some of these types may provide error codes. An error code reports additional information about the error. Error codes are produced only for some exceptions. An example of the notation used to show an exception and error code is shown below.

#PF(fault code)

This example refers to a page-fault exception under conditions where an error code naming a type of fault is reported. Under some conditions, exceptions which produce error codes may not be able to report an accurate code. In this case, the error code is zero, as shown below.

#PF(0)

Part I
Application Programming

Basic Programming Model 2

CHAPTER 2
BASIC PROGRAMMING MODEL

This chapter describes the application programming environment (except for the floating-point features) as seen by assembly-language programmers. The chapter introduces the architectural features which directly affect the design and implementation of application programs. Floating-point applications are described separately in Part III.

The basic programming model consists of these parts:

- Memory organization
- Data types
- Registers
- Instruction format
- Operand selection
- Interrupts and exceptions

Note that input/output is not included as part of the basic programming model. System designers may choose to make I/O instructions available to applications or may choose to reserve these functions for the operating system. For this reason, the I/O features of the i486™ processor are discussed in Part II.

This chapter contains a section for each feature of the architecture normally visible to applications.

2.1 MEMORY ORGANIZATION

The memory on the bus of an i486 processor is called *physical memory*. It is organized as a sequence of 8-bit bytes. Each byte is assigned a unique address, called a *physical address*, which ranges from zero to a maximum of $2^{32} - 1$ (4 gigabytes). Memory management is a hardware mechanism for making reliable and efficient use of memory. When memory management is used, programs do not directly address physical memory. Programs address a memory model, called *virtual memory*.

Memory management consists of segmentation and paging. Segmentation is a mechanism for providing multiple, independent address spaces. Paging is a mechanism to support a model of a large address space in RAM using a small amount of RAM and some disk storage. Either or both of these mechanisms may be used. An address issued by a program is a *logical address*. Segmentation hardware translates a logical address into an address for a continuous, unsegmented address space, called a *linear address*. Paging hardware translates a linear address into a physical address.

Memory may appear as a single, addressable space like physical memory. Or, it may appear as one or more independent memory spaces, called *segments*. Segments can be assigned specifically for holding a program's code (instructions), data, or stack. In fact, a single program may have up to 16,383 segments of different sizes and kinds. Segments can be used to increase the reliability of programs and systems. For example, a program's stack can be put into a different segment than its code to prevent the stack from growing into the code space and overwriting instructions with data.

Whether or not multiple segments are used, logical addresses are translated into linear addresses by treating the address as an offset into a segment. Each segment has a *segment descriptor*, which holds its base address and size limit. If the offset does not exceed the limit, and no other condition exists which would prevent reading the segment, the offset and base address are added together to form the linear address.

The linear address produced by segmentation is used directly as the physical address if bit 31 of the CR0 register is clear (the CR0 register is discussed in Chapter 4). This register bit controls whether paging is used or not used. If the bit is set, the paging hardware is used to translate the linear address into the physical address.

The paging hardware gives another level of organization to memory. It breaks the linear address space into fixed blocks of 4K bytes, called *pages*. The logical address space is mapped into the linear address space, which is mapped into some number of pages. A page may be in memory or on disk. When a logical address is issued, it is translated into an address for a page in memory, or an exception is issued. An exception gives the operating system a chance to read the page from disk and update the page mapping. The program which generated the exception then can be restarted without generating an exception.

If multiple segments are used, they are part of the programming environment seen by application programmers. If paging is used, it is normally invisible to the application programmer. It only becomes visible when there is an interaction between the application program and the paging algorithm used by the operating system. When all of the pages in memory are used, the operating system uses its paging algorithm to decide which memory pages should be sent to disk. All paging algorithms (except random algorithms) have some kind of worst-case behavior which may be exercised by some kinds of application programs.

The architecture of the i486 processor gives designers the freedom to choose a different memory model for each program, even when more than one program is running at the same time. The model of memory organization can range between the following extremes:

- A "flat" address space where the code, stack, and data spaces are mapped to the same linear addresses. To the greatest extent possible, this eliminates segmentation by allowing any type of memory reference to access any type of data.
- A segmented address space with separate segments for the code, data, and stack spaces. As many as 16,383 linear address spaces of up to 4 gigabytes each can be used.

Both models can provide memory protection. Models intermediate between these extremes also can be chosen. The reasons for choosing a particular memory model and the manner in which system programmers implement a model are discussed in Part II—System Programming.

2.1.1 Unsegmented or "Flat" Model

The simplest memory model is the flat model. Although there isn't a mode bit or control register which turns off the segmentation mechanism, the same effect can be achieved by mapping all segments to the same linear addresses. This will cause all memory operations to refer to the same memory space.

In a flat model, segments may cover the entire 4 gigabyte range of physical addresses, or they may cover only those addresses which are mapped to physical memory. The advantage of the smaller address space is it provides a minimum level of hardware protection against software bugs; an exception will occur if any logical address refers to an address for which no memory exists.

2.1.2 Segmented Model

In a segmented model of memory organization, the logical address space consists of as many as 16,383 segments of up to 4 gigabytes each, or a total as large as 2^{46} bytes (64 terabytes). The processor maps this 64 terabyte logical address space onto the physical address space (up to 4 gigabytes) by the address translation mechanism described in Chapter 5. Application programmers may ignore the details of this mapping. The advantage of the segmented model is that offsets within each address space are separately checked and access to each segment can be individually controlled.

A pointer into a segmented address space consists of two parts (see Figure 2-1).

1. A *segment selector*, which is a 16-bit field which identifies a segment.
2. An *offset*, which is a 32-bit byte address within a segment.

The processor uses the segment selector to find the linear address of the beginning of the segment, called the *base address*. Programs access memory using fixed offsets from this base address, so an object-code module may be loaded into memory and run without changing the addresses it uses (dynamic linking). The size of a segment is defined by the programmer, so a segment can be exactly the size of the module it contains.

2.2 DATA TYPES

Bytes, words, and doublewords are the principal data types (see Figure 2-2). A byte is eight bits. The bits are numbered 0 through 7, bit 0 being the least significant bit (LSB).

A word is two bytes occupying any two consecutive addresses. A word contains 16 bits. The bits of a word are numbered from 0 through 15, bit 0 again being the least significant bit. The byte containing bit 0 of the word is called the *low byte*; the byte containing bit 15 is called the *high byte*. On the i486 processor, the low byte is stored in the byte with the lower address. The address of the low byte also is the address of the word. The address of the high byte is used only when the upper half of the word is being accessed separately from the lower half.

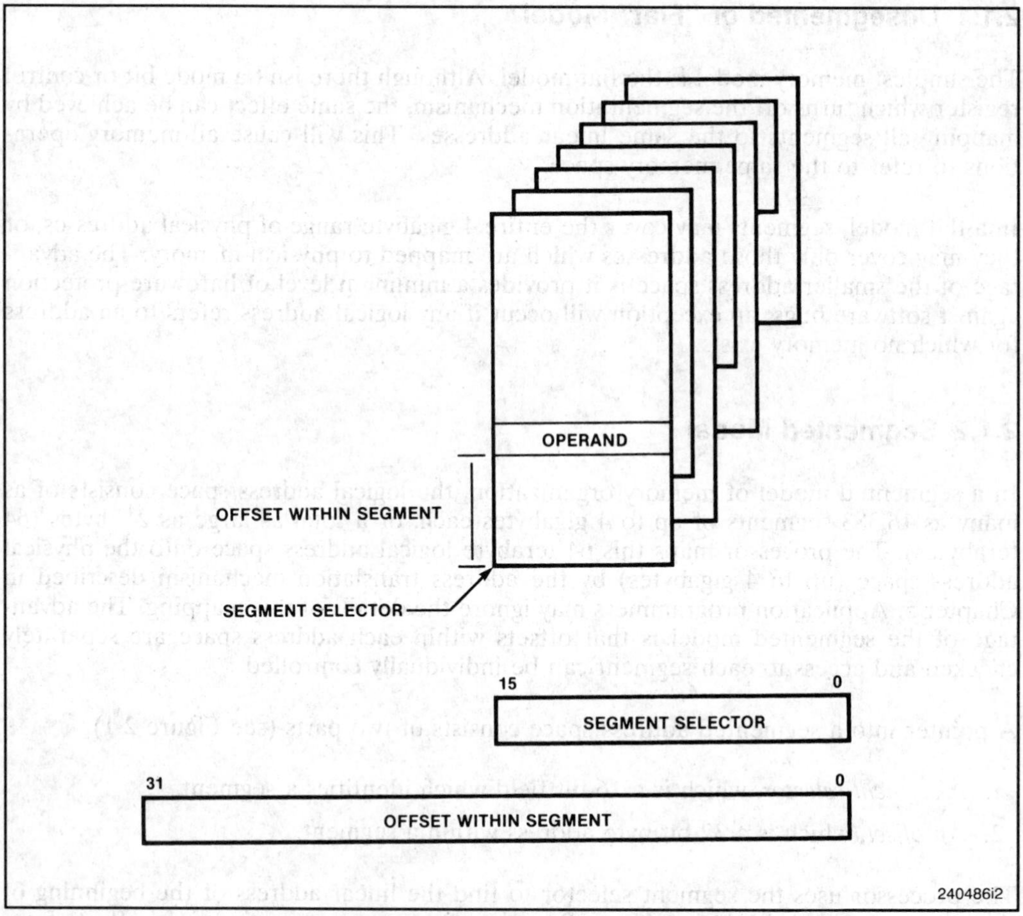

Figure 2-1. Segmented Addressing

A doubleword is four bytes occupying any four consecutive addresses. A doubleword contains 32 bits. The bits of a doubleword are numbered from 0 through 31, bit 0 again being the least significant bit. The word containing bit 0 of the doubleword is called the *low word*; the word containing bit 31 is called the *high word*. The low word is stored in the two bytes with the lower addresses. The address of the lowest byte is the address of the doubleword. The higher addresses are used only when the upper word is being accessed separately from the lower word, or when individual bytes are being accessed. Figure 2-3 illustrates the arrangement of bytes within words and doublewords.

Note that words do not need to be aligned at even-numbered addresses and doublewords do not need to be aligned at addresses evenly divisible by four. This allows maximum flexibility in data structures (e.g., records containing mixed byte, word, and doubleword items) and efficiency in memory utilization. Because the i486 processor has

7
0
BYTE
BYTE
15
7
0
HIGH BYTE
LOW BYTE
WORD
address N + 1
address N
31
15
0
HIGH WORD
LOW WORD
DOUBLEWORD
address N + 3
address N + 2
address N + 1
address N
240486i3

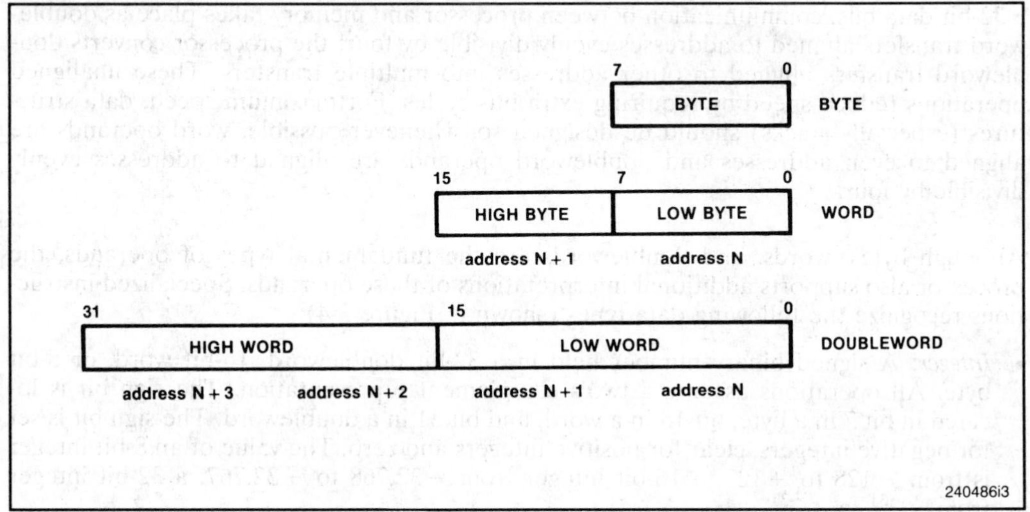

Figure 2-2. Fundamental Data Types

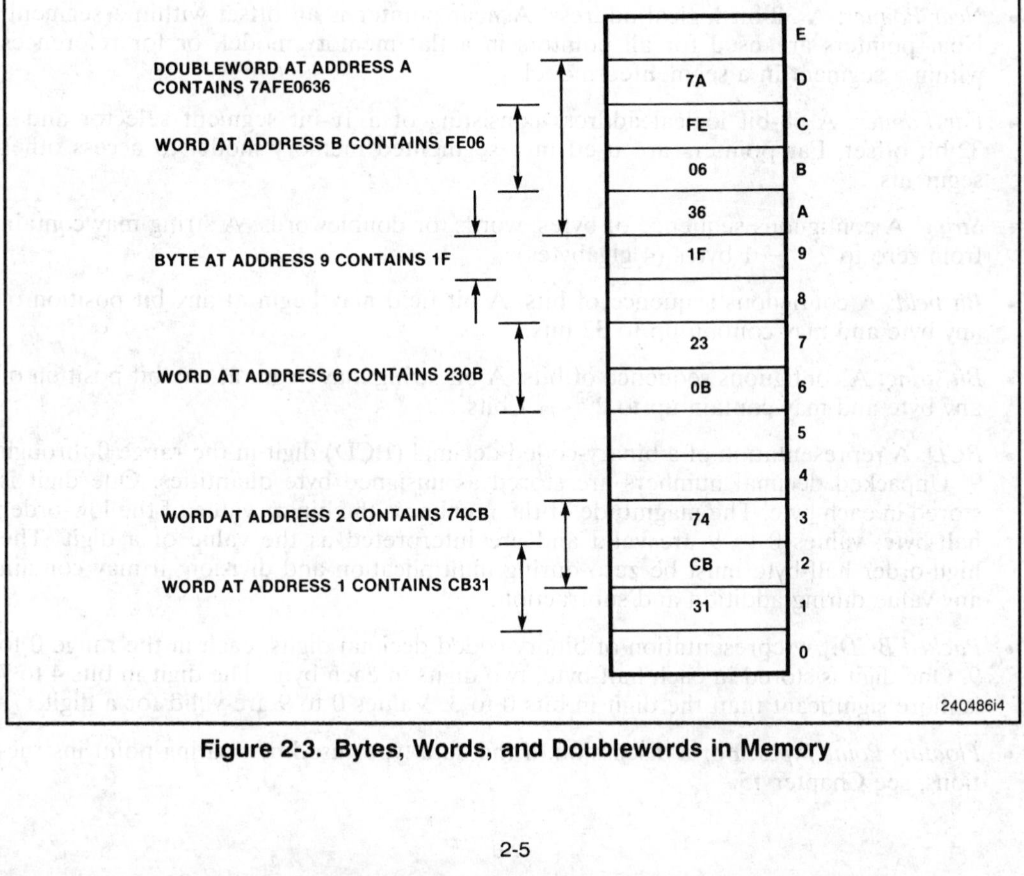

DOUBLEWORD AT ADDRESS A CONTAINS 7AFE0636
WORD AT ADDRESS B CONTAINS FE06
BYTE AT ADDRESS 9 CONTAINS 1F
WORD AT ADDRESS 6 CONTAINS 230B
WORD AT ADDRESS 2 CONTAINS 74CB
WORD AT ADDRESS 1 CONTAINS CB31
E
7A
D
FE
C
06
B
36
A
1F
9
8
23
7
0B
6
5
4
74
3
CB
2
31
1
0
240486i4

Figure 2-3. Bytes, Words, and Doublewords in Memory

a 32-bit data bus, communication between processor and memory takes place as doubleword transfers aligned to addresses evenly divisible by four; the processor converts doubleword transfers aligned to other addresses into multiple transfers. These unaligned operations reduce speed by requiring extra bus cycles. For maximum speed, data structures (especially stacks) should be designed so, whenever possible, word operands are aligned to even addresses and doubleword operands are aligned to addresses evenly divisible by four.

Although bytes, words, and doublewords are the fundamental types of operands, the processor also supports additional interpretations of these operands. Specialized instructions recognize the following data types (shown in Figure 2-4):

- *Integer*: A signed binary number held in a 32-bit doubleword, 16-bit word, or 8-bit byte. All operations assume a two's complement representation. The sign bit is located in bit 7 in a byte, bit 15 in a word, and bit 31 in a doubleword. The sign bit is set for negative integers, clear for positive integers and zero. The value of an 8-bit integer is from −128 to +127; a 16-bit integer from −32,768 to +32,767; a 32-bit integer from -2^{31} to $+2^{31}-1$.
- *Ordinal*: An unsigned binary number contained in a 32-bit doubleword, 16-bit word, or 8-bit byte. The value of an 8-bit ordinal is from 0 to 255; a 16-bit ordinal from 0 to 65,535; a 32-bit ordinal from 0 to $2^{32} - 1$.
- *Near Pointer*: A 32-bit logical address. A near pointer is an offset within a segment. Near pointers are used for all pointers in a flat memory model, or for references within a segment in a segmented model.
- *Far Pointer*: A 48-bit logical address consisting of a 16-bit segment selector and a 32-bit offset. Far pointers are used in a segmented memory model to access other segments.
- *String*: A contiguous sequence of bytes, words, or doublewords. A string may contain from zero to $2^{32} - 1$ bytes (4 gigabytes).
- *Bit field*: A contiguous sequence of bits. A bit field may begin at any bit position of any byte and may contain up to 32 bits.
- *Bit string*: A contiguous sequence of bits. A bit string may begin at any bit position of any byte and may contain up to $2^{32} - 1$ bits.
- *BCD*: A representation of a binary-coded decimal (BCD) digit in the range 0 through 9. Unpacked decimal numbers are stored as unsigned byte quantities. One digit is stored in each byte. The magnitude of the number is the binary value of the low-order half-byte; values 0 to 9 are valid and are interpreted as the value of a digit. The high-order half-byte must be zero during multiplication and division; it may contain any value during addition and subtraction.
- *Packed BCD*: A representation of binary-coded decimal digits, each in the range 0 to 9. One digit is stored in each half-byte, two digits in each byte. The digit in bits 4 to 7 is more significant than the digit in bits 0 to 3. Values 0 to 9 are valid for a digit.
- *Floating-Point Types*: For a discussion of the data types used by floating-point instructions, see Chapter 15.

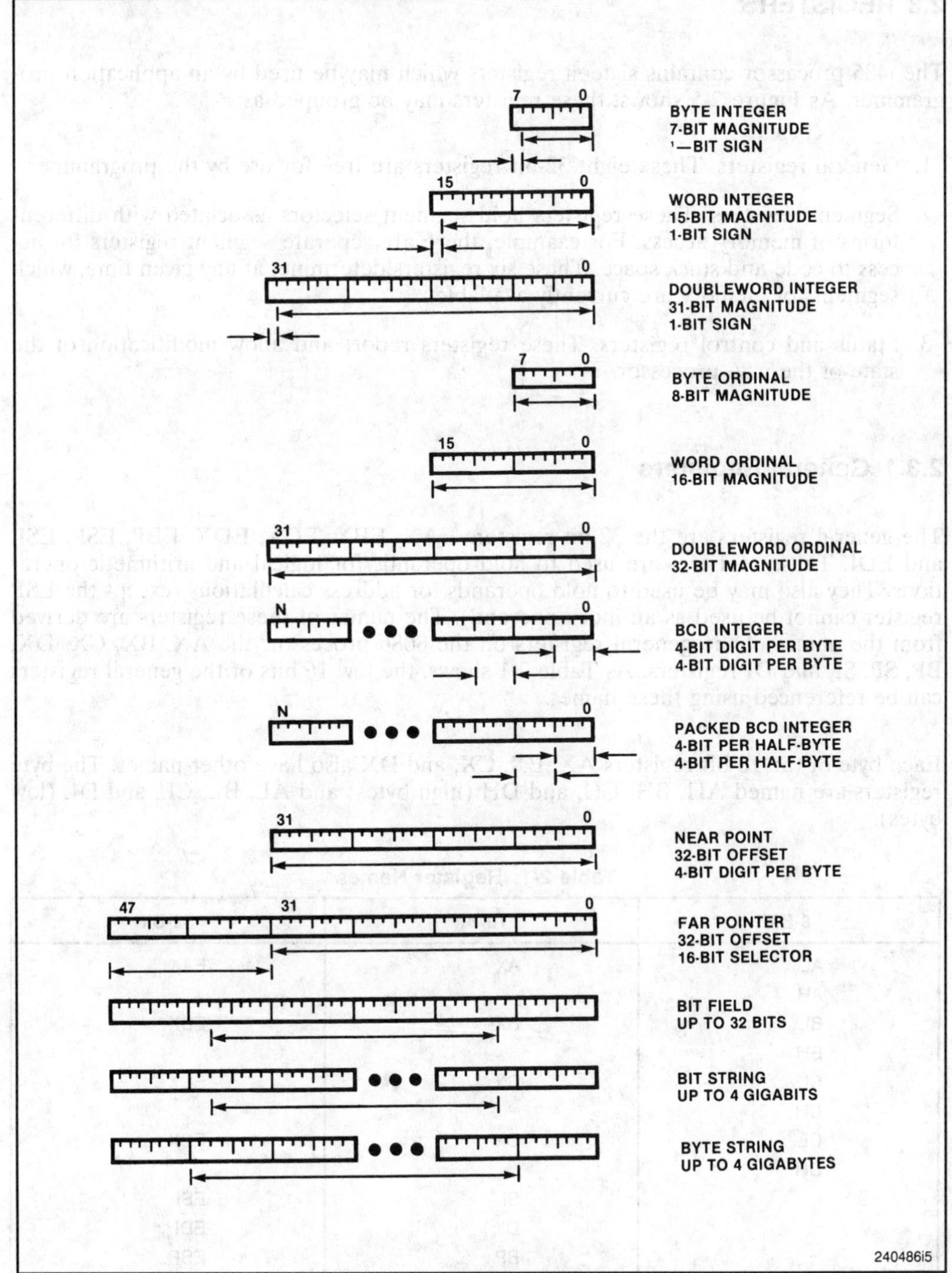

Figure 2-4. Data Types

2.3 REGISTERS

The i486 processor contains sixteen registers which may be used by an application programmer. As Figure 2-5 shows, these registers may be grouped as:

1. General registers. These eight 32-bit registers are free for use by the programmer.
2. Segment registers. These registers hold segment selectors associated with different forms of memory access. For example, there are separate segment registers for access to code and stack space. These six registers determine, at any given time, which segments of memory are currently available.
3. Status and control registers. These registers report and allow modification of the state of the i486 processor.

2.3.1 General Registers

The general registers are the 32-bit registers EAX, EBX, ECX, EDX, EBP, ESP, ESI, and EDI. These registers are used to hold operands for logical and arithmetic operations. They also may be used to hold operands for address calculations (except the ESP register cannot be used as an index operand). The names of these registers are derived from the names of the general registers on the 8086 processor, the AX, BX, CX, DX, BP, SP, SI, and DI registers. As Table 2-1 shows, the low 16 bits of the general registers can be referenced using these names.

Each byte of the 16-bit registers AX, BX, CX, and DX also have other names. The byte registers are named AH, BH, CH, and DH (high bytes) and AL, BL, CL, and DL (low bytes).

Table 2-1. Register Names

8-Bit	16-Bit	32-Bit
AL AH	AX	EAX
BL BH	BX	EBX
CL CH	CX	ECX
DL DH	DX	EDX
	SI	ESI
	DI	EDI
	BP	EBP
	SP	ESP

GENERAL REGISTERS

31	23	15	7	0	16-BIT	32-BIT
		AH	AL		AX	EAX
		DH	DL		DX	EDX
		CH	CL		CX	ECX
		BH	BL		BX	EBX
		BP				EBP
		SI				ESI
		DI				EDI
		SP				ESP

SEGMENT REGISTERS

15	0
CS	
SS	
DS	
ES	
FS	
GS	

STATUS AND CONTROL REGISTERS

31	0
EFLAGS	
EIP	

240486i6

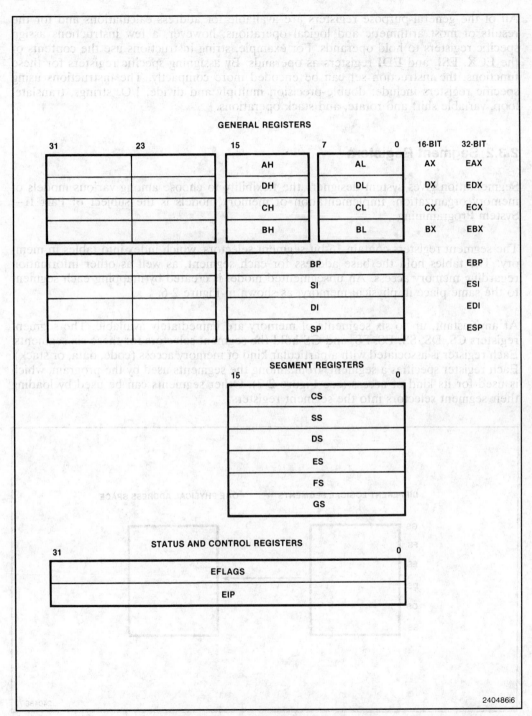

Figure 2-5. Application Register Set

All of the general-purpose registers are available for address calculations and for the results of most arithmetic and logical operations; however, a few instructions assign specific registers to hold operands. For example, string instructions use the contents of the ECX, ESI, and EDI registers as operands. By assigning specific registers for these functions, the instruction set can be encoded more compactly. The instructions using specific registers include: double-precision multiply and divide, I/O, strings, translate, loop, variable shift and rotate, and stack operations.

2.3.2 Segment Registers

Segmentation gives system designers the flexibility to choose among various models of memory organization. Implementation of memory models is the subject of Part II–System Programming.

The segment registers contain 16-bit segment selectors, which index into tables in memory. The tables hold the base address for each segment, as well as other information regarding memory access. An unsegmented model is created by mapping each segment to the same place in physical memory, as shown in Figure 2-6.

At any instant, up to six segments of memory are immediately available. The segment registers CS, DS, SS, ES, FS, and GS hold the segment selectors for these six segments. Each register is associated with a particular kind of memory access (code, data, or stack). Each register specifies a segment, from among the segments used by the program, which is used for its kind of access (see Figure 2-7). Other segments can be used by loading their segment selectors into the segment registers.

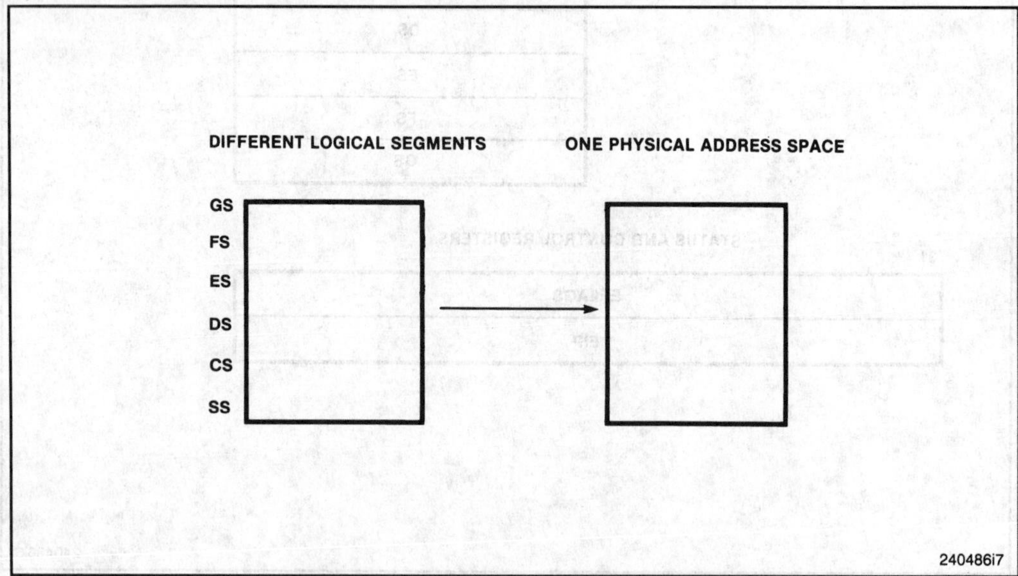

Figure 2-6. An Unsegmented Memory

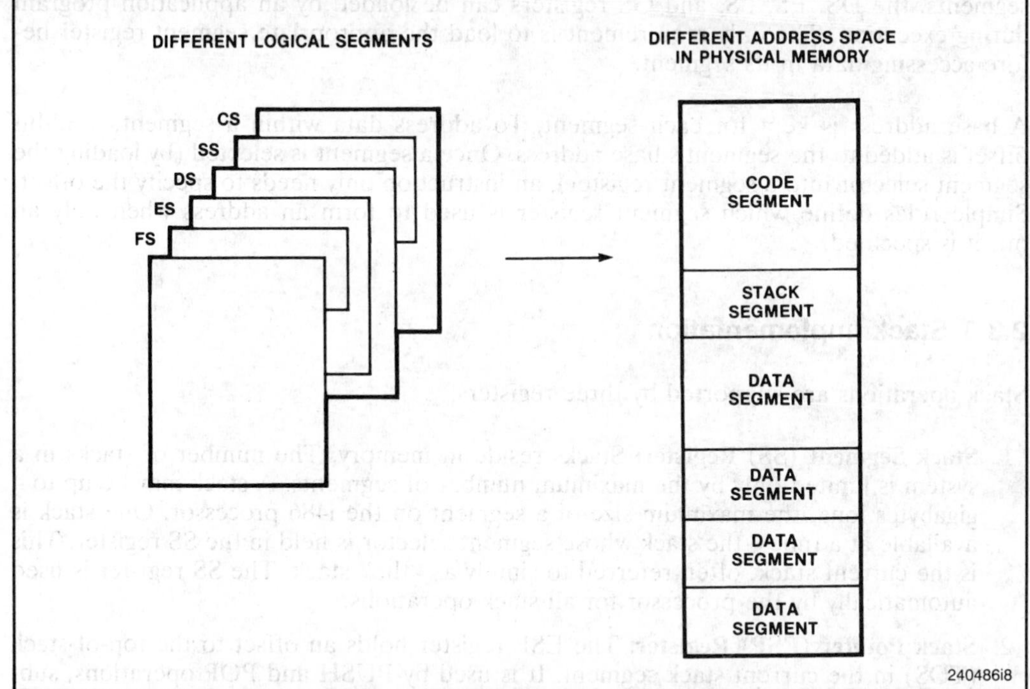

Figure 2-7. A Segmented Memory

The segment containing the instructions being executed is called the *code segment*. Its segment selector is held in the CS register. The i486 processor fetches instructions from the code segment, using the contents of the EIP register as an offset into the segment. The CS register is loaded as the result of interrupts, exceptions, and instructions which transfer control between segments (e.g., the CALL, IRET and JMP instructions).

Before a procedure is called, a region of memory needs to be allocated for a stack. The stack is used to hold the return address, parameters passed by the calling routine, and temporary variables allocated by the procedure. All stack operations use the SS register to find the stack segment. Unlike the CS register, the SS register can be loaded explicitly, which permits application programs to set up stacks.

The DS, ES, FS, and GS registers allow as many as four data segments to be available simultaneously. Four data segments give efficient and secure access to different types of data structures. For example, separate data segments can be created for the data structures of the current module, data exported from a higher-level module, a dynamically-created data structure, and data shared with another program. If a bug causes a program to run wild, the segmentation mechanism can limit the damage to only those segments allocated to the program. An operand within a data segment is addressed by specifying its offset either in an instruction or a general register.

Depending on the structure of data (i.e., the way data is partitioned into segments), a program may require access to more than four data segments. To access additional segments, the DS, ES, FS, and GS registers can be loaded by an application program during execution. The only requirement is to load the appropriate segment register before accessing data in its segment.

A base address is kept for each segment. To address data within a segment, a 32-bit offset is added to the segment's base address. Once a segment is selected (by loading the segment selector into a segment register), an instruction only needs to specify the offset. Simple rules define which segment register is used to form an address when only an offset is specified.

2.3.3 Stack Implementation

Stack operations are supported by three registers:

1. **Stack Segment (SS) Register:** Stacks reside in memory. The number of stacks in a system is limited only by the maximum number of segments. A stack may be up to 4 gigabytes long, the maximum size of a segment on the i486 processor. One stack is available at a time—the stack whose segment selector is held in the SS register. This is the current stack, often referred to simply as "the" stack. The SS register is used automatically by the processor for all stack operations.
2. **Stack Pointer (ESP) Register:** The ESP register holds an offset to the top-of-stack (TOS) in the current stack segment. It is used by PUSH and POP operations, subroutine calls and returns, exceptions, and interrupts. When an item is pushed onto the stack (see Figure 2-8), the processor decrements the ESP register, then writes

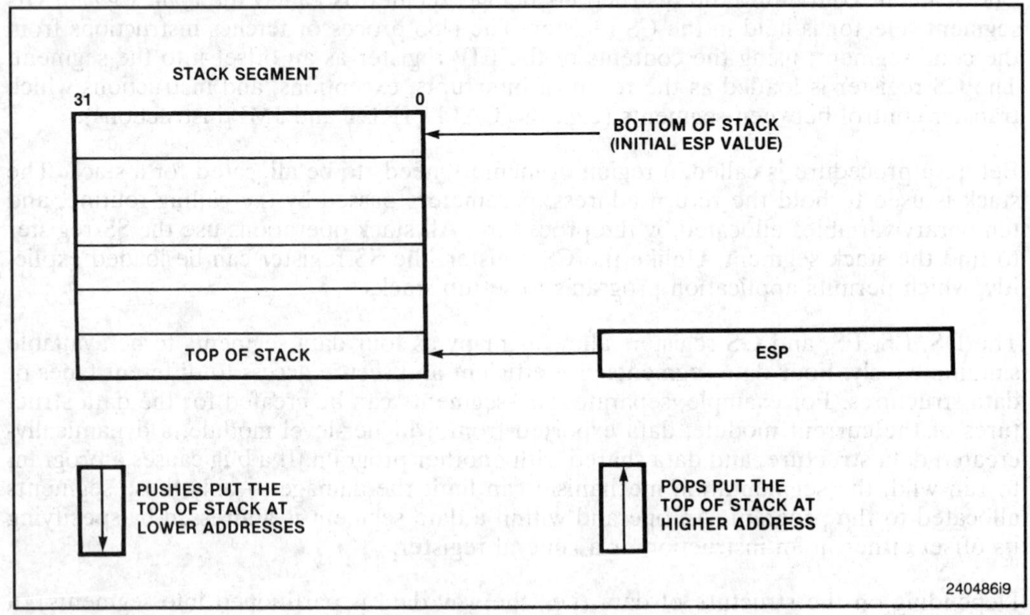

Figure 2-8. Stacks

the item at the new TOS. When an item is popped off the stack, the processor copies it from the TOS, then increments the ESP register. In other words, the stack grows *down* in memory toward lesser addresses.

3. **Stack-Frame Base Pointer (EBP) Register:** The EBP register typically is used to access data structures passed on the stack. For example, on entering a subroutine the stack contains the return address and some number of data structures passed to the subroutine. The subroutine adds to the stack whenever it needs to create space for temporary local variables. As a result, the stack pointer moves around as temporary variables are pushed and popped. If the stack pointer is copied into the base pointer before anything is pushed on the stack, the base pointer can be used to reference data structures with fixed offsets. If this is not done, the offset to access a particular data structure would change whenever a temporary variable is allocated or de-allocated.

   When the EBP register is used to address memory, the current stack segment is selected (i.e., the SS segment). Because the stack segment does not have to be specified, instruction encoding is more compact. The EBP register also can be used to address other segments.

   Instructions, such as the ENTER and LEAVE instructions, are provided which automatically set up the EBP register for convenient access to variables.

2.3.4 Flags Register

Condition codes (e.g., carry, sign, overflow) and mode bits are kept in a 32-bit register named EFLAGS. Figure 2-9 defines the bits within this register. The flags control certain operations and indicate the status of the i486 processor.

The flags may be considered in three groups: status flags, control flags, and system flags. Discussion of the system flags occurs in Part II.

2.3.4.1 STATUS FLAGS

The status flags of the EFLAGS register report the kind of result produced from the execution of arithmetic instructions. The MOV instruction does not affect these flags. Conditional jumps and subroutine calls allow a program to sense the state of the status flags and respond to them. For example, when the counter controlling a loop is decremented to zero, the state of the ZF flag changes, and this change can be used to suppress the conditional jump to the start of the loop.

The status flags are shown in Table 2-2.

2.3.4.2 CONTROL FLAG

The control flag DF of the EFLAGS register controls string instructions.

DF (Direction Flag, bit 10)

31 … 18 17 16 15 14 13 12 11 10 9 8 7 6 5 4 3 2 1 0

0	0	0	0	0	0	0	0	0	0	0	0	0	AC	VM	RF	0	NT	IOPL	OF	DF	IF	TF	SF	ZF	0	AF	0	PF	1	CF

X ALIGNMENT CHECK
X VIRTUAL 8086 MODE (VM)
X RESUME FLAG (RF)
X NESTED FLAG (NF)
X I/O PRIVILEGE LEVEL (IOPL)
S OVERFLOW FLAG (OF)
C DIRECTION FLAG (DF)
X INTERRUPT ENABLE FLAG (IF)
X TRAP FLAT (TF)
S SIGN FLAG (SF)
S ZERO FLAG (ZF)
S AUXILIARY CARRY FLAG (AF)
S PARITY FLAG (PF)
S CARRY FLAT (CF)

S INDICATES A STATUS FLAG
C INDICATES A CONTROL FLAG
X INDICATES A SYSTEM FLAG

BIT POSITIONS SHOWN AS 0 OR 1 ARE INTEL RESERVED
DO NOT USE. ALWAYS SET THEM TO THE VALUE PREVIOUSLY READ.

240486i10

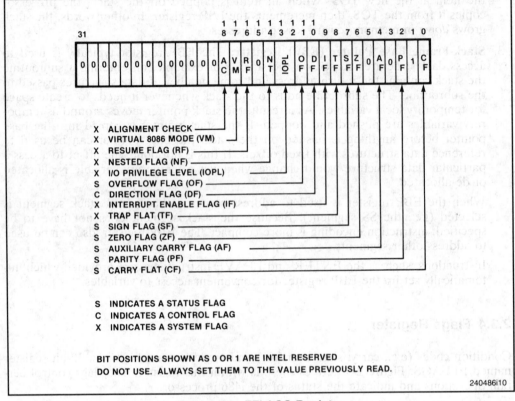

Figure 2-9. EFLAGS Register

Table 2-2. Status Flags

Name	Purpose	Condition Reported
OF	overflow	Result exceeds positive or negative limit of number range
SF	sign	Result is negative (less than zero)
ZF	zero	Result is zero
AF	auxiliary carry	Carry out of bit position 3 (used for BCD)
PF	parity	Low byte of result has even parity (even number of set bits)
CF	carry flag	Carry out of most significant bit of result

Setting the DF flag causes string instructions to auto-decrement, that is, to process strings from high addresses to low addresses. Clearing the DF flag causes string instructions to auto-increment, or to process strings from low addresses to high addresses.

2.3.4.3 INSTRUCTION POINTER

The instruction pointer (EIP) register contains the offset into the current code segment for the next instruction to execute. The instruction pointer is not directly available to the programmer; it is controlled implicitly by control-transfer instructions (jumps, returns, etc.), interrupts, and exceptions.

The EIP register is advanced from one instruction boundary to the next. Because of instruction prefetching, it is only an approximate indication of the bus activity which loads instructions into the processor.

The i486 processor does not fetch single instructions. The processor prefetches aligned 128-bit blocks of instruction code in advance of instruction execution. (An aligned 128-bit block begins at an address which is clear in its low four bits.) These blocks are fetched without regard to the boundaries between instructions. By the time an instruction starts to execute, it already has been loaded into the processor and decoded. This is a performance feature, because it allows instruction execution to be overlapped with instruction prefetch and decode.

When a jump or call is executed, the processor prefetches the entire aligned block containing the destination address. Instructions which have been prefetched or decoded are discarded. If a prefetch would generate an exception, such as a prefetch beyond the end of the code segment, the exception is not reported until the execution of an instruction containing at least one exception-generating byte. If the instruction is discarded, no exception is generated.

In real mode prefetching may cause the processor to access addresses not anticipated by programmers. In protected mode exceptions are correctly reported when these addresses are executed. There may not be hardware mechanisms which account for real mode behavior of the processor. For example, if a system does not return the RDY# signal (the signal which terminates a bus cycle) for bus cycles to unimplemented addresses, prefetching must be prevented from referencing these addresses. If a system implements parity checking, prefetching must be prevented from accessing addresses beyond the end of parity-protected memory. (Alternatively, RDY# can be returned even for bus cycles to unimplemented addresses, and parity errors can be ignored on prefetches beyond the end of parity-protected memory.)

Prefetching can be kept from referencing a particular address by placing enough distance between the address and the last executable byte. For example, to keep prefetching away from addresses in the block from 10000H to 1000FH, the last executable byte should be no closer than 0FFEEH. This places one free byte followed by one free, aligned, 128-bit block between the last byte of the last instruction and the address which must not be referenced. The prefetching behavior of the i486 processor is implementation-dependent; future Intel® products may have different prefetching behavior.

2.4 INSTRUCTION FORMAT

The information encoded in an instruction includes a specification of the operation to be performed, the type of the operands to be manipulated, and the location of these operands. If an operand is located in memory, the instruction also must select, explicitly or implicitly, the segment which contains the operand.

An instruction may have various parts and formats. The exact format of instructions is shown in Appendix B; the parts of an instruction are described below. Of these parts, only the opcode is always present. The other parts may or may not be present, depending on the operation involved and the location and type of the operands. The parts of an instruction, in order of occurrence, are listed below:

- **Prefixes:** one or more bytes preceding an instruction which modify the operation of the instruction. The following prefixes can be used by application programs:
  1. Segment override – explicitly specifies which segment register an instruction should use, instead of the default segment register.
  2. Address size – switches between 16- and 32-bit addressing. Either size can be the default; this prefix selects the non-default size.
  3. Operand size – switches between 16- and 32-bit data size. Either size can be the default; this prefix selects the non-default size.
  4. Repeat – used with a string instruction to cause the instruction to be repeated for each element of the string.
- **Opcode:** specifies the operation performed by the instruction. Some operations have several different opcodes, each specifying a different form of the operation.
- **Register specifier:** an instruction may specify one or two register operands. Register specifiers occur either in the same byte as the opcode or in the same byte as the addressing-mode specifier.
- **Addressing-mode specifier:** when present, specifies whether an operand is a register or memory location; if in memory, specifies whether a displacement, a base register, an index register, and scaling are to be used.
- **SIB (scale, index, base) byte:** when the addressing-mode specifier indicates an index register will be used to calculate the address of an operand, a SIB byte is included in the instruction to encode the base register, the index register, and a scaling factor.
- **Displacement:** when the addressing-mode specifier indicates a displacement will be used to compute the address of an operand, the displacement is encoded in the instruction. A displacement is a signed integer of 32, 16, or 8 bits. The 8-bit form is used in the common case when the displacement is sufficiently small. The processor extends an 8-bit displacement to 16 or 32 bits, taking into account the sign.
- **Immediate operand:** when present, directly provides the value of an operand. Immediate operands may be bytes, words, or doublewords. In cases where an 8-bit immediate operand is used with a 16- or 32-bit operand, the processor extends the eight-bit operand to an integer of the same sign and magnitude in the larger size. In the same way, a 16-bit operand is extended to 32-bits.

2.5 OPERAND SELECTION

An instruction acts on zero or more operands. An example of a zero-operand instruction is the NOP instruction (no operation). An operand can be held in any of these places:

- In the instruction itself (an immediate operand).
- In a register (in the case of 32-bit operands, EAX, EBX, ECX, EDX, ESI, EDI, ESP, or EBP; in the case of 16-bit operands AX, BX, CX, DX, SI, DI, SP, or BP; in the case of 8-bit operands AH, AL, BH, BL, CH, CL, DH, or DL; the segment registers; or the EFLAGS register for flag operations). Use of 16-bit register operands requires use of the 16-bit operand size prefix (a byte with the value 67H preceding the instruction).
- In memory.
- At an I/O port.

Access to operands is very fast. Register and immediate operands are available on-chip—the latter because they are prefetched as part of interpreting the instruction. Memory operands residing in the on-chip cache can be accessed just as fast.

Of the instructions which have operands, some specify operands implicitly; others specify operands explicitly; still others use a combination of both. For example:

Implicit operand: `AAM`

By definition, AAM (ASCII adjust for multiplication) operates on the contents of the AX register.

Explicit operand: `XCHG EAX, EBX`

The operands to be exchanged are encoded in the instruction with the opcode.

Implicit and explicit operands: `PUSH COUNTER`

The memory variable COUNTER (the explicit operand) is copied to the top of the stack (the implicit operand).

Note that most instructions have implicit operands. All arithmetic instructions, for example, update the EFLAGS register.

An instruction can *explicitly* reference one or two operands. Two-operand instructions, such as MOV, ADD, and XOR, generally overwrite one of the two participating operands with the result. This is the difference between the *source operand* (the one unaffected by the operation) and the *destination operand* (the one overwritten by the result).

For most instructions, one of the two explicitly specified operands – either the source or the destination – can be either in a register or in memory. The other operand must be in a register or it must be an immediate source operand. This puts the explicit two-operand instructions into the following groups:

- Register to register
- Register to memory
- Memory to register
- Immediate to register
- Immediate to memory

Certain string instructions and stack manipulation instructions, however, transfer data from memory to memory. Both operands of some string instructions are in memory and are specified implicitly. Push and pop stack operations allow transfer between memory operands and the memory-based stack.

Several three-operand instructions are provided, such as the IMUL, SHRD, and SHLD instructions. Two of the three operands are specified explicitly, as for the two-operand instructions, while a third is taken from the ECX register or supplied as an immediate. Other three-operand instructions, such as the string instructions when used with a repeat prefix, take all their operands from registers.

2.5.1 Immediate Operands

Certain instructions use data from the instruction itself as one (and sometimes two) of the operands. Such an operand is called an *immediate* operand. It may be a byte, word, or doubleword. For example:

```
SHR PATTERN, 2
```

One byte of the instruction holds the value 2, the number of bits by which to shift the variable PATTERN.

```
TEST PATTERN, 0FFFF00FFH
```

A doubleword of the instruction holds the mask which is used to test the variable PATTERN.

```
IMUL CX, MEMWORD, 3
```

A word in memory is multiplied by an immediate 3 and stored into the CX register.

All arithmetic instructions (except divide) allow the source operand to be an immediate value. When the destination is the EAX or AL register, the instruction encoding is one byte shorter than with the other general registers.

2.5.2 Register Operands

Operands may be located in one of the 32-bit general registers (EAX, EBX, ECX, EDX, ESI, EDI, ESP, or EBP), in one of the 16-bit general registers (AX, BX, CX, DX, SI, DI, SP, or BP), or in one of the 8-bit general registers (AH, BH, CH, DH, AL, BL, CL, or DL).

The i486 processor has instructions for referencing the segment registers (CS, DS, ES, SS, FS, and GS). These instructions are used by application programs only if system designers have chosen a segmented memory model.

The i486 processor also has instructions for changing the state of individual flags in the EFLAGS register. Instructions have been provided for setting and clearing flags which often need to be accessed. The other flags, which are not accessed so often, can be changed by pushing the contents of the EFLAGS register on the stack, making changes to it while it's on the stack, and popping it back into the register.

2.5.3 Memory Operands

Instructions with explicit operands in memory must reference the segment containing the operand and the offset from the beginning of the segment to the operand. Segments are specified using a segment-override prefix, which is a byte placed at the beginning of an instruction. If no segment is specified, simple rules assign the segment by default. The offset is specified in one of the following ways:

1. Most instructions which access memory contain a byte for specifying the addressing method of the operand. The byte, called the *modR/M* byte, comes after the opcode and specifies whether the operand is in a register or in memory. If the operand is in memory, the address is calculated from a segment register and any of the following values: a base register, an index register, a scaling factor, and a displacement. When an index register is used, the modR/M byte also is followed by another byte to specify the index register and scaling factor. This form of addressing is the most flexible.

2. A few instructions use implied address modes:

   A MOV instruction with the AL or EAX register as either source or destination can address memory with a doubleword encoded in the instruction. This special form of the MOV instruction allows no base register, index register, or scaling factor to be used. This form is one byte shorter than the general-purpose form.

   String operations address memory in the DS segment using the ESI register, (the MOVS, CMPS, OUTS, LODS, and SCAS instructions) or using the ES segment and EDI register (the MOVS, CMPS, INS, and STOS instructions).

   Stack operations address memory in the SS segment using the ESP register (the PUSH, POP, PUSHA, PUSHAD, POPA, POPAD, PUSHF, PUSHFD, POPF, POPFD, CALL, RET, IRET, and IRETD instructions, exceptions, and interrupts).

2.5.3.1 SEGMENT SELECTION

Explicit specification of a segment is optional. If a segment is not specified using a segment-override prefix, the processor automatically chooses a segment according to the rules of Table 2-3. (If a flat model of memory organization is used, the rules for selecting segments are not apparent to application programs.)

Different kinds of memory access have different default segments. Data operands usually use the main data segment (the DS segment). However, the ESP and EBP registers are used for addressing the stack, so when either register is used, the stack segment (the SS segment) is selected.

Segment-override prefixes are provided for each of the segment registers. Only the following special cases have a default segment selection which is not affected by a segment-override prefix:

- Destination strings in string instructions use the ES segment
- Destination of a push or source of a pop uses the SS segment
- Instruction fetches use the CS segment

2.5.3.2 EFFECTIVE-ADDRESS COMPUTATION

The modR/M byte provides the most flexible form of addressing. Instructions which have a modR/M byte after the opcode are the most common in the instruction set. For memory operands specified by a modR/M byte, the offset within the selected segment is the sum of three components:

- A displacement
- A base register
- An index register (the index register may be multiplied by a factor of 2, 4, or 8)

Table 2-3. Default Segment Selection Rules

Type of Reference	Segment Used Register Used	Default Selection Rule
Instructions	Code Segment CS register	Automatic with instruction fetch.
Stack	Stack Segment SS register	All stack pushes and pops. Any memory reference which uses ESP or EBP as a base register.
Local Data	Data Segment DS register	All data references except when relative to stack or string destination.
Destination Strings	E-Space Segment ES register	Destination of string instructions.

The offset which results from adding these components is called an *effective address*. Each of these components may have either a positive or negative value. Figure 2-10 illustrates the full set of possibilities for modR/M addressing.

The displacement component, because it is encoded in the instruction, is useful for relative addressing by fixed amounts, such as:

- Location of simple scalar operands.
- Beginning of a statically allocated array.
- Offset to a field within a record.

The base and index components have similar functions. Both use the same set of general registers. Both can be used for addressing which changes during program execution, such as:

- Location of procedure parameters and local variables on the stack.
- The beginning of one record among several occurrences of the same record type or in an array of records.
- The beginning of one dimension of multiple dimension array.
- The beginning of a dynamically allocated array.

The uses of general registers as base or index components differ in the following respects:

- The ESP register cannot be used as an index register.
- When the ESP or EBP register is used as the base, the SS segment is the default selection. In all other cases, the DS segment is the default selection.

The scaling factor permits efficient indexing into an array when the array elements are 2, 4, or 8 bytes. The scaling of the index register is done in hardware at the time the address is evaluated. This eliminates an extra shift or multiply instruction.

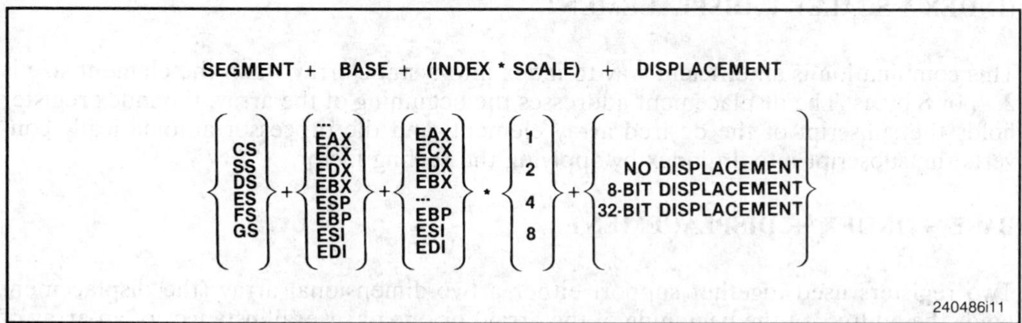

Figure 2-10. Effective Address Computation

The base, index, and displacement components may be used in any combination; any of these components may be null. A scale factor can be used only when an index also is used. Each possible combination is useful for data structures commonly used by programmers in high-level languages and assembly language. Suggested uses for some combinations of address components are described below.

DISPLACEMENT

The displacement alone indicates the offset of the operand. This form of addressing is used to access a statically allocated scalar operand. A byte, word, or doubleword displacement can be used.

BASE

The offset to the operand is specified indirectly in one of the general registers, as for "based" variables.

BASE + DISPLACEMENT

A register and a displacement can be used together for two distinct purposes:

1. Index into static array when the element size is not 2, 4, or 8 bytes. The displacement component encodes the offset of the beginning of the array. The register holds the results of a calculation to determine the offset to a specific element within the array.
2. Access a field of a record. The base register holds the address of the beginning of the record, while the displacement is an offset to the field.

An important special case of this combination is access to parameters in a procedure activation record. A procedure activation record is the stack frame created when a subroutine is entered. In this case, the EBP register is the best choice for the base register, because it automatically selects the stack segment. This is a compact encoding for this common function.

(INDEX * SCALE) + DISPLACEMENT

This combination is an efficient way to index into a static array when the element size is 2, 4, or 8 bytes. The displacement addresses the beginning of the array, the index register holds the subscript of the desired array element, and the processor automatically converts the subscript into an index by applying the scaling factor.

BASE + INDEX + DISPLACEMENT

Two registers used together support either a two-dimensional array (the displacement holds the address of the beginning of the array) or one of several instances of an array of records (the displacement is an offset to a field within the record).

BASE + (INDEX * SCALE) + DISPLACEMENT

This combination provides efficient indexing of a two-dimensional array when the elements of the array are 2, 4, or 8 bytes in size.

2.6 INTERRUPTS AND EXCEPTIONS

The i486 processor has two mechanisms for interrupting program execution:

1. *Exceptions* are synchronous events which are responses of the processor to certain conditions detected during the execution of an instruction.
2. *Interrupts* are asynchronous events typically triggered by external devices needing attention.

Interrupts and exceptions are alike in that both cause the processor to temporarily suspend the program being run in order to run a program of higher priority. The major distinction between these two kinds of interrupts is their origin. An exception is always reproducible by re-executing the program which caused the exception, while an interrupt can have a complex, timing-dependent relationship with programs.

Application programmers normally are not concerned with handling exceptions or interrupts. The operating system, monitor, or device driver handles them. More information on interrupts for system programmers may be found in Chapter 9. Certain kinds of exceptions, however, are relevant to application programming, and many operating systems give application programs the opportunity to service these exceptions. However, the operating system defines the interface between the application program and the exception mechanism of the i486 processor. Table 2-4 lists the interrupts and exceptions.

- A divide-error exception results when the DIV or IDIV instruction is executed with a zero denominator or when the quotient is too large for the destination operand. (See Chapter 3 for more information on the DIV and IDIV instructions.)
- A debug exception may be sent back to an application program if it results from the TF (trap) flag.
- A breakpoint exception results when an INT3 instruction is executed. This instruction is used by some debuggers to stop program execution at specific points.
- An overflow exception results when the INTO instruction is executed and the OF (overflow) flag is set. See Chapter 3 for a discussion of the INTO instruction.
- A bounds-check exception results when the BOUND instruction is executed with an array index which falls outside the bounds of the array. See Chapter 3 for a discussion of the BOUND instruction.
- The device-not-available exception occurs whenever the processor encounters an escape instruction and either the TS (task switched) or the EM (emulate coprocessor) bit of the CR0 control register is set.

Table 2-4. Exceptions and Interrupts

Vector Number	Description
0	Divide Error
1	Debugger Call
2	NMI Interrupt
3	Breakpoint
4	INTO-detected Overflow
5	BOUND Range Exceeded
6	Invalid Opcode
7	Device Not Available
8	Double Fault
9	(Intel® reserved. Do not use. Not used by i486™ CPU.)
10	Invalid Task State Segment
11	Segment Not Present
12	Stack Exception
13	General Protection
14	Page Fault
15	(Intel reserved. Do not use.)
16	Floating-Point Error
17	Alignment Check
18-31	(Intel reserved. Do not use.)
32-255	Maskable Interrupts

- An alignment-check exception is generated for unaligned memory operations in user mode (privilege level 3), provided both AM and AC are set. Memory operations at supervisor mode (privilege levels 0, 1, and 2), or memory operations which default to supervisor mode, do not generate this exception.

The INT instruction generates an interrupt whenever it is executed; the processor treats this interrupt as an exception. Its effects (and the effects of all other exceptions) are determined by exception handler routines in the application program or the operating system. The INT instruction itself is discussed in Chapter 3. See Chapter 9 for a more complete description of exceptions.

Exceptions caused by segmentation and paging are handled differently than interrupts. Normally, the contents of the program counter (EIP register) are saved on the stack when an exception or interrupt is generated. But exceptions resulting from segmentation and paging restore the contents of some processor registers to their state *before* interpretation of the instruction began. The saved contents of the program counter address the instruction which caused the exception, rather than the instruction after it. This lets the operating system fix the exception-generating condition and restart the program which generated the exception. This mechanism is completely transparent to the program.

Application Programming 3

CHAPTER 3
APPLICATION PROGRAMMING

This chapter is an overview of the integer instructions which programmers can use to write application software for the i486™ processor. The instructions are grouped by categories of related functions. (Additional application instructions for operating on floating-point operands are described in Part III.)

The instructions not discussed in this chapter or Part III normally are used only by operating-system programmers. Part II describes these system-level instructions.

These instruction descriptions are for the i486 processor in protected mode. The instruction set in this mode is a 32-bit superset of the instruction set used in Intel® 16-bit processors. In real-address mode or virtual-8086 mode, the i486 processor appears to have the architecture of a fast, enhanced 8086 processor with instruction set extensions. See Chapters 21, 22, 23, 24 and 25 for more information about running the 16-bit instruction set. All of the instructions described in this chapter are available in all modes.

The instruction set descriptions in Chapter 26 contain more detailed information on all instructions, including encoding, operation, timing, effect on flags, and exceptions which may be generated.

3.1 DATA MOVEMENT INSTRUCTIONS

These instructions provide convenient methods for moving bytes, words, or doublewords between memory and the processor registers. They come in three types:

1. General-purpose data movement instructions.
2. Stack manipulation instructions.
3. Type-conversion instructions.

3.1.1 General-Purpose Data Movement Instructions

MOV (Move) transfers a byte, word, or doubleword from the source operand to the destination operand. The MOV instruction is useful for transferring data along any of these paths:

- To a register from memory
- To memory from a register
- Between general registers
- Immediate data to a register
- Immediate data to memory

The MOV instruction cannot move from memory to memory or from a segment register to a segment register. Memory-to-memory moves can be performed, however, by the string move instruction MOVS. A special form of the MOV instruction is provided for transferring data between the AL or EAX registers and a location in memory specified by a 32-bit offset encoded in the instruction. This form of the instruction does not allow a segment override, index register, or scaling factor to be used. The encoding of this form is one byte shorter than the encoding of the general-purpose MOV instruction. A similar encoding is provided for moving an 8-, 16-, or 32-bit immediate into any of the general registers.

XCHG (Exchange) swaps the contents of two operands. This instruction takes the place of three MOV instructions. It does not require a temporary location to save the contents of one operand while the other is being loaded. The XCHG instruction is especially useful for implementing semaphores or similar data structures for process synchronization.

The XCHG instruction can swap two byte operands, two word operands, or two doubleword operands. The operands for the XCHG instruction may be two register operands, or a register operand and a memory operand. When used with a memory operand, XCHG automatically activates the LOCK signal. (See Chapter 13 for more information on bus locking).

3.1.2 Stack Manipulation Instructions

PUSH (Push) decrements the stack pointer (ESP register), then copies the source operand to the top of stack (see Figure 3-1). The PUSH instruction often is used to place parameters on the stack before calling a procedure. Inside a procedure, it can be used to reserve space on the stack for temporary variables. The PUSH instruction operates on

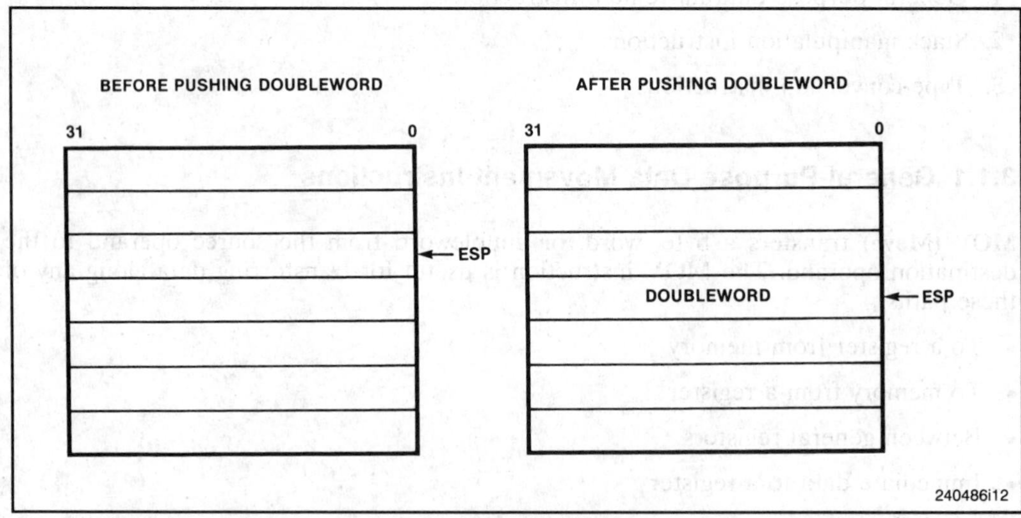

Figure 3-1. PUSH Instruction

memory operands, immediate operands, and register operands (including segment registers). A special form of the PUSH instruction is available for pushing a 32-bit general register on the stack. This form has an encoding which is one byte shorter than the general-purpose form.

PUSHA (Push All Registers) saves the contents of the eight general registers on the stack (see Figure 3-2). This instruction simplifies procedure calls by reducing the number of instructions required to save the contents of the general registers. The processor pushes the general registers on the stack in the following order: EAX, ECX, EDX, EBX, the initial value of ESP before EAX was pushed, EBP, ESI, and EDI. The effect of the PUSHA instruction is reversed using the POPA instruction.

POP (Pop) transfers the word or doubleword at the current top of stack (indicated by the ESP register) to the destination operand, and then increments the ESP register to point to the new top of stack. See Figure 3-3. POP moves information from the stack to a general register, segment register, or to memory. A special form of the POP instruction is available for popping a doubleword from the stack to a general register. This form has an encoding which is one byte shorter than the general-purpose form.

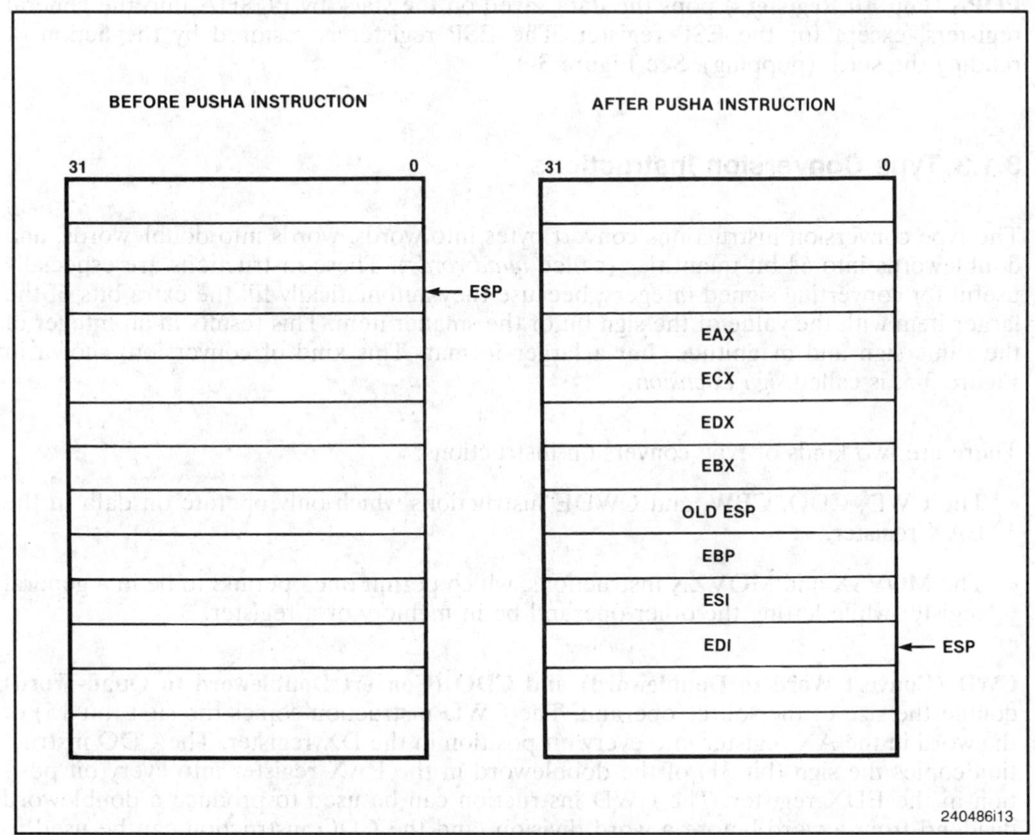

Figure 3-2. PUSHA Instruction

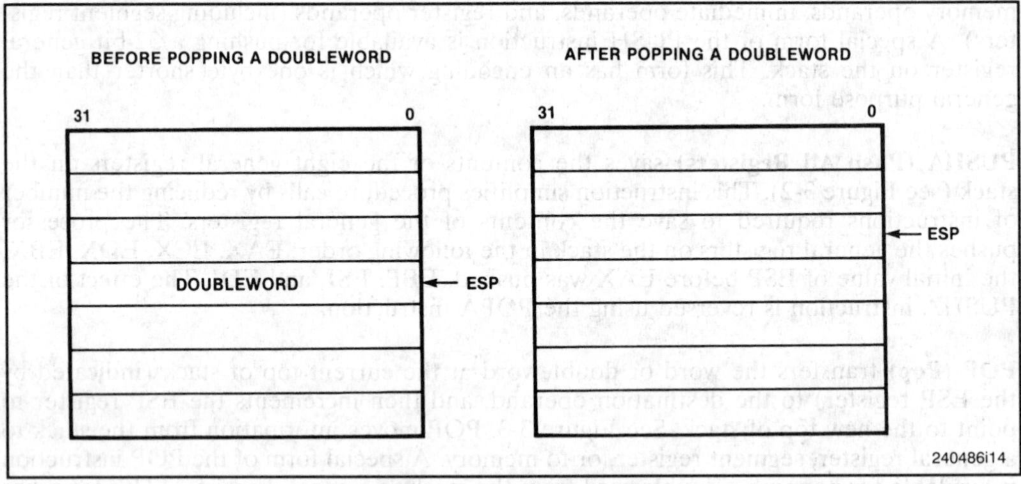

Figure 3-3. POP Instruction

POPA (Pop All Registers) pops the data saved on the stack by PUSHA into the general registers, except for the ESP register. The ESP register is restored by the action of reading the stack (popping). See Figure 3-4.

3.1.3 Type Conversion Instructions

The type conversion instructions convert bytes into words, words into doublewords, and doublewords into 64-bit quantities (called *quadwords*). These instructions are especially useful for converting signed integers, because they automatically fill the extra bits of the larger item with the value of the sign bit of the smaller item. This results in an integer of the same sign and magnitude, but a larger format. This kind of conversion, shown in Figure 3-5, is called *sign extension*.

There are two kinds of type conversion instructions:

- The CWD, CDQ, CBW, and CWDE instructions which only operate on data in the EAX register.
- The MOVSX and MOVZX instructions, which permit one operand to be in a general register while letting the other operand be in memory or a register.

CWD (Convert Word to Doubleword) and **CDQ (Convert Doubleword to Quad-Word)** double the size of the source operand. The CWD instruction copies the sign (bit 15) of the word in the AX register into every bit position in the DX register. The CDQ instruction copies the sign (bit 31) of the doubleword in the EAX register into every bit position in the EDX register. The CWD instruction can be used to produce a doubleword dividend from a word before a word division, and the CDQ instruction can be used to produce a quadword dividend from a doubleword before doubleword division.

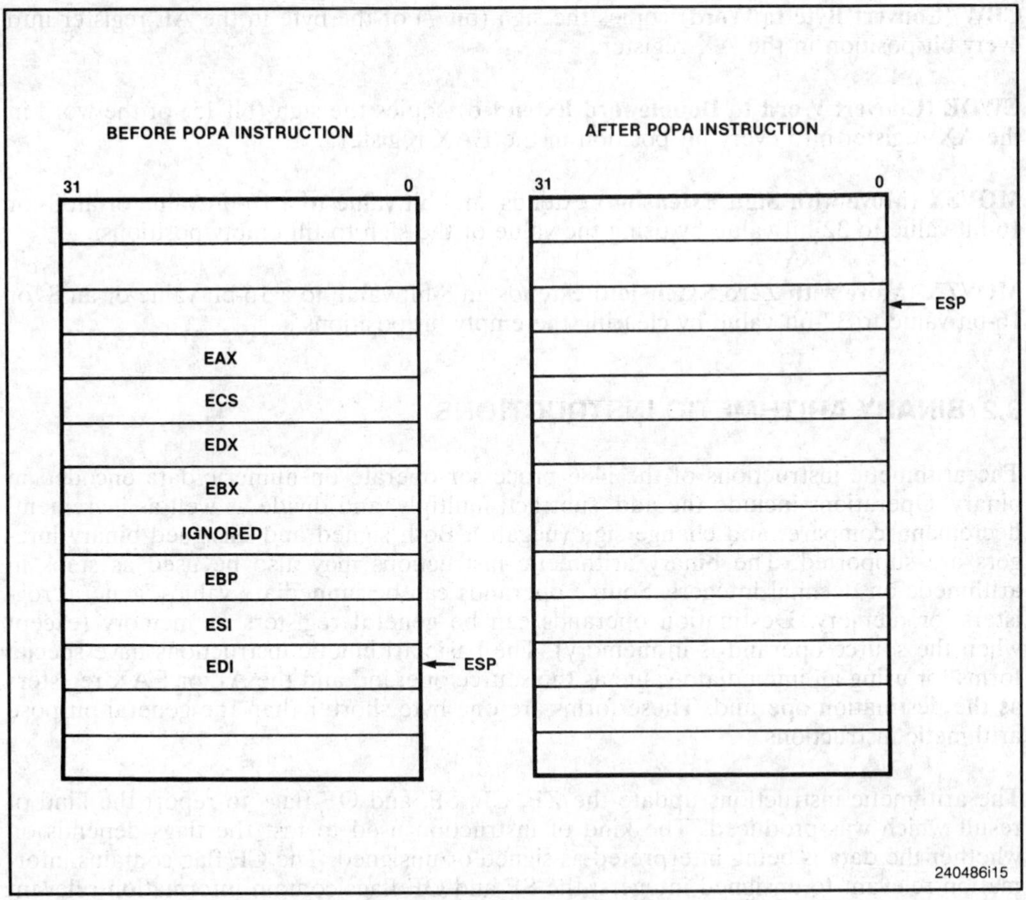

BEFORE POPA INSTRUCTION
AFTER POPA INSTRUCTION
31
0
EAX
ECS
EDX
EBX
IGNORED
EBP
ESI
EDI
ESP
ESP
240486i15

Figure 3-4. POPA Instruction

15
0
S N N N N N N N N N N N N N N N
BEFORE SIGN EXTENSION
31
15
0
S S S S S S S S S S S S S S S S S N N N N N N N N N N N N N N N
AFTER SIGN EXTENSION
240486i16

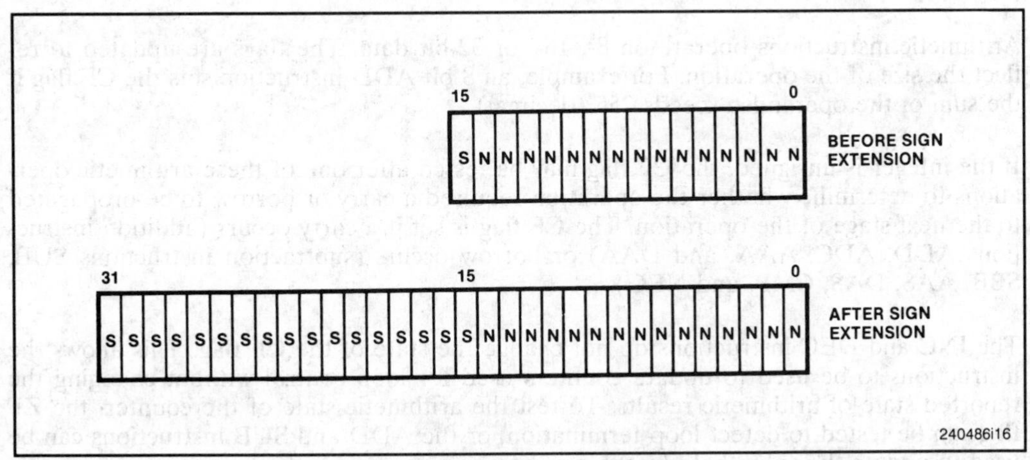

Figure 3-5. Sign Extension

CBW (Convert Byte to Word) copies the sign (bit 7) of the byte in the AL register into every bit position in the AX register.

CWDE (Convert Word to Doubleword Extended) copies the sign (bit 15) of the word in the AX register into every bit position in the EAX register.

MOVSX (Move with Sign Extension) extends an 8-bit value to a 16-bit value or an 8- or 16-bit value to 32-bit value by using the value of the sign to fill empty positions.

MOVZX (Move with Zero Extension) extends an 8-bit value to a 16-bit value or an 8- or 16-bit value to 32-bit value by clearing the empty bit positions.

3.2 BINARY ARITHMETIC INSTRUCTIONS

The arithmetic instructions of the i486 processor operate on numeric data encoded in binary. Operations include the add, subtract, multiply, and divide as well as increment, decrement, compare, and change sign (negate). Both signed and unsigned binary integers are supported. The binary arithmetic instructions may also be used as steps in arithmetic on decimal integers. Source operands can be immediate values, general registers, or memory. Destination operands can be general registers or memory (except when the source operand is in memory). The basic arithmetic instructions have special forms for using an immediate value as the source operand and the AL or EAX registers as the destination operand. These forms are one byte shorter than the general-purpose arithmetic instructions.

The arithmetic instructions update the ZF, CF, SF, and OF flags to report the kind of result which was produced. The kind of instruction used to test the flags depends on whether the data is being interpreted as signed or unsigned. The CF flag contains information relevant to unsigned integers; the SF and OF flags contain information relevant to signed integers. The ZF flag is relevant to both signed and unsigned integers; the ZF flag is set when all bits of the result are clear.

Arithmetic instructions operate on 8-, 16-, or 32-bit data. The flags are updated to reflect the size of the operation. For example, an 8-bit ADD instruction sets the CF flag if the sum of the operands exceeds 255 (decimal).

If the integer is unsigned, the CF flag may be tested after one of these arithmetic operations to determine whether the operation required a carry or borrow to be propagated to the next stage of the operation. The CF flag is set if a carry occurs (addition instructions ADD, ADC, AAA, and DAA) or borrow occurs (subtraction instructions SUB, SBB, AAS, DAS, CMP, and NEG).

The INC and DEC instructions do not change the state of the CF flag. This allows the instructions to be used to update counters used for loop control without changing the reported state of arithmetic results. To test the arithmetic state of the counter, the ZF flag can be tested to detect loop termination, or the ADD and SUB instructions can be used to update the value held by the counter.

The SF and OF flags support signed integer arithmetic. The SF flag has the value of the sign bit of the result. The most significant bit (MSB) of the magnitude of a signed integer is the bit next to the sign—bit 6 of a byte, bit 14 of a word, or bit 30 of a doubleword. The OF flag is set in either of these cases:

- A carry was generated from the MSB into the sign bit but no carry was generated out of the sign bit (addition instructions ADD, ADC, INC, AAA, and DAA). In other words, the result was greater than the greatest positive number which could be represented in two's complement form.
- A carry was generated from the sign bit into the MSB but no carry was generated into the sign bit (subtraction instructions SUB, SBB, DEC, AAS, DAS, CMP, and NEG). In other words, the result was smaller than the smallest negative number which could be represented in two's complement form.

These status flags are tested by either kind of conditional instruction: J*cc* (jump on condition *cc*) or SET*cc* (byte set on condition).

3.2.1 Addition and Subtraction Instructions

ADD (Add Integers) replaces the destination operand with the sum of the source and destination operands. The OF, SF, ZF, AF, PF, and CF flags are affected.

ADC (Add Integers with Carry) replaces the destination operand with the sum of the source and destination operands, plus 1 if the CF flag is set. If the CF flag is clear, the ADC instruction performs the same operation as the ADD instruction. An ADC instruction is used to propagate carry when adding numbers in stages, for example when using 32-bit ADD instructions to sum quadword operands. The OF, SF, ZF, AF, PF, and CF flags are affected.

INC (Increment) adds 1 to the destination operand. The INC instruction preserves the state of the CF flag. This allows the use of INC instructions to update counters in loops without disturbing the status flags resulting from an arithmetic operation used for loop control. The ZF flag can be used to detect when carry would have occurred. Use an ADD instruction with an immediate value of 1 to perform an increment which updates the CF flag. A one-byte form of this instruction is available when the operand is a general register. The OF, SF, ZF, AF, and PF flags are affected.

SUB (Subtract Integers) subtracts the source operand from the destination operand and replaces the destination operand with the result. If a borrow is required, the CF flag is set. The operands may be signed or unsigned bytes, words, or doublewords. The OF, SF, ZF, AF, PF, and CF flags are affected.

SBB (Subtract Integers with Borrow) subtracts the source operand from the destination operand and replaces the destination operand with the result, minus 1 if the CF flag is set. If the CF flag is clear, the SBB instruction performs the same operation as the SUB instruction. An SBB instruction is used to propagate borrow when subtracting numbers in stages, for example when using 32-bit SUB instructions to subtract one quadword operand from another. The OF, SF, ZF, AF, PF, and CF flags are affected.

DEC (Decrement) subtracts 1 from the destination operand. The DEC instruction preserves the state of the CF flag. This allows the use of the DEC instruction to update counters in loops without disturbing the status flags resulting from an arithmetic operation used for loop control. Use a SUB instruction with an immediate value of 1 to perform a decrement which updates the CF flag. A one-byte form of this instruction is available when the operand is a general register. The OF, SF, ZF, AF, and PF flags are affected.

3.2.2 Comparison and Sign Change Instruction

CMP (Compare) subtracts the source operand from the destination operand. It updates the OF, SF, ZF, AF, PF, and CF flags, but does not modify the source or destination operands. A subsequent J*cc* or SET*cc* instruction can test the flags.

NEG (Negate) subtracts a signed integer operand from zero. The effect of the NEG instruction is to change the sign of a two's complement operand while keeping its magnitude. The OF, SF, ZF, AF, PF, and CF flags are affected.

3.2.3 Multiplication Instructions

The i486 processor has separate multiply instructions for unsigned and signed operands. The MUL instruction operates on unsigned integers, while the IMUL instruction operates on signed integers as well as unsigned.

MUL (Unsigned Integer Multiply) performs an unsigned multiplication of the source operand and the AL, AX, or EAX register. If the source is a byte, the processor multiplies it by the value held in the AL register and returns the double-length result in the AH and AL registers. If the source operand is a word, the processor multiplies it by the value held in the AX register and returns the double-length result in the DX and AX registers. If the source operand is a doubleword, the processor multiplies it by the value held in the EAX register and returns the quadword result in the EDX and EAX registers. The MUL instruction sets the CF and OF flags when the upper half of the result is non-zero; otherwise, the flags are cleared. The state of the SF, ZF, AF, and PF flags is undefined.

IMUL (Signed Integer Multiply) performs a signed multiplication operation. The IMUL instruction has three forms:

1. A one-operand form. The operand may be a byte, word, or doubleword located in memory or in a general register. This instruction uses the EAX and EDX registers as implicit operands in the same way as the MUL instruction.
2. A two-operand form. One of the source operands is in a general register while the other may be in a general register or memory. The result replaces the general-register operand.
3. A three-operand form; two are source operands and one is the destination. One of the source operands is an immediate value supplied by the instruction; the second may be in memory or in a general register. The result is stored in a general register.

The immediate operand is a two's complement signed integer. If the immediate operand is a byte, the processor automatically sign-extends it to the size of the second operand before performing the multiplication.

The three forms are similar in most respects:

- The length of the product is calculated to twice the length of the operands.
- The CF and OF flags are set when significant bits are carried into the upper half of the result. The CF and OF flags are cleared when the upper half of the result is the sign-extension of the lower half. The state of the SF, ZF, AF, and PF flags is undefined.

However, forms 2 and 3 differ because the product is truncated to the length of the operands before it is stored in the destination register. Because of this truncation, the OF flag should be tested to ensure that no significant bits are lost. (For ways to test the OF flag, see the JO, INTO, and PUSHF instructions.)

Forms 2 and 3 of IMUL also may be used with unsigned operands because, whether the operands are signed or unsigned, the lower half of the product is the same. The CF and OF flags, however, cannot be used to determine if the upper half of the result is non-zero.

3.2.4 Division Instructions

The i486 processor has separate division instructions for unsigned and signed operands. The DIV instruction operates on unsigned integers, while the IDIV instruction operates on both signed and unsigned integers. In either case, a divide-error exception is generated if the divisor is zero or if the quotient is too large for the AL, AX, or EAX register.

DIV (Unsigned Integer Divide) performs an unsigned division of the AL, AX, or EAX register by the source operand. The dividend (the accumulator) is twice the size of the divisor (the source operand); the quotient and remainder have the same size as the divisor, as shown in Table 3-1.

Non-integral results are truncated toward 0. The remainder is always smaller than the divisor. For unsigned byte division, the largest quotient is 255. For unsigned word division, the largest quotient is 65,535. For unsigned doubleword division the largest quotient is $2^{32}-1$. The state of the OF, SF, ZF, AF, PF, and CF flags is undefined.

Table 3-1. Operands for Division

Operand Size (Divisor)	Dividend	Quotient	Remainder
Byte	AX register	AL register	AH register
Word	DX and AX	AX register	DX register
Doubleword	EDX and EAX	EAX register	EDX register

IDIV (Signed Integer Divide) performs a signed division of the accumulator by the source operand. The IDIV instruction uses the same registers as the DIV instruction.

For signed byte division, the maximum positive quotient is +127, and the minimum negative quotient is −128. For signed word division, the maximum positive quotient is +32,767, and the minimum negative quotient is −32,768. For signed doubleword division the maximum positive quotient is $2^{32}-1$, the minimum negative quotient is -2^{31}. Non-integral results are truncated towards 0. The remainder always has the same sign as the dividend and is less than the divisor in magnitude. The state of the OF, SF, ZF, AF, PF, and CF flags is undefined.

3.3 DECIMAL ARITHMETIC INSTRUCTIONS

Decimal arithmetic is performed by combining the binary arithmetic instructions (already discussed in the prior section) with the decimal arithmetic instructions. The decimal arithmetic instructions are used in one of the following ways:

- To adjust the results of a previous binary arithmetic operation to produce a valid packed or unpacked decimal result.
- To adjust the inputs to a subsequent binary arithmetic operation so that the operation will produce a valid packed or unpacked decimal result. These instructions operate only on the AL or AH registers. Most use the AF flag.

3.3.1 Packed BCD Adjustment Instructions

DAA (Decimal Adjust after Addition) adjusts the result of adding two valid packed decimal operands in the AL register. A DAA instruction must follow the addition of two pairs of packed decimal numbers (one digit in each half-byte) to obtain a pair of valid packed decimal digits as results. The CF flag is set if a carry occurs. The SF, ZF, AF, PF, and CF flags are affected. The state of the OF flag is undefined.

DAS (Decimal Adjust after Subtraction) adjusts the result of subtracting two valid packed decimal operands in the AL register. A DAS instruction must always follow the subtraction of one pair of packed decimal numbers (one digit in each half-byte) from another to obtain a pair of valid packed decimal digits as results. The CF flag is set if a borrow is needed. The SF, ZF, AF, PF, and CF flags are affected. The state of the OF flag is undefined.

3.3.2 Unpacked BCD Adjustment Instructions

AAA (ASCII Adjust after Addition) changes the contents of the AL register to a valid unpacked decimal number, and clears the upper 4 bits. An AAA instruction must follow the addition of two unpacked decimal operands in the AL register. The CF flag is set and the contents of the AH register are incremented if a carry occurs. The AF and CF flags are affected. The state of the OF, SF, ZF, and PF flags is undefined.

AAS (ASCII Adjust after Subtraction) changes the contents of the AL register to a valid unpacked decimal number, and clears the upper 4 bits. An AAS instruction must follow the subtraction of one unpacked decimal operand from another in the AL register. The CF flag is set and the contents of the AH register are decremented if a borrow is needed. The AF and CF flags are affected. The state of the OF, SF, ZF, and PF flags is undefined.

AAM (ASCII Adjust after Multiplication) corrects the result of a multiplication of two valid unpacked decimal numbers. An AAM instruction must follow the multiplication of two decimal numbers to produce a valid decimal result. The upper digit is left in the AH register, the lower digit in the AL register. The SF, ZF, and PF flags are affected. The state of the AF, OF, and CF flags is undefined.

AAD (ASCII Adjust before Division) modifies the numerator in the AH and AL registers to prepare for the division of two valid unpacked decimal operands, so that the quotient produced by the division will be a valid unpacked decimal number. The AH register should contain the upper digit and the AL register should contain the lower digit. This instruction adjusts the value and places the result in the AL register. The AH register will be clear. The SF, ZF, and PF flags are affected. The state of the AF, OF, and CF flags is undefined.

3.4 LOGICAL INSTRUCTIONS

The logical instructions have two operands. Source operands can be immediate values, general registers, or memory. Destination operands can be general registers or memory (except when the source operand is in memory). The logical instructions modify the state of the flags. Short forms of the instructions are available when the an immediate source operand is applied to a destination operand in the AL or EAX registers. The group of logical instructions includes:

- Boolean operation instructions
- Bit test and modify instructions
- Bit scan instructions
- Rotate and shift instructions
- Byte set on condition

3.4.1 Boolean Operation Instructions

The logical operations are performed by the AND, OR, XOR, and NOT instructions.

NOT (Not) inverts the bits in the specified operand to form a one's complement of the operand. The NOT instruction is a unary operation which uses a single operand in a register or memory. NOT has no effect on the flags.

The AND, OR, and XOR instructions perform the standard logical operations "and," "or," and "exclusive or." These instructions can use the following combinations of operands:

- Two register operands
- A general register operand with a memory operand
- An immediate operand with either a general register operand or a memory operand

The AND, OR, and XOR instructions clear the OF and CF flags, leave the AF flag undefined, and update the SF, ZF, and PF flags.

3.4.2 Bit Test and Modify Instructions

This group of instructions operates on a single bit which can be in memory or in a general register. The location of the bit is specified as an offset from the low end of the operand. The value of the offset either may be given by an immediate byte in the instruction or may be contained in a general register.

These instructions first assign the value of the selected bit to the CF flag. Then a new value is assigned to the selected bit, as determined by the operation. The state of the OF, SF, ZF, AF, and PF flags is undefined. Table 3-2 defines these instructions.

3.4.3 Bit Scan Instructions

These instructions scan a word or doubleword for a set bit and store the bit index (an integer representing the bit position) of the first set bit into a register. The bit string being scanned may be in a register or in memory. The ZF flag is set if the entire word is clear, otherwise the ZF flag is cleared. In the former case, the value of the destination register is left undefined. The state of the OF, SF, AF, PF, and CF flags is undefined.

BSF (Bit Scan Forward) scans low-to-high (from bit 0 toward the upper bit positions).

BSR (Bit Scan Reverse) scans high-to-low (from the uppermost bit toward bit 0).

3.4.4 Shift and Rotate Instructions

The shift and rotate instructions rearrange the bits within an operand.

Table 3-2. Bit Test and Modify Instructions

Instruction	Effect on CF Flag	Effect on Selected Bit
BT (Bit Test)	CF flag ← Selected Bit	no effect
BTS (Bit Test and Set)	CF flag ← Selected Bit	Selected Bit ← 1
BTR (Bit Test and Reset)	CF flag ← Selected Bit	Selected Bit ← 0
BTC (Bit Test and Complement)	CF flag ← Selected Bit	Selected Bit ← – (Selected Bit)

These instructions fall into the following classes:

- Shift instructions
- Double shift instructions
- Rotate instructions

3.4.4.1 SHIFT INSTRUCTIONS

Shift instructions apply an arithmetic or logical shift to bytes, words, and doublewords. An arithmetic shift right copies the sign bit into empty bit positions on the upper end of the operand, while a logical shift right fills clears the empty bit positions. An arithmetic shift is a fast way to perform a simple calculation. For example, an arithmetic shift right by one bit position divides an integer by two. A logical shift right divides an unsigned integer or a positive integer, but a signed negative integer loses its sign bit.

The arithmetic and logical shift right instructions, SAR and SHR, differ only in their treatment of the bit positions emptied by shifting the contents of the operand. Note that there is no difference between an arithmetic shift left and a logical shift left. Two names, SAL and SHL, are supported for this instruction in the assembler.

A count specifies the number of bit positions to shift an operand. Bits can be shifted up to 31 places. A shift instruction can give the count in any of three ways. One form of shift instruction always shifts by one bit position. The second form gives the count as an immediate operand. The third form gives the count as the value contained in the CL register. This last form allows the count to be a result from a calculation. Only the low five bits of the CL register are used.

When the number of bit positions to shift is zero, no flags are affected. Otherwise, the CF flag is left with the value of the last bit shifted out of the operand. In a single-bit shift, the OF flag is set if the value of the uppermost bit (sign bit) was changed by the operation. Otherwise, the OF flag is cleared. After a shift of more than one bit position, the state of the OF flag is undefined. On a shift of one or more bit positions, the SF, ZF, PF, and CF flags are affected, and the state of the AF flag is undefined.

SAL (Shift Arithmetic Left) shifts the destination byte, word, or doubleword operand left by one bit position or by the number of bits specified in the count operand (an immediate value or a value contained in the CL register). Empty bit positions are cleared. See Figure 3-6.

SHL (Shift Logical Left) is another name for the SAL instruction. It is supported in the assembler.

SHR (Shift Logical Right) shifts the destination byte, word, or doubleword operand right by one bit position or by the number of bits specified in the count operand (an immediate value or a value contained in the CL register). Empty bit positions are cleared. See Figure 3-7.

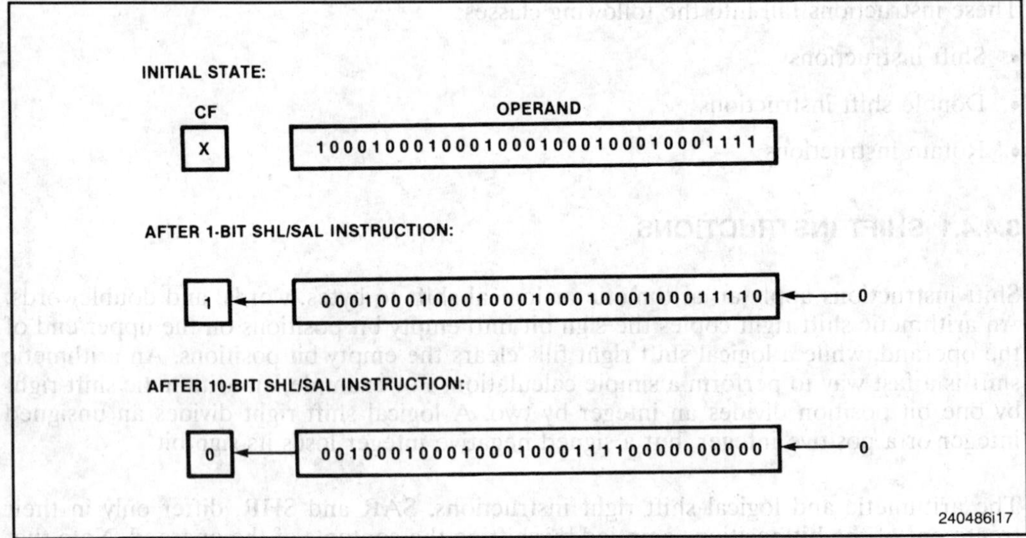

Figure 3-6. SHL/SAL Instruction

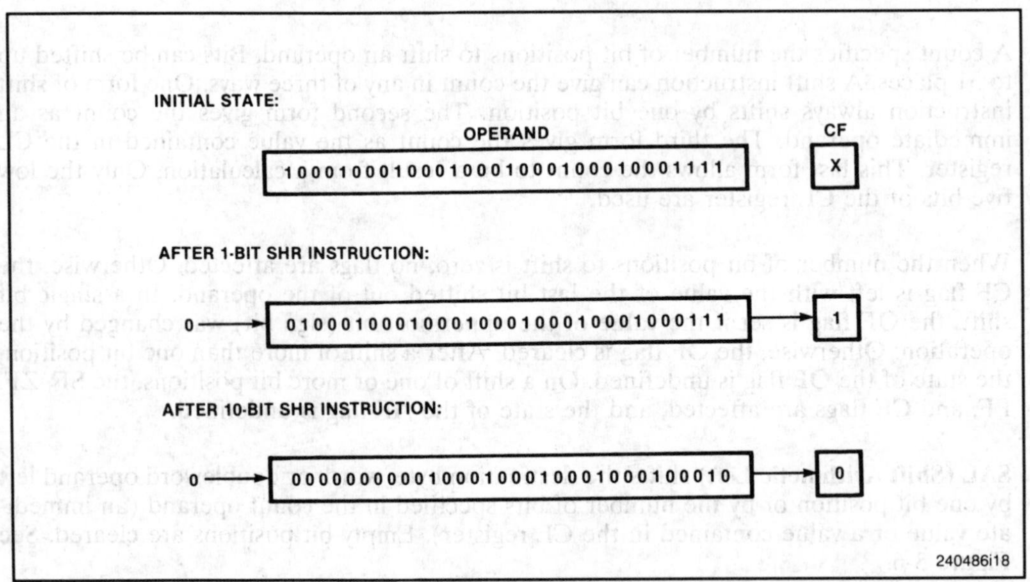

Figure 3-7. SHR Instruction

SAR (Shift Arithmetic Right) shifts the destination byte, word, or doubleword operand to the right by one bit position or by the number of bits specified in the count operand (an immediate value or a value contained in the CL register). The sign of the operand is preserved by clearing empty bit positions if the operand is positive, or setting the empty bits if the operand is negative. See Figure 3-8.

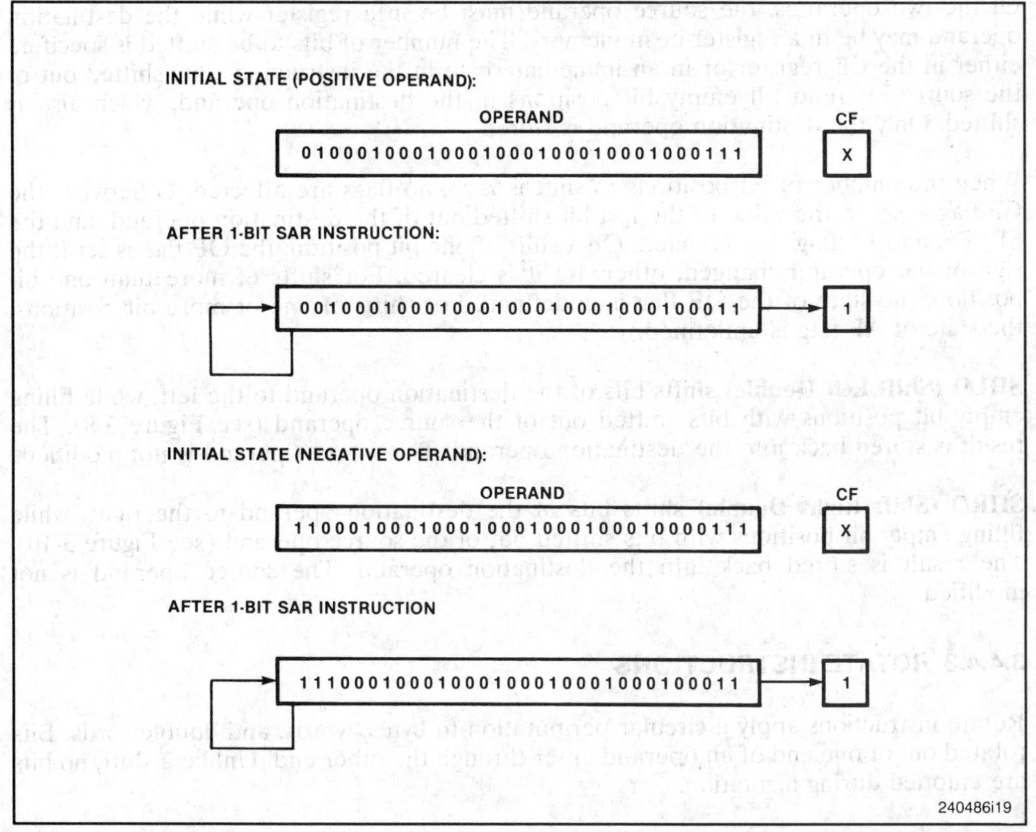

Figure 3-8. SAR Instruction

Even though this instruction can be used to divide integers by an integer power of two, **the type of division is not the same as that produced by the IDIV instruction**. The quotient from the IDIV instruction is rounded toward zero, whereas the "quotient" of the SAR instruction is rounded toward negative infinity. This difference is apparent only for negative numbers. For example, when the IDIV instruction is used to divide −9 by 4, the result is −2 with a remainder of −1. If the SAR instruction is used to shift −9 right by two bits, the result is −3. The "remainder" of this kind of division is +13; however, the SAR instruction stores only the high-order bit of the remainder (in the CF flag).

3.4.4.2 DOUBLE-SHIFT INSTRUCTIONS

These instructions provide the basic operations needed to implement operations on long unaligned bit strings. The double shifts operate either on word or doubleword operands, as follows:

- Take two word operands and produce a one-word result (32-bit shift).
- Take two doubleword operands and produce a doubleword result (64-bit shift).

Of the two operands, the source operand must be in a register while the destination operand may be in a register or in memory. The number of bits to be shifted is specified either in the CL register or in an immediate byte in the instruction. Bits shifted out of the source operand fill empty bit positions in the destination operand, which also is shifted. Only the destination operand is stored.

When the number of bit positions to shift is zero, no flags are affected. Otherwise, the CF flag is set to the value of the last bit shifted out of the destination operand, and the SF, ZF, and PF flags are affected. On a shift of one bit position, the OF flag is set if the sign of the operand changed, otherwise it is cleared. For shifts of more than one bit position, the state of the OF flag is undefined. For shifts of one or more bit positions, the state of AF flag is undefined.

SHLD (Shift Left Double) shifts bits of the destination operand to the left, while filling empty bit positions with bits shifted out of the source operand (see Figure 3-9). The result is stored back into the destination operand. The source operand is not modified.

SHRD (Shift Right Double) shifts bits of the destination operand to the right, while filling empty bit positions with bits shifted out of the source operand (see Figure 3-10). The result is stored back into the destination operand. The source operand is not modified.

3.4.4.3 ROTATE INSTRUCTIONS

Rotate instructions apply a circular permutation to bytes, words, and doublewords. Bits rotated out of one end of an operand enter through the other end. Unlike a shift, no bits are emptied during a rotation.

Rotate instructions use only the CF and OF flags. The CF flag may act as an extension of the operand in two of the rotate instructions, allowing a bit to be isolated and then tested by a conditional jump instruction (JC or JNC). The CF flag always contains the value of the last bit rotated out of the operand, even if the instruction does not use the CF flag as an extension of the operand. The state of the SF, ZF, AF, and PF flags is not affected.

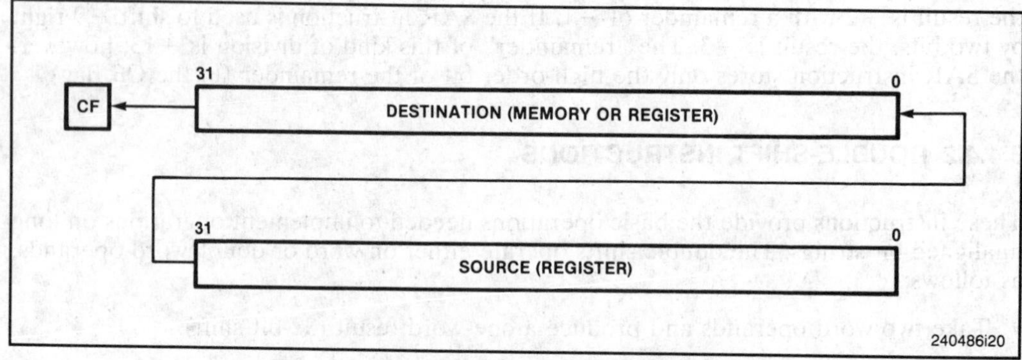

Figure 3-9. SHLD Instruction

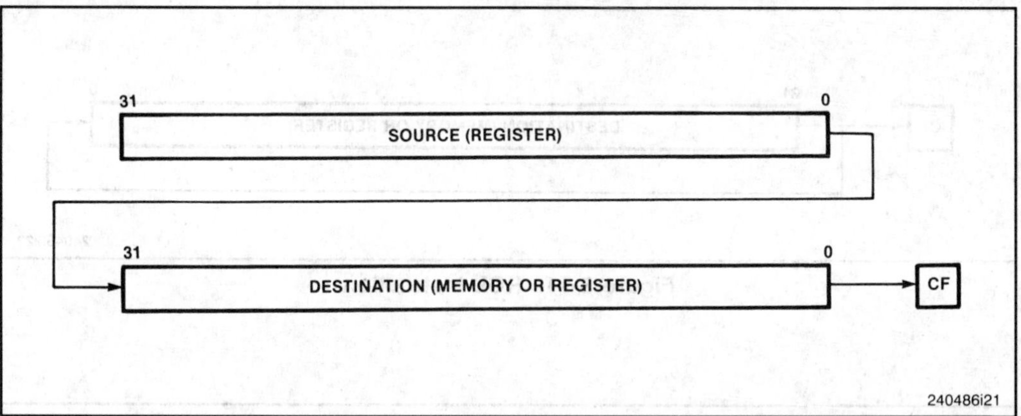

Figure 3-10. SHRD Instruction

In a single-bit rotation, the OF flag is set if the operation changes the uppermost bit (sign bit) of the destination operand. If the sign bit retains its original value, the OF flag is cleared. After a rotate of more than one bit position, the value of the OF flag is undefined.

ROL (Rotate Left) rotates the byte, word, or doubleword destination operand left by one bit position or by the number of bits specified in the count operand (an immediate value or a value contained in the CL register). For each bit position of the rotation, the bit which exits from the left of the operand returns at the right. See Figure 3-11.

ROR (Rotate Right) rotates the byte, word, or doubleword destination operand right by one bit position or by the number of bits specified in the count operand (an immediate value or a value contained in the CL register). For each bit position of the rotation, the bit which exits from the right of the operand returns at the left. See Figure 3-12.

RCL (Rotate Through Carry Left) rotates bits in the byte, word, or doubleword destination operand left by one bit position or by the number of bits specified in the count operand (an immediate value or a value contained in the CL register).

This instruction differs from ROL in that it treats the CF flag as a one-bit extension on the upper end of the destination operand. Each bit which exits from the left side of the operand moves into the CF flag. At the same time, the bit in the CF flag enters the right side. See Figure 3-13.

RCR (Rotate Through Carry Right) rotates bits in the byte, word, or doubleword destination operand right by one bit position or by the number of bits specified in the count operand (an immediate value or a value contained in the CL register).

This instruction differs from ROR in that it treats CF as a one-bit extension on the lower end of the destination operand. Each bit which exits from the right side of the operand moves into the CF flag. At the same time, the bit in the CF flag enters the left side. See Figure 3-14.

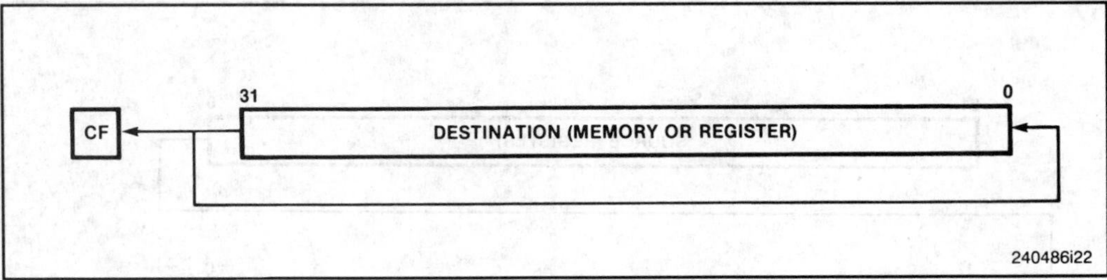

Figure 3-11. ROL Instruction

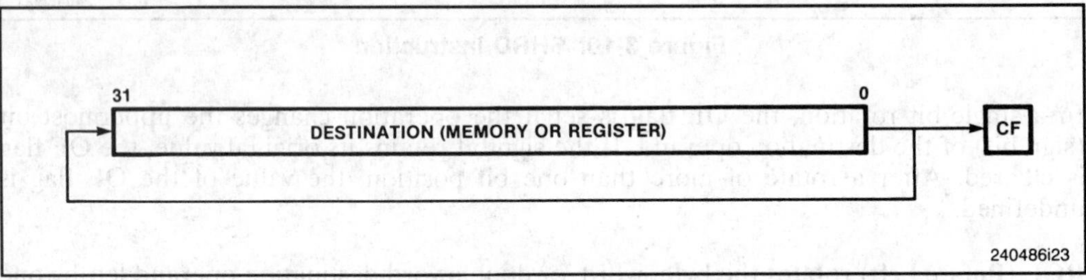

Figure 3-12. ROR Instruction

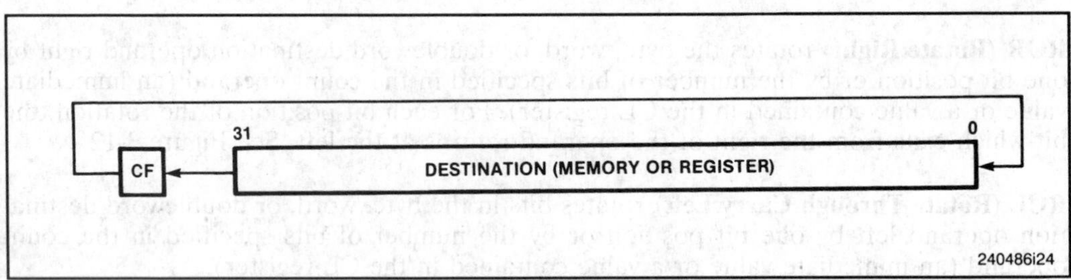

Figure 3-13. RCL Instruction

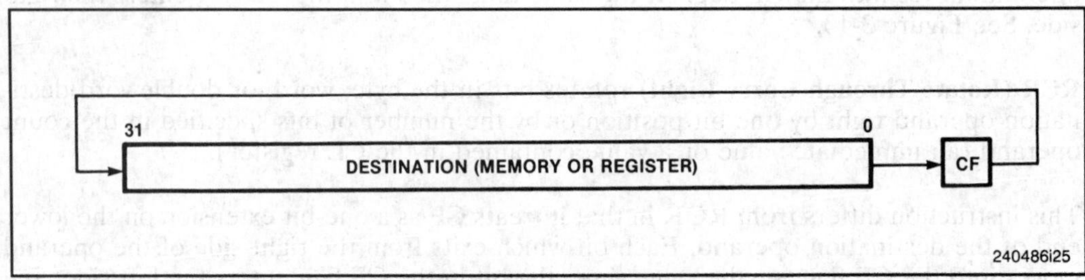

Figure 3-14. RCR Instruction

3.4.4.4 FAST "bit blt" USING DOUBLE-SHIFT INSTRUCTIONS

One purpose of the double shift instructions is to implement a bit string move, with arbitrary misalignment of the bit strings. This is called a "bit blt" (BIT BLock Transfer). A simple example is to move a bit string from an arbitrary offset into a doubleword-aligned byte string. A left-to-right string is moved 32 bits at a time if a double shift is used inside the move loop.

```
        MOV    ESI,ScrAddr
        MOV    EDI,DestAddr
        MOV    EBX,WordCnt
        MOV    CL,RelOffset ; relative offset Dest-Src
        MOV    EDX,[ESI]    ; load first word of source
        ADD    ESI,4        ; bump source address
BltLoop:
        LODS                ; new low order part in EAX
        SHLD EDX,EAX,CL     ; EDX overwritten with aligned stuff
        XCHG EDX,EAX        ; Swap high and low words
        STOS                ; Write out next aligned chunk
        DEC  EBX            ; Decrement loop count
        JNZ  BltLoop
```

This loop is simple, yet allows the data to be moved in 32-bit chunks for the highest possible performance. Without a double shift, the best which can be achieved is 16 bits per loop iteration by using a 32-bit shift, and replacing the XCHG instruction with a ROR instruction by 16 to swap the high and low words of registers. A more general loop than shown above would require some extra masking on the first doubleword moved (before the main loop), and on the last doubleword moved (after the main loop), but would have the same 32-bits per loop iteration as the code above.

3.4.4.5 FAST BIT STRING INSERT AND EXTRACT

The double shift instructions also make possible:

- Fast insertion of a bit string from a register into an arbitrary bit location in a larger bit string in memory, without disturbing the bits on either side of the inserted bits
- Fast extraction of a bit string into a register from an arbitrary bit location in a larger bit string in memory, without disturbing the bits on either side of the extracted bits

The following coded examples illustrate bit insertion and extraction under various conditions:

1. Bit String Insertion into Memory (when the bit string is 1-25 bits long, i.e., spans four bytes or less):

```
; Insert a right-justified bit string from a register into
; a bit string in memory.
;
; Assumptions:
; 1. The base of the string array is doubleword aligned.
```

```
; 2. The length of the bit string is an immediate value
;     and the bit offset is held in a register.
;
; The ESI register holds the right-justified bit string
; to be inserted.
; The EDI register holds the bit offset of the start of the
; substring.
; The EAX register and ECX are also used.
;
MOV   ECX,EDI                    ; save original offset
SHR   EDI,3                      ; divide offset by 8 (byte addr)
AND   CL,7H                      ; get low three bits of offset
MOV   EAX, [EDI]strg_base        ; move string dword into EAX
ROR   EAX,CL                     ; right justify old bit field
SHRD  EAX,ESI,length             ; bring in new bits
ROL   EAX,length                 ; right justify new bit field
ROL   EAX,CL                     ; bring to final position
MOV   [EDI]strg_base,EAX         ; replace doubleword in memory
```

2. Bit String Insertion into Memory (when the bit string is 1-31 bits long, i.e., spans five bytes or less):

```
; Insert a right-justified bit string from a register into
; a bit string in memory.
;
; Assumptions:
; 1. The base of the string array is doubleword aligned.
; 2. The length of the bit string is an immediate value
;     and the bit offset is held in a register.
;
; The ESI register holds the right-justified bit string
; to be inserted.
; The EDI register holds the bit offset of the start of the
; substring.
; The EAX, EBX, ECX, and EDI registers also are used.
;
MOV   ECX,EDI                    ; temp storage for offset
SHR   EDI,5                      ; divide offset by 32 (dwords)
SHL   EDI,2                      ; multiply by 4 (byte address)
AND   CL,1FH                     ; get low five bits of offset
MOV   EAX,[EDI]strg_base         ; move low string dword into EAX
MOV   EDX,[EDI]strg_base+4       ; other string dword into EDX
MOV   EBX,EAX                    ; temp storage for part of string
SHRD  EAX,EDX,CL                 ; shift by offset within dword
SHRD  EAX,EBX,CL                 ; shift by offset within dword
SHRD  EAX,ESI,length             ; bring in new bits
ROL   EAX,length                 ; right justify new bit field
MOV   EBX,EAX                    ; temp storage for string
SHLD  EAX,EDX,CL                 ; shift by offset within word
SHLD  EDX,EBX,CL                 ; shift by offset within word
```

```
MOV   [EDI]strg_base,EAX        ; replace dword in memory
MOV   [EDI]strg_base+4,EDX      ; replace dword in memory
```

3. Bit String Insertion into Memory (when the bit string is exactly 32 bits long, i.e., spans four or five bytes):

```
; Insert right-justified bit string from a register into
; a bit string in memory.
;
; Assumptions:
; 1. The base of the string array is doubleword aligned.
; 2. The length of the bit string is 32 bits
;     and the bit offset is held in a register.
;
; The ESI register holds the 32-bit string to be inserted.
; The EDI register holds the bit offset to the start of the
; substring.
; The EAX, EBX, ECX, and EDI registers also are used.
;
MOV   EDX,EDI                   ; save original offset
SHR   EDI,5                     ; divide offset by 32 (dwords)
SHL   EDI,2                     ; multiply by 4 (byte address)
AND   CL,1FH                    ; isolate low five bits of offset
MOV   EAX,[EDI]strg_base        ; move low string dword into EAX
MOV   EDX,[EDI]strg_base+4      ; other string dword into EDX
MOV   EBX,EAX                   ; temp storage for part of string
SHRD  EAX,EDX                   ; shift by offset within dword
SHRD  EDX,EBX                   ; shift by offset within dword
MOV   EAX,ESI                   ; move 32-bit field into position
MOV   EBX,EAX                   ; temp storage for part of string
SHLD  EAX,EDX                   ; shift by offset within word
SHLD  EDX,EBX                   ; shift by offset within word
MOV   [EDI]strg_base,EAX        ; replace dword in memory
MOV   [EDI]strg_base,+4,EDX     ; replace dword in memory
```

4. Bit String Extraction from Memory (when the bit string is 1-25 bits long, i.e., spans four bytes or less):

```
; Extract a right-justified bit string into a register from
; a bit string in memory.
;
; Assumptions:
; 1) The base of the string array is doubleword aligned.
; 2) The length of the bit string is an immediate value
;    and the bit offset is held in a register.
;
; The EAX register hold the right-justified, zero-padded
; bit string that was extracted.
; The EDI register holds the bit offset of the start of the
; substring.
; The EDI, and ECX registers also are used.
;
```

```
MOV   ECX,EDI                   ; temp storage for offset
SHR   EDI,3                     ; divide offset by 8 (byte addr)
AND   CL,7H                     ; get low three bits of offset
MOV   EAX,[EDI]strg_base        ; move string dword into EAX
SHR   EAX,CL                    ; shift by offset within dword
AND   EAX,mask                  ; extracted bit field in EAX
```

5. Bit String Extraction from Memory (when bit string is 1-32 bits long, i.e., spans five bytes or less):

```
; Extract a right-justified bit string into a register from a
; bit string in memory.
;
; Assumptions:
; 1) The base of the string array is doubleword aligned.
; 2) The length of the bit string is an immediate
;    value and the bit offset is held in a register.
;
; The EAX register holds the right-justified, zero-padded
; bit string that was extracted.
; The EDI register holds the bit offset of the start of the
; substring.
; The EAX, EBX, and ECX registers also are used.
;
MOV   ECX,EDI                   ; temp storage for offset
SHR   EDI,5                     ; divide offset by 32 (dwords)
SHL   EDI,2                     ; multiply by 4 (byte address)
AND   CL,1FH                    ; get low five bits of offset in
MOV   EAX,[EDI]strg_base        ; move low string dword into EAX
MOV   EAX,[EDI]strg_base +4     ; other string dword into EDX
SHRD  EAX,EDX,CL                ; shift right by offset in dword
AND   EAX,mask                  ; extracted bit field in EAX
```

3.4.5 Byte-Set-On-Condition Instructions

This group of instructions sets a byte to the value of zero or one, depending on any of the 16 conditions defined by the status flags. The byte may be in a register or in memory. These instructions are especially useful for implementing Boolean expressions in high-level languages such as Pascal.

Some languages represent a logical one as an integer with all bits set. This can be done by using the SET*cc* instruction with the mutually exclusive condition, then decrementing the result.

SET*cc* (Set Byte on Condition *cc*) loads the value 1 into a byte if condition *cc* is true; clears the byte otherwise. See Appendix D for a definition of the possible conditions.

3.4.6 Test Instruction

TEST (Test) performs the logical "and" of the two operands, clears the OF and CF flags, leaves the AF flag undefined, and updates the SF, ZF, and PF flags. The flags can be tested by conditional control transfer instructions or the byte-set-on-condition instructions. The operands may be bytes, words, or doublewords.

The difference between the TEST and AND instructions is the TEST instruction does not alter the destination operand. The difference between the TEST and BT instructions is the TEST instruction can test the value of multiple bits in one operation, while the BT instruction tests a single bit.

3.5 CONTROL TRANSFER INSTRUCTIONS

The i486 processor provides both conditional and unconditional control transfer instructions to direct the flow of execution. Conditional transfers are executed only for certain combinations of the state of the flags. Unconditional control transfers are always executed.

3.5.1 Unconditional Transfer Instructions

The JMP, CALL, RET, INT and IRET instructions transfer execution to a destination in a code segment. The destination can be within the same code segment (*near* transfer) or in a different code segment (*far* transfer). The forms of these instructions which transfer execution to other segments are discussed in a later section of this chapter. If the model of memory organization used in a particular application does not make segments visible to application programmers, far transfers will not be used.

3.5.1.1 JUMP INSTRUCTION

JMP (Jump) unconditionally transfers execution to the destination. The JMP instruction is a one-way transfer of execution; it does not save a return address on the stack.

The JMP instruction transfers execution from the current routine to a different routine. The address of the routine is specified in the instruction, in a register, or in memory. The location of the address determines whether it is interpreted as a relative address or an absolute address.

Relative Address. A relative jump uses a displacement (immediate mode constant used for address calculation) held in the instruction. The displacement is signed and variable-length (byte or doubleword). The destination address is formed by adding the displacement to the address held in the EIP register. The EIP register then contains the address of the next instruction to be executed.

Absolute Address. An absolute jump is used with a 32-bit segment offset in either of the following ways:

1. The program can jump to an address in a general register. This 32-bit value is copied into the EIP register and execution continues.
2. The destination address can be a memory operand specified using the standard addressing modes. The operand is copied into the EIP register and execution continues.

3.5.1.2 CALL INSTRUCTIONS

CALL (Call Procedure) transfers execution and saves the address of the instruction following the CALL instruction for later use by a RET (Return) instruction. CALL pushes the current contents of the EIP register on the stack. The RET instruction in the called procedure uses this address to transfer execution back to the calling program.

CALL instructions, like JMP instructions, have relative and absolute forms.

Indirect CALL instructions specify an absolute address in one of the following ways:

1. The program can jump to an address in a general register. This 32-bit value is copied into the EIP register, the return address is pushed on the stack, and execution continues.
2. The destination address can be a memory operand specified using the standard addressing modes. The operand is copied into the EIP register, the return address is pushed on the stack, and execution continues.

3.5.1.3 RETURN AND RETURN-FROM-INTERRUPT INSTRUCTIONS

RET (Return From Procedure) terminates a procedure and transfers execution to the instruction following the CALL instruction which originally invoked the procedure. The RET instruction restores the contents of the EIP register which were pushed on the stack when the procedure was called.

The RET instructions have an optional immediate operand. When present, this constant is added to the contents of the ESP register, which has the effect of removing any parameters pushed on the stack before the procedure call.

IRET (Return From Interrupt) returns control to an interrupted procedure. The IRET instruction differs from the RET instruction in that it also restores the EFLAGS register from the stack. The contents of the EFLAGS register are stored on the stack when an interrupt occurs.

3.5.2 Conditional Transfer Instructions

The conditional transfer instructions are jumps which transfer execution if the states in the EFLAGS register match conditions specified in the instruction.

3.5.2.1 CONDITIONAL JUMP INSTRUCTIONS

Table 3-3 shows the mnemonics for the jump instructions. The instructions listed as pairs are alternate names for the same instruction. The assembler provides these names for greater clarity in program listings.

A form of the conditional jump instructions is available which uses a displacement added to the contents of the EIP register if the specified condition is true. The displacement may be a byte or doubleword. The displacement is signed; it can be used to jump forward or backward.

3.5.2.2 LOOP INSTRUCTIONS

The loop instructions are conditional jumps which use a value placed in the ECX register as a count for the number of times to run a loop. All loop instructions decrement the contents of the ECX register on each reposition and terminate when zero is reached. Four of the five loop instructions accept the ZF flag as a condition for terminating the loop before the count reaches zero.

LOOP (Loop While ECX Not Zero) is a conditional jump instruction which decrements the contents of the ECX register before testing for the loop-terminating condition. If contents of the ECX register are non-zero, the program jumps to the destination specified in the instruction. The LOOP instruction causes the execution of a block of code to be repeated until the count reaches zero. When zero is reached, execution is transferred

Table 3-3. Conditional Jump Instructions

Mnemonic	Flag States	Description
Unsigned Conditional Jumps		
JA/JNBE	(CF or ZF)=0	above/not below nor equal
JAE/JNB	CF=0	above or equal/not below
JB/JNAE	CF=1	below/not above nor equal
JBE/JNA	(CF or ZF)=1	below or equal/not above
JC	CF=1	carry
JE/JZ	ZF=1	equal/zero
JNC	CF=0	not carry
JNE/JNZ	ZF=0	not equal/not zero
JNP/JPO	PF=0	not parity/parity odd
JP/JPE	PF=1	parity/parity even
Signed Conditional Jumps		
JG/JNLE	((SF xor OF) or ZF) =0	greater/not less nor equal
JGE/JNL	(SF xor OF)=0	greater or equal/not less
JL/JNGE	(SF xor OF)=1	less/not greater nor equal
JLE/JNG	((SF xor OF) or ZF)=1	less or equal/not greater
JNO	OF=0	not overflow
JNS	SF=0	not sign (non-negative)
JO	OF=1	overflow
JS	SF=1	sign (negative)

to the instruction immediately following the LOOP instruction. If the value in the ECX register is zero when the instruction is first called, the count is pre-decremented to 0FFFFFFFFH and the LOOP runs 2^{32} times.

LOOPE (Loop While Equal) and **LOOPZ (Loop While Zero)** are synonyms for the same instruction. These instructions are conditional jumps which decrement the contents of the ECX register before testing for the loop-terminating condition. If the contents of the ECX register are non-zero and the ZF flag is set, the program jumps to the destination specified in the instruction. When zero is reached or the ZF flag is clear, execution is transferred to the instruction immediately following the LOOPE/LOOPZ instruction.

LOOPNE (Loop While Not Equal) and **LOOPNZ (Loop While Not Zero)** are synonyms for the same instruction. These instructions are conditional jumps which decrement the contents of the ECX register before testing for the loop-terminating condition. If the contents of the ECX register are non-zero and the ZF flag is clear, the program jumps to the destination specified in the instruction. When zero is reached or the ZF flag is set, execution is transferred to the instruction immediately following the LOOPE/LOOPZ instruction.

3.5.2.3 EXECUTING A LOOP OR REPEAT ZERO TIMES

JECXZ (Jump if ECX Zero) jumps to the destination specified in the instruction if the ECX register holds a value of zero. The JECXZ instruction is used in combination with the LOOP instruction and with the string scan and compare instructions. Because these instructions decrement the contents of the ECX register before testing for zero, a loop will run 2^{32} times if the loop is entered with a zero value in the ECX register. The JECXZ instruction is used to create loops which fall through without executing when the initial value is zero. A JECXZ instruction at the beginning of a loop can be used to jump out of the loop if the count is zero. When used with repeated string scan and compare instructions, the JECXZ instruction can determine whether the loop terminated due to the count or due to satisfaction of the scan or compare conditions.

3.5.3 Software Interrupts

The INT, INTO, and BOUND instructions allow the programmer to specify a transfer of execution to an exception or interrupt handler.

INT*n* (Software Interrupt) calls the handler specified by an interrupt vector encoded in the instruction. The INT instruction may specify any interrupt type. This instruction is used to support multiple types of software interrupts or to test the operation of interrupt service routines. The interrupt service routine terminates with an IRET instruction, which returns execution to the instruction following the INT instruction.

INTO (Interrupt on Overflow) calls the handler for the overflow exception, if the OF flag is set. If the flag is clear, execution continues without calling the handler. The OF flag is set by arithmetic, logical, and string instructions. This instruction supports the use of software interrupts for handling error conditions, such as arithmetic overflow.

BOUND (Detect Value Out of Range) compares the signed value held in a general register against an upper and lower limit. The handler for the bounds-check exception is called if the value held in the register is less than the lower bound or greater than the upper bound. This instruction supports the use of software interrupts for bounds checking, such as checking an array index to make sure it falls within the range defined for the array.

The BOUND instruction has two operands. The first operand specifies the general register being tested. The second operand is the base address of two words or doublewords at adjacent locations in memory. The lower limit is the word or doubleword with the lower address; the upper limit has the higher address. The BOUND instruction assumes that the upper limit and lower limit are in adjacent memory locations. These limit values cannot be register operands; if they are, an invalid-opcode exception occurs.

The upper and lower limits of an array can reside just before the array itself. This puts the array bounds at a constant offset from the beginning of the array. Because the address of the array already will be present in a register, this practice avoids extra bus cycles to obtain the effective address of the array bounds.

3.6 STRING OPERATIONS

String operations manipulate large data structures in memory, such as alphanumeric character strings. See also the section on I/O for information about the string I/O instructions (also known as block I/O instructions).

The string operations are made by putting string instructions (which execute only one iteration of an operation) together with other features of the instruction set, such as repeat prefixes. The string instructions are:

MOVS – Move String
CMPS – Compare string
SCAS – Scan string
LODS – Load string
STOS – Store string

After a string instruction executes, the string source and destination registers point to the next elements in their strings. These registers automatically increment or decrement their contents by the number of bytes occupied by each string element. A string element can be a byte, word, or doubleword. The string registers are:

ESI – Source index register
EDI – Destination index register

String operations can begin at higher addresses and work toward lower ones, or they can begin at lower addresses and work toward higher ones. The direction is controlled by:

DF – Direction flag

If the DF flag is clear, the registers are incremented. If the flag is set, the registers are decremented. These instructions set and clear the flag:

STD – Set direction flag instruction
CLD – Clear direction flag instruction

To operate on more than one element of a string, a repeat prefix must be used, such as:

REP – Repeat while the ECX register not zero
REPE/REPZ – Repeat while the ECX register not zero and the ZF flag is set
REPNE/REPNZ – Repeat while the ECX register not zero and the ZF flag is clear

Exceptions or interrupts which occur during a string instruction leave the registers in a state which allows the string instruction to be restarted. The source and destination registers point to the next string elements, the EIP register points to the string instruction, and the ECX register has the value it held following the last successful iteration. All that is necessary to restart the operation is to service the interrupt or fix the source of the exception, then execute an IRET instruction.

3.6.1 Repeat Prefixes

The repeat prefixes **REP (Repeat While ECX Not Zero)**, **REPE/REPZ (Repeat While Equal/Zero)**, and **REPNE/REPNZ (Repeat While Not Equal/Not Zero)** specify repeated operation of a string instruction. This form of iteration allows string operations to proceed much faster than would be possible with a software loop.

When a string instruction has a repeat prefix, the operation executes until one of the termination conditions specified by the prefix is satisfied.

For each repetition of the instruction, the string operation may be suspended by an exception or interrupt. After the exception or interrupt has been serviced, the string operation can restart where it left off. This mechanism allows long string operations to proceed without affecting the interrupt response time of the system.

All three prefixes shown in Table 3-4 cause the instruction to repeat until the ECX register is decremented to zero, if no other termination condition is satisfied. The repeat prefixes differ in their other termination condition. The REP prefix has no other termination condition. The REPE/REPZ and REPNE/REPNZ prefixes are used exclusively with the SCAS (Scan String) and CMPS (Compare String) instructions. The REPE/REPZ prefix terminates if the ZF flag is clear. The REPNE/REPNZ prefix terminates if

Table 3-4. Repeat Instructions

Repeat Prefix	Termination Condition 1	Termination Condition 2
REP	ECX=0	none
REPE/REPZ	ECX=0	ZF=0
REPNE/REPNZ	ECX=0	ZF=1

the ZF flag is set. The ZF flag does not require initialization before execution of a repeated string instruction, because both the SCAS and CMPS instructions affect the ZF flag according to the results of the comparisons they make.

3.6.2 Indexing and Direction Flag Control

Although the general registers are completely interchangeable under most conditions, the string instructions require the use of two specific registers. The source and destination strings are in memory addressed by the ESI and EDI registers. The ESI register points to source operands. By default, the ESI register is used with the DS segment register. A segment-override prefix allows the ESI register to be used with the CS, SS, ES, FS, or GS segment registers. The EDI register points to destination operands. It uses the segment indicated by the ES segment register; no segment override is allowed. The use of two different segment registers in one instruction permits operations between strings in different segments.

When ESI and EDI are used in string instructions, they automatically are incremented or decremented after each iteration. String operations can begin at higher addresses and work toward lower ones, or they can begin at lower addresses and work toward higher ones. The direction is controlled by the DF flag. If the flag is clear, the registers are incremented. If the flag is set, the registers are decremented. The STD and CLD instructions set and clear this flag. Programmers should always put a known value in the DF flag before using a string instruction.

3.6.3 String Instructions

MOVS (Move String) moves the string element addressed by the ESI register to the location addressed by the EDI register. The MOVSB instruction moves bytes, the MOVSW instruction moves words, and the MOVSD instruction moves doublewords. The MOVS instruction, when accompanied by the REP prefix, operates as a memory-to-memory block transfer. To set up this operation, the program must initialize the ECX, ESI, and EDI registers. The ECX register specifies the number of elements in the block.

CMPS (Compare Strings) subtracts the destination string element from the source string element and updates the AF, SF, PF, CF and OF flags. Neither string element is written back to memory. If the string elements are equal, the ZF flag is set; otherwise, it is cleared. CMPSB compares bytes, CMPSW compares words, and CMPSD compares doublewords.

SCAS (Scan String) subtracts the destination string element from the EAX, AX, or AL register (depending on operand length) and updates the AF, SF, ZF, PF, CF and OF flags. The string and the register are not modified. If the values are equal, the ZF flag is set; otherwise, it is cleared. The SCASB instruction scans bytes; the SCASW instruction scans words; the SCASD instruction scans doublewords.

When the REPE/REPZ or REPNE/REPNZ prefix modifies either the SCAS or CMPS instructions, the loop which is formed is terminated by the loop counter or the effect the SCAS or CMPS instruction has on the ZF flag.

LODS (Load String) places the source string element addressed by the ESI register into the EAX register for doubleword strings, into the AX register for word strings, or into the AL register for byte strings. This instruction usually is used in a loop, where other instructions process each element of the string as they appear in the register.

STOS (Store String) places the source string element from the EAX, AX, or AL register into the string addressed by the EDI register. This instruction usually is used in a loop, where it writes to memory the result of processing a string element read from memory with the LODS instruction. A REP STOS instruction is the fastest way to initialize a large block of memory.

3.7 INSTRUCTIONS FOR BLOCK-STRUCTURED LANGUAGES

These instructions provide machine-language support for implementing block-structured languages, such as C and Pascal. They include ENTER and LEAVE, which simplify procedure entry and exit in compiler-generated code. They support a structure of pointers and local variables on the stack called a *stack frame*.

ENTER (Enter Procedure) creates a stack frame compatible with the scope rules of block-structured languages. In these languages, a procedure has access to its own variables and some number of other variables defined elsewhere in the program. The scope of a procedure is the set of variables to which it has access. The rules for scope vary among languages; they may be based on the nesting of procedures, the division of the program into separately-compiled files, or some other modularization scheme.

The ENTER instruction has two operands. The first specifies the number of bytes to be reserved on the stack for dynamic storage in the procedure being entered. Dynamic storage is the memory allocated for variables created when the procedure is called, also known as automatic variables. The second parameter is the lexical nesting level (from 0 to 31) of the procedure. The nesting level is the depth of a procedure in the hierarchy of a block-structured program. The lexical level has no particular relationship to either the protection privilege level or to the I/O privilege level.

The lexical nesting level determines the number of stack frame pointers to copy into the new stack frame from the preceding frame. A stack frame pointer is a doubleword used to access the variables of a procedure. The set of stack frame pointers used by a procedure to access the variables of other procedures is called the *display*. The first doubleword in the display is a pointer to the previous stack frame. This pointer is used by a LEAVE instruction to undo the effect of an ENTER instruction by discarding the current stack frame.

Example: `ENTER 2048,3`

Allocates 2K bytes of dynamic storage on the stack and sets up pointers to two previous stack frames in the stack frame for this procedure.

After the ENTER instruction creates the display for a procedure, it allocates the dynamic (automatic) local variables for the procedure by decrementing the contents of the ESP register by the number of bytes specified in the first parameter. This new value in the ESP register serves as the initial top-of-stack for all PUSH and POP operations within the procedure.

To allow a procedure to address its display, the ENTER instruction leaves the EBP register pointing to the first doubleword in the display. Because stacks grow down, this is actually the doubleword with the highest address in the display. Data manipulation instructions which specify the EBP register as a base register automatically address locations within the stack segment instead of the data segment.

The ENTER instruction can be used in two ways: nested and non-nested. If the lexical level is 0, the non-nested form is used. The non-nested form pushes the contents of the EBP register on the stack, copies the contents of the ESP register into the EBP register, and subtracts the first operand from the contents of the ESP register to allocate dynamic storage. The non-nested form differs from the nested form in that no stack frame pointers are copied. The nested form of the ENTER instruction occurs when the second parameter (lexical level) is not zero.

Figure 3-15 shows the formal definition of the ENTER instruction. STORAGE is the number of bytes of dynamic storage to allocate for local variables, and LEVEL is the lexical nesting level.

The main procedure (in which all other procedures are nested) operates at the highest lexical level, level 1. The first procedure it calls operates at the next deeper lexical level, level 2. A level 2 procedure can access the variables of the main program, which are at

```
Push EBP
Set a temporary value FRAME_PTR := ESP
If LEVEL  0 then
        Repeat LEVEL – 1) times:
                EBP := EBP  – 4
                Push the doubleword pointed to by EBP
        End repeat
        Push FRAME_PTR
End if
EBP := FRAME_PTR
ESP := ESP – STORAGE
```

Figure 3-15. Formal Definition of the ENTER Instruction

fixed locations specified by the compiler. In the case of level 1, the ENTER instruction allocates only the requested dynamic storage on the stack because there is no previous display to copy.

A procedure which calls another procedure at a lower lexical level gives the called procedure access to the variables of the caller. The ENTER instruction provides this access by placing a pointer to the calling procedure's stack frame in the display.

A procedure which calls another procedure at the same lexical level should not give access to its variables. In this case, the ENTER instruction copies only that part of the display from the calling procedure which refers to previously nested procedures operating at higher lexical levels. The new stack frame does not include the pointer for addressing the calling procedure's stack frame.

The ENTER instruction treats a re-entrant procedure as a call to a procedure at the same lexical level. In this case, each succeeding iteration of the re-entrant procedure can address only its own variables and the variables of the procedures within which it is nested. A re-entrant procedure always can address its own variables; it does not require pointers to the stack frames of previous iterations.

By copying only the stack frame pointers of procedures at higher lexical levels, the ENTER instruction makes certain that procedures access only those variables of higher lexical levels, not those at parallel lexical levels (see Figure 3-16).

Block-structured languages can use the lexical levels defined by ENTER to control access to the variables of nested procedures. In the figure, for example, if PROCEDURE A calls PROCEDURE B which, in turn, calls PROCEDURE C, then PROCEDURE C

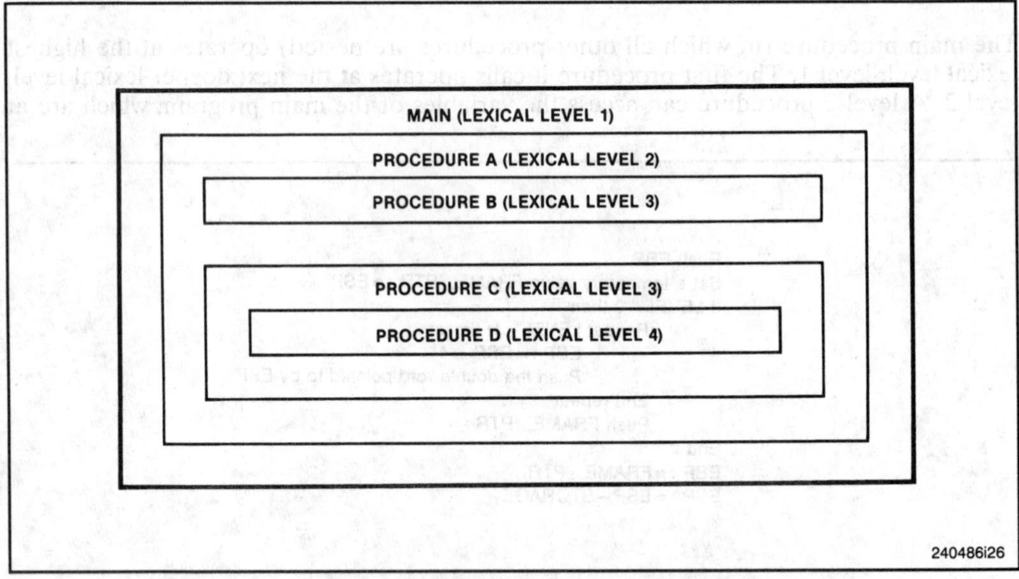

Figure 3-16. Nested Procedures

will have access to the variables of MAIN and PROCEDURE A, but not those of PROCEDURE B because they are at the same lexical level. The following definition describes the access to variables for the nested procedures in the figure.

1. MAIN has variables at fixed locations.
2. PROCEDURE A can access only the variables of MAIN.
3. PROCEDURE B can access only the variables of PROCEDURE A and MAIN. PROCEDURE B cannot access the variables of PROCEDURE C or PROCEDURE D.
4. PROCEDURE C can access only the variables of PROCEDURE A and MAIN. PROCEDURE C cannot access the variables of PROCEDURE B or PROCEDURE D.
5. PROCEDURE D can access the variables of PROCEDURE C, PROCEDURE A, and MAIN. PROCEDURE D cannot access the variables of PROCEDURE B.

In the following diagram, an ENTER instruction at the beginning of the MAIN program creates three doublewords of dynamic storage for MAIN, but copies no pointers from other stack frames (See Figure 3-17). The first doubleword in the display holds a copy of the last value in the EBP register before the ENTER instruction was executed. The second doubleword (which, because stacks grow down, is stored at a lower address) holds a copy of the contents of the EBP register following the ENTER instruction. After the instruction is executed, the EBP register points to the first doubleword pushed on the stack, and the ESP register points to the last doubleword in the stack frame.

When MAIN calls PROCEDURE A, the ENTER instruction creates a new display (See Figure 3-18). The first doubleword is the last value held in MAIN's EBP register. The second doubleword is a pointer to MAIN's stack frame which is copied from the second doubleword in MAIN's display. This happens to be another copy of the last value held in MAIN's EBP register. PROCEDURE A can access variables in MAIN because MAIN

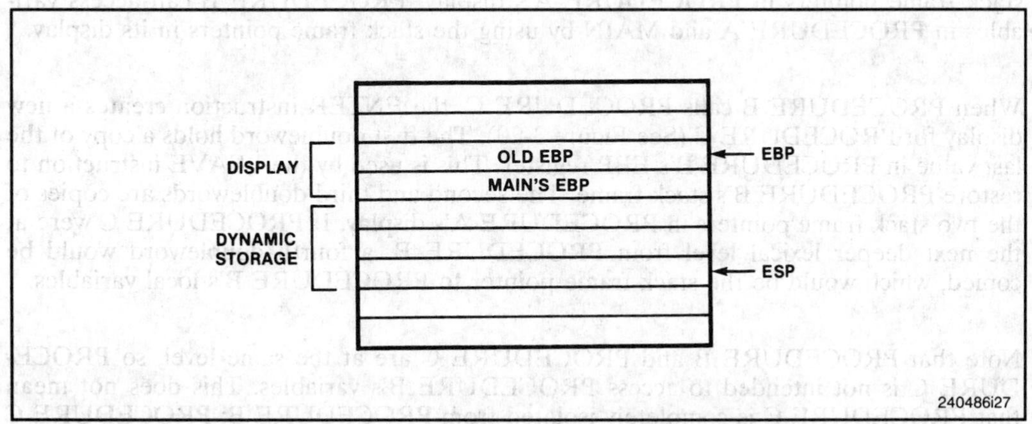

Figure 3-17. Stack Frame After Entering MAIN

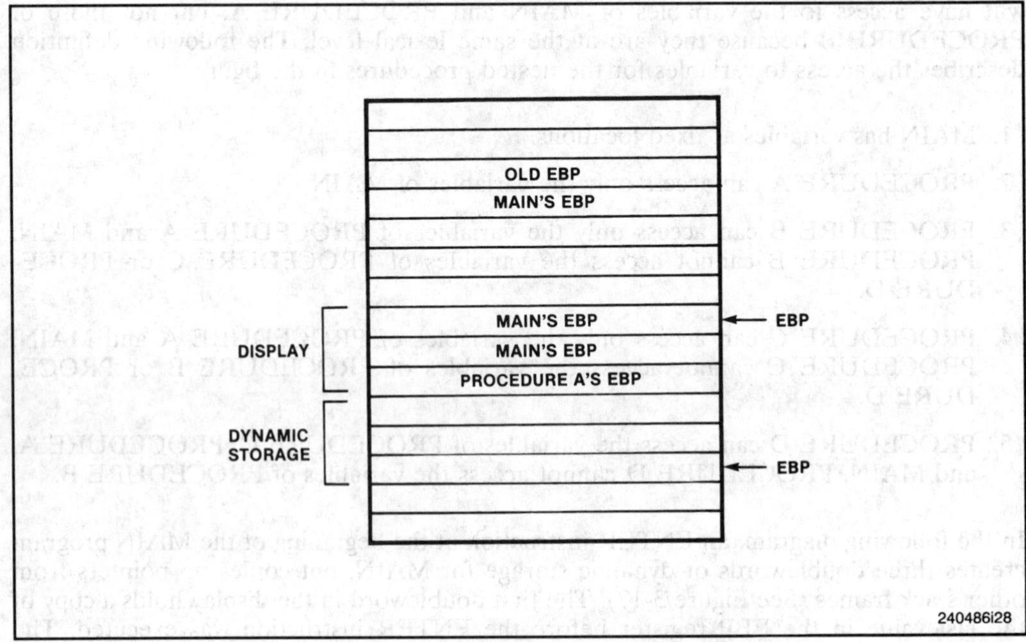

Figure 3-18. Stack Frame After Entering PROCEDURE A

is at level 1. Therefore the base address for the dynamic storage used in MAIN is the current address in the EBP register, plus four bytes to account for the saved contents of MAIN's EBP register. All dynamic variables for MAIN are at fixed, positive offsets from this value.

When PROCEDURE A calls PROCEDURE B, the ENTER instruction creates a new display (See Figure 3-19). The first doubleword holds a copy of the last value in PROCEDURE A's EBP register. The second and third doublewords are copies of the two stack frame pointers in PROCEDURE A's display. PROCEDURE B can access variables in PROCEDURE A and MAIN by using the stack frame pointers in its display.

When PROCEDURE B calls PROCEDURE C, the ENTER instruction creates a new display for PROCEDURE C (See Figure 3-20). The first doubleword holds a copy of the last value in PROCEDURE B's EBP register. This is used by the LEAVE instruction to restore PROCEDURE B's stack frame. The second and third doublewords are copies of the two stack frame pointers in PROCEDURE A's display. If PROCEDURE C were at the next deeper lexical level from PROCEDURE B, a fourth doubleword would be copied, which would be the stack frame pointer to PROCEDURE B's local variables.

Note that PROCEDURE B and PROCEDURE C are at the same level, so PROCEDURE C is not intended to access PROCEDURE B's variables. This does not mean that PROCEDURE C is completely isolated from PROCEDURE B; PROCEDURE C is called by PROCEDURE B, so the pointer to the returning stack frame is a pointer to

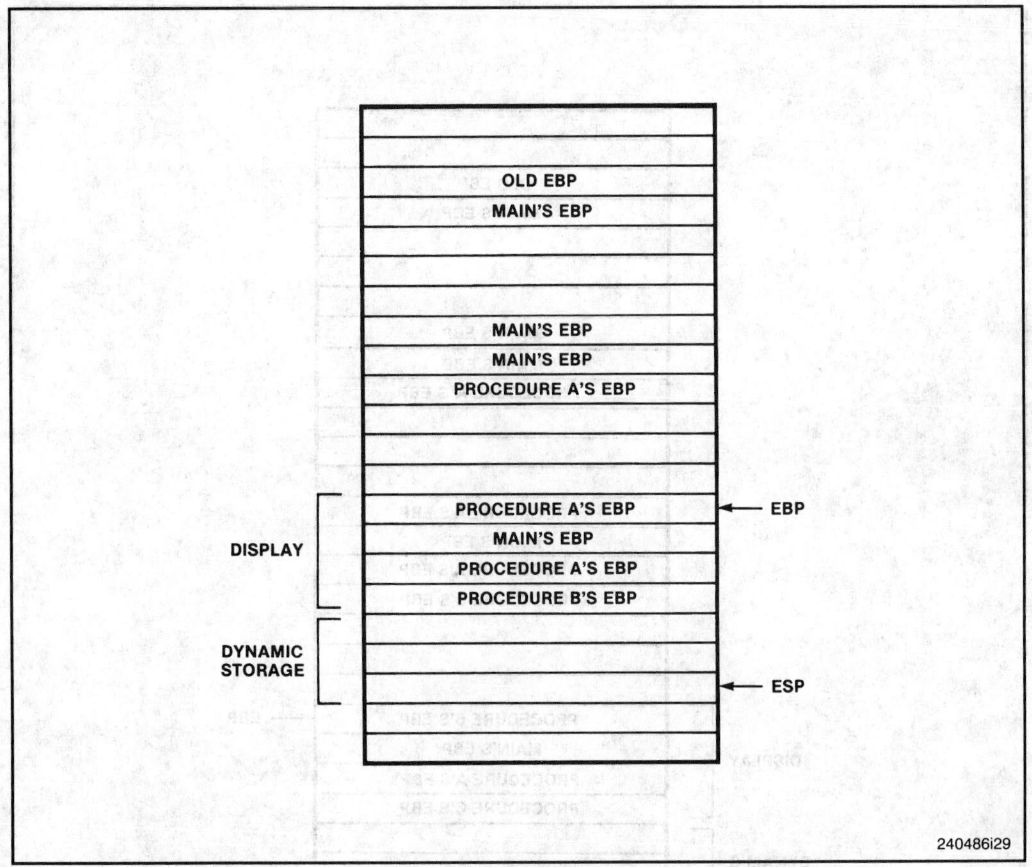

Figure 3-19. Stack Frame After Entering PROCEDURE B

PROCEDURE B's stack frame. In addition, PROCEDURE B can pass parameters to PROCEDURE C either on the stack or through variables global to both procedures (i.e., variables in the scope of both procedures).

LEAVE (Leave Procedure) reverses the action of the previous ENTER instruction. The LEAVE instruction does not have any operands. The LEAVE instruction copies the contents of the EBP register into the ESP register to release all stack space allocated to the procedure. Then the LEAVE instruction restores the old value of the EBP register from the stack. This simultaneously restores the ESP register to its original value. A subsequent RET instruction then can remove any arguments and the return address pushed on the stack by the calling program for use by the procedure.

3.8 FLAG CONTROL INSTRUCTIONS

The flag control instructions change the state of bits in the EFLAGS register, as shown in Table 3-5.

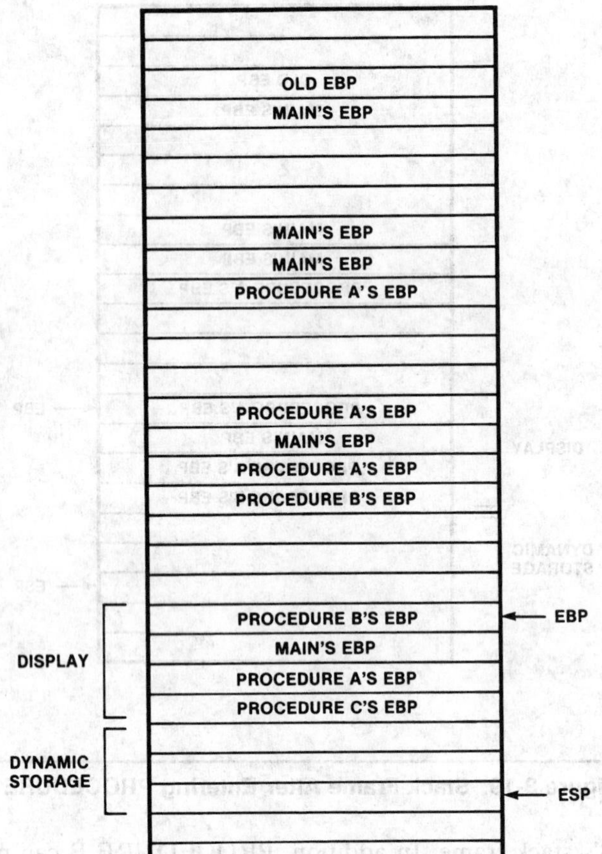

OLD EBP
MAIN'S EBP
MAIN'S EBP
MAIN'S EBP
PROCEDURE A'S EBP
PROCEDURE A'S EBP
MAIN'S EBP
PROCEDURE A'S EBP
PROCEDURE B'S EBP
DISPLAY
PROCEDURE B'S EBP ← EBP
MAIN'S EBP
PROCEDURE A'S EBP
PROCEDURE C'S EBP
DYNAMIC STORAGE
← ESP

240486i30

Figure 3-20. Stack Frame After Entering PROCEDURE C

Table 3-5. Flag Control Instructions

Instruction	Effect
STC (Set Carry Flag)	CF ← 1
CLC (Clear Carry Flag)	CF ← 0
CMC (Complement Carry Flag)	CF ← − (CF)
CLD (Clear Direction Flag)	DF ← 0
STD (Set Direction Flag)	DF ← 1

3.8.1 Carry and Direction Flag Control Instructions

The carry flag instructions are useful with instructions like the rotate-with-carry instructions RCL and RCR. They can initialize the carry flag, CF, to a known state before execution of an instruction which copies the flag into an operand.

The direction flag control instructions set or clear the direction flag, DF, which controls the direction of string processing. If the DF flag is clear, the processor increments the string index registers, ESI and EDI, after each iteration of a string instruction. If the DF flag is set, the processor decrements these index registers.

3.8.2 Flag Transfer Instructions

Though specific instructions exist to alter the CF and DF flags, there is no direct method of altering the other application-oriented flags. The flag transfer instructions allow a program to change the state of the other flag bits using the bit manipulation instructions once these flags have been moved to the stack or the AH register.

The LAHF and SAHF instructions deal with five of the status flags, which are used primarily by the arithmetic and logical instructions.

LAHF (Load AH from Flags) copies the SF, ZF, AF, PF, and CF flags to the AH register bits 7, 6, 4, 2, and 0, respectively (see Figure 3-21). The contents of the remaining bits 5, 3, and 1 are left undefined. The contents of the EFLAGS register remain unchanged.

SAHF (Store AH into Flags) copies bits 7, 6, 4, 2, and 0 from the AH register into the SF, ZF, AF, PF, and CF flags, respectively (see Figure 3-21).

The PUSHF and POPF instructions are not only useful for storing the flags in memory where they can be examined and modified, but also are useful for preserving the state of the EFLAGS register while executing a subroutine.

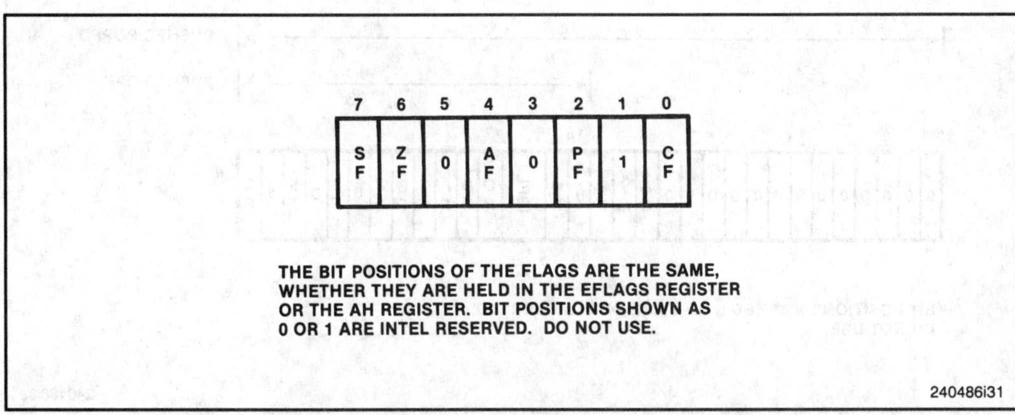
7 6 5 4 3 2 1 0
SF ZF 0 AF 0 PF 1 CF
THE BIT POSITIONS OF THE FLAGS ARE THE SAME, WHETHER THEY ARE HELD IN THE EFLAGS REGISTER OR THE AH REGISTER. BIT POSITIONS SHOWN AS 0 OR 1 ARE INTEL RESERVED. DO NOT USE.
240486i31

Figure 3-21. Low Byte of EFLAGS Register

PUSHF (Push Flags) pushes the lower word of the EFLAGS register onto the stack (see Figure 3-22). The PUSHFD instruction pushes the entire EFLAGS register onto the stack (the RF flag reads as clear, however).

POPF (Pop Flags) pops a word from the stack into the EFLAGS register. Only bits 14, 11, 10, 8, 7, 6, 4, 2, and 0 are affected with all uses of this instruction. If the privilege level of the current code segment is 0 (most privileged), the IOPL bits (bits 13 and 12) also are affected. If the I/O privilege level (IOPL) is 0, the IF flag (bit 9) also is affected. The POPFD instruction pops a doubleword into the EFLAGS register, and it can change the state of the AC bit (bit 18) as well as the bits affected by a POPF instruction.

3.9 NUMERIC INSTRUCTIONS

The i486 processor includes hardware and instructions for high-precision numeric operations on a variety of numeric data types, including 80-bit *extended real* and 64-bit *long integer*. Arithmetic, comparison, transcendental, and data transfer instructions are available. Frequently-used constants are also provided, to enhance the speed of numeric calculations.

The numeric instructions are embedded in the instruction stream of the i486 processor, as though they were being executed by a single device having both integer and floating-point capabilities. But the floating-point unit of the i486 CPU actually works in parallel with the integer unit, resulting in higher performance.

Part III of this manual, Chapters 14–18, describe the numeric instructions in more detail.

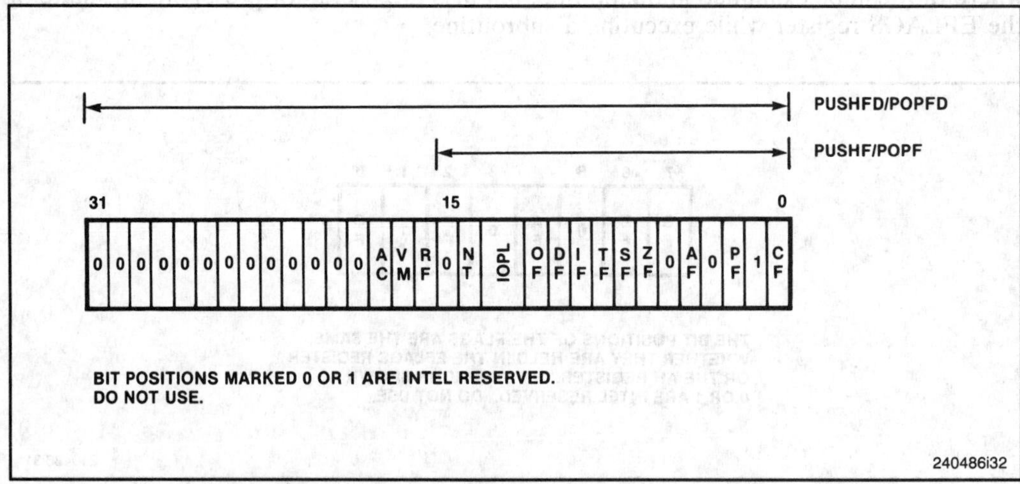

Figure 3-22. Flags Used with PUSHF and POPF

3.10 SEGMENT REGISTER INSTRUCTIONS

There are several distinct types of instructions which use segment registers. They are grouped together here because, if system designers choose an unsegmented model of memory organization, none of these instructions are used. The instructions which deal with segment registers are:

1. Segment-register transfer instructions.

```
MOV   SegReg, ...
MOV   ..., SegReg
PUSH  SegReg
POP   SegReg
```

2. Control transfers to another executable segment.

```
JMP   far
CALL  far
RET   far
```

3. Data pointer instructions.

```
LDS   reg, 48-bit memory operand
LES   reg, 48-bit memory operand
LFS   reg, 48-bit memory operand
LGS   reg, 48-bit memory operand
LSS   reg, 48-bit memory operand
```

4. Note that the following interrupt-related instructions also are used in unsegmented systems. Although they can transfer execution between segments when segmentation is used, this is transparent to the application programmer.

```
INT n
INTO
BOUND
IRET
```

3.10.1 Segment-Register Transfer Instructions

Forms of the MOV, POP, and PUSH instructions also are used to load and store segment registers. These forms operate like the general-register forms, except that one operand is a segment register. The MOV instruction cannot copy the contents of a segment register into another segment register.

The POP and MOV instructions cannot place a value in the CS register (code segment); only the far control-transfer instructions affect the CS register. When the destination is the SS register (stack segment), interrupts are disabled until after the next instruction.

On the 386™ DX processor, loading a segment register always resulted in locked read and write cycles to set the Accessed bit. On the i486 processor, locked cycles are generated only if the Accessed bit is not already set.

No 16-bit operand size prefix is needed when transferring data between a segment register and a 32-bit general register.

3.10.2 Far Control Transfer Instructions

The far control-transfer instructions transfer execution to a destination in another segment by replacing the contents of the CS register. The destination is specified by a far pointer, which is a 16-bit segment selector and a 32-bit offset into the segment. The far pointer can be an immediate operand or an operand in memory.

Far CALL. An intersegment CALL instruction places the values held in the EIP and CS registers on the stack.

Far RET. An intersegment RET instruction restores the values of the CS and EIP registers from the stack.

3.10.3 Data Pointer Instructions

The data pointer instructions load a far pointer into the processor registers. A far pointer consists of a 16-bit segment selector, which is loaded into a segment register, and a 32-bit offset into the segment, which is loaded into a general register.

LDS (Load Pointer Using DS) copies a far pointer from the source operand into the DS register and a general register. The source operand must be a memory operand, and the destination operand must be a general register.

> **Example:** `LDS ESI, STRING_X`
>
> Loads the DS register with the segment selector for the segment addressed by STRING_X, and loads the offset within the segment to STRING_X into the ESI register. Specifying the ESI register as the destination operand is a convenient way to prepare for a string operation, when the source string is not in the current data segment.

LES (Load Pointer Using ES) has the same effect as the LDS instruction, except the segment selector is loaded into the ES register rather than the DS register.

> **Example:** `LES EDI, DESTINATION_X`
>
> Loads the ES register with the segment selector for the segment addressed by DESTINATION_X, and loads the offset within the segment to DESTINATION_X into the EDI register. This instruction is a convenient way to select a destination for string operation if the desired location is not in the current E-data segment.

LFS (Load Pointer Using FS) has the same effect as the LDS instruction, except the FS register receives the segment selector rather than the DS register.

LGS (Load Pointer Using GS) has the same effect as the LDS instruction, except the GS register receives the segment selector rather than the DS register.

LSS (Load Pointer Using SS) has the same effect as the LDS instruction, except the SS register receives the segment selector rather than the DS register. This instruction is especially important, because it allows the two registers which identify the stack (the SS and ESP registers) to be changed in one uninterruptible operation. Unlike the other instructions which can load the SS register, interrupts are not inhibited at the end of the LSS instruction. The other instructions, such as POP SS, turn off interrupts to permit the following instruction to load the ESP register without an intervening interrupt. Since both the SS and ESP registers can be loaded by the LSS instruction, there is no need to disable or re-enable interrupts.

3.11 MISCELLANEOUS INSTRUCTIONS

The following instructions do not fit in any of the previous categories, but are no less important.

The BSWAP, XADD, and CMPXCHG instructions are not available on 386 DX or SX microprocessors. A 386 CPU can perform the same operations in multiple instructions. To use these instructions, always include functionally-equivalent code for 386 CPUs. Use the code in Figure 3-23 to determine whether these instructions can be used.

3.11.1 Address Calculation Instruction

LEA (Load Effective Address) puts the 32-bit offset to a source operand in memory (rather than its contents) into the destination operand. The source operand must be in memory, and the destination operand must be a general register. This instruction is especially useful for initializing the ESI or EDI registers before the execution of string instructions or initializing the EBX register before an XLAT instruction. The LEA instruction can perform any indexing or scaling which may be needed.

Example: `LEA EBX, EBCDIC_TABLE`

Causes the processor to place the address of the starting location of the table labeled EBCDIC_TABLE into EBX.

3.11.2 No-Operation Instruction

NOP (No Operation) occupies a byte of code space. When executed, it increments the EIP register to point at the next instruction, but affects nothing else.

```
$title("Determine CPU id for 386 or i486 CPUs")

    name    CPU_ID
    public  is386

code    segment    er public use32
;
;    Identify the current CPU being executed.
;    Return with EAX=0 for i486 CPU or EAX=1 for 386 CPU.
;    Leave ESP, EBP, EBX, ESI, and EDI unchanged.
;
is386    proc    near

    mov     edx,esp             ; Save current stack pointer to align it
    and     esp,not 3           ; Align stack to avoid AC fault
    pushfd                      ; Push EFLAGS
    pop     eax                 ; Get EFLAGS value
    mov     ecx,eax             ; Save original EFLAGS
    xor     eax,40000H          ; Flip AC bit in EFLAGS
    push    eax                 ; Copy to EFLAGS
    popfd
    pushfd                      ; Get new EFLAGS value
    pop     eax                 ; Put into eax
    xor     eax,ecx             ; See if AC bit changed
                                ; EAX=4000H if 386 CPU, 0 if i486 CPU
    shr     eax,18              ; Set EAX=1 if 386 CPU, 0 if i486 CPU
    and     eax,1               ; Ignore all other bits
    push    ecx
    popfd                       ; Restore original EFLAGS register
    mov     esp,edx             ; Restore original stack pointer
    ret
is386    endp

code    ends
    end
```

Figure 3-23. CPU_ID Detection Code

3.11.3 Translate Instruction

XLATB (Translate) replaces the contents of the AL register with a byte read from a translation table in memory. The contents of the AL register are interpreted as an unsigned index into this table, with the contents of the EBX register used as the base address. The XLAT instruction does the same operation and loads its result into the same register, but it gets the byte operand from memory. This function is used to convert character codes from one alphabet into another. For example, an ASCII code could be used to look up its EBCDIC equivalent.

3.11.4 Byte Swap Instruction

BSWAP (Byte Swap) reverses the byte order in a 32-bit register operand. Bit positions 7..0 are exchanged with 31..24, and bit positions 15..8 are exchanged with 23..16. This instruction is useful for converting between "big-endian" and "little-endian" data formats. Executing this instruction twice in a row leaves the register in the same value as before. This instruction also speeds execution of decimal arithmetic by operating on four digits at a time as shown in Figure 3-24. See introduction for Section 3.11 regarding 386 processors when using BSWAP.

3.11.5 Exchange-and-Add Instruction

XADD (Exchange and Add) takes two operands: a source operand in a register and a destination operand in a register or memory. The source operand is replaced with the destination operand, and the destination operand is replaced with the sum of the source and destination operands. The flags reflect the result of the addition. This instruction can be combined with LOCK in a multiprocessing system to allow multiple processors to execute one do loop. See introduction for Section 3.11 regarding 386 processors when using XADD.

3.11.6 Compare-and-Exchange Instruction

CMPXCHG (Compare and Exchange) takes three operands: a source operand in a register, a destination operand in a register or memory, and the accumulator (i.e., the AL, AX, or EAX register, depending on operand size). If the values in the destination operand and the accumulator are equal, the destination operand is replaced with the source operand. Otherwise, the original value of the destination operand is loaded into the accumulator. The flags reflect the result which would have been obtained by subtracting the destination operand from the accumulator. The ZF flag is set if the values in the destination operand and the accumulator were equal, otherwise it is cleared.

The CMPXCHG instruction is useful for testing and modifying semaphores. It performs a check to see if a semaphore is free, and if so mark it allocated else get the id of the current owner in one uninterruptible operation. In a single processor system, it eliminates the need to switch to level 0 to disable interrupts to execute multiple instructions. For multiple processor systems, CMPXCHG can be combined with LOCK to perform all bus cycles atomically. See introduction for Section 3.11 regarding 386 processors when using CMPXCHG.

```
$title('ASCII Add/Subtract With BSWAP')

    name    ASCII_arith

code    segment    er public use32
;
;    Add a string of 4 ASCII decimal digits together.
;    The upper nibble MUST be 3.
;    DS:[ESI] points at operand 1
;    DS:[EBX] points at operand 2
;    DS:[EDI] points at the destination
;

add10    proc    near

;
;    Perform ASCII add using BSWAP instruction on i486 CPU.
;
    mov     eax,[esi]          ; Get low four digits of first operand
    bswap   eax                ; Put into big-endian form
    add     eax,96969696H      ; Adjust for addition so carries work
    mov     ecx,[ebx]          ; Get low four digits of second operand
    bswap   ecx                ; Put into big endian form
    add     eax,ecx            ; Do the add with inter-digit carry
    rcr     ch,1               ; Save the carry flag
    mov     edx,eax            ; Save the value
    and     eax,0F0F0F0F0H     ; Extract upper nibble
    sub     edx,eax            ; Zero out upper nibble of each byte
    shr     eax,4              ; Prepare for fixup
    and     eax,0A0A0A0AH      ; If non-zero upper nibble then form
                               ; 10 as adjustment value to lower nibble
    add     eax,edx            ; Form adjusted lower nibble value
                               ; upper nibbles may be 1 from adjustment
    or      eax,30303030H      ; Convert back to ASCII
    bswap   eax                ; Back to little-endian
    mov     [edi],eax          ; Set destination
    rcl     ch,1               ; Restore carry
    ret
add10    endp

;
;    Subtract a string of 4 ASCII decimal digits together.
;    The upper nibble must be 3.
;    DS:[ESI] points at operand 1
;    DS:[EBX] points at operand 2    [ESI]-[EBX]
;    DS:[EDI] points at the destination
;

sub10    proc    near

;
;    Perform ASCII subtract using BSWAP instruction on i486 CPU.
```

Figure 3-24. ASCII Arithmetic Using BSWAP (Part 1 of 2)

```
    mov    eax,[esi]          ; Get low four digits of first operand
    bswap  eax                ; Put into big-endian form
    mov    ecx,[ebx]          ; Get low four digits of second operand
    bswap  ecx                ; Put into big endian form
    sub    eax,ecx            ; Do the subtract with inter-digit borrow
    rcr    ch,1               ; Save the carry flag
    mov    edx,eax            ; Save the value
    and    eax,0F0F0F0F0H     ; Extract upper nibble, F if borrow happened
    sub    edx,eax            ; Zero out upper nibble of each byte
    shr    eax,4              ; Prepare for fixup
    and    eax,0A0A0A0AH      ; If non-zero upper nibble then form
                              ; 10 as adjustment value to lower nibble
    add    eax,edx            ; Form adjusted lower nibble value
                              ; upper nibbles may be 1 from adjustment
    or     eax,30303030H      ; Convert back to ASCII
    bswap  eax                ; Back to little-endian
    mov    [edi],eax          ; Set destination
    rcl    ch,1               ; Restore borrow
    ret

sub10    endp

code     ends
    end
```

Figure 3-24. ASCII Arithmetic Using BSWAP (Part 2 of 2)

Part II
System Programming

System Architecture 4

CHAPTER 4
SYSTEM ARCHITECTURE

Many of the architectural features of the i486™ processor are used only by system programmers. This chapter presents an overview of these features. Application programmers may need to read this chapter, and the following chapters which describe the use of these features, in order to understand the hardware facilities used by system programmers to create a reliable and secure environment for application programs. The system-level architecture also supports powerful debugging features which application programmers may wish to use during program development.

The system-level features of the architecture include:

Memory Management
Protection
Multitasking
Input/Output
Exceptions and Interrupts
Initialization
Coprocessing and Multiprocessing
Debugging
Cache Management

These features are supported by registers and instructions, all of which are introduced in the following sections. The purpose of this chapter is not to explain each feature in detail, but rather to place the remaining chapters of Part II in perspective. When a register or instruction is mentioned, it is accompanied by an explanation or a reference to a following chapter.

4.1 SYSTEM REGISTERS

The registers intended for use by system programmers fall into these categories:

EFLAGS Register
Memory-Management Registers
Control Registers
Debug Registers
Test Registers

The system registers control the execution environment of application programs. Most systems restrict access to these facilities by application programs (although systems can be built where all programs run at the most privileged level, in which case application programs are allowed to modify these facilities).

4.1.1 System Flags

The system flags of the EFLAGS register control I/O, maskable interrupts, debugging, task switching, and the virtual-8086 mode. An application program should ignore these flags, and should not attempt to change their state. In most systems, an attempt to change the state of a system flag by an application program results in an exception. These flags are shown in Figure 4-1.

AC (Alignment Check Mode, bit 18)

Setting the AC flag and the AM bit in the CR0 register enables alignment checking on memory references. An alignment-check exception is generated when reference is made to an unaligned operand, such as a word at an odd byte address or a doubleword at an address which is not an integral multiple of four. Alignment-check exceptions are generated only in user mode (privilege level 3). Memory references which default to privilege level 0, such as segment descriptor loads, do not generate this exception even when caused by a memory reference in user-mode.

The alignment check interrupt can be used to check alignment of data. This is useful when exchanging data with other processors like i860™ 64-bit microprocessor which require all data to be aligned. The alignment check interrupt can also be used by interpreters to flag some pointers as special by misaligning the pointer. This eliminates overhead of checking each pointer and only handle the special pointer when used.

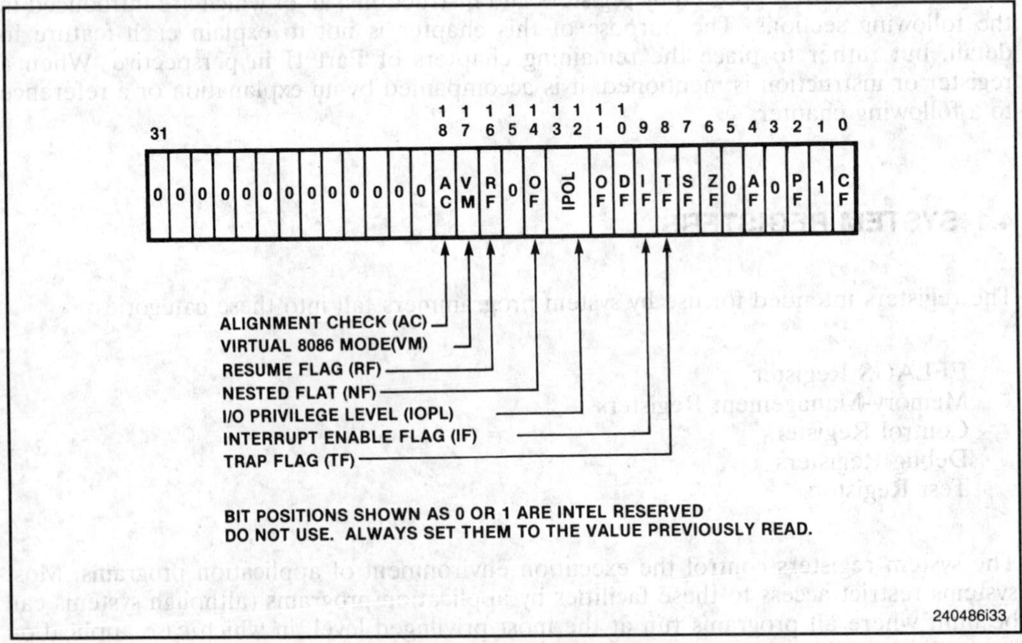

Figure 4-1. System Flags

VM (Virtual-8086 Mode, bit 17)

Setting the VM flag places the processor in virtual-8086 mode, which is an emulation of the programming environment of an 8086 processor. See Chapter 23 for more information.

RF (Resume Flag, bit 16)

The RF flag temporarily disables debug exceptions so that an instruction can be restarted after a debug exception without immediately causing another debug exception. When the debugger is entered, this flag allows it to run normally rather than recursively calling itself until the stack overflows. The RF flag is not affected by the POPF instruction, but it is affected by the POPFD and IRET instructions. See Chapter 9 and Chapter 11 for details.

NT (Nested Task, bit 14)

The processor uses the nested task flag to control chaining of interrupted and called tasks. The NT flag affects the operation of the IRET instruction. The NT flag is affected by the POPF, POPFD, and IRET instructions. Improper changes to the state of this flag can generate unexpected exceptions in application programs. See Chapter 7 and Chapter 9 for more information on nested tasks.

IOPL (I/O Privilege Level, bits 12 and 13)

The I/O privilege level is used by the protection mechanism to control access to the I/O address space. The privilege level of the code segment currently executing (CPL) and the IOPL determine whether this field can be modified by the POPF, POPFD, and IRET instructions. See Chapter 8 for more information.

IF (Interrupt-Enable Flag, bit 9)

Setting the IF flag puts the processor in a mode in which it responds to maskable interrupt requests (INTR interrupts). Clearing the IF flag disables these interrupts. The IF flag has no effect on either exceptions or nonmaskable interrupts (NMI interrupts). The CPL and IOPL determine whether this field can be modified by the CLI, STI, POPF, POPFD, and IRET instructions. See Chapter 9 for more details about interrupts.

TF (Trap Flag, bit 8)

Setting the TF flag puts the processor into single-step mode for debugging. In this mode, the processor generates a debug exception after each instruction, which allows a program to be inspected as it executes each instruction. Single-stepping is just one of several debugging features of the i486 processor. If an application program sets the TF flag using the POPF, POPFD, or IRET instructions, a debug exception is generated. See Chapter 9 and Chapter 11 for more information.

4.1.2 Memory-Management Registers

Four registers of the i486 processor specify the location of the data structures which control segmented memory management, as shown in Figure 4-2. Special instructions are provided for loading and storing these registers. The GDTR and IDTR registers may be loaded with instructions which get a six-byte block of data from memory. The LDTR and TR registers may be loaded with instructions which take a 16-bit segment selector as an operand. The remaining bytes of these registers are then loaded automatically by the processor from the descriptor referenced by the operand.

Most systems will protect the instructions which load memory-management registers from use by application programs (although a system in which no protection is used is possible).

GDTR Global Descriptor Table Register

This register holds the 32-bit base address and 16-bit segment limit for the global descriptor table (GDT). When a reference is made to data in memory, a segment selector is used to find a segment descriptor in the GDT or LDT. A segment descriptor contains the base address for a segment. See Chapter 5 for an explanation of segmentation.

LDTR Local Descriptor Table Register

This register holds the 32-bit base address, 16-bit segment limit, and 16-bit segment selector for the local descriptor table (LDT). The segment which contains the LDT has a segment descriptor in the GDT. There is no segment descriptor for the GDT. When a reference is made to data in memory, a segment selector is used to find a segment descriptor in the GDT or LDT. A segment descriptor contains the base address for a segment. See Chapter 5 for an explanation of segmentation.

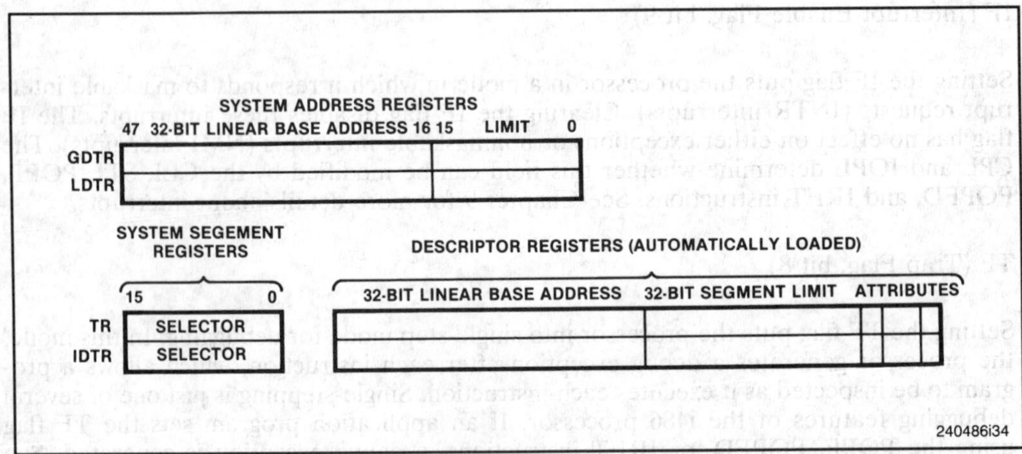

Figure 4-2. Memory Management Registers

IDTR Interrupt Descriptor Table Register

This register holds the 32-bit base address and 16-bit segment limit for the interrupt descriptor table (IDT). When an interrupt occurs, the interrupt vector is used as an index to get a gate descriptor from this table. The gate descriptor contains a pointer used to start up the interrupt handler. See Chapter 9 for details of the interrupt mechanism.

TR Task Register

This register holds the 32-bit base address, 16-bit segment limit, descriptor attributes, and 16-bit segment selector for the task currently being executed. It references a task state segment (TSS) descriptor in the global descriptor table. See Chapter 7 for a description of the multitasking features of the i486 processor.

4.1.3 Control Registers

Figure 4-3 shows the format of the control registers CR0, CR1, CR2, and CR3. Most systems prevent application programs from loading the control registers (although an unprotected system would allow this). Application programs can read this register to determine if a numerics coprocessor is present. Forms of the MOV instruction allow the register to be loaded from or stored in general registers. For example:

```
MOV    EAX,  CR0
MOV    CR3,  EBX
```

The CR0 register contains system control flags, which control modes or indicate states which apply generally to the processor, rather than to the execution of an individual task. A program should not attempt to change any of the reserved bit positions. Reserved bits should always be set to the value previously read.

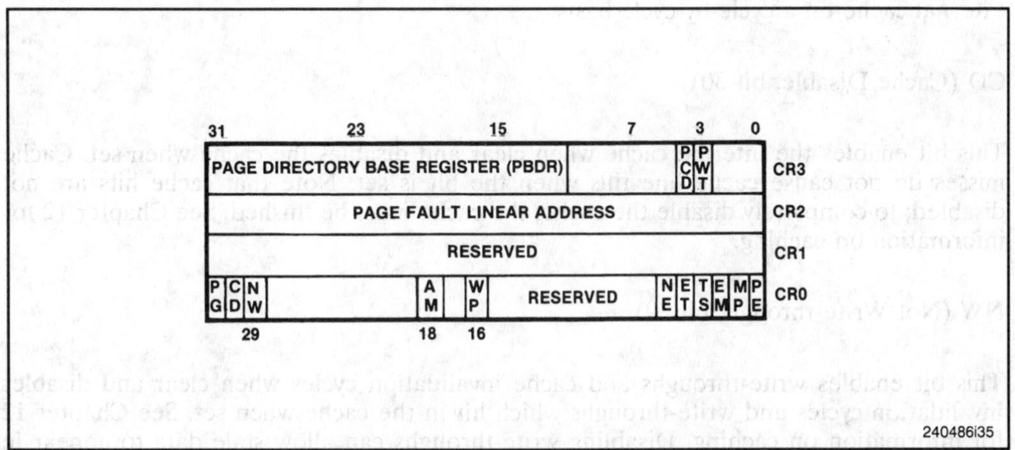

Figure 4-3. Control Registers

The LMSW instruction can only modify the lower 16 bits of CR0.

PG (Paging, bit 31)

This bit enables paging when set and disables paging when clear. See Chapter 5 for more information about paging. See Chapter 10 for information on how to enable paging.

When an exception is generated during paging, the CR2 register has the 32-bit linear address which caused the exception. See Chapter 9 for more information about handling exceptions generated during paging (page faults).

When paging is used, the CR3 register has the 20 most-significant bits of the address of the page directory (the first-level page table). The CR3 register is also known as the page-directory base register (PDBR). Note that the page directory must be aligned to a page boundary, so the low 12 bits of the register are ignored. Unlike the 386™ DX processor, the i486 processor assigns functions to two of these bits. These are:

PCD (Page-Level Cache Disable, bit 4 of CR3)

The state of this bit is driven on the PCD pin during bus cycles which are not paged, such as interrupt acknowledge cycles, when paging is enabled. It is driven during all bus cycles when paging is not enabled. The PCD pin is used to control caching in an external cache on a cycle-by-cycle basis.

PWT (Page-Level Writes Transparent, bit 3 of CR3)

The state of this bit is driven on the PWT pin during bus cycles which are not paged, such as interrupt acknowledge cycles, when paging is enabled. It is driven during all bus cycles when paging is not enabled. The PWT pin is used to control write-through in an external cache on a cycle-by-cycle basis.

CD (Cache Disable, bit 30)

This bit enables the internal cache when clear and disables the cache when set. Cache misses do not cause cache line fills when the bit is set. Note that cache hits are not disabled; to completely disable the cache, the cache must be flushed. See Chapter 12 for information on caching.

NW (Not Write-through, bit 29)

This bit enables write-throughs and cache invalidation cycles when clear and disables invalidation cycles and write-throughs which hit in the cache when set. See Chapter 12 for information on caching. Disabling write-throughs can allow stale data to appear in the cache.

AM (Alignment Mask, bit 18)

This bit allows alignment checking when set and disables alignment checking when clear. Alignment checking is performed only when the AM bit is set, the AC flag is set, and the CPL is 3 (user mode).

WP (Write Protect, bit 16)

When set, this bit write-protects user-level pages against supervisor-mode access. When this bit is clear, read-only user-level pages can be written by a supervisor process. This feature is useful for implementing the copy-on-write method of creating a new process (forking) used by some operating systems, such as UNIX.

NE (Numeric Error, bit 5)

This bit enables the standard mechanism for reporting floating-point numeric errors when set. When NE is clear and the IGNNE# input is active, numeric errors are ignored. When the NE bit is clear and the IGNNE# input is inactive, a numeric error causes the processor to stop and wait for an interrupt. The interrupt is generated by using the FERR# pin to drive an input to the interrupt controller (the FERR# pin emulates the ERROR# pin of the 80287 and 387™ DX coprocessors). The NE bit, IGNNE# pin, and FERR# pin are used with external logic to implement PC-style error reporting.

ET (Extension Type, bit 4)

This bit is one to indicate support of 387 DX math coprocessor instructions (Intel® reserved).

TS (Task Switched, bit 3)

The processor sets the TS bit with every task switch and tests it when interpreting floating-point arithmetic instructions. This bit allows delaying save/restore of numeric content until the numeric data is actually used. The CLTS instruction will clear this bit.

EM (Emulation, bit 2)

When either the EM and TS bits are set, execution of a WAIT or numeric instruction generates the coprocessor-not-available exception. EM can be set to cause exception 7 on any WAIT or numeric instruction.

MP (Math Present, bit 1)

On the 80286 and 386 DX processors, the MP bit controls the function of the WAIT instruction, which is used to synchronize with a coprocessor. When running programs on the i486 processor, this bit should be set.

PE (Protection Enable, bit 0)

Setting the PE bit enables segment-level protection. See Chapter 6 for more information about protection. See Chapter 10 and Chapter 22 for information on how to enable paging.

4.1.4 Debug Registers

The debug registers bring advanced debugging abilities to the i486 processor, including data breakpoints and the ability to set instruction breakpoints without modifying code segments (useful in debugging ROM-based software). Only programs executing at the highest privilege level can access these registers. See Chapter 11 for a complete description of their formats and use. The debug registers are shown in Figure 4-4.

4.1.5 Test Registers

The test registers are not a formal part of the architecture. They are an implementation-dependent facility provided for testing the translation lookaside buffer (TLB) and the cache. See Chapter 10 for a complete description of their formats and use. The test registers are shown in Figure 4-5.

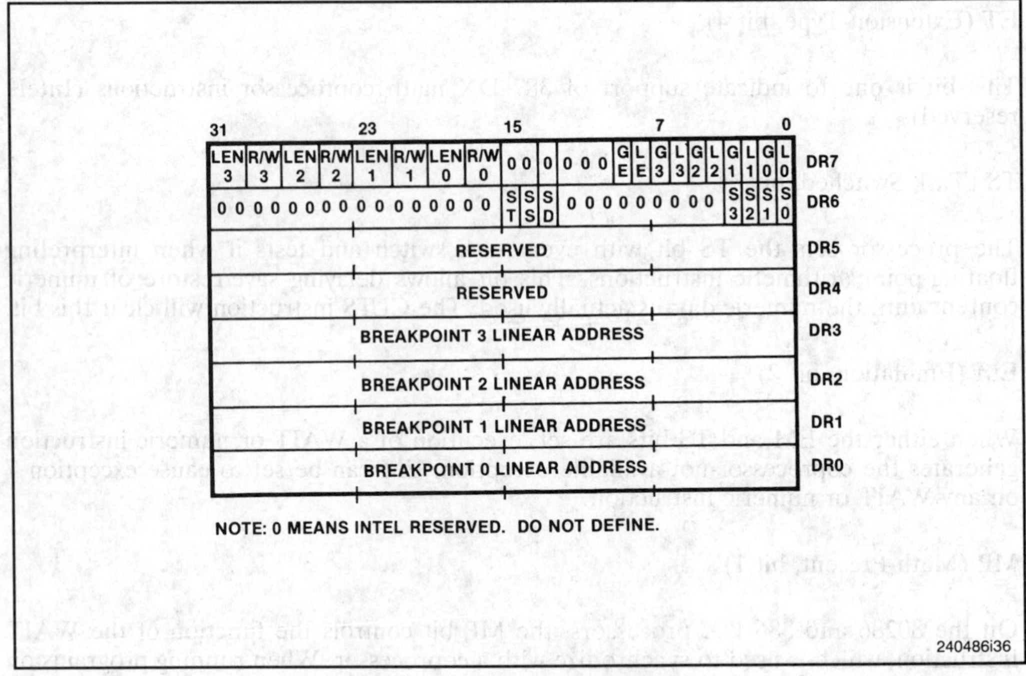

Figure 4-4. Debug Registers

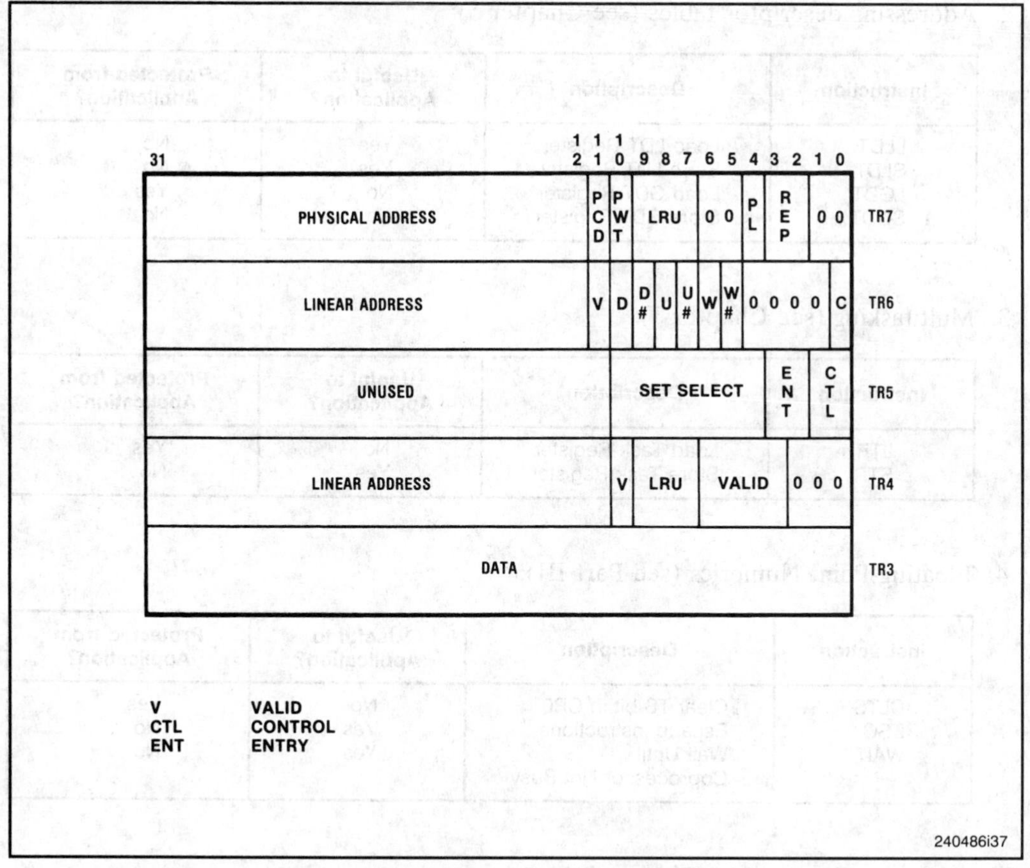

Figure 4-5. Test Registers

4.2 SYSTEM INSTRUCTIONS

System instructions deal with functions such as:

1. Verification of pointer parameters (see Chapter 6):

Instruction	Description	Useful to Application?	Protected from Application?
ARPL	Adjust RPL	No	No
LAR	Load Access Rights	Yes	No
LSL	Load Segment Limit	Yes	No
VERR	Verify for Reading	Yes	No
VERW	Verify for Writing	Yes	No

2. Addressing descriptor tables (see Chapter 5):

Instruction	Description	Useful to Application?	Protected from Application?
LLDT	Load LDT Register	Yes	No
SLDT	Store LDT Register	Yes	No
LGDT	Load GDT Register	No	Yes
SGDT	Store GDT Register	No	No

3. Multitasking (see Chapter 7):

Instruction	Description	Useful to Application?	Protected from Application?
LTR	Load Task Register	No	Yes
STR	Store Task Register	Yes	No

4. Floating-Point Numerics (see Part III):

Instruction	Description	Useful to Application?	Protected from Application?
CLTS	Clear TS bit in CR0	No	Yes
ESC	Escape Instructions	Yes	No
WAIT	Wait Until Coprocessor Not Busy	Yes	No

5. Input and Output (see Chapter 8):

Instruction	Description	Useful to Application?	Protected from Application?
IN	Input	Yes	Can be
OUT	Output	Yes	Can be
INS	Input String	Yes	Can be
OUTS	Output String	Yes	Can be

6. Interrupt control (see Chapter 9):

Instruction	Description	Useful to Application?	Protected from Application?
CLI	Clear IF flag	Can be	Can be
STI	Store IF flag	Can be	Can be
LIDT	Load IDT Register	No	Yes
SIDT	Store IDT Register	No	No

7. Debugging (see Chapter 11):

Instruction	Description	Useful to Application?	Protected from Application?
MOV	Load and store debug registers	No	Yes

8. Cache Management:

Instruction	Description	Useful to Application?	Protected from Application?
INVD	Invalidate cache, no write-back	No	Yes
WBINVD	Invalidate cache, with write-back	No	Yes
INVLPG	Invalidate TLB entry	No	Yes

9. System Control:

Instruction	Description	Useful to Application?	Protected from Application?
SMSW	Store MSW	No	No
LMSW	Load MSW	No	Yes
MOV	Load And Store Control Register	No	Yes
HLT	Halt Processor	No	Yes
LOCK	Bus Lock	No	Can Be

The SMSW and LMSW instructions are provided for compatibility with the 80286 processor. A program for the i486 processor should not use these instructions. A program should access the Control Registers using forms of the MOV instruction. The LMSW instruction does not affect the PG, CD, NW, AM, WP, NE or ET bits, and it cannot be used to clear the PE bit.

The HLT instruction stops the processor until an enabled interrupt or RESET signal is received. (Note that the NMI interrupt is always enabled.) A special bus cycle is generated by the processor to indicate halt mode has been entered. Hardware may respond to this signal in a number of ways. An indicator light on the front panel may be turned on. An NMI interrupt for recording diagnostic information may be generated. Reset initialization may be invoked. Software designers may need to be aware of the response of hardware to halt mode.

The LOCK instruction prefix is used to invoke a locked (atomic) read-modify-write operation when modifying a memory operand. The LOCK# signal is asserted and the processor does not respond to requests for bus control during a locked operation. This mechanism is used to allow reliable communications between processors in multiprocessor systems.

In addition to the chapters mentioned above, detailed information about each of these instructions can be found in the instruction reference chapter, Chapter 26.

Memory Management 5

CHAPTER 5
MEMORY MANAGEMENT

Memory management is a hardware mechanism which lets operating systems create simplified environments for running programs. For example, when several programs are running at the same time, they must each be given an independent address space. If they all had to share the same address space, each would have to perform difficult and time-consuming checks to avoid interfering with the others.

Memory management consists of segmentation and paging. Segmentation is used to give each program several independent, protected address spaces. Paging is used to support an environment where large address spaces are simulated using a small amount of RAM and some disk storage. System designers may choose to use either or both of these mechanisms. When several programs are running at the same time, either mechanism can be used to protect programs against interference from other programs.

Segmentation allows memory to be completely unstructured and simple, like the memory model of an 8-bit processor, or highly structured with address translation and protection. The memory management features apply to units called *segments*. Each segment is an independent, protected address space. Access to segments is controlled by data which describes its size, the privilege level required to access it, the kinds of memory references which can be made to it (instruction fetch, stack push or pop, read operation, write operation, etc.), and whether it is present in memory.

Segmentation is used to control memory access, which is useful for catching bugs during program development and for increasing the reliability of the final product. It also is used to simplify the linkage of object code modules. There is no reason to write position-independent code when full use is made of the segmentation mechanism, because all memory references can be made relative to the base addresses of a module's code and data segments. Segmentation can be used to create ROM-based software modules, in which fixed addresses (fixed, in the sense that they cannot be changed) are offsets from a segment's base address. Different software systems can have the ROM modules at different physical addresses because the segmentation mechanism will direct all memory references to the right place.

In a simple memory architecture, all addresses refer to the same address space. This is the memory model used by 8-bit microprocessors, such as the 8080 processor, where the logical address is the physical address. The i486™ processor can be used in this way by mapping all segments into the same address space and keeping paging disabled. This might be done where an older design is being updated to 32-bit technology without also adopting the new architectural features.

An application also could make partial use of segmentation. A frequent cause of software failures is the growth of the stack into the instruction code or data of a program. Segmentation can be used to prevent this. The stack can be put in an address space separate from the address space for either code or data. Stack addresses always would refer to the memory in the stack segment, while data addresses always would refer to memory in the data segment. The stack segment would have a maximum size enforced by hardware. Any attempt to grow the stack beyond this size would generate an exception.

A complex system of programs may make full use of segmentation. For example, a system in which programs share data in real time can have precise control of access to that data. Program bugs appear as exceptions generated when a program makes improper access. This is useful as an aid to debugging during program development, and it also may be used to trigger error-recovery procedures in systems delivered to the end user.

Segmentation hardware translates a segmented (logical) address into an address for a continuous, unsegmented address space, called a linear address. If paging is enabled, paging hardware translates a linear address into a physical address. If paging is not enabled, the linear address is used as the physical address. The physical address appears on the address bus coming out of the processor.

Paging is a mechanism used to simulate a large, unsegmented address space using a small, fragmented address space and some disk storage. Paging provides access to data structures larger than the available memory space by keeping them partly in memory and partly on disk.

Paging is applied to units of 4K bytes called *pages*. When a program attempts to access a page which is on disk, the program is interrupted in a special way. Unlike other exceptions and interrupts, an exception generated due to address translation restores the contents of the processor registers to values which allow the exception-generating instruction to be re-executed. This special treatment is called *instruction restart*. It allows the operating system to read the page from disk, update the mapping of linear addresses to physical addresses for that page, and restart the program. This process is transparent to the program.

If an operating system never sets bit 31 of the CR0 register (the PG bit), the paging mechanism will never be enabled. Linear addresses will be used as physical addresses. This might be done where a design using a 16-bit processor is being updated to use a 32-bit processor. An operating system written for a 16-bit processor does not use paging because the size of its address space is so small (64K bytes) that it is more efficient to swap entire segments between RAM and disk, rather than individual pages.

Paging would be enabled for operating systems which can support demand-paged virtual memory, such as UNIX. Paging is transparent to application software, so an operating system intended to support application programs written for 16-bit processors may run those programs with paging enabled. Unlike paging, segmentation is not transparent to application programs. Programs which use segmentation must be run with the segments they were designed to use.

5.1 SELECTING A SEGMENTATION MODEL

A model for the segmentation of memory is chosen on the basis of reliability and performance. For example, a system which has several programs sharing data in real time would get maximum performance from a model which checks memory references in hardware. This would be a multi-segment model.

At the other extreme, a system which has just one program may get higher performance from an unsegmented or "flat" model. The elimination of "far" pointers and segment-override prefixes reduces code size and increases execution speed. Context switching is faster, because the contents of the segment registers no longer have to be saved or restored.

Some of the benefits of segmentation also can be provided by paging. For example, data can be shared by mapping the same pages onto the address space of each program.

5.1.1 Flat Model

The simplest model is the flat model. In this model, all segments are mapped to the entire physical address space. A segment offset can refer to either code or data areas. To the greatest extent possible, this model removes the segmentation mechanism from the architecture seen by either the system designer or the application programmer. This might be done for a programming environment like UNIX, which supports paging but does not support segmentation.

A segment is defined by a segment descriptor. At least two segment descriptors must be created for a flat model, one for code references and one for data references. Both descriptors have the same base address value. Whenever memory is accessed, the contents of one of the segment registers are used to select a segment descriptor. The segment descriptor provides the base address of the segment and its limit, as well as access control information (see Figure 5-1).

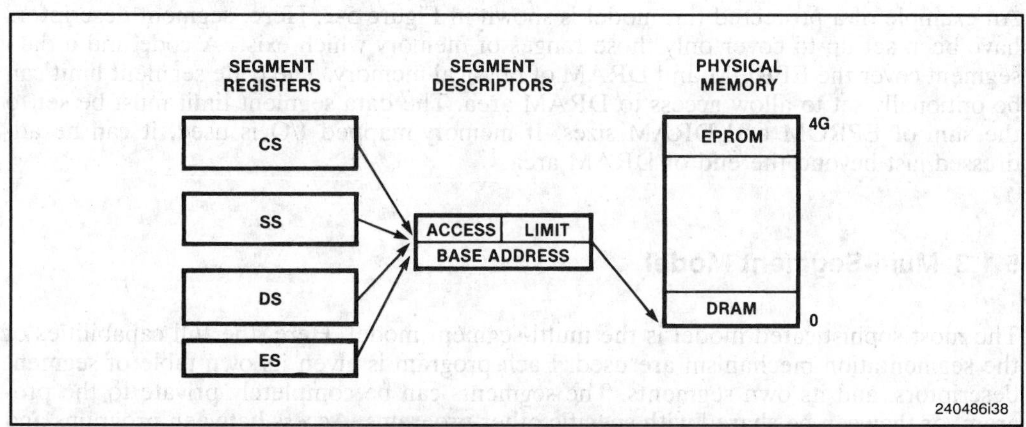

Figure 5-1. Flat Model

ROM usually is put at the top of the physical address space, because the processor begins execution at 0FFFFFFF0H. RAM is placed at the bottom of the address space because the initial base address for the DS data segment after reset initialization is 0.

For a flat model, each descriptor has a base address of 0 and a segment limit of 4 gigabytes. By setting the segment limit to 4 gigabytes, the segmentation mechanism is kept from generating exceptions for memory references which fall outside of a segment. Exceptions could still be generated by the paging or segmentation protection mechanisms, but these also can be removed from the memory model.

5.1.2 Protected Flat Model

The protected flat model is like the flat model, except the segment limits are set to include only the range of addresses for which memory actually exists. A general-protection exception will be generated on any attempt to access unimplemented memory. This might be used for systems in which the paging mechanism is disabled, because it provides a minimum level of hardware protection against some kinds of program bugs.

In this model, the segmentation hardware prevents programs from addressing nonexistent memory locations. The consequences of being allowed access to these memory locations are hardware-dependent. For example, if the processor does not receive a READY# signal (the signal used to acknowledge and terminate a bus cycle), the bus cycle does not terminate and program execution stops.

Although no program should make an attempt to access these memory locations, an attempt may occur as a result of program bugs. Without hardware checking of addresses, it is possible that a bug could suddenly stop program execution. With hardware checking, programs fail in a controlled way. A diagnostic message can appear and recovery procedures can be attempted.

An example of a protected flat model is shown in Figure 5-2. Here, segment descriptors have been set up to cover only those ranges of memory which exist. A code and a data segment cover the EPROM and DRAM of physical memory. The code segment limit can be optionally set to allow access to DRAM area. The data segment limit must be set to the sum of EPROM and DRAM sizes. If memory-mapped I/O is used, it can be addressed just beyond the end of DRAM area.

5.1.3 Multi-Segment Model

The most sophisticated model is the multi-segment model. Here, the full capabilities of the segmentation mechanism are used. Each program is given its own table of segment descriptors, and its own segments. The segments can be completely private to the program, or they can be shared with specific other programs. Access between programs and particular segments can be individually controlled.

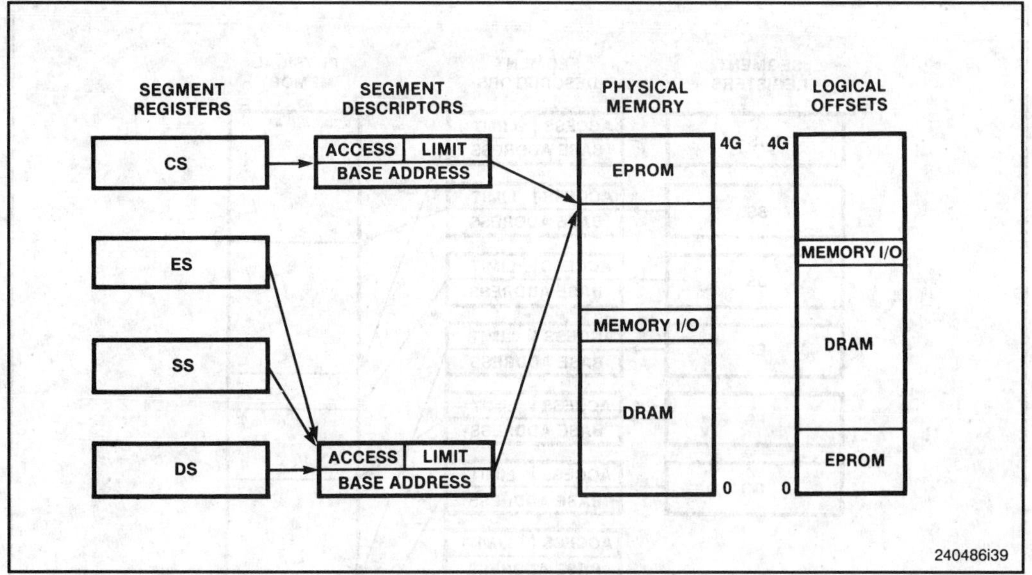

Figure 5-2. Protected Flat Model

Up to six segments can be ready for immediate use. These are the segments which have segment selectors loaded in the segment registers. Other segments are accessed by loading their segment selectors into the segment registers (see Figure 5-3).

Each segment is a separate address space. Even though they may be placed in adjacent blocks of physical memory, the segmentation mechanism prevents access to the contents of one segment by reading beyond the end of another. Every memory operation is checked against the limit specified for the segment it uses. An attempt to address memory beyond the end of the segment generates a general-protection exception.

The segmentation mechanism only enforces the address range specified in the segment descriptor. It is the responsibility of the operating system to allocate separate address ranges to each segment. There may be situations in which it is desirable to have segments which share the same range of addresses. For example, a system may have both code and data stored in a ROM. A code segment descriptor would be used when the ROM is accessed for instruction fetches. A data segment descriptor would be used when the ROM is accessed as data.

5.2 SEGMENT TRANSLATION

A logical address consists of the 16-bit segment selector for its segment and a 32-bit offset into the segment. A logical address is translated into a linear address by adding the offset to the base address of the segment. The base address comes from the *segment descriptor*, a data structure in memory which provides the size and location of a segment, as well as access control information. The segment descriptor comes from one of two tables, the global descriptor table (GDT) or the local descriptor table (LDT). There is

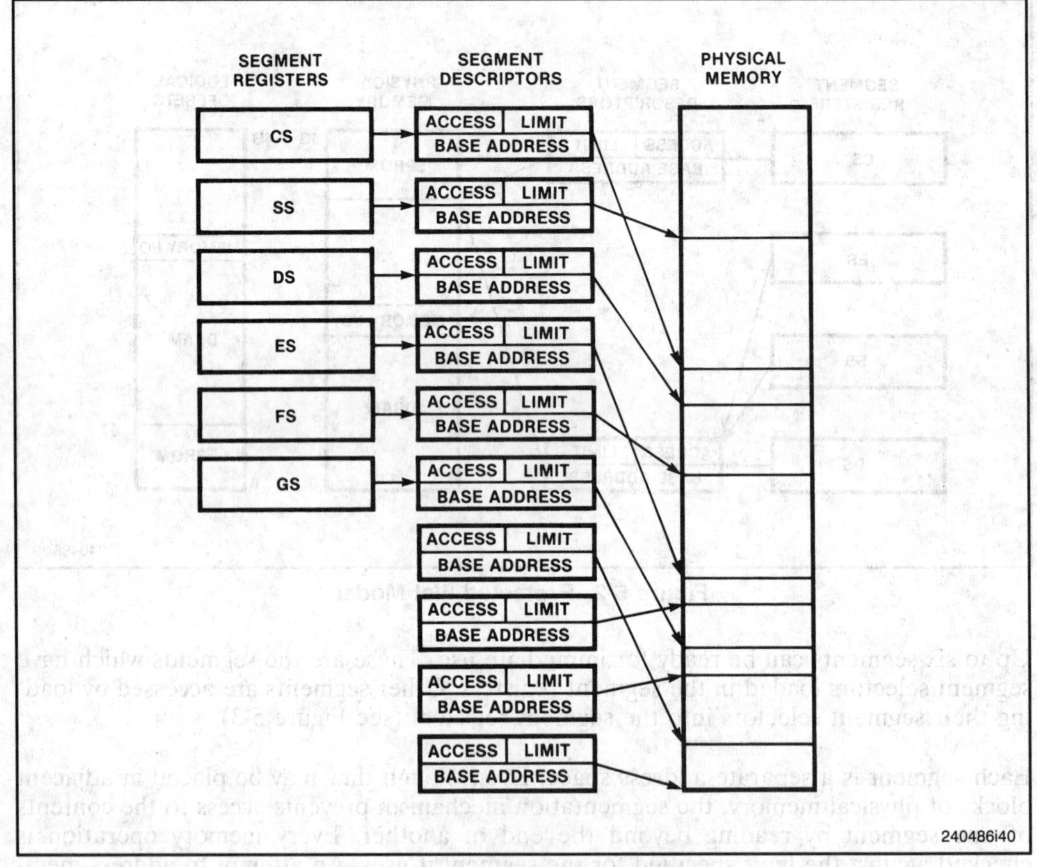

Figure 5-3. Multi-Segment Model

one GDT for all programs in the system, and one LDT for each separate program being run. If the operating system allows, different programs can share the same LDT. The system also may be set up with no LDTs; all programs will then use the GDT.

Every logical address is associated with a segment (even if the system maps all segments into the same linear address space). Although a program may have thousands of segments, only six may be available for immediate use. These are the six segments whose segment selectors are loaded in the processor. The segment selector holds information used to translate the logical address into the corresponding linear address.

Separate *segment registers* exist in the processor for each kind of memory reference (code space, stack space, and data spaces). They hold the segment selectors for the segments currently in use. Access to other segments requires loading a segment register using a form of the MOV instruction. Up to four data spaces may be available at the same time, thus providing a total of six segment registers.

When a segment selector is loaded, the base address, segment limit, and access control information also are loaded into the segment register. The processor does not reference the descriptor tables again until another segment selector is loaded. The information saved in the processor allows it to translate addresses without making extra bus cycles. In systems in which multiple processors have access to the same descriptor tables, it is the responsibility of software to reload the segment registers when the descriptor tables are modified. If this is not done, an old segment descriptor cached in a segment register might be used after its memory-resident version has been modified.

The segment selector contains a 13-bit index into one of the descriptor tables. The index is scaled by eight (the number of bytes in a segment descriptor) and added to the 32-bit base address of the descriptor table. The base address comes from either the global descriptor table register (GDTR) or the local descriptor table register (LDTR). These registers hold the linear address of the beginning of the descriptor tables. A bit in the segment selector specifies which table to use, as shown in Figure 5-4.

The translated address is the linear address, as shown in Figure 5-5. If paging is not used, it is also the physical address. If paging is used, a second level of address translation produces the physical address. This translation is described in Section 5.3.

5.2.1 Segment Registers

Each kind of memory reference is associated with a segment register. Code, data, and stack references each access the segments specified by the contents of their segment registers. More segments can be made available by loading their segment selectors into these registers during program execution.

Every segment register has a "visible" part and an "invisible" part, as shown in Figure 5-6. There are forms of the MOV instruction to load the visible part of these segment registers. The invisible part is loaded by the processor.

The operations which load these registers are instructions for application programs (described in Chapter 3). There are two kinds of these instructions:

1. Direct load instructions such as the MOV, POP, LDS, LSS, LGS, and LFS instructions. These instructions explicitly reference the segment registers.
2. Implied load instructions such as the far pointer versions of the CALL and JMP instructions. These instructions change the contents of the CS register as an incidental part of their function.

When these instructions are used, the visible part of the segment register is loaded with a segment selector. The processor automatically fetches the base address, limit, type, and other information from the descriptor table and loads the invisible part of the segment register.

Because most instructions refer to segments whose selectors already have been loaded into segment registers, the processor can add the logical-address offset to the segment base address with no performance penalty.

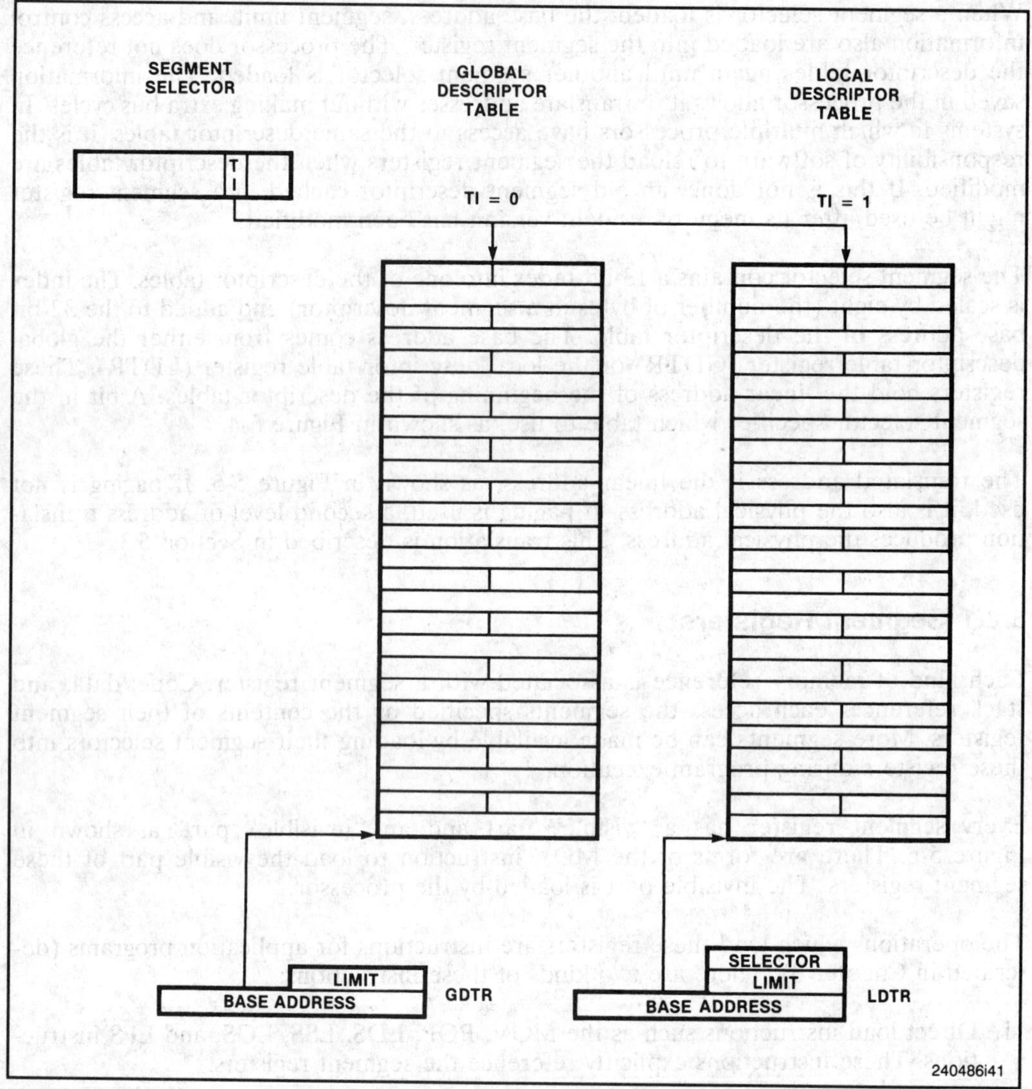

Figure 5-4. TI Bit Selects Descriptor Table

5.2.2 Segment Selectors

A segment selector points to the information which defines a segment, called a segment descriptor. A program may have more segments than the six whose segment selectors occupy segment registers. When this is true, the program uses forms of the MOV instruction to change the contents of these registers when it needs to access a new segment.

A segment selector identifies a segment descriptor by specifying a descriptor table and a descriptor within that table. Segment selectors are visible to application programs as a

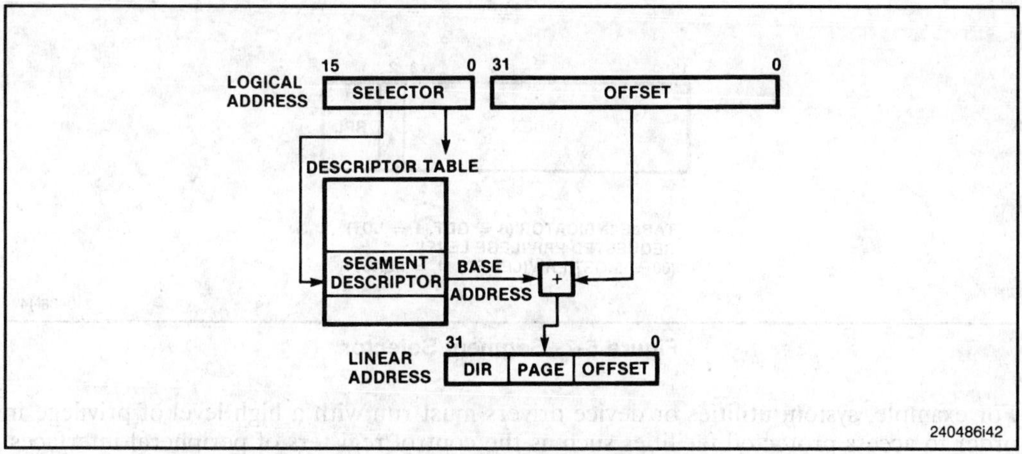

Figure 5-5. Segment Translation

VISIBLE PART	INVISIBLE PART	
SELECTOR	BASE ADDRESS, LIMIT, ETC.	CS
		SS
		DS
		ES
		FS
		GS

240486i43

Figure 5-6. Segment Registers

part of a pointer variable, but the values of selectors are usually assigned or modified by link editors or linking loaders, not application programs. Figure 5-7 shows the format of a segment selector.

Index: Selects one of 8192 descriptors in a descriptor table. The processor multiplies the index value by 8 (the number of bytes in a segment descriptor) and adds the result to the base address of the descriptor table (from the GDTR or LDTR register).

Table Indicator bit: Specifies the descriptor table to use. A clear bit selects the GDT; a set bit selects the current LDT.

Requester Privilege Level: When this field contains a privilege level having a greater value (i.e., less privileged) than the program, it overrides the program's privilege level. When a program uses a less privileged segment selector, memory accesses take place at the lesser privilege level. This is used to guard against a security violation in which a less privileged program uses a more privileged program to access protected data.

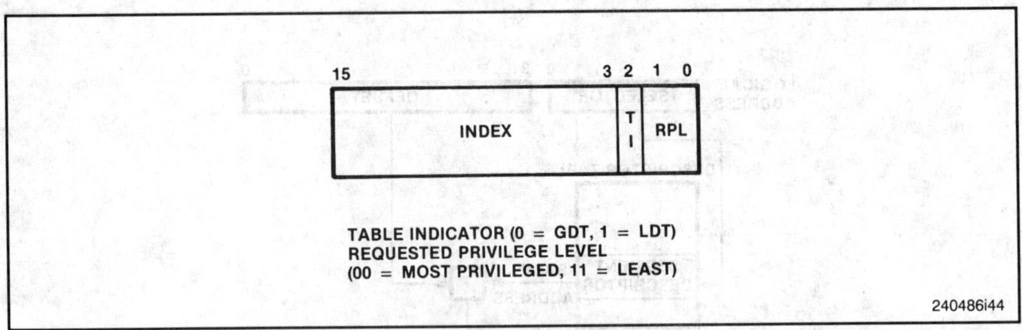

Figure 5-7. Segment Selector

For example, system utilities or device drivers must run with a high level of privilege in order to access protected facilities such as the control registers of peripheral interfaces. But they must not interfere with other protected facilities, even if a request to do so is received from a less privileged program. If a program requested reading a sector of disk into memory occupied by a more privileged program, such as the operating system, the RPL can be used to generate a general-protection exception when the less privileged segment selector is used. This exception occurs even though the program using the segment selector would have a sufficient privilege level to perform the operation on its own.

Because the first entry of the GDT is not used by the processor, a selector which has an index of 0 and a table indicator of 0 (i.e., a selector which points to the first entry of the GDT) is used as a "null selector." The processor does not generate an exception when a segment register (other than the CS or SS registers) is loaded with a null selector. It does, however, generate an exception when a segment register holding a null selector is used to access memory. This feature can be used to initialize unused segment registers.

5.2.3 Segment Descriptors

A segment descriptor is a data structure in memory which provides the processor with the size and location of a segment, as well as control and status information. Descriptors typically are created by compilers, linkers, loaders, or the operating system, but not application programs. Figure 5-8 illustrates the two general descriptor formats. The system segment descriptor is described more fully in Chapter 6. All types of segment descriptors take one of these formats.

Base: Defines the location of the segment within the 4 gigabyte physical address space. The processor puts together the three base address fields to form a single 32-bit value. Segment base values should be aligned to 16 byte boundaries to allow programs to maximize performance by aligning code/data on 16 byte boundaries.

Granularity bit: Turns on scaling of the Limit field by a factor of 4096 (2^{12}). When the bit is clear, the segment limit is interpreted in units of one byte; when set, the segment limit is interpreted in units of 4K bytes (one page). Note that the twelve least significant

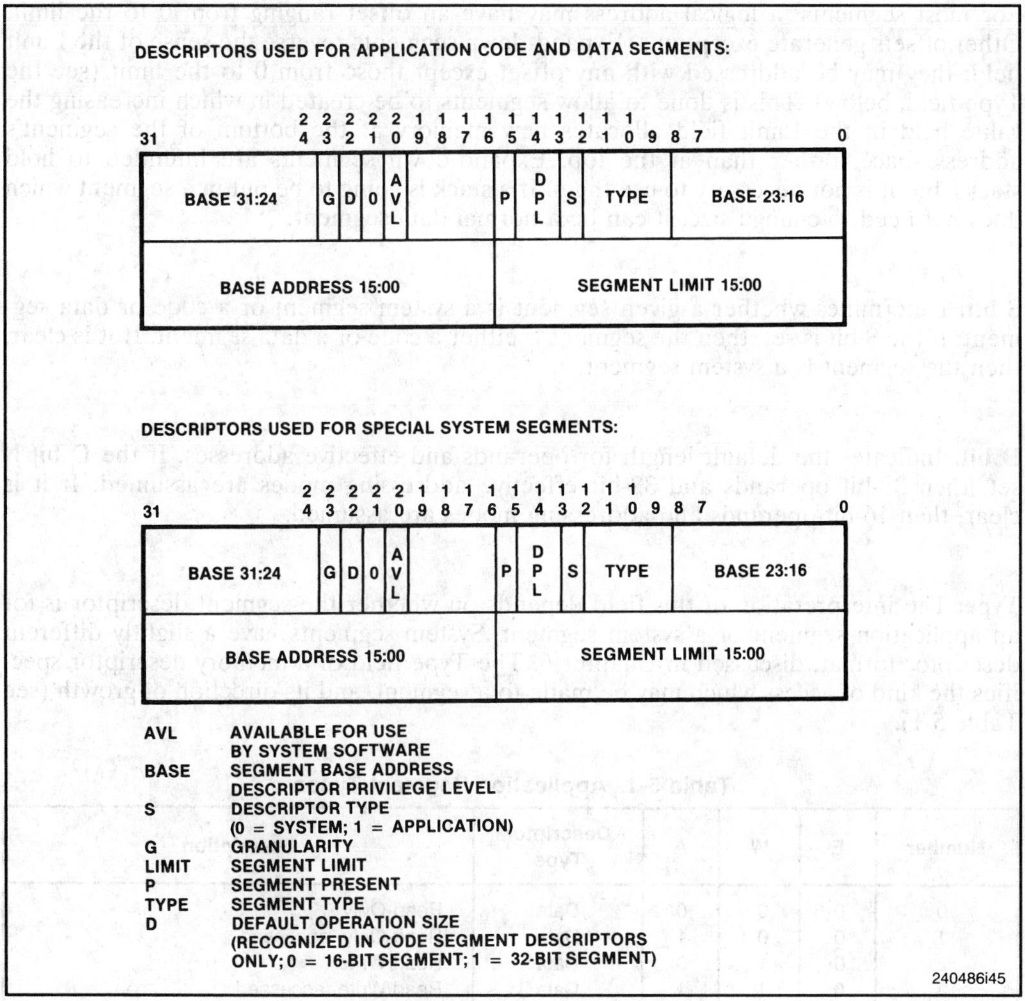

DESCRIPTORS USED FOR APPLICATION CODE AND DATA SEGMENTS:

31–24	23	22	21	20	19–16	15	14–13	12	11–8	7–0
BASE 31:24	G	D	0	AVL		P	DPL	S	TYPE	BASE 23:16

31–16	15–0
BASE ADDRESS 15:00	SEGMENT LIMIT 15:00

DESCRIPTORS USED FOR SPECIAL SYSTEM SEGMENTS:

31–24	23	22	21	20	19–16	15	14–13	12	11–8	7–0
BASE 31:24	G	D	0	AVL		P	DPL	S	TYPE	BASE 23:16

31–16	15–0
BASE ADDRESS 15:00	SEGMENT LIMIT 15:00

AVL	AVAILABLE FOR USE BY SYSTEM SOFTWARE
BASE	SEGMENT BASE ADDRESS
	DESCRIPTOR PRIVILEGE LEVEL
S	DESCRIPTOR TYPE (0 = SYSTEM; 1 = APPLICATION)
G	GRANULARITY
LIMIT	SEGMENT LIMIT
P	SEGMENT PRESENT
TYPE	SEGMENT TYPE
D	DEFAULT OPERATION SIZE (RECOGNIZED IN CODE SEGMENT DESCRIPTORS ONLY; 0 = 16-BIT SEGMENT; 1 = 32-BIT SEGMENT)

240486i45

Figure 5-8. Segment Descriptors

bits of the address are not tested when scaling is used. For example, a limit of 0 with the Granularity bit set results in valid offsets from 0 to 4095. Also note that only the Limit field is affected. The base address remains byte granular.

Limit: Defines the size of the segment. The processor puts together the two limit fields to form a 20-bit value. The processor interprets the limit in one of two ways, depending on the setting of the Granularity bit:

1. If the Granularity bit is clear, the Limit has a value from 1 byte to 1 megabyte, in increments of 1 byte.
2. If the Granularity bit is set, the Limit has a value from 4 kilobytes to 4 gigabytes, in increments of 4K bytes.

For most segments, a logical address may have an offset ranging from 0 to the limit. Other offsets generate exceptions. Expand-down segments reverse the sense of the Limit field; they may be addressed with any offset except those from 0 to the limit (see the Type field, below). This is done to allow segments to be created in which increasing the value held in the Limit field allocates new memory at the bottom of the segment's address space, rather than at the top. Expand-down segments are intended to hold stacks, but it is not necessary to use them. If a stack is going to be put in a segment which does not need to change size, it can be a normal data segment.

S bit: Determines whether a given segment is a system segment or a code or data segment. If the S bit is set, then the segment is either a code or a data segment. If it is clear, then the segment is a system segment.

D bit: Indicates the default length for operands and effective addresses. If the D bit is set, then 32-bit operands and 32-bit effective addressing modes are assumed. If it is clear, then 16-bit operands and addressing modes are assumed.

Type: The interpretation of this field depends on whether the segment descriptor is for an application segment or a system segment. System segments have a slightly different descriptor format, discussed in Chapter 6. The Type field of a memory descriptor specifies the kind of access which may be made to a segment, and its direction of growth (see Table 5-1).

Table 5-1. Application Segment Types

Number	E	W	A	Descriptor Type	Description
0	0	0	0	Data	Read-Only
1	0	0	1	Data	Read-Only, accessed
2	0	1	0	Data	Read/Write
3	0	1	1	Data	Read/Write, accessed
4	1	0	0	Data	Read-Only, expand-down
5	1	0	1	Data	Read-Only, expand-down, accessed
6	1	1	0	Data	Read/Write, expand-down
7	1	1	1	Data	Read/Write, expand-down, accessed
Number	**C**	**R**	**A**	**Descriptor Type**	**Description**
8	0	0	0	Code	Execute-Only
9	0	0	1	Code	Execute-Only, accessed
10	0	1	0	Code	Execute/Read
11	0	1	1	Code	Execute/Read, accessed
12	1	0	0	Code	Execute-Only, conforming
13	1	0	1	Code	Execute-Only, conforming, accessed
14	1	1	0	Code	Execute/Read-Only, conforming
15	1	1	1	Code	Execute/Read-Only, conforming, accessed

For data segments, the three lowest bits of the type field can be interpreted as expand-down (E), write enable (W), and accessed (A). For code segments, the three lowest bits of the type field can be interpreted as conforming (C), read enable (R), and accessed (A).

Data segments can be read-only or read/write. Stack segments are data segments which must be read/write. Loading the SS register with a segment selector for any other type of segment generates a general-protection exception. If the stack segment needs to be able to change size, it can be an expand-down data segment. The meaning of the segment limit is reversed for an expand-down segment. While an offset in the range from 0 to the segment limit is valid for other kinds of segments (outside this range a general-protection exception is generated), in an expand-down segment these offsets are the ones which generate exceptions. The valid offsets in an expand-down segment are those which generate exceptions in the other kinds of segments. Expand-up segments must be addressed by offsets which are equal or less than the segment limit. Offsets into expand-down segments always must be greater than the segment limit. This interpretation of the segment limit causes memory space to be allocated at the bottom of the segment when the segment limit is increased, which is correct for stack segments because they grow toward lower addresses. If the stack is given a segment which does not change size, it does not need to be an expand-down segment.

Code segments can be execute-only or execute/read. An execute/read segment might be used, for example, when constants have been placed with instruction code in a ROM. In this case, the constants can be read either by using an instruction with a CS override prefix or by placing a segment selector for the code segment in a segment register for a data segment.

Code segments can be either conforming or non-conforming. A transfer of execution into a more privileged conforming segment keeps the current privilege level. A transfer into a non-conforming segment at a different privilege level results in a general-protection exception, unless a task gate is used (see Chapter 6 for a discussion of multitasking). System utilities which do not access protected facilities, such as data-conversion functions (e.g., EBCDIC/ASCII translation, Huffman encoding/decoding, math library) and some types of exceptions (e.g., Divide Error, INTO-detected overflow, and BOUND range exceeded) may be loaded in conforming code segments.

The Type field also reports whether the segment has been accessed. Segment descriptors initially report a segment as having been accessed. If the Type field then is set to a value for a segment which has not been accessed, the processor restores the value if the segment is accessed. By clearing and testing the low bit of the Type field, software can monitor segment usage (the low bit of the Type field also is called the Accessed bit).

For example, a program development system might clear all of the Accessed bits for the segments of an application. If the application crashes, the states of these bits can be used to generate a map of all the segments accessed by the application. Unlike the breakpoints provided by the debugging mechanism (Chapter 11), the usage information applies to segments rather than physical addresses.

The processor may update the Type field when a segment is accessed, even if the access is a read cycle. If the descriptor tables have been put in ROM, it may be necessary for hardware to prevent the ROM from being enabled onto the data bus during a write cycle. It also may be necessary to return the READY# signal to the processor when a write cycle to ROM occurs, otherwise the cycle does not terminate. These features of the hardware design are necessary for using ROM-based descriptor tables with the 386™ DX processor, which always sets the Accessed bit when a segment descriptor is loaded. The i486 processor, however, only sets the Accessed bit if it is not already set. Writes to descriptor tables in ROM can be avoided by setting the Accessed bits in every descriptor.

DPL (Descriptor Privilege Level): Defines the privilege level of the segment. This is used to control access to the segment, using the protection mechanism described in Chapter 6.

Segment-Present bit: If this bit is clear, the processor generates a segment-not-present exception when a selector for the descriptor is loaded into a segment register. This is used to detect access to segments which have become unavailable. A segment can become unavailable when the system needs to create free memory. Items in memory, such as character fonts or device drivers, which currently are not being used are de-allocated. An item is de-allocated by marking the segment "not present" (this is done by clearing the Segment-Present bit). The memory occupied by the segment then can be put to another use. The next time the de-allocated item is needed, the segment-not-present exception will indicate the segment needs to be loaded into memory. When this kind of memory management is provided in a manner invisible to application programs, it is called *virtual memory*. A system may maintain a total amount of virtual memory far larger than physical memory by keeping only a few segments present in physical memory at any one time.

Figure 5-9 shows the format of a descriptor when the Segment-Present bit is clear. When this bit is clear, the operating system is free to use the locations marked Available to store its own data, such as information regarding the whereabouts of the missing segment.

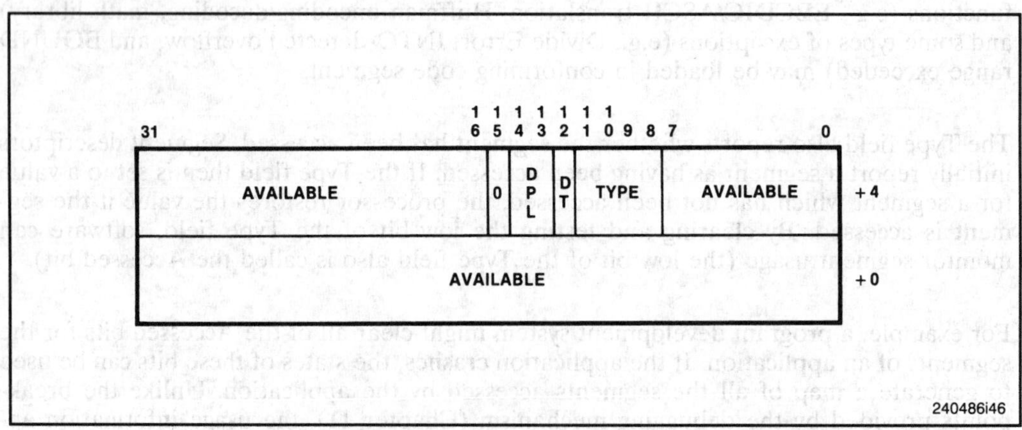

Figure 5-9. Segment Descriptor (Segment Not Present)

5.2.4 Segment Descriptor Tables

A segment descriptor table is an array of segment descriptors. There are two kinds of descriptor tables:

- The global descriptor table (GDT)
- The local descriptor tables (LDT)

There is one GDT for all tasks, and an LDT for each task being run. A descriptor table is an array of segment descriptors, as shown in Figure 5-10. A descriptor table is variable in length and may contain up to 8192 (2^{13}) descriptors. The first descriptor in the GDT is not used by the processor. A segment selector to this "null descriptor" does not

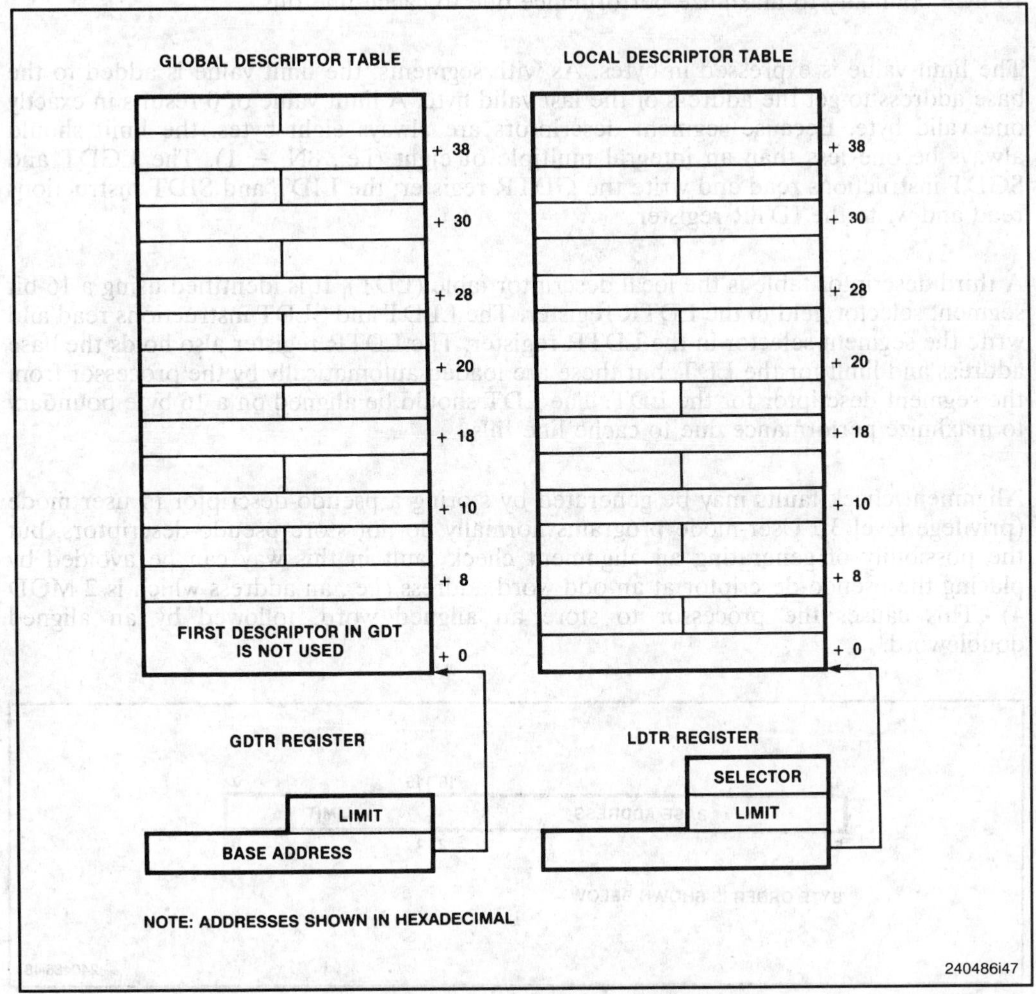

Figure 5-10. Descriptor Tables

generate an exception when loaded into a segment register, but it always generates an exception when an attempt is made to access memory using the descriptor. By initializing the segment registers with this segment selector, accidental reference to unused segment registers can be guaranteed to generate an exception.

5.2.5 Descriptor Table Base Registers

The processor finds the global descriptor table (GDT) and interrupt descriptor table (IDT) using the GDTR and IDTR registers. These registers hold 32-bit base addresses for tables in the linear address space. They also hold 16-bit limit values for the size of these tables. When the registers are loaded or stored, a 48-bit "pseudo-descriptor" is accessed in memory, as shown in Figure 5-11. The GDT and IDT should be aligned on a 16 byte boundary to maximize performance due to cache line fills.

The limit value is expressed in bytes. As with segments, the limit value is added to the base address to get the address of the last valid byte. A limit value of 0 results in exactly one valid byte. Because segment descriptors are always eight bytes, the limit should always be one less than an integral multiple of eight (i.e., 8N − 1). The LGDT and SGDT instructions read and write the GDTR register; the LIDT and SIDT instructions read and write the IDTR register.

A third descriptor table is the local descriptor table (LDT). It is identified using a 16-bit segment selector held in the LDTR register. The LLDT and SLDT instructions read and write the segment selector in the LDTR register. The LDTR register also holds the base address and limit for the LDT, but these are loaded automatically by the processor from the segment descriptor for the LDT. The LDT should be aligned on a 16 byte boundary to maximize performance due to cache line fills.

Alignment check faults may be generated by storing a pseudo-descriptor in user mode (privilege level 3). User-mode programs normally do not store pseudo-descriptors, but the possibility of generating an alignment check fault in this way can be avoided by placing the pseudo-descriptor at an odd word address (i.e., an address which is 2 MOD 4). This causes the processor to store an aligned word, followed by an aligned doubleword.

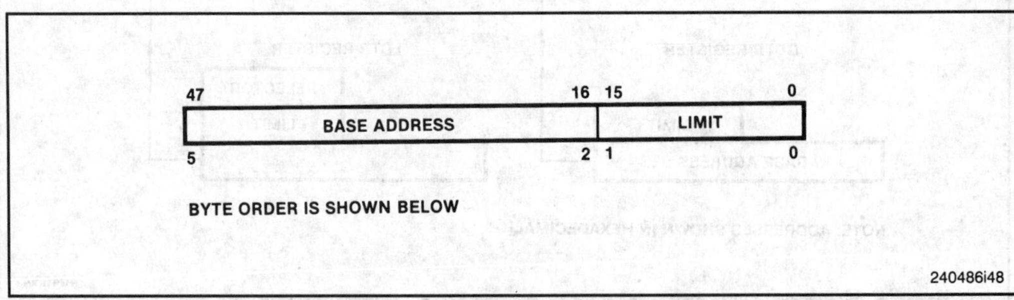

Figure 5-11. Pseudo-Descriptor Format

5.3 Page Translation

A linear address is a 32-bit address into a uniform, unsegmented address space. This address space may be a large physical address space (i.e., an address space composed of 4 gigabytes of RAM), or paging can be used to simulate this address space using a small amount of RAM and some disk storage. When paging is used, a linear address is translated into its corresponding physical address, or an exception is generated. The exception gives the operating system a chance to read the page from disk (perhaps sending a different page out to disk in the process), then restart the instruction which generated the exception.

Paging is different from segmentation through its use of small, fixed-size pages. Unlike segments, which usually are the same size as the data structures they hold, on the i486 processor, pages are always 4K bytes. If segmentation is the only form of address translation which is used, a data structure which is present in physical memory will have all of its parts in memory. If paging is used, a data structure may be partly in memory and partly in disk storage.

The information which maps linear addresses into physical addresses and exceptions is held in data structures in memory called *page tables*. As with segmentation, this information is cached in processor registers to minimize the number of bus cycles required for address translation. Unlike segmentation, these processor registers are completely invisible to application programs. (For testing purposes, these registers are visible to programs running with maximum privileges; see Chapter 10 for details.)

The paging mechanism treats the 32-bit linear address as having three parts, two 10-bit indexes into the page tables and a 12-bit offset into the page addressed by the page tables. Because both the virtual pages in the linear address space and the physical pages of memory are aligned to 4K-byte page boundaries, there is no need to modify the low 12 bits of the address. These 12 bits pass straight through the paging hardware, whether paging is enabled or not. Note that this is different from segmentation, because segments can start at any byte address.

The upper 20 bits of the address are used to index into the page tables. If every page in the linear address space were mapped by a single page table in RAM, 4 megabytes would be needed. This is not done. Instead, two levels of page tables are used. The top level page table is called the *page directory*. It maps the upper 10 bits of the linear address to the second level of page tables. The second level of page tables maps the middle 10 bits of the linear address to the base address of a page in physical memory (called a *page frame address*).

An exception may be generated based on the contents of the page table or the page directory. An exception gives the operating system a chance to bring in a page table from disk storage. By allowing the second-level page tables to be sent to disk, the paging mechanism can support mapping of the entire linear address space using only a few pages in memory.

The CR3 register holds the page frame address of the page directory. For this reason, it also is called the page directory base register or PDBR. The upper 10 bits of the linear address are scaled by four (the number of bytes in a page table entry) and added to the value in the PDBR register to get the physical address of an entry in the page directory. Because the page frame address is always clear in its lowest 12 bits, this addition is performed by concatenation (replacement of the low 12 bits with the scaled index).

When the entry in the page directory is accessed, a number of checks are performed. Exceptions may be generated if the page is protected or is not present in memory. If no exception is generated, the upper 20 bits of the page table entry are used as the page frame address of a second-level page table. The middle 10 bits of the linear address are scaled by four (again, the size of a page table entry) and concatenated with the page frame address to get the physical address of an entry in the second-level page table.

Again, access checks are performed, and exceptions may be generated. If no exception occurs, the upper 20 bits of the second-level page table entry are concatenated with the lowest 12 bits of the linear address to form the physical address of the operand (data) in memory.

Although this process may seem complex, it all takes place with very little overhead. The processor has a cache for page table entries called the translation lookaside buffer (TLB). The TLB satisfies most requests for reading the page tables. Extra bus cycles occur only when a new page is accessed. The page size (4K bytes) is large enough so that very few bus cycles are made to the page tables, compared to the number of bus cycles made to instructions and data. At the same time, the page size is small enough to make efficient use of memory. (No matter how small a data structure is, it occupies at least one page of memory.)

5.3.1 PG Bit Enables Paging

If paging is enabled, a second stage of address translation is used to generate the physical address from the linear address. If paging is not enabled, the linear address is used as the physical address.

Paging is enabled when bit 31 (the PG bit) of the CR0 register is set. This bit usually is set by the operating system during software initialization. The PG bit must be set if the operating system is running more than one program in virtual-8086 mode or if demand-paged virtual memory is used.

5.3.2 Linear Address

Figure 5-12 shows the format of a linear address.

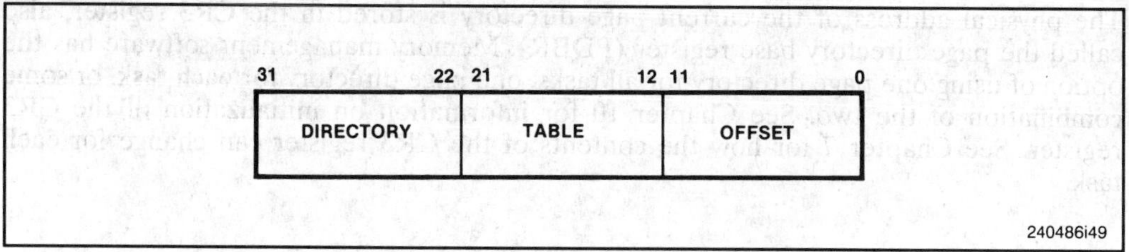

Figure 5-12. Format of a Linear Address

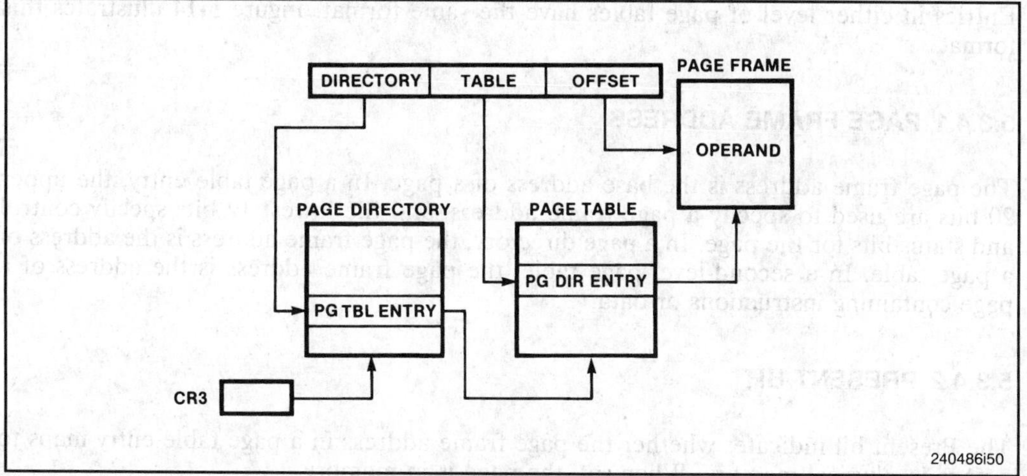

Figure 5-13. Page Translation

Figure 5-13 shows how the processor translates the DIRECTORY, TABLE, and OFFSET fields of a linear address into the physical address using two levels of page tables. The paging mechanism uses the DIRECTORY field as an index into a page directory, the TABLE field as an index into the page table determined by the page directory, and the OFFSET field to address an operand within the page specified by the page table.

5.3.3 Page Tables

A page table is an array of 32-bit entries. A page table is itself a page, and contains 4096 bytes of memory or, at most, 1K 32-bit entries. All pages, including page directories and page tables, are aligned to 4K-byte boundaries.

Two levels of tables are used to address a page of memory. The top level is called the page directory. It addresses up to 1K page tables in the second level. A page table in the second level addresses up to 1K pages in physical memory. All the tables addressed by one page directory, therefore, can address 1M or 2^{20} pages. Because each page contains 4K or 2^{12} bytes, the tables of one page directory can span the entire linear address space of the i486 processor ($2^{20} \times 2^{12} = 2^{32}$).

The physical address of the current page directory is stored in the CR3 register, also called the page directory base register (PDBR). Memory management software has the option of using one page directory for all tasks, one page directory for each task, or some combination of the two. See Chapter 10 for information on initialization of the CR3 register. See Chapter 7 for how the contents of the CR3 register can change for each task.

5.3.4 Page-Table Entries

Entries in either level of page tables have the same format. Figure 5-14 illustrates this format.

5.3.4.1 PAGE FRAME ADDRESS

The page frame address is the base address of a page. In a page table entry, the upper 20 bits are used to specify a page frame address, and the lowest 12 bits specify control and status bits for the page. In a page directory, the page frame address is the address of a page table. In a second-level page table, the page frame address is the address of a page containing instructions or data.

5.3.4.2 PRESENT BIT

The Present bit indicates whether the page frame address in a page table entry maps to a page in physical memory. When set, the page is in memory.

When the Present bit is clear, the page is not in memory, and the rest of the page table entry is available for the operating system, for example, to store information regarding the whereabouts of the missing page. Figure 5-15 illustrates the format of a page table entry when the Present bit is clear.

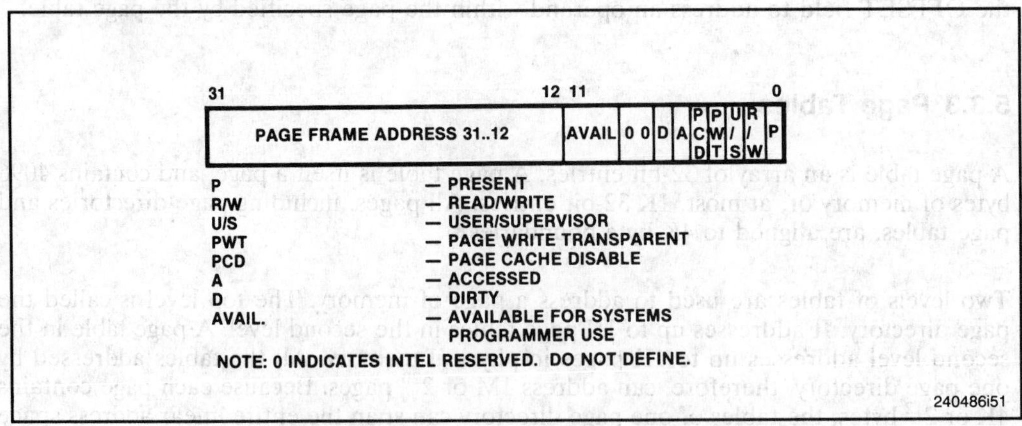

Figure 5-14. Format of a Page Table Entry

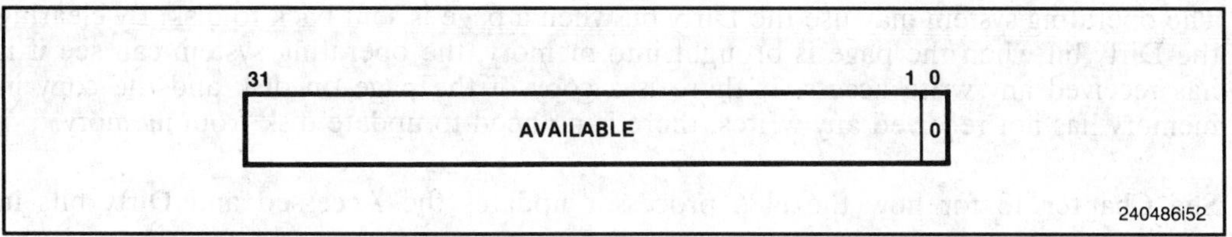

Figure 5-15. Format of a Page Table Entry for a Not-Present Page

If the Present bit is clear in either level of page tables when an attempt is made to use a page table entry for address translation, a page-fault exception is generated. In systems which support demand-paged virtual memory, the following sequence of events then occurs:

1. The operating system copies the page from disk storage into physical memory.
2. The operating system loads the page frame address into the page table entry and sets its Present bit. Other bits, such as the R/W bit, may be set, too.
3. Because a copy of the old page table entry may still exist in the translation lookaside buffer (TLB), the operating system empties it. See Section 5.3.5 for a discussion of the TLB and how to empty it.
4. The program which caused the exception is then restarted.

Since there is no Present bit in CR3 to indicate when the page directory is not resident in memory, the page directory pointed to by CR3 should always be present in physical memory.

5.3.4.3 ACCESSED AND DIRTY BITS

These bits provide data about page usage in both levels of page tables. The Accessed bit is used to report read or write access to a page or second-level page table. The Dirty bit is used to report write access to a page.

With the exception of the Dirty bit in a page directory entry, these bits are set by the hardware; however, the processor does not clear either of these bits. The processor sets the Accessed bits in both levels of page tables before a read or write operation to a page. The processor sets the Dirty bit in the second-level page table before a write operation to an address mapped by that page table entry. The Dirty bit in directory entries is undefined.

The operating system may use the Accessed bit when it needs to create some free memory by sending a page or second-level page table to disk storage. By periodically clearing the Accessed bits in the page tables, it can see which pages have been used recently. Pages which have not been used are candidates for sending out to disk.

The operating system may use the Dirty bit when a page is sent back to disk. By clearing the Dirty bit when the page is brought into memory, the operating system can see if it has received any write access. If there is a copy of the page on disk and the copy in memory has not received any writes, there is no need to update disk from memory.

See Chapter 13 for how the i486 processor updates the Accessed and Dirty bits in multiprocessor systems.

5.3.4.4 READ/WRITE AND USER/SUPERVISOR BITS

The Read/Write and User/Supervisor bits are used for protection checks applied to pages, which the processor performs at the same time as address translation. See Chapter 6 for more information on protection.

5.3.4.5 PAGE-LEVEL CACHE CONTROL BITS

The PCD and PWT bits are used for page-level cache management. Software can control the caching of individual pages or second-level page tables using these bits. See Chapter 12 for more information on caching.

5.3.5 Translation Lookaside Buffer

The processor stores the most recently used page table entries in an on-chip cache called the translation lookaside buffer or TLB. Most paging is performed using the contents of the TLB. Bus cycles to the page tables are performed only when a new page is used.

The TLB is invisible to application programs, but not to operating systems. Operating-system programmers must flush the TLB (dispose of its page table entries) when entries in the page tables are changed. If this is not done, old data which has not received the changes might get used for address translation. A change to an entry for a page which is not present in memory does not require flushing the TLB, because entries for not-present pages are not cached.

The TLB is flushed when the CR3 register is loaded. The CR3 register can be loaded in either of two ways:

1. Explicit loading using MOV instructions, such as:
   ```
   MV CR3, EAX
   ```
2. Implicit loading by a task switch which changes the contents of the CR3 register. (See Chapter 7 for more information on task switching.)

An individual entry in the TLB can be flushed using an INVLPG instruction. This is useful when the mapping of an individual page is changed.

5.4 COMBINING SEGMENT AND PAGE TRANSLATION

Figure 5-16 combines Figure 5-5 and Figure 5-13 to summarize both stages of translation from a logical address to a physical address when paging is enabled. Options available in both stages of address translation can be used to support several different styles of memory management.

5.4.1 Flat Model

When the i486 processor is used to run software written without segments, it may be desirable to remove the segmentation features of the i486 processor. The i486 processor does not have a mode bit for disabling segmentation, but the same effect can be achieved by mapping the stack, code, and data spaces to the same range of linear addresses. The 32-bit offsets used by i486 processor instructions can cover the entire linear address space.

When paging is used, the segments can be mapped to the entire linear address space. If more than one program is being run at the same time, the paging mechanism can be used to give each program a separate address space.

16 0 32 0
LOGICAL ADDRESS
SELECTOR
OFFSET
DESCIPTOR TABLE
SEGMENT DESCRIPTOR
+
LINEAR ADDRESS
DIRECTORY
TABLE
OFFSET
PAGE FRAME
OPERAND
PAGE DIRECTORY
PAGE TABLE
PG TBL ENTRY
PG DIR ENTRY
CR3

240486i53

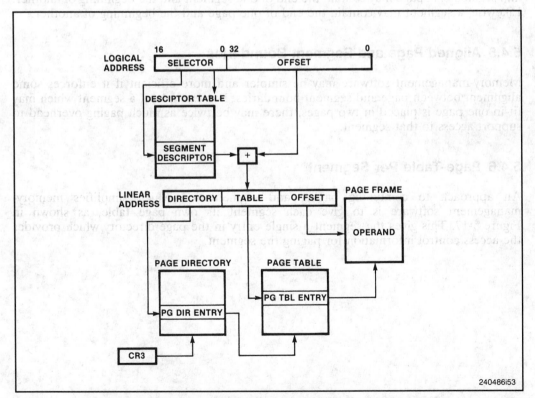

Figure 5-16. Combined Segment and Page Address Translation

5.4.2 Segments Spanning Several Pages

The architecture allows segments which are larger the size of a page (4K bytes). For example, a large data structure may span thousands of pages. If paging were not used, access to any part of the data structure would require the entire data structure to be present in physical memory. With paging, only the page containing the part being accessed needs to be in memory.

5.4.3 Pages Spanning Several Segments

Segments also may be smaller than the size of a page. If one of these segments is placed in a page which is not shared with another segment, the extra memory is wasted. For example, a small data structure, such as a 1-byte semaphore, occupies 4K bytes if it is placed in a page by itself. If many semaphores are used, it is more efficient to pack them into a single page.

5.4.4 Non-Aligned Page and Segment Boundaries

The architecture does not enforce any correspondence between the boundaries of pages and segments. A page may contain the end of one segment and the beginning of another. Likewise, a segment may contain the end of one page and the beginning of another.

5.4.5 Aligned Page and Segment Boundaries

Memory-management software may be simpler and more efficient if it enforces some alignment between page and segment boundaries. For example, if a segment which may fit in one page is placed in two pages, there may be twice as much paging overhead to support access to that segment.

5.4.6 Page-Table Per Segment

An approach to combining paging and segmentation which simplifies memory-management software is to give each segment its own page table, as shown in Figure 5-17. This gives the segment a single entry in the page directory which provides the access control information for paging the segment.

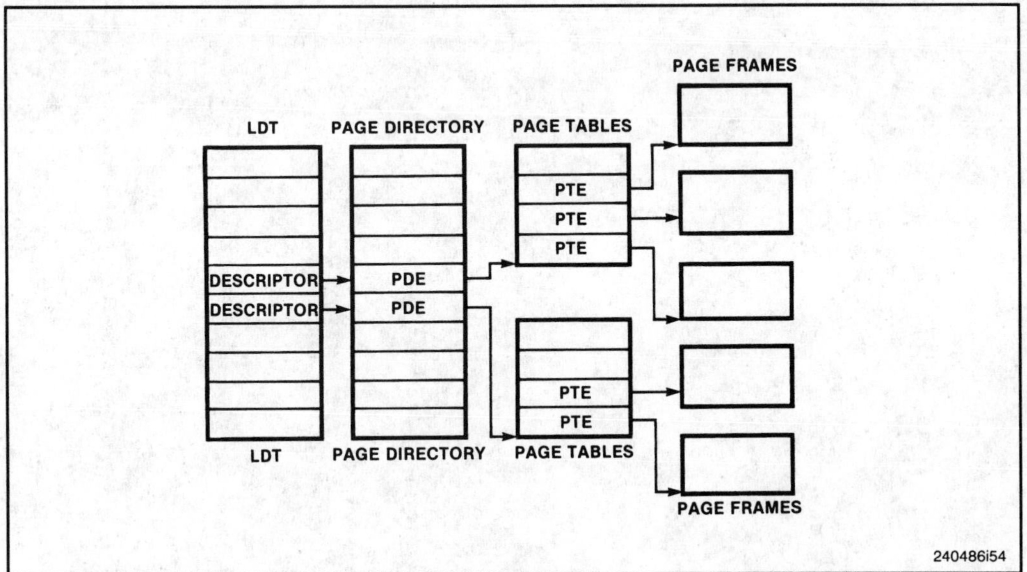

Figure 5-17. Each Segment Can Have Its Own Page Table

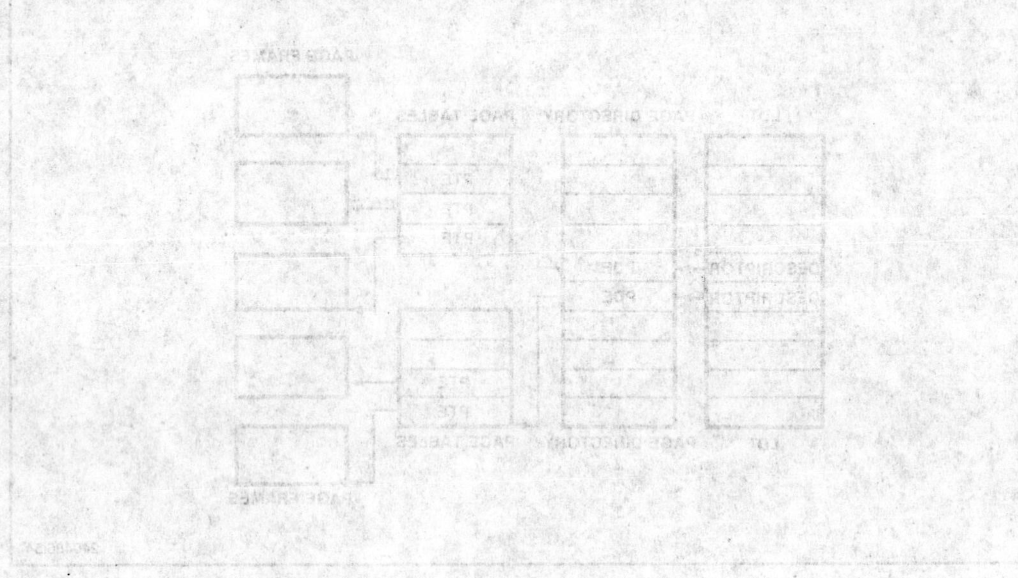

Protection 6

CHAPTER 6
PROTECTION

Protection is necessary for reliable multitasking. Protection can be used to prevent tasks from interfering with each other. For example, protection can keep one task from overwriting the instructions or data of another task.

During program development, the protection mechanism can give a clearer picture of program bugs. When a program makes an unexpected reference to the wrong memory space, the protection mechanism can block the event and report its occurrence.

In end-user systems, the protection mechanism can guard against the possibility of software failures caused by undetected program bugs. If a program fails, its effects can be confined to a limited domain. The operating system can be protected against damage, so diagnostic information can be recorded and automatic recovery may be attempted.

Protection may be applied to segments and pages. Two bits in a processor register define the privilege level of the program currently running (called the current privilege level or CPL). The CPL is checked during address translation for segmentation and paging.

Although there is no control register or mode bit for turning off the protection mechanism, the same effect can be achieved by assigning privilege level 0 (the highest level of privilege) to all segment selectors, segment descriptors, and page table entries.

6.1 SEGMENT-LEVEL PROTECTION

Protection provides the ability to limit the amount of interference a malfunctioning program can inflict on other programs and their data. Protection is a valuable aid in software development because it allows software tools (operating system, debugger, etc.) to survive in memory undamaged. When an application program fails, the software is available to report diagnostic messages, and the debugger is available for post-mortem analysis of memory and registers. In production, protection can make software more reliable by giving the system an opportunity to initiate recovery procedures.

Each memory reference is checked to verify that it satisfies the protection checks. All checks are made before the memory cycle is started; any violation prevents the cycle from starting and results in an exception. Because checks are performed in parallel with address translation, there is no performance penalty. There are five protection checks:

1. Type check
2. Limit check
3. Restriction of addressable domain
4. Restriction of procedure entry points
5. Restriction of instruction set

A protection violation results in an exception. See Chapter 9 for an explanation of the exception mechanism. This chapter describes the protection violations which lead to exceptions.

6.2 SEGMENT DESCRIPTORS AND PROTECTION

Figure 6-1 shows the fields of a segment descriptor which are used by the protection mechanism. Individual bits in the Type field also are referred to by the names of their functions.

Protection parameters are placed in the descriptor when it is created. In general, application programmers do not need to be concerned about protection parameters.

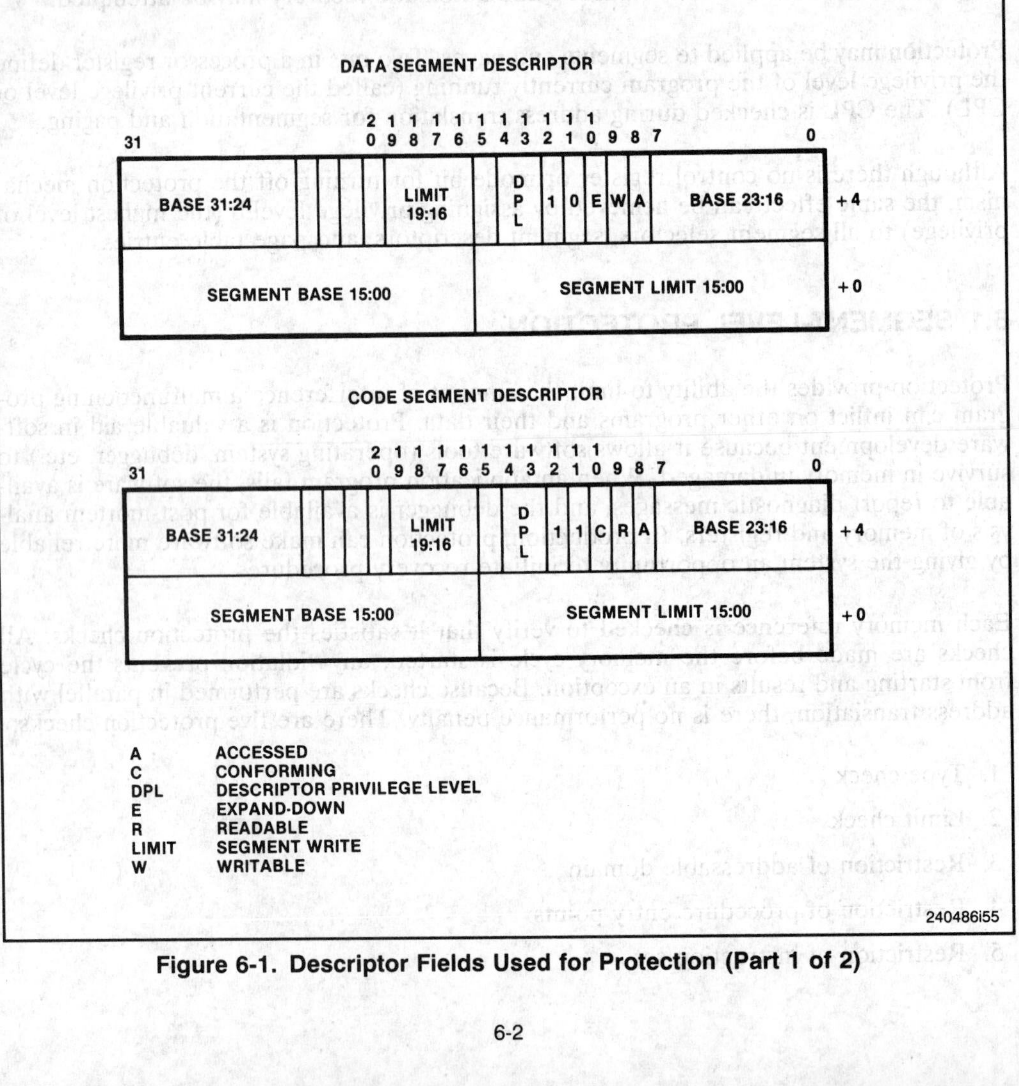

Figure 6-1. Descriptor Fields Used for Protection (Part 1 of 2)

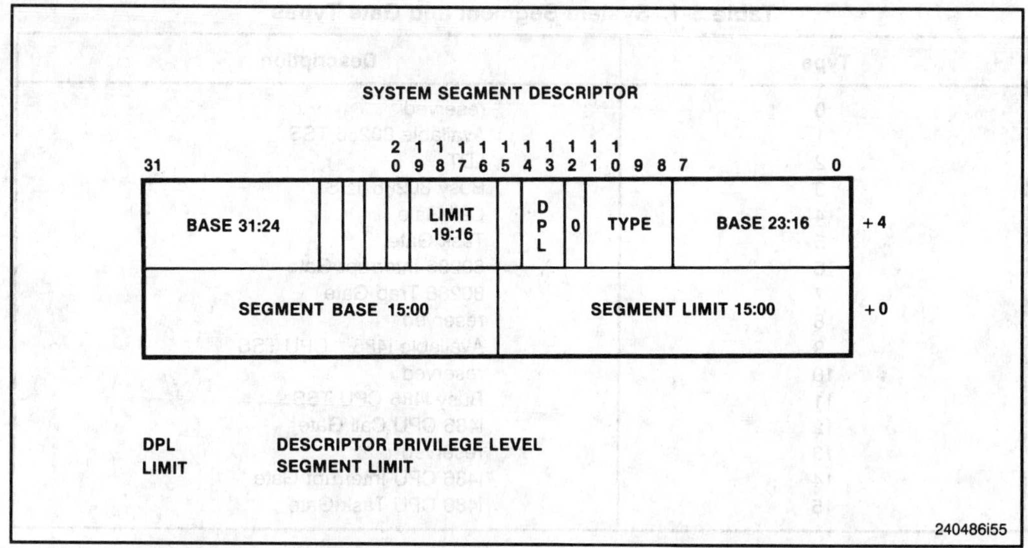

Figure 6-1. Descriptor Fields Used for Protection (Part 2 of 2)

When a program loads a segment selector into a segment register, the processor loads both the base address of the segment and the protection information. The invisible part of each segment register has storage for the base, limit, type, and privilege level. While this information is resident in the segment register, subsequent protection checks on the same segment can be performed with no performance penalty.

6.2.1 Type Checking

In addition to the descriptors for application code and data segments, the i486™ processor has descriptors for system segments and gates. These are data structures used for managing tasks (Chapter 7) and exceptions and interrupts (Chapter 9). Table 6-1 lists all the types defined for system segments and gates. Note that not all descriptors define segments; gate descriptors hold pointers to procedure entry points.

The Type fields of code and data segment descriptors include bits which further define the purpose of the segment (see Figure 6-1):

- The Writable bit in a data-segment descriptor controls whether programs can write to the segment.
- The Readable bit in an executable-segment descriptor specifies whether programs can read from the segment (e.g., to access constants stored in the code space). A readable, executable segment may be read in two ways:
  1. With the CS register, by using a CS override prefix.
  2. By loading a selector for the descriptor into a data-segment register (the DS, ES, FS, or GS registers).

Table 6-1. System Segment and Gate Types

Type	Description
0	reserved
1	Available 80286 TSS
2	LDT
3	Busy 80286 TSS
4	Call Gate
5	Task Gate
6	80286 Interrupt Gate
7	80286 Trap Gate
8	reserved
9	Available i486™ CPU TSS
10	reserved
11	Busy i486 CPU TSS
12	i486 CPU Call Gate
13	reserved
14	i486 CPU Interrupt Gate
15	i486 CPU Task Gate

Type checking can be used to detect programming errors which would attempt to use segments in ways not intended by the programmer. The processor examines type information on two kinds of occasions:

1. When a selector for a descriptor is loaded into a segment register. Certain segment registers can contain only certain descriptor types; for example:
   - The CS register only can be loaded with a selector for an executable segment.
   - Selectors of executable segments which are not readable cannot be loaded into data-segment registers.
   - Only selectors of writable data segments can be loaded into the SS register.
2. Certain segments can be used by instructions only in certain predefined ways; for example:
   - No instruction may write into an executable segment.
   - No instruction may write into a data segment if the writable bit is not set.
   - No instruction may read an executable segment unless the readable bit is set.

6.2.2 Limit Checking

The Limit field of a segment descriptor prevents programs from addressing outside the segment. The effective value of the limit depends on the setting of the G bit (Granularity bit). For data segments, the limit also depends on the E bit (Expansion Direction bit). The E bit is a designation for one bit of the Type field, when referring to data segment descriptors.

When the G bit is clear, the limit is the value of the 20-bit Limit field in the descriptor. In this case, the limit ranges from 0 to 0FFFFFH ($2^{20} - 1$ or 1 megabyte). When the G bit is set, the processor scales the value in the Limit field by a factor of 2^{12}. In this case the limit ranges from 0FFFH ($2^{12} - 1$ or 4K bytes) to 0FFFFFFFFH ($2^{32} - 1$ or 4 gigabytes). Note that when scaling is used, the lower twelve bits of the address are not checked against the limit; when the G bit is set and the segment limit is 0, valid offsets within the segment are 0 through 4095.

For all types of segments except expand-down data segments (stack segments), the value of the limit is one less than the size, in bytes, of the segment. The processor causes a general-protection exception in any of these cases:

- Attempt to access a memory byte at an address > limit
- Attempt to access a memory word at an address > (limit − 1)
- Attempt to access a memory doubleword at an address > (limit − 3)

For expand-down data segments, the limit has the same function but is interpreted differently. In these cases the range of valid offsets is from (limit + 1) to $2^{32} - 1$. An expand-down segment has maximum size when the segment limit is 0.

Limit checking catches programming errors such as runaway subscripts and invalid pointer calculations. These errors are detected when they occur, so identification of the cause is easier. Without limit checking, these errors could overwrite critical memory in another module, and the existence of these errors would not be discovered until the damaged module crashed, an event which may occur long after the actual error. Protection can block these errors and report their source.

In addition to limit checking on segments, there is limit checking on the descriptor tables. The GDTR and IDTR registers contain a 16-bit limit value. It is used by the processor to prevent programs from selecting a segment descriptor outside the descriptor table. The limit of a descriptor table identifies the last valid byte of the table. Because each descriptor is eight bytes long, a table which contains up to N descriptors should have a limit of 8N − 1.

A descriptor may be given a zero value. This refers to the first descriptor in the GDT, which is not used. Although this descriptor may be loaded into a segment register, any attempt to reference memory using this descriptor will generate a general-protection exception.

6.2.3 Privilege Levels

The protection mechanism recognizes four privilege levels, numbered from 0 to 3. The greater numbers mean lesser privileges. If all other protection checks are satisfied, a general-protection exception is generated if a program attempts to access a segment using a less privileged level (greater privilege number) than that applied to the segment.

Although no control register or mode bit is provided for turning off the protection mechanism, the same effect can be achieved by assigning all privilege levels the value of 0. (The PE bit in the CR0 register is not an enabling bit for the protection mechanism alone; it is used to enable "protected mode," the mode of program execution in which the full 32-bit architecture is available. When protected mode is disabled, the processor operates in "real-address mode," where it appears as a fast, enhanced 8086 processor.)

Privilege levels can be used to improve the reliability of operating systems. By giving the operating system the highest privilege level, it is protected from damage by bugs in other programs. If a program crashes, the operating system has a chance to generate a diagnostic message and attempt recovery procedures.

Another level of privilege can be established for other parts of the system software, such as the programs which handle peripheral devices, called *device drivers*. If a device driver crashes, the operating system should be able to report a diagnostic message, so it makes sense to protect the operating system against bugs in device drivers. A device driver, however, may service an important peripheral such as a disk drive. If the application program crashed, the device driver should not corrupt the directory structure of the disk, so it makes sense to protect device drivers against bugs in applications. Device drivers should be given an intermediate privilege level between the operating system and the application programs. Application programs are given the lowest privilege level.

Figure 6-2 shows how these levels of privilege can be interpreted as rings of protection. The center is for the segments containing the most critical software, usually the kernel of an operating system. Outer rings are for less critical software.

The following data structures contain privilege levels:

- The lowest two bits of the CS segment register hold the *current privilege level (CPL)*. This is the privilege level of the program being run. The lowest two bits of the SS register also hold a copy of the CPL. Normally, the CPL is equal to the privilege level of the code segment from which instructions are being fetched. The CPL changes when control is transferred to a code segment with a different privilege level.

- Segment descriptors contain a field called the *descriptor privilege level (DPL)*. The DPL is the privilege level applied to a segment.

- Segment selectors contain a field called the *requested privilege level (RPL)*. The RPL is intended to represent the privilege level of the procedure which created the selector. If the RPL is a less privileged level than the CPL, it overrides the CPL. When a more privileged program receives a segment selector from a less privileged program, the RPL causes the memory access take place at the less privileged level.

Privilege levels are checked when the selector of a descriptor is loaded into a segment register. The checks used for data access differ from those used for transfers of execution among executable segments; therefore, the two types of access are considered separately in the following sections.

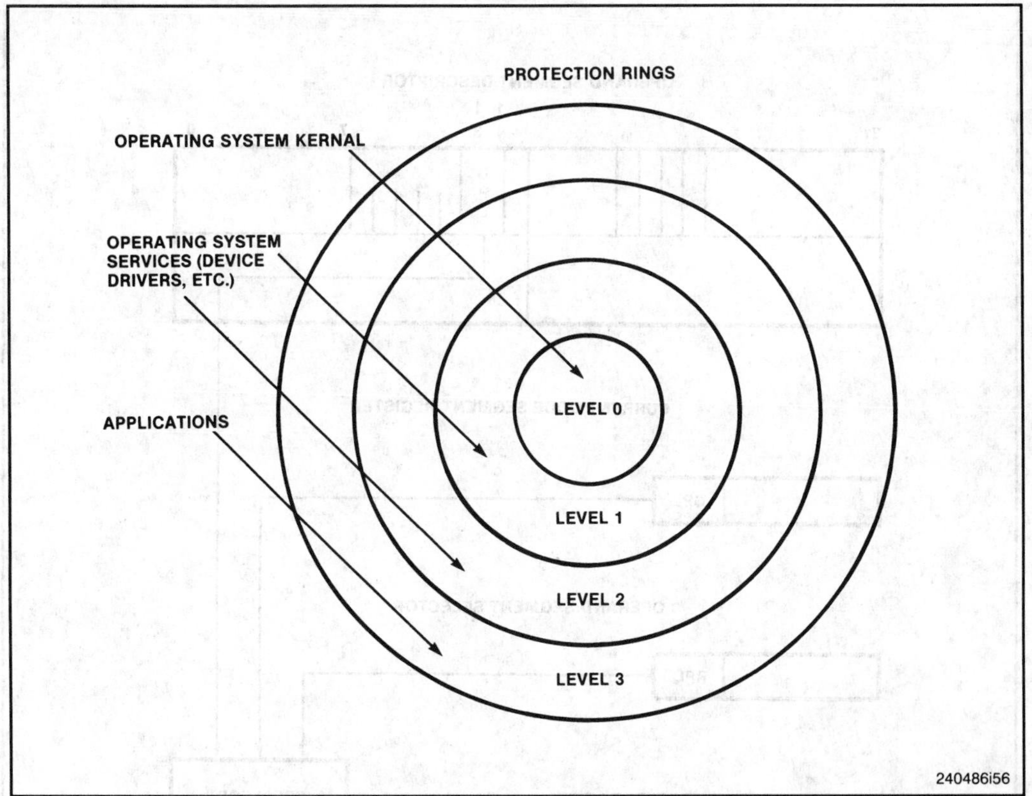

Figure 6-2. Protection Rings

6.3 RESTRICTING ACCESS TO DATA

To address operands in memory, a segment selector for a data segment must be loaded into a data-segment register (the DS, ES, FS, GS, or SS registers). The processor checks the segment's privilege levels. The check is performed when the segment selector is loaded. As Figure 6-3 shows, three different privilege levels enter into this type of privilege check.

The three privilege levels which are checked are:

1. The CPL (current privilege level) of the program. This is held in the two least-significant bit positions of the CS register.
2. The DPL (descriptor privilege level) of the segment descriptor of the segment containing the operand.
3. The RPL (requestor's privilege level) of the selector used to specify the segment containing the operand. This is held in the two lowest bit positions of the segment register used to access the operand (the SS, DS, ES, FS, or GS registers). If the operand is in the stack segment, the RPL is the same as the CPL.

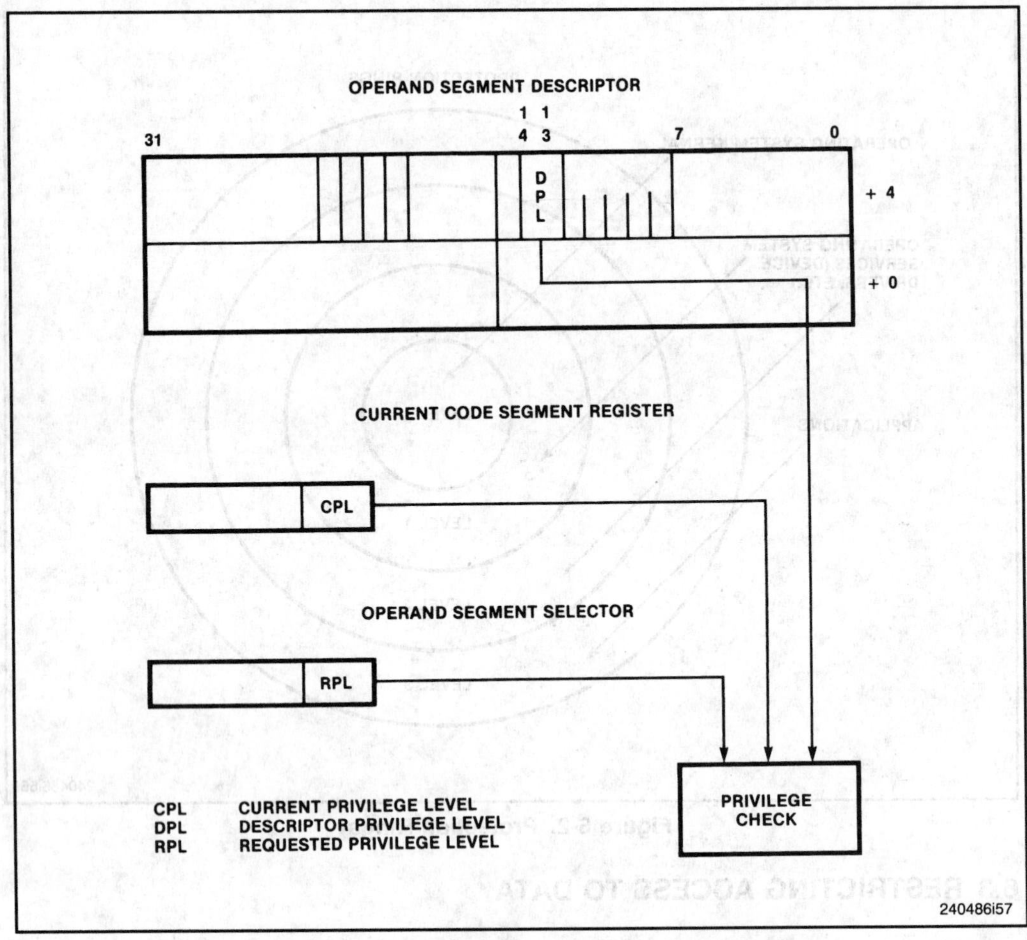

Figure 6-3. Privilege Check for Data Access

Instructions may load a segment register only if the DPL of the segment is the same or a less privileged level (greater privilege number) than the less privileged of the CPL and the selector's RPL.

The addressable domain of a task varies as its CPL changes. When the CPL is 0, data segments at all privilege levels are accessible; when the CPL is 1, only data segments at privilege levels 1 through 3 are accessible; when the CPL is 3, only data segments at privilege level 3 are accessible.

6.3.1 Accessing Data in Code Segments

It may be desirable to store data in a code segment, for example, when both code and data are provided in ROM. Code segments may legitimately hold constants; it is not possible to write to a segment defined as a code segment, unless a data segment is mapped to the same address space. The following methods of accessing data in code segments are possible:

1. Load a data-segment register with a segment selector for a nonconforming, readable, executable segment.
2. Load a data-segment register with a segment selector for a conforming, readable, executable segment.
3. Use a code-segment override prefix to read a readable, executable segment whose selector already is loaded in the CS register.

The same rules for access to data segments apply to case 1. Case 2 is always valid because the privilege level of a code segment with a set Conforming bit is effectively the same as the CPL, regardless of its DPL. Case 3 is always valid because the DPL of the code segment selected by the CS register is the CPL.

6.4 RESTRICTING CONTROL TRANSFERS

With the i486 processor, control transfers are provided by the JMP, CALL, RET, INT, and IRET instructions, as well as by the exception and interrupt mechanisms. Exceptions and interrupts are special cases discussed in Chapter 9. This chapter discusses only the JMP, CALL, and RET instructions.

The "near" forms of the JMP, CALL, and RET instructions transfer program control within the current code segment, and therefore are subject only to limit checking. The processor checks that the destination of the JMP, CALL, or RET instruction does not exceed the limit of the current code segment. This limit is cached in the CS register, so protection checks for near transfers require no performance penalty.

The operands of the "far" forms of the JMP and CALL instruction refer to other segments, so the processor performs privilege checking. There are two ways a JMP or CALL instruction can refer to another segment:

1. The operand selects the descriptor of another executable segment.
2. The operand selects a call gate descriptor. This gated form of transfer is discussed in Chapter 7.

As Figure 6-4 shows, two different privilege levels enter into a privilege check for a control transfer which does not use a call gate:

1. The CPL (current privilege level).
2. The DPL of the descriptor of the destination code segment.

Normally the CPL is equal to the DPL of the segment which the processor is currently executing. The CPL may, however, be greater (less privileged) than the DPL if the current code segment is a *conforming segment* (as indicated by the Type field of its

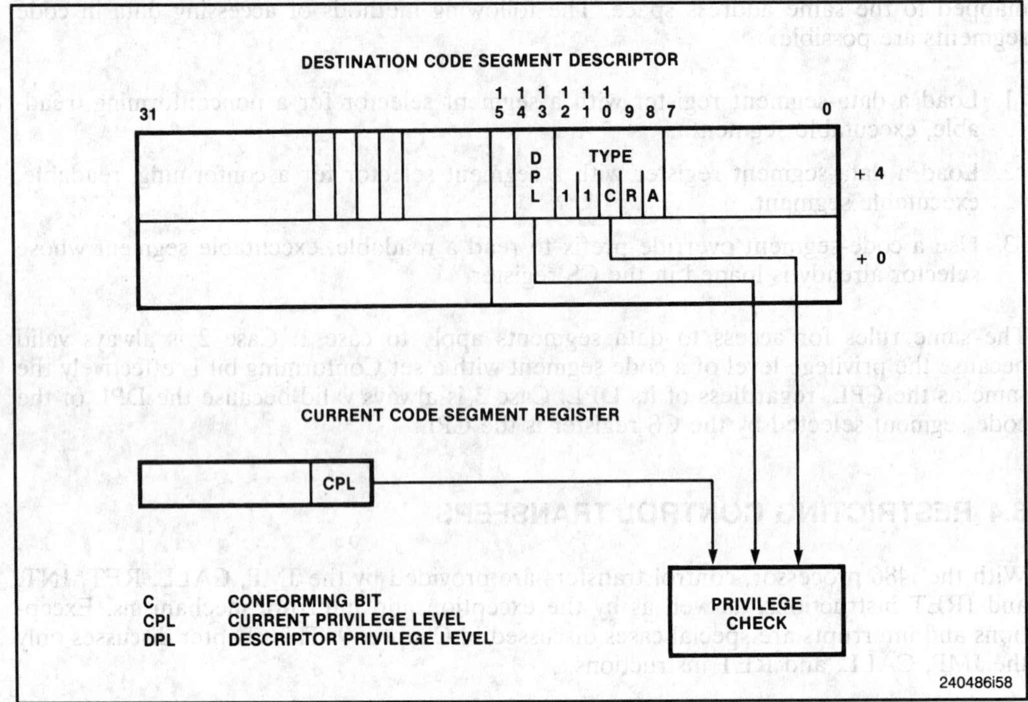

Figure 6-4. Privilege Check for Control Transfer Without Gate

segment descriptor). A conforming segment runs at the privilege level of the calling procedure. The processor keeps a record of the CPL cached in the CS register; this value can be different from the DPL in the segment descriptor of the current code segment.

The processor only permits a JMP or CALL instruction directly into another segment if one of the following privilege rules is satisfied:

- The DPL of the segment is equal to the current CPL.
- The segment is a conforming code segment, and its DPL is less (more privileged) than the current CPL.

Conforming segments are used for programs, such as math libraries and some kinds of exception handlers, which support applications but do not require access to protected system facilities. When control is transferred to a conforming segment, the CPL does not change, even if the selector used to address the segment has a different RPL. This is the only condition in which the CPL may be different from the DPL of the current code segment.

Most code segments are not conforming. For these segments, control can be transferred without a gate only to other code segments at the same level of privilege. It is sometimes necessary, however, to transfer control to higher privilege levels. This is accomplished with the CALL instruction using call-gate descriptors, which is explained in Chapter 7. The JMP instruction may never transfer control to a nonconforming segment whose DPL does not equal the CPL.

6.5 GATE DESCRIPTORS

To provide protection for control transfers among executable segments at different privilege levels, the i486 processor uses *gate descriptors*. There are four kinds of gate descriptors:

- Call gates
- Trap gates
- Interrupt gates
- Task gates

Task gates are used for task switching and are discussed in Chapter 7. Chapter 9 explains how trap gates and interrupt gates are used by exceptions and interrupts. This chapter is concerned only with call gates. Call gates are a form of protected control transfer. They are used for control transfers between different privilege levels. They only need to be used in systems in which more than one privilege level is used. Figure 6-5 illustrates the format of a call gate.

A call gate has two main functions:

1. To define an entry point of a procedure.
2. To specify the privilege level required to enter a procedure.

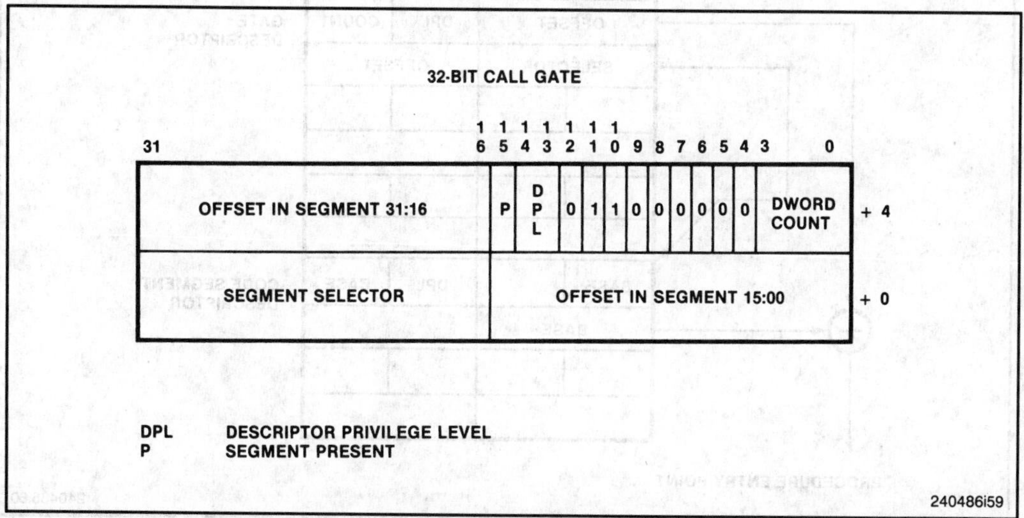

Figure 6-5. Call Gate

Call gate descriptors are used by CALL and JUMP instructions in the same manner as code segment descriptors. When the hardware recognizes that the segment selector for the destination refers to a gate descriptor, the operation of the instruction is determined by the contents of the call gate. A call gate descriptor may reside in the GDT or in an LDT, but not in the interrupt descriptor table (IDT).

The selector and offset fields of a gate form a pointer to the entry point of a procedure. A call gate guarantees that all control transfers to other segments go to a valid entry point, rather than to the middle of a procedure (or worse, to the middle of an instruction). The operand of the control transfer instruction is not the segment selector and offset within the segment to the procedure's entry point. Instead, the segment selector points to a gate descriptor, and the offset is not used. Figure 6-6 shows this form of addressing.

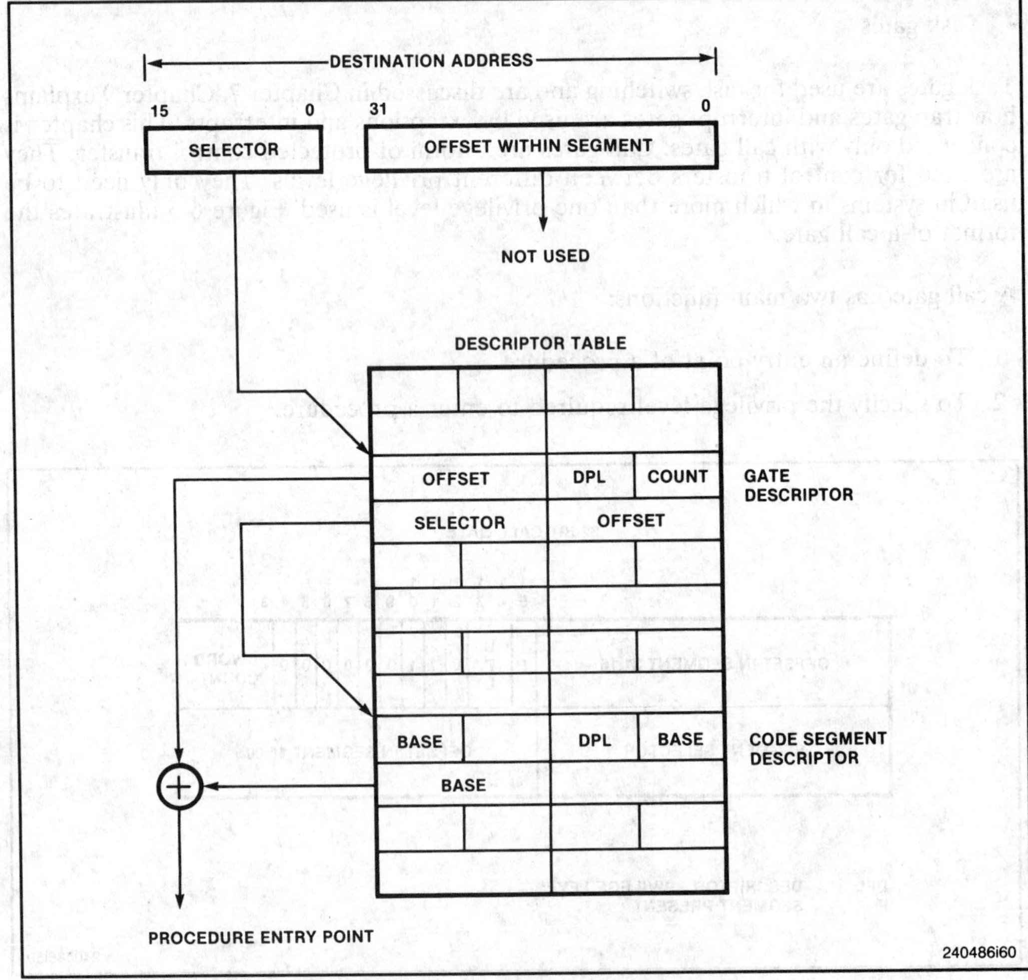

Figure 6-6. Call Gate Mechanism

As shown in Figure 6-7, four different privilege levels are used to check the validity of a control transfer through a call gate.

The privilege levels checked during a transfer of execution through a call gate are:

1. The CPL (current privilege level).
2. The RPL (requestor's privilege level) of the segment selector used to specify the call gate.
3. The DPL (descriptor privilege level) of the gate descriptor.
4. The DPL of the segment descriptor of the destination code segment.

The DPL field of the gate descriptor determines from which privilege levels the gate may be used. One code segment can have several procedures which are intended for use from different privilege levels. For example, an operating system may have some services which are intended to be used by both the operating system and application software, such as routines to handle character I/O, while other services may be intended only for use by operating system, such as routines which initialize device drivers.

Gates can be used for control transfers to more privileged levels or to the same privilege level (though they are not necessary for transfers to the same level). Only CALL instructions can use gates to transfer to less privileged levels. A JMP instruction may use a gate only to transfer control to a code segment with the same privilege level, or to a conforming code segment with the same or a more privileged level.

For a JMP instruction to a nonconforming segment, both of the following privilege rules must be satisfied; otherwise, a general-protection exception is generated.

MAX (CPL,RPL) ≤ gate DPL
destination code segment DPL = CPL

For a CALL instruction (or for a JMP instruction to a conforming segment), both of the following privilege rules must be satisfied; otherwise, a general-protection exception is generated.

MAX (CPL,RPL) ≤ gate DPL
destination code segment DPL ≤ CPL

6.5.1 Stack Switching

A procedure call to a more privileged level does the following:

1. Changes the CPL.
2. Transfers control (execution).
3. Switches stacks.

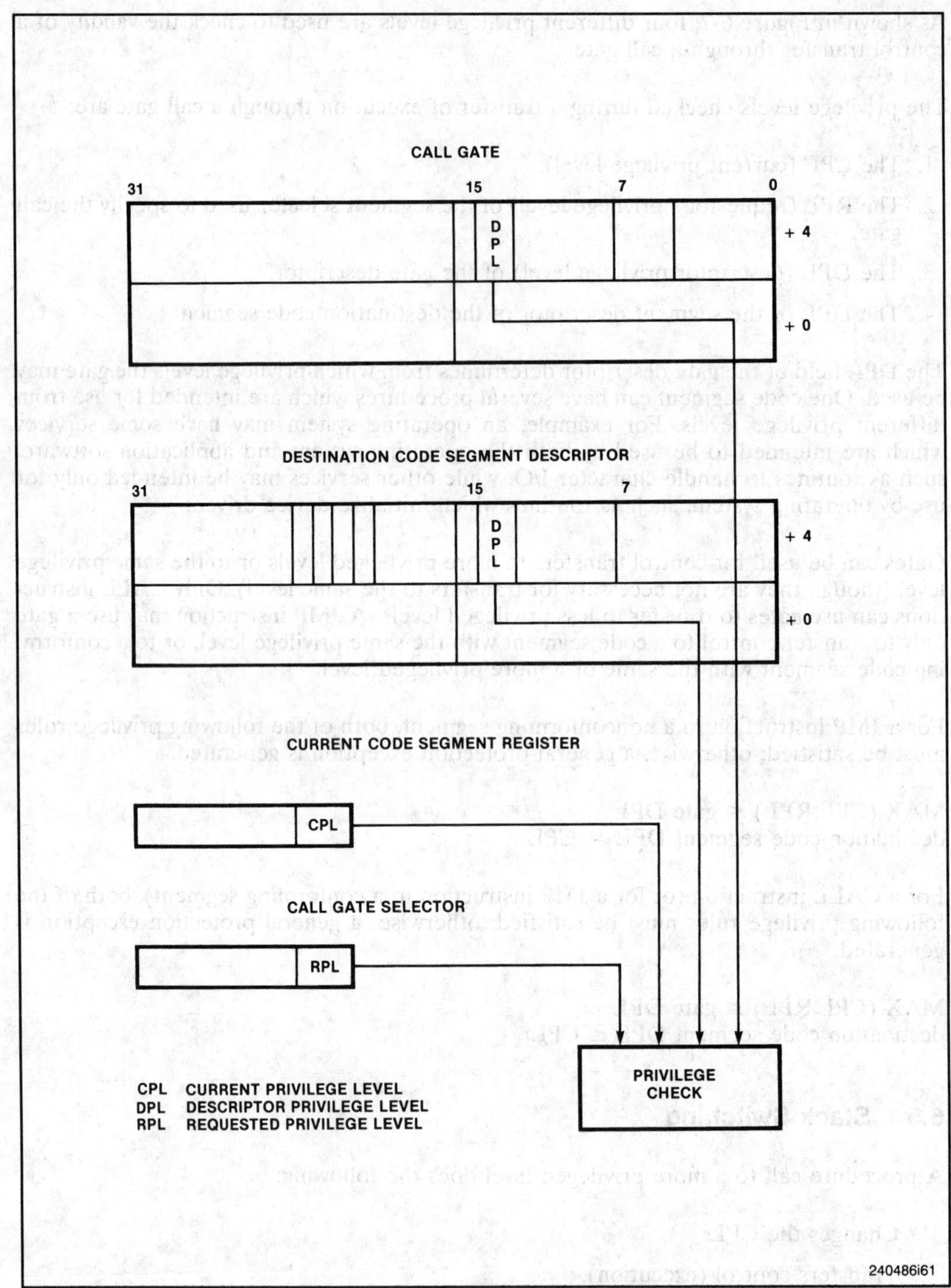

Figure 6-7. Privilege Check for Control Transfer with Call Gate

All inner protection rings (privilege levels 0, 1, and 2), have their own stacks for receiving calls from less privileged levels. If the caller were to provide the stack, and the stack was too small, the called procedure might crash as a result of insufficient stack space. Instead, less privileged programs are prevented from crashing more privileged programs by creating a new stack when a call is made to a more privileged level. The new stack is created, parameters are copied from the old stack, the contents of registers are saved, and execution proceeds normally. When the procedure returns, the contents of the saved registers restore the original stack. A complete description of the task switching mechanism is provided in Chapter 7.

The processor finds the space to create new stacks using the task state segment (TSS), as shown in Figure 6-8. Each task has its own TSS. The TSS contains initial stack pointers for the inner protection rings. The operating system is responsible for creating each TSS and initializing its stack pointers. An initial stack pointer consists of a segment selector and an initial value for the ESP register (an initial offset into the segment). The initial stack pointers are strictly read-only values. The processor does not change them while the task runs. These stack pointers are used only to create new stacks when calls are made to more privileged levels. These stacks disappear when the called procedure returns. The next time the procedure is called, a new stack is created using the initial stack pointer.

32-BIT TASK STATE SEGMENT

31	0	Offset
		64
	SS2	18
ESP2		14
	SS1	10
ESP1		0C
	SS0	8
ESP0		4
		0

NOTE: ADDRESSES ARE IN HEXADECIMAL

240486i62

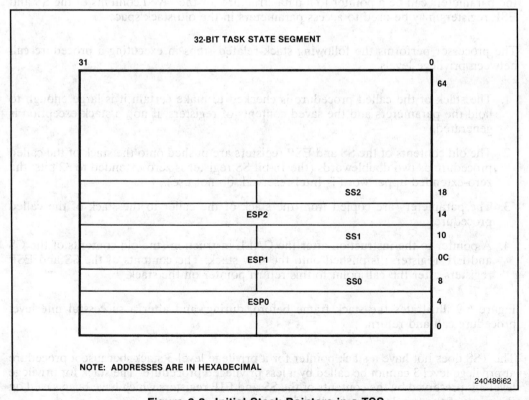

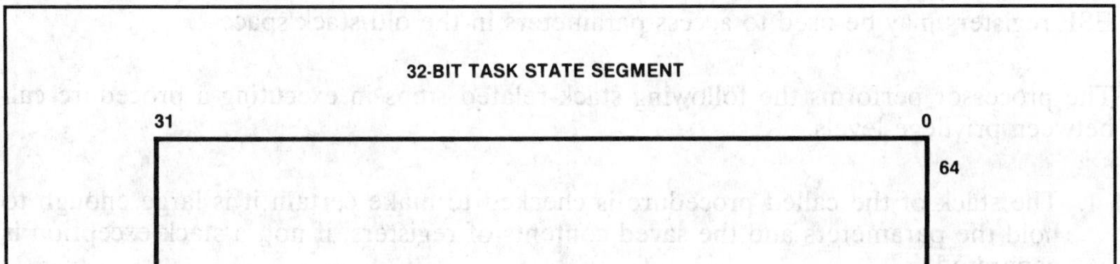

Figure 6-8. Initial Stack Pointers in a TSS

When a call gate is used to change privilege levels, a new stack is created by loading an address from the TSS. The processor uses the DPL of the destination code segment (the new CPL) to select the initial stack pointer for privilege level 0, 1, or 2.

The DPL of the new stack segment must equal the new CPL; if not, a stack-fault exception is generated. It is the responsibility of the operating system to create stacks and stack-segment descriptors for all privilege levels which are used. The stacks must be read/write as specified in the Type field of their segment descriptors. They must contain enough space, as specified in the Limit field, to hold the contents of the SS and ESP registers, the return address, and the parameters and temporary variables required by the called procedure.

As with calls within a privilege level, parameters for the procedure are placed on the stack. The parameters are copied to the new stack. The parameters can be accessed within the called procedure using the same relative addresses which would have been used if no stack switching had occurred. The count field of a call gate tells the processor how many doublewords (up to 31) to copy from the caller's stack to the stack of the called procedure. If the count is 0, no parameters are copied.

If more than 31 doublewords of data need to be passed to the called procedure, one of the parameters can be a pointer to a data structure, or the saved contents of the SS and ESP registers may be used to access parameters in the old stack space.

The processor performs the following stack-related steps in executing a procedure call between privilege levels.

1. The stack of the called procedure is checked to make certain it is large enough to hold the parameters and the saved contents of registers; if not, a stack exception is generated.

2. The old contents of the SS and ESP registers are pushed onto the stack of the called procedure as two doublewords (the 16-bit SS register is zero-extended to 32 bits; the zero-extended upper word is Intel reserved; do not use).

3. The parameters are copied from the stack of the caller to the stack of the called procedure.

4. A pointer to the instruction after the CALL instruction (the old contents of the CS and EIP registers) is pushed onto the new stack. The contents of the SS and ESP registers after the call point to this return pointer on the stack.

Figure 6-9 illustrates the stack frame before, during, and after a successful interlevel procedure call and return.

The TSS does not have a stack pointer for a privilege level 3 stack, because a procedure at privilege level 3 cannot be called by a less privileged procedure. The stack for privilege level 3 is preserved by the contents of the SS and EIP registers which have been saved on the stack of the privilege level called from level 3.

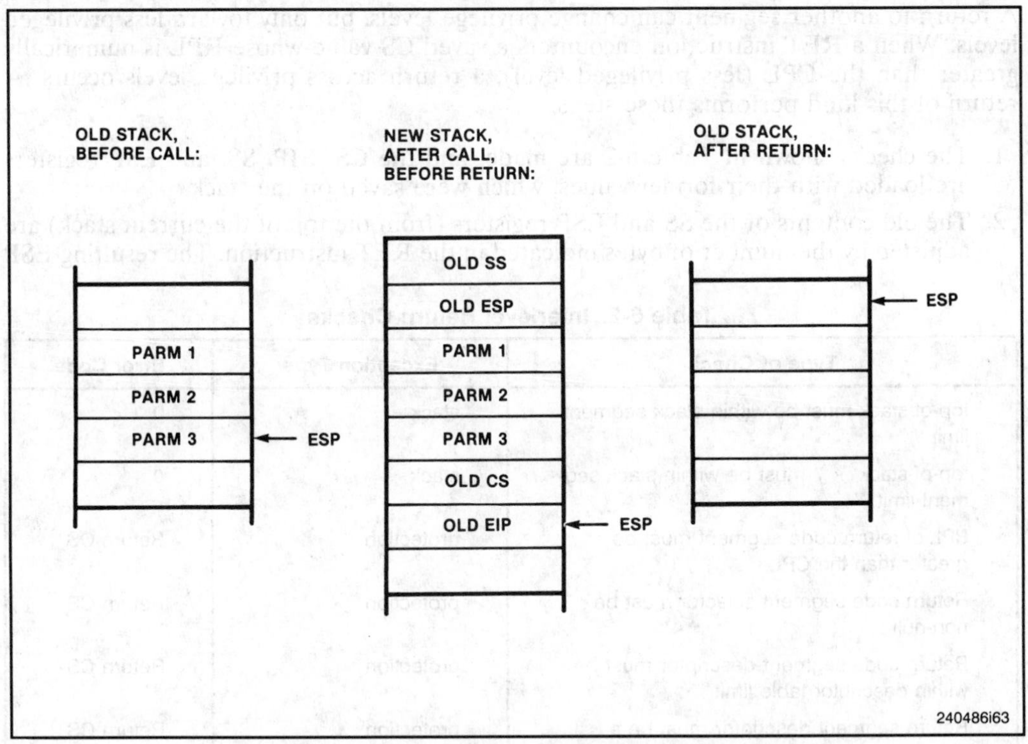

Figure 6-9. Stack Frame During Interlevel Call

A call using a call gate does not check the values of the words copied onto the new stack. The called procedure should check each parameter for validity. A later section discusses how the ARPL, VERR, VERW, LSL, and LAR instructions can be used to check pointer values.

6.5.2 Returning from a Procedure

The "near" forms of the RET instruction only transfer control within the current code segment, therefore are subject only to limit checking. The offset to the instruction following the CALL instruction is popped from the stack into the EIP register. The processor checks that this offset does not exceed the limit of the current code segment.

The "far" form of the RET instruction pops the return address which was pushed onto the stack by an earlier far CALL instruction. Under normal conditions, the return pointer is valid, because it was generated by a CALL or INT instruction. Nevertheless, the processor performs privilege checking because of the possibility that the current procedure altered the pointer or failed to maintain the stack properly. The RPL of the code-segment selector popped off the stack by the return instruction should have the privilege level of the calling procedure.

A return to another segment can change privilege levels, but only toward less privileged levels. When a RET instruction encounters a saved CS value whose RPL is numerically greater than the CPL (less privileged level), a return across privilege levels occurs. A return of this kind performs these steps:

1. The checks shown in Table 6-2 are made, and the CS, EIP, SS, and ESP registers are loaded with their former values, which were saved on the stack.
2. The old contents of the SS and ESP registers (from the top of the current stack) are adjusted by the number of bytes indicated in the RET instruction. The resulting ESP

Table 6-2. Interlevel Return Checks

Type of Check	Exception Type	Error Code
top-of-stack must be within stack segment limit	stack	0
top-of-stack + 7 must be within stack segment limit	stack	0
RPL of return code segment must be greater than the CPL	protection	Return CS
Return code segment selector must be non-null	protection	Return CS
Return code segment descriptor must be within descriptor table limit	protection	Return CS
Return segment descriptor must be a code segment	protection	Return CS
Return code segment is present	segment not present	Return CS
DPL of return non-conforming code segment must equal RPL of return code segment selector, or DPL of return conforming code segment must be less than or equal to RPL of return code segment selector	protection	Return CS
ESP + N + 15* must be within the stack segment limit	stack fault	Return CS
segment selector at ESP + N + 12* must be non-null	protection	Return CS
segment descriptor at ESP + N + 12* must be within descriptor table limit	protection	Return CS
stack segment descriptor must be read/write	protection	Return CS
stack segment must be present	stack fault	Return CS
old stack segment DPL must be equal to RPL of old code segment	protection	Return CS
old stack segment selector must have an RPL equal to the DPL of the old stack segment	protection	Return CS

*N is the value of the immediate operand supplied with the RET instruction.

value is not checked against the limit of the stack segment. If the ESP value is beyond the limit, that fact is not recognized until the next stack operation. (The contents of the SS and ESP registers for the returning procedure are not preserved; normally, their values are the same as those contained in the TSS.)

3. The contents of the DS, ES, FS, and GS segment registers are checked. If any of these registers refer to segments whose DPL is less than the new CPL (excluding conforming code segments), the segment register is loaded with the null selector (Index = 0, TI = 0). The RET instruction itself does not signal exceptions in these cases; however, any subsequent memory reference using a segment register containing the null selector will cause a general-protection exception. This prevents less privileged code from accessing more privileged segments using selectors left in the segment registers by a more privileged procedure.

6.6 INSTRUCTIONS RESERVED FOR THE OPERATING SYSTEM

Instructions which can affect the protection mechanism or influence general system performance can only be executed by trusted procedures. The i486 processor has two classes of such instructions:

1. Privileged instructions—those used for system control.
2. Sensitive instructions—those used for I/O and I/O-related activities.

6.6.1 Privileged Instructions

The instructions which affect protected facilities can be executed only when the CPL is 0 (most privileged). If one of these instructions is executed when the CPL is not 0, a general-protection exception is generated. These instructions include:

CLTS	—Clear Task-Switched Flag
HLT	—Halt Processor
LGDT	—Load GDT Register
LIDT	—Load IDT Register
LLDT	—Load LDT Register
LMSW	—Load Machine Status Word
LTR	—Load Task Register
MOV to/from CR0	—Move to Control Register 0
MOV to/from DRn	—Move to Debug Register n
MOV to/from TRn	—Move to Test Register n

6.6.2 Sensitive Instructions

Instructions which deal with I/O need to be protected, but they also need to be used by procedures executing at privilege levels other than 0 (the most privileged level). The mechanisms for protection of I/O operations are covered in detail in Chapter 8.

6.7 INSTRUCTIONS FOR POINTER VALIDATION

Pointer validation is necessary for maintaining isolation between privilege levels. It consists of the following steps:

1. Check if the supplier of the pointer is allowed to access the segment.
2. Check if the segment type is compatible with its use.
3. Check if the pointer offset exceeds the segment limit.

Although the i486 processor automatically performs checks 2 and 3 during instruction execution, software must assist in performing the first check. The ARPL instruction is provided for this purpose. Software also can use steps 2 and 3 to check for potential violations, rather than waiting for an exception to be generated. The LAR, LSL, VERR, and VERW instructions are provided for this purpose.

An additional check, the alignment check, can be applied in user mode. When both the AM bit in CR0 and the AC flag are set, unaligned memory references generate exceptions. This is useful for programs which use the low two bits of pointers to identify the type of data structure they address. For example, a subroutine in a math library may accept pointers to numeric data structures. If the type of this structure is assigned a code of 10 (binary) in the lowest two bits of pointers to this type, math subroutines can correct for the type code by adding a displacement of −10 (binary). If the subroutine should ever receive the wrong pointer type, an unaligned reference would be produced, which would generate an exception. Alignment checking accelerates the processing of programs written in symbolic-processing (i.e., Artificial Intelligence) languages such as Lisp, Prolog, Smalltalk, and C++. It can be used to speed up pointer tag type checking.

LAR (Load Access Rights) is used to verify that a pointer refers to a segment of a compatible privilege level and type. The LAR instruction has one operand—a segment selector for a descriptor whose access rights are to be checked. The segment descriptor must be readable at a privilege level which is numerically greater (less privileged) than the CPL and the selector's RPL. If the descriptor is readable, the LAR instruction gets the second doubleword of the descriptor, masks this value with 00FxFF00H, stores the result into the specified 32-bit destination register, and sets the ZF flag. (The x indicates that the corresponding four bits of the stored value are undefined.) Once loaded, the access rights can be tested. All valid descriptor types can be tested by the LAR instruction. If the RPL or CPL is greater than the DPL, or if the segment selector would exceed the limit for the descriptor table, no access rights are returned, and the ZF flag is cleared. Conforming code segments may be accessed from any privilege level.

LSL (Load Segment Limit) allows software to test the limit of a segment descriptor. If the descriptor referenced by the segment selector (in memory or a register) is readable at the CPL, the LSL instruction loads the specified 32-bit register with a 32-bit, byte granular limit calculated from the concatenated limit fields and the G bit of the descriptor. This only can be done for descriptors which describe segments (data, code, task state, and local descriptor tables); gate descriptors are inaccessible. (Table 6-3 lists in detail which types are valid and which are not.) Interpreting the limit is a function of the

Table 6-3. Valid Descriptor Types for LSL Instruction

Type Code	Descriptor Type	Valid?
0	reserved	no
1	reserved	no
2	LDT	yes
3	reserved	no
4	reserved	no
5	Task Gate	no
6	reserved	no
7	reserved	no
8	reserved	no
9	Available i486™ CPU TSS	yes
A	reserved	no
B	Busy i486 CPU TSS	yes
C	i486 CPU Call Gate	no
D	reserved	no
E	i486 CPU Interrupt Gate	no
F	i486 CPU Trap Gate	no

segment type. For example, downward-expandable data segments (stack segments) treat the limit differently than other kinds of segments. For both the LAR and LSL instructions, the ZF flag is set if the load was successful; otherwise, the ZF flag is cleared.

6.7.1 Descriptor Validation

The i486 processor has two instructions, VERR and VERW, which determine whether a segment selector points to a segment which can be read or written using the CPL. Neither instruction causes a protection fault if the segment cannot be accessed.

VERR (Verify for Reading) verifies a segment for reading and sets the ZF flag if that segment is readable using the CPL. The VERR instruction checks the following:

- The segment selector points to a segment descriptor within the bounds of the GDT or an LDT.
- The segment selector indexes to a code or data segment descriptor.
- The segment is readable and has a compatible privilege level.

The privilege check for data segments and nonconforming code segments verifies that the DPL must be a less privileged level than either the CPL or the selector's RPL. Conforming segments are not checked for privilege level.

VERW (Verify for Writing) provides the same capability as the VERR instruction for verifying writability. Like the VERR instruction, the VERW instruction sets the ZF flag if the segment can be written. The instruction verifies the descriptor is within bounds, is a segment descriptor, is writable, and has a DPL which is a less privileged level than either the CPL or the selector's RPL. Code segments are never writable, whether conforming or not.

6.7.2 Pointer Integrity and RPL

The requested privilege level (RPL) can prevent accidental use of pointers which crash more privileged code from a less privileged level.

A common example is a file system procedure, FREAD (file_id, n_bytes, buffer_ptr). This hypothetical procedure reads data from a disk file into a buffer, overwriting whatever is already there. It services requests from programs operating at the application level, but it must run in a privileged mode in order to read from the system I/O buffer. If the application program passed this procedure a bad buffer pointer, one which pointed at critical code or data in a privileged address space, the procedure could cause damage which would crash the system.

Use of the RPL can avoid this problem. The RPL allows a privilege override to be assigned to a selector. This privilege override is intended to be the privilege level of the code segment which generated the segment selector. In the above example, the RPL would be the CPL of the application program which called the system level procedure. The i486 processor automatically checks any segment selector loaded into a segment register to determine whether its RPL allows access.

To take advantage of the processor's checking of the RPL, the called procedure need only check that all segment selectors passed to it have an RPL for the same or a less privileged level as the original caller's CPL. This guarantees that the segment selectors are not more privileged than their source. If a selector is used to access a segment which the source would not be able to access directly, i.e. the RPL is less privileged than the segment's DPL, a general-protection exception is generated when the selector is loaded into a segment register.

ARPL (Adjust Requested Privilege Level) adjusts the RPL field of a segment selector to be the larger (less privileged) of its original value and the value of the RPL field for a segment selector stored in a general register. The RPL fields are the two least significant bits of the segment selector and the register. The latter normally is a copy of the caller's CS register on the stack. If the adjustment changes the selector's RPL, the ZF flag is set; otherwise, the ZF flag is cleared.

6.8 PAGE-LEVEL PROTECTION

Protection applies to both segments and pages. When the flat model for memory segmentation has been used, page-level protection prevents programs from interfering with each other.

Each memory reference is checked to verify that it satisfies the protection checks. All checks are made before the memory cycle is started; any violation prevents the cycle from starting and results in an exception. Because checks are performed in parallel with address translation, there is no performance penalty. There are two page-level protection checks:

1. Restriction of addressable domain
2. Type checking

A protection violation results in an exception. See Chapter 9 for an explanation of the exception mechanism. This chapter describes the protection violations which lead to exceptions.

6.8.1 Page-Table Entries Hold Protection Parameters

Figure 6-10 highlights the fields of a page table entry which control access to pages. The protection checks are applied for both first- and second-level page tables.

6.8.1.1 RESTRICTING ADDRESSABLE DOMAIN

Privilege is interpreted differently for pages and segments. With segments, there are four privilege levels, ranging from 0 (most privileged) to 3 (least privileged). With pages, there are two levels of privilege:

1. Supervisor level (U/S = 0) – for the operating system, other system software (such as device drivers), and protected system data (such as page tables)
2. User level (U/S = 1) – for application code and data.

The privilege levels used for segmentation are mapped into the privilege levels used for paging. If the CPL is 0, 1, or 2, the processor is running at supervisor level. If the CPL is 3, the processor is running at user level.When the processor is running at supervisor level, all pages are accessible. When the processor is running at user level, only pages from the user level are accessible.

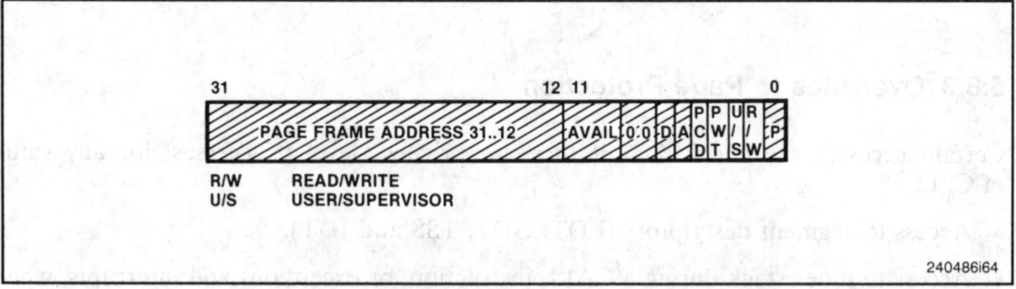

Figure 6-10. Protection Fields of a Page Table Entry

6.8.1.2 TYPE CHECKING

Only two types of pages are recognized by the protection mechanism:

1. Read-only access (R/W=0)
2. Read/write access (R/W=1)

When the processor is running at supervisor level with the WP bit in the CR0 register clear (its state following reset initialization), all pages are both readable and writable (write-protection is ignored). When the processor is running at user level, only pages which belong to user level and are marked for read/write access are writable. User-level pages which are read/write or read-only are readable. Pages from the supervisor level are neither readable nor writable from user level. A general-protection exception is generated on any attempt to violate the protection rules.

Unlike the 386™ DX processor, the i486 processor allows user-mode pages to be write-protected against supervisor mode access. Setting the WP bit in the CR0 register enables supervisor-mode sensitivity to user-mode, write-protected pages. This feature is useful for implementing the *copy-on-write* strategy used by some operating systems, such as UNIX, for task creation (also called *forking* or *spawning*).

When a new task is created, it is possible to copy the entire address space of the parent task. This gives the child task a complete, duplicate set of the parent's segments and pages. The copy-on-write strategy saves memory space and time by mapping the child's segments and pages to the same segments and pages used by the parent task. A private copy of a page gets created only when one of the tasks writes to the page.

6.8.2 Combining Protection of Both Levels of Page Tables

For any one page, the protection attributes of its page directory entry (first-level page table) may differ from those of its second-level page table entry. The i486 processor checks the protection for a page by examining the protection specified in both the page directory (first-level page table) and the second-level page table. Table 6-4 shows the protection provided by the possible combinations of protection attributes when the WP bit is clear.

6.8.3 Overrides to Page Protection

Certain accesses are checked as if they are privilege-level 0 accesses, for any value of CPL:

- Access to segment descriptors (LDT, GDT, TSS and IDT).
- Access to inner stack during a CALL instruction, or exceptions and interrupts, when a change of privilege level occurs.

Table 6-4. Combined Page Directory and Page Table Protection

Page Directory Entry		Page Table Entry		Combined Effect	
Privilege	Access Type	Privilege	Access Type	Privilege	Access Type
User	Read-Only	User	Read-Only	User	Read-Only
User	Read-Only	User	Read-Write	User	Read-Only
User	Read-Write	User	Read-Only	User	Read-Only
User	Read-Write	User	Read-Write	User	Read/Write
User	Read-Only	Supervisor	Read-Only	User	Read-Only
User	Read-Only	Supervisor	Read-Write	User	Read-Only
User	Read-Write	Supervisor	Read-Only	User	Read-Only
User	Read-Write	Supervisor	Read-Write	User	Read/Write
Supervisor	Read-Only	User	Read-Only	User	Read-Only
Supervisor	Read-Only	User	Read-Write	User	Read-Only
Supervisor	Read-Write	User	Read-Only	User	Read-Only
Supervisor	Read-Write	User	Read-Write	User	Read/Write
Supervisor	Read-Only	Supervisor	Read-Only	Supervisor	Read/Write
Supervisor	Read-Only	Supervisor	Read-Write	Supervisor	Read/Write
Supervisor	Read-Write	Supervisor	Read-Only	Supervisor	Read/Write
Supervisor	Read-Write	Supervisor	Read-Write	Supervisor	Read/Write

6.9 COMBINING PAGE AND SEGMENT PROTECTION

When paging is enabled, the i486 processor first evaluates segment protection, then evaluates page protection. If the processor detects a protection violation at either the segment level or the page level, the operation does not go through; an exception occurs instead. If an exception is generated by segmentation, no paging exception is generated for the operation.

For example, it is possible to define a large data segment which has some parts which are read-only and other parts which are read-write. In this case, the page directory (or page table) entries for the read-only parts would have the U/S and R/W bits specifying no write access for all the pages described by that directory entry (or for individual pages specified in the second-level page tables). This technique might be used, for example, to define a large data segment, part of which is read-only (for shared data or ROMmed constants). This defines a "flat" data space as one large segment, with "flat" pointers used to access this "flat" space, while protecting shared data, shared files mapped into the virtual space, and supervisor areas.

Multitasking 7

CHAPTER 7
MULTITASKING

The i486™ processor provides hardware support for multitasking. A *task* is a program which is running, or waiting to run while another program is running. A task is invoked by an interrupt, exception, jump, or call. When one of these forms of transferring execution is used with a destination specified by an entry in one of the descriptor tables, this descriptor can be a type which causes a new task to begin execution after saving the state of the current task. There are two types of task-related descriptors which can occur in a descriptor table: task state segment descriptors and task gates. When execution is passed to either kind of descriptor, a *task switch* occurs.

A task switch is like a procedure call, but it saves more processor state information. A procedure call only saves the contents of the general registers, and it might save the contents of only one register (the EIP register). A procedure call pushes the contents of the saved registers on the stack, in order that a procedure may call itself. When a procedure calls itself, it is said to be *re-entrant*.

A task switch transfers execution to a completely new environment, the environment of a task. This requires saving the contents of nearly all the processor registers, such as the EFLAGS register. Unlike procedures, tasks are not re-entrant. A task switch does not push anything on the stack. The processor state information is saved in a data structure in memory, called a *task state segment*.

The registers and data structures which support multitasking are:

- Task state segment
- Task state segment descriptor
- Task register
- Task gate descriptor

With these structures, the i486 processor can switch execution from one task to another, with the context of the original task saved to allow the task to be restarted. In addition to the simple task switch, the i486 processor offers two other task-management features:

1. Interrupts and exceptions can cause task switches (if needed in the system design). The processor not only performs a task switch to handle the interrupt or exception, but it automatically switches back when the interrupt or exception returns. Interrupts may occur during interrupt tasks.

2. With each switch to another task, the i486 processor also can switch to another LDT. This can be used to give each task a different logical-to-physical address mapping. This is an additional protection feature, because tasks can be isolated and prevented from interfering with one another. The PDBR register also is reloaded. This allows the paging mechanism to be used to enforce the isolation between tasks.

Use of the multitasking mechanism is optional. In some applications, it may not be the best way to manage program execution. Where extremely fast response to interrupts is needed, the time required to save the processor state may be too great. A possible compromise in these situations is to use the task-related data structures, but perform task switching in software. This allows a smaller processor state to be saved. This technique can be one of the optimizations used to enhance system performance after the basic functions of a system have been implemented.

7.1 TASK STATE SEGMENT

The processor state information needed to restore a task is saved in a type of segment, called a *task state segment* or TSS. Figure 7-1 shows the format of a TSS for an i486 CPU task (compatibility with 80286 tasks is provided by a different kind of TSS; see Chapter 21). The fields of a TSS are divided into two main categories:

1. Dynamic fields the processor updates with each task switch. These fields store:
   - The general registers (EAX, ECX, EDX, EBX, ESP, EBP, ESI, and EDI).
   - The segment registers (ES, CS, SS, DS, FS, and GS).
   - The flags register (EFLAGS).
   - The instruction pointer (EIP).
   - The selector for the TSS of the previous task (updated only when a return is expected).
2. Static fields the processor reads, but does not change. These fields are set up when a task is created. These fields store:
   - The selector for the task's LDT.
   - The logical address of the stacks for privilege levels 0, 1, and 2.
   - The T-bit (debug trap bit) which, when set, causes the processor to raise a debug exception when a task switch occurs. (See Chapter 11 for more information on debugging).
   - The base address for the I/O permission bit map. If present, this map is stored in the TSS at higher addresses. The base address points to the beginning of the map. (See Chapter 8 for more information about the I/O permission bit map.)

If paging is used, it is important to avoid placing a page boundary within the part of the TSS which is read by the processor during a task switch (the first 108 bytes). If a page boundary is placed within this part of the TSS, the pages on either side of the boundary must be present at the same time. It is an unrecoverable error to receive a page fault or general-protection exception after the processor has started to read the TSS.

7.2 TSS DESCRIPTOR

The task state segment, like all other segments, is defined by a descriptor. Figure 7-2 shows the format of a TSS descriptor.

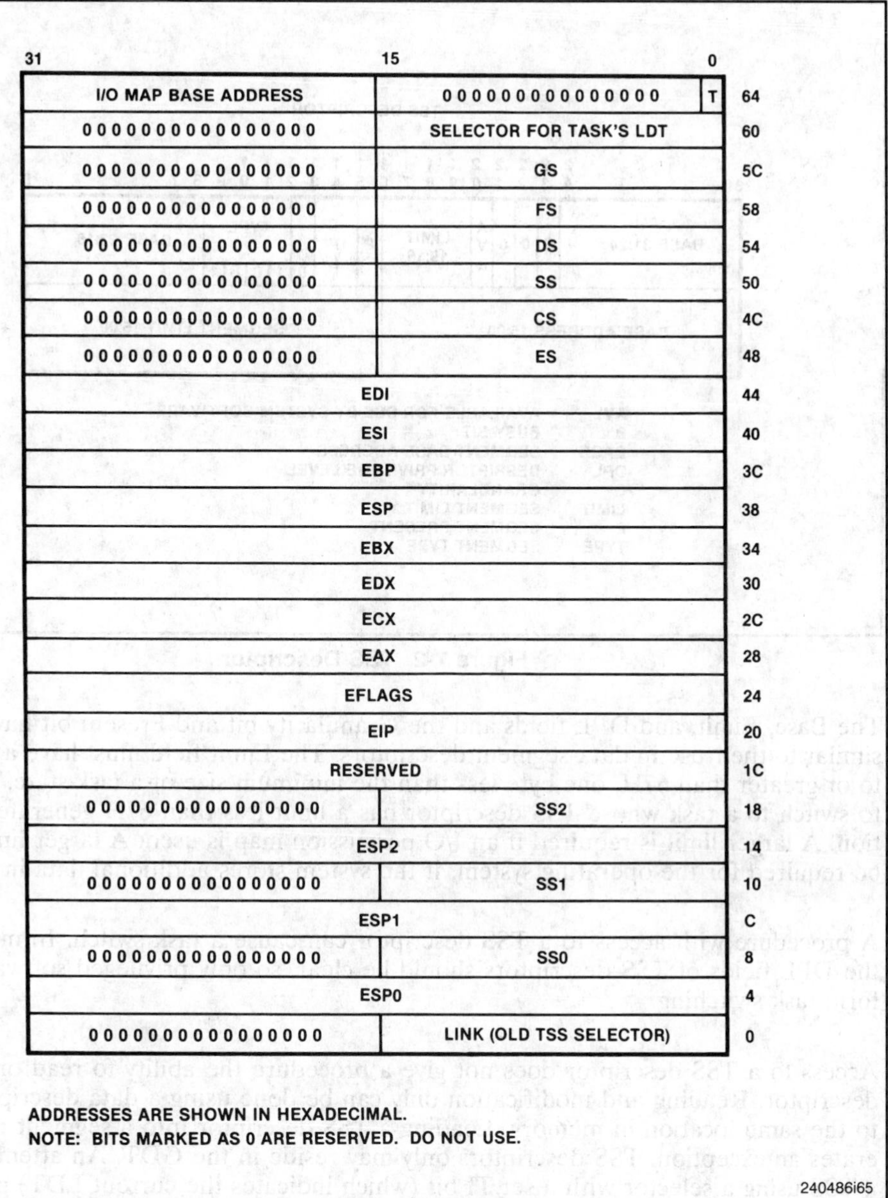

Figure 7-1. Task State Segment

The Busy bit in the Type field indicates whether the task is busy. A busy task is currently running or waiting to run. A Type field with a value of 9 indicates an inactive task; a value of 11 (decimal) indicates a busy task. Tasks are not re-entrant. The i486 processor uses the Busy bit to detect an attempt to call a task whose execution has been interrupted.

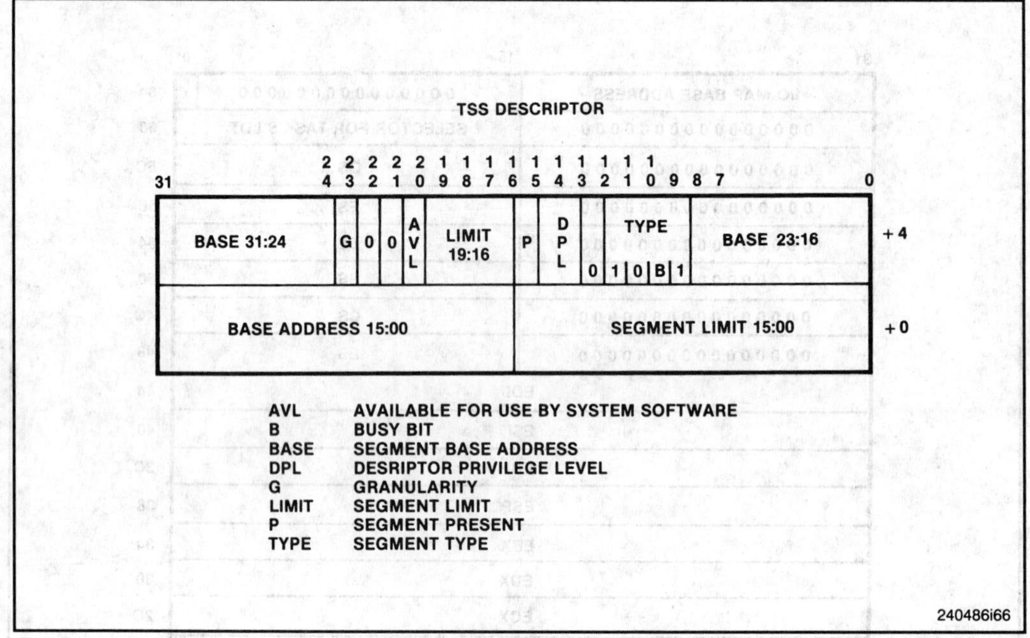

Figure 7-2. TSS Descriptor

The Base, Limit, and DPL fields and the Granularity bit and Present bit have functions similar to their use in data-segment descriptors. The Limit field must have a value equal to or greater than 67H, one byte less than the minimum size of a task state. An attempt to switch to a task whose TSS descriptor has a limit less than 67H generates an exception. A larger limit is required if an I/O permission map is used. A larger limit also may be required for the operating system, if the system stores additional data in the TSS.

A procedure with access to a TSS descriptor can cause a task switch. In most systems, the DPL fields of TSS descriptors should be clear, so only privileged software can perform task switching.

Access to a TSS descriptor does not give a procedure the ability to read or modify the descriptor. Reading and modification only can be done using a data descriptor mapped to the same location in memory. Loading a TSS descriptor into a segment register generates an exception. TSS descriptors only may reside in the GDT. An attempt to access a TSS using a selector with a set TI bit (which indicates the current LDT) generates an exception.

7.3 TASK REGISTER

The task register (TR) is used to find the current TSS. Figure 7-3 shows the path by which the processor accesses the TSS.

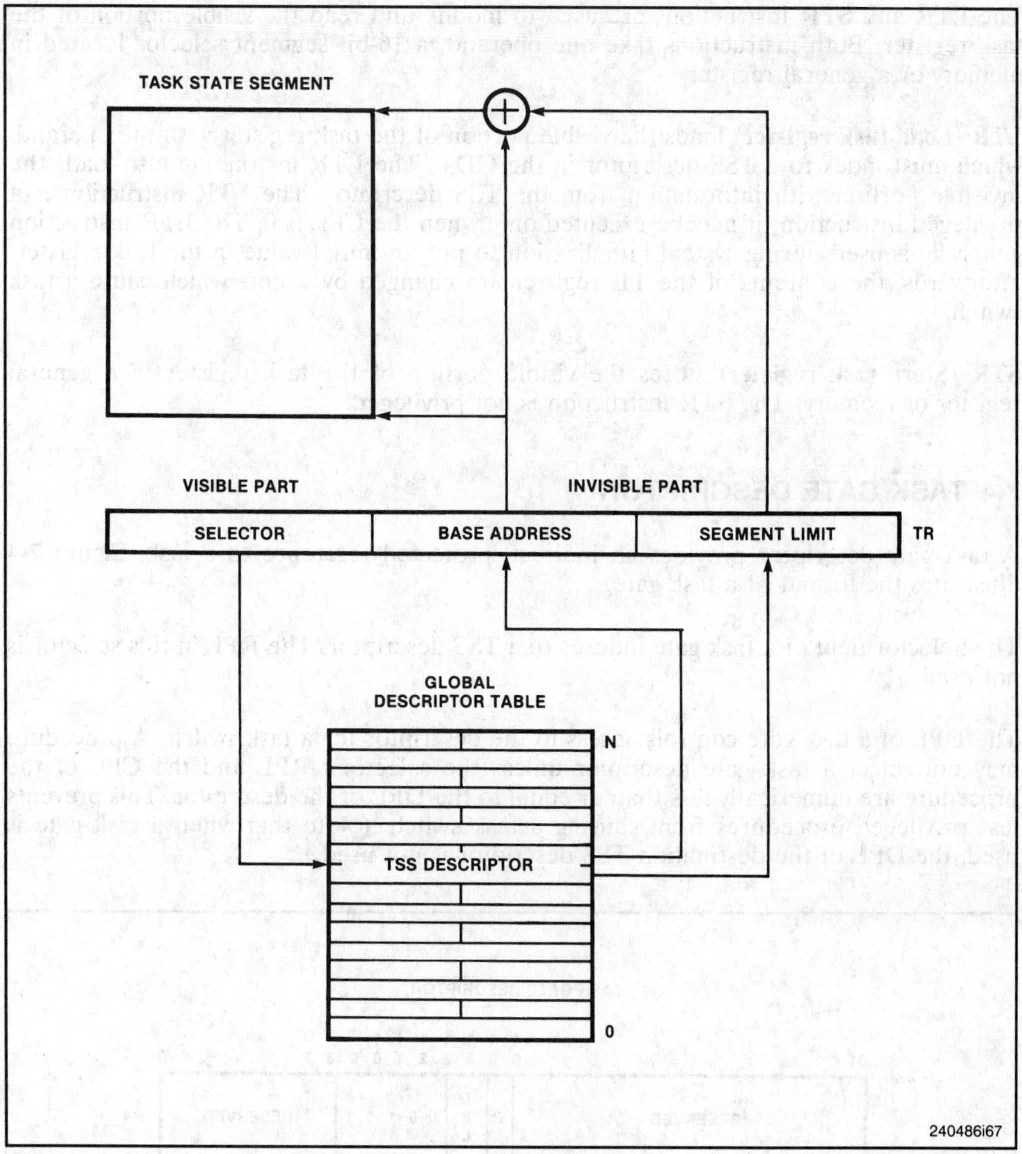

Figure 7-3. TR Register

The task register has both a "visible" part (i.e., a part which can be read and changed by software) and an "invisible" part (i.e., a part maintained by the processor and inaccessible to software). The selector in the visible portion indexes to a TSS descriptor in the GDT. The processor uses the invisible portion of the TR register to retain the base and limit values from the TSS descriptor. Keeping these values in a register makes execution of the task more efficient, because the processor does not need to fetch these values from memory to reference the TSS of the current task.

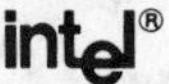

The LTR and STR instructions are used to modify and read the visible portion of the task register. Both instructions take one operand, a 16-bit segment selector located in memory or a general register.

LTR (Load task register) loads the visible portion of the task register with the operand, which must index to a TSS descriptor in the GDT. The LTR instruction also loads the invisible portion with information from the TSS descriptor. The LTR instruction is a privileged instruction; it may be executed only when the CPL is 0. The LTR instruction generally is used during system initialization to put an initial value in the task register; afterwards, the contents of the TR register are changed by events which cause a task switch.

STR (Store task register) stores the visible portion of the task register in a general register or memory. The STR instruction is not privileged.

7.4 TASK GATE DESCRIPTOR

A task gate descriptor provides an indirect, protected reference to a task. Figure 7-4 illustrates the format of a task gate.

The Selector field of a task gate indexes to a TSS descriptor. The RPL in this selector is not used.

The DPL of a task gate controls access to the descriptor for a task switch. A procedure may not select a task gate descriptor unless the selector's RPL and the CPL of the procedure are numerically less than or equal to the DPL of the descriptor. This prevents less privileged procedures from causing a task switch. (Note that when a task gate is used, the DPL of the destination TSS descriptor is not used.)

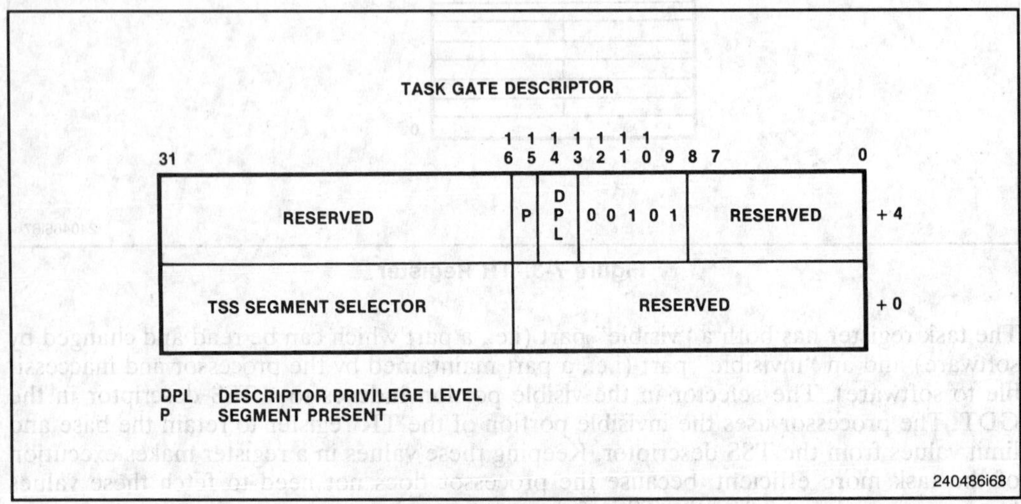

Figure 7-4. Task Gate Descriptor

A procedure with access to a task gate can cause a task switch, as can a procedure with access to a TSS descriptor. Both task gates and TSS descriptors are provided to satisfy three needs:

1. The need for a task to have only one Busy bit. Because the Busy bit is stored in the TSS descriptor, each task should have only one such descriptor. There may, however, be several task gates which select a single TSS descriptor.
2. The need to provide selective access to tasks. Task gates fill this need, because they can reside in an LDT and can have a DPL which is different from the TSS descriptor's DPL. A procedure which does not have sufficient privilege to use the TSS descriptor in the GDT (which usually has a DPL of 0) can still call another task if it has access to a task gate in its LDT. With task gates, the operating system can limit task switching to specific tasks.
3. The need for an interrupt or exception to cause a task switch. Task gates also may reside in the IDT, which allows interrupts and exceptions to cause task switching. When an interrupt or exception supplies a vector to a task gate, the i486 processor switches to the indicated task.

Figure 7-5 illustrates how both a task gate in an LDT and a task gate in the IDT can identify the same task.

7.5 TASK SWITCHING

The i486 processor transfers execution to another task in any of four cases:

1. The current task executes a JMP or CALL to a TSS descriptor.
2. The current task executes a JMP or CALL to a task gate.
3. An interrupt or exception indexes to a task gate in the IDT.
4. The current task executes an IRET when the NT flag is set.

The JMP, CALL, and IRET instructions, as well as interrupts and exceptions, are all ordinary mechanisms of the i486 processor which can be used in circumstances in which no task switch occurs. The descriptor type (when a task is called) or the NT flag (when the task returns) make the difference between the standard mechanism and the form which causes a task switch.

To cause a task switch, a JMP or CALL instruction can transfer execution to either a TSS descriptor or a task gate. The effect is the same in either case: the i486 processor transfers execution to the specified task.

An exception or interrupt causes a task switch when it indexes to a task gate in the IDT. If it indexes to an interrupt or trap gate in the IDT, a task switch does not occur. See Chapter 9 for more information on the interrupt mechanism.

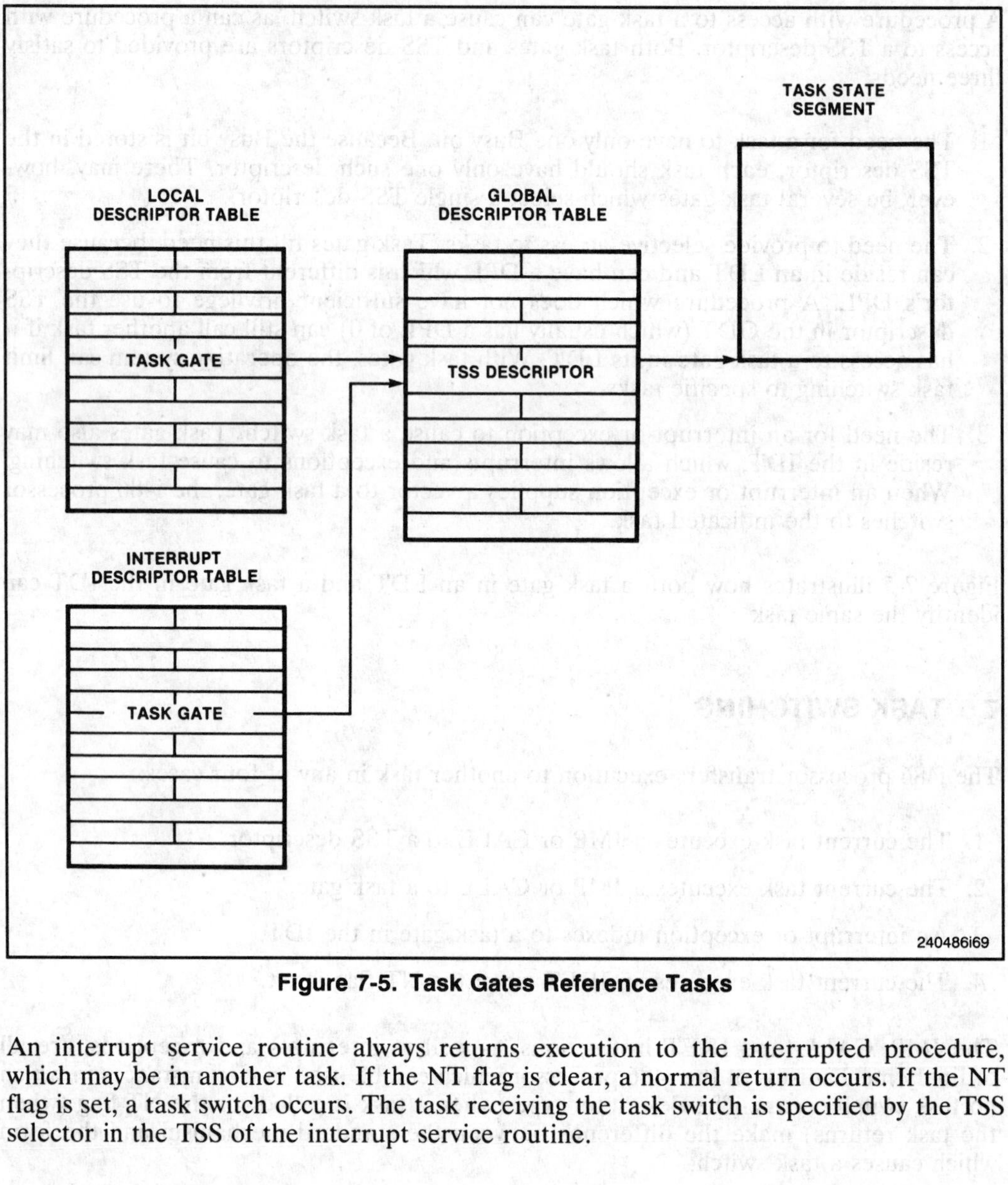

TASK STATE SEGMENT

LOCAL DESCRIPTOR TABLE

GLOBAL DESCRIPTOR TABLE

TASK GATE

TSS DESCRIPTOR

INTERRUPT DESCRIPTOR TABLE

TASK GATE

240486i69

Figure 7-5. Task Gates Reference Tasks

An interrupt service routine always returns execution to the interrupted procedure, which may be in another task. If the NT flag is clear, a normal return occurs. If the NT flag is set, a task switch occurs. The task receiving the task switch is specified by the TSS selector in the TSS of the interrupt service routine.

A task switch has these steps:

1. Check that the current task is allowed to switch to the new task. Data-access privilege rules apply to JMP and CALL instructions. The DPL of the TSS descriptor and the task gate must be greater than or equal to both the CPL and the RPL of the gate selector. Exceptions, interrupts, and IRET instructions are permitted to switch tasks regardless of the DPL of the destination task gate or TSS descriptor.

2. Check that the TSS descriptor of the new task is marked present and has a valid limit (greater than or equal to 67H). Any errors up to this point occur in the context of the current task. These errors restore any changes made in the processor state when an attempt is made to execute the error-generating instruction. This lets the return address for the exception handler point to the error-generating instruction, rather than the instruction following the error-generating instruction. The exception handler can fix the condition which caused the error, and restart the task. The intervention of the exception handler can be completely transparent to the application program.

3. Save the state of the current task. The processor finds the base address of the current TSS in the task register. The processor registers are copied into the current TSS (the EAX, ECX, EDX, EBX, ESP, EBP, ESI, EDI, ES, CS, SS, DS, FS, GS, and EFLAGS registers).

4. Load the TR register with the selector to the new task's TSS descriptor, set the new task's Busy bit, and set the TS bit in the CR0 register. The selector is either the operand of a JMP or CALL instruction, or it is taken from a task gate.

5. Load the new task's state from its TSS and continue execution. The registers loaded are the LDTR register; the EFLAGS register; the general registers EIP, EAX, ECX, EDX, EBX, ESP, EBP, ESI, EDI; and the segment registers ES, CS, SS, DS, FS, and GS. Any errors detected in this step occur in the context of the new task. To an exception handler, the first instruction of the new task appears not to have executed.

Note that the state of the old task is always saved when a task switch occurs. If the task is resumed, execution starts with the instruction which normally would have been next. The registers are restored to the values they held when the task stopped running.

Every task switch sets the TS (task switched) bit in the CR0 register. The TS bit is useful to system software for coordinating the operations of the integer unit with the floating-point unit or a coprocessor. The TS bit indicates that the context of the floating-point unit or coprocessor may be different from that of the current task. Chapter 10 discusses the TS bit and coprocessors in more detail.

Exception service routines for exceptions caused by task switching (exceptions resulting from steps 5 through 17 shown in Table 7-1) may be subject to recursive calls if they attempt to reload the segment selector which generated the exception. The cause of the exception (or the first of multiple causes) should be fixed before reloading the selector.

The privilege level at which the old task was running has no relation to the privilege level of the new task. Because the tasks are isolated by their separate address spaces and task state segments, and because privilege rules control access to a TSS, no privilege checks are needed to perform a task switch. The new task begins executing at the privilege level indicated by the RPL of new contents of the CS register, which are loaded from the TSS.

Table 7-1. Checks Made during a Task Switch

Step	Condition Checked	Exception[1]	Error Code Reference
1	TSS descriptor is present in memory	NP	New Task's TSS
2	TSS descriptor is not busy	GP	New Task's TSS
3	TSS segment limit greater than or equal to 103	TS	New Task's TSS
4	Registers are loaded from the values in the TSS		
5	LDT selector of new task is valid[2]	TS	New Task's TSS
6	Code segment DPL matches selector RPL	TS	New Code Segment
7	SS selector is valid[2]	GP	New Stack Segment
8	Stack segment is present in memory	SF	New Stack Segment
9	Stack segment DPL matches CPL	SF	New Stack Segment
10	LDT of new task is present in memory	TS	New Task's TSS
11	CS selector is valid[2]	TS	New Code Segment
12	Code segment is present in memory	NP	New Code Segment
13	Stack segment DPL matches selector RPL	GP	New Stack Segment
14	DS, ES, FS, and GS selectors are valid[2]	GP	New Data Segment
15	DS, ES, FS, and GS segments are readable	GP	New Data Segment
16	DS, ES, FS, and GS segments are present in memory	NP	New Data Segment
17	DS, ES, FS, and GS segment DPL greater than or equal to CPL (unless these are conforming segments)	GP	New Data Segment

NOTES: Future Intel® processors may use a different order of checks.

1. NP = Segment-not-present exception, GP = General-protection exception, TS = Invalid-TSS exception, SF = Stack exception.
2. A selector is valid if it is in a compatible type of table (e.g., an LDT selector may not be in any table except the GDT), occupies an address within the table's segment limit, and refers to a compatible type of descriptor (e.g., a selector in the CS register only is valid when it indexes to a descriptor for a code segment; the descriptor type is specified in its Type field).

7.6 TASK LINKING

The Link field of the TSS and the NT flag are used to return execution to the previous task. The NT flag indicates whether the currently executing task is nested within the execution of another task, and the Link field of the current task's TSS holds the TSS selector for the higher-level task, if there is one (see Figure 7-6).

When an interrupt, exception, jump, or call causes a task switch, the i486 processor copies the segment selector for the current task state segment into the TSS for the new task and sets the NT flag. The NT flag indicates the Link field of the TSS has been loaded with a saved TSS selector. The new task releases control by executing an IRET instruction. When an IRET instruction is executed, the NT flag is checked. If it is set, the processor does a task switch to the previous task. Table 7-2 summarizes the uses of the fields in a TSS which are affected by task switching.

Note that the NT flag may be modified by software executing at any privilege level. It is possible for a program to set its NT bit and execute an IRET instruction, which would have the effect of invoking the task specified in the Link field of the current task's TSS. To keep spurious task switches from succeeding, the operating system should initialize the Link field of every TSS it creates.

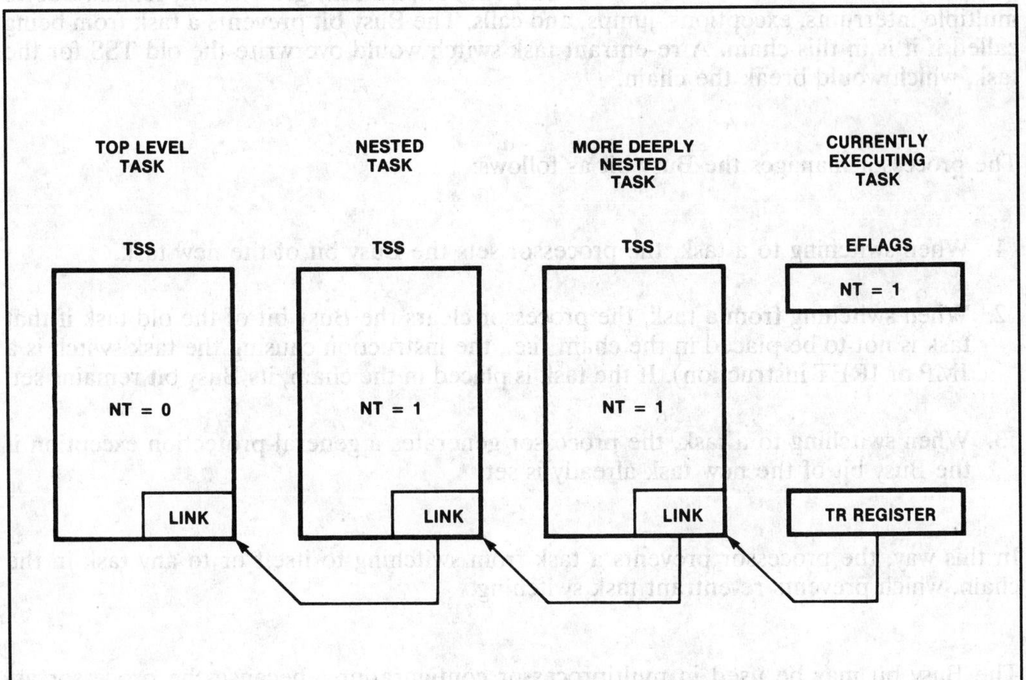

TOP LEVEL TASK
NESTED TASK
MORE DEEPLY NESTED TASK
CURRENTLY EXECUTING TASK
TSS
TSS
TSS
EFLAGS
NT = 1
NT = 0
NT = 1
NT = 1
LINK
LINK
LINK
TR REGISTER
240486i70

Figure 7-6. Nested Tasks

Table 7-2.. Effect of a Task Switch on Busy, NT, and Link Fields

Field	Effect of Jump	Effect of CALL Instruction or Interrupt	Effect of IRET Instruction
Busy bit of new task	Bit is set. Must have been clear before.	Bit is set. Must have been clear before.	No change. Must be set.
Busy bit of old task	Bit is cleared.	No change. Bit is currently set.	Bit is cleared.
NT flag of new task	Flag is cleared.	Flag is set.	No change.
NT flag of old task	No change.	No change.	Flag is cleared.
Link field of new task.	No change.	Loaded with selector for old task's TSS.	No change.
Link field of old task.	No change.	No change.	No change.

7.6.1 Busy Bit Prevents Loops

The Busy bit of the TSS descriptor prevents re-entrant task switching. There is only one saved task context, the context saved in the TSS, therefore a task only may be called once before it terminates. The chain of suspended tasks may grow to any length, due to multiple interrupts, exceptions, jumps, and calls. The Busy bit prevents a task from being called if it is in this chain. A re-entrant task switch would overwrite the old TSS for the task, which would break the chain.

The processor manages the Busy bit as follows:

1. When switching to a task, the processor sets the Busy bit of the new task.

2. When switching from a task, the processor clears the Busy bit of the old task if that task is not to be placed in the chain (i.e., the instruction causing the task switch is a JMP or IRET instruction). If the task is placed in the chain, its Busy bit remains set.

3. When switching to a task, the processor generates a general-protection exception if the Busy bit of the new task already is set.

In this way, the processor prevents a task from switching to itself or to any task in the chain, which prevents re-entrant task switching.

The Busy bit may be used in multiprocessor configurations, because the processor asserts a bus lock when it sets or clears the Busy bit. This keeps two processors from invoking the same task at the same time. (See Chapter 13 for more information on multiprocessing.)

7.6.2 Modifying Task Linkages

Modification of the chain of suspended tasks may be needed to resume an interrupted task before the task which interrupted it. A reliable way to do this is:

1. Disable interrupts.
2. First change the Link field in the TSS of the interrupting task, then clear the Busy bit in the TSS descriptor of the task being removed from the chain.
3. Re-enable interrupts.

7.7 TASK ADDRESS SPACE

The LDT selector and PDBR (CR3) field of the TSS can be used to give each task its own LDT and page tables. Because segment descriptors in the LDTs are the connections between tasks and segments, separate LDTs for each task can be used to set up individual control over these connections. Access to any particular segment can be given to any particular task by placing a segment descriptor for that segment in the LDT for that task. If paging is enabled, each task can have its own set of page tables for mapping linear addresses to physical addresses.

It also is possible for tasks to have the same LDT. This is a simple and memory-efficient way to allow some tasks to communicate with or control each other, without dropping the protection barriers for the entire system.

Because all tasks have access to the GDT, it also is possible to create shared segments accessed through segment descriptors in this table.

7.7.1 Task Linear-to-Physical Space Mapping

The choices for arranging the linear-to-physical mappings of tasks fall into two general classes:

1. One linear-to-physical mapping shared among all tasks. When paging is not enabled, this is the only choice. Without paging, all linear addresses map to the same physical addresses. When paging is enabled, this form of linear-to-physical mapping is obtained by using one page directory for all tasks. The linear space may exceed the available physical space if demand-paged virtual memory is supported.
2. Independent linear-to-physical mappings for each task. This form of mapping comes from using a different page directory for each task. Because the PDBR (page directory base register) is loaded from the TSS with each task switch, each task may have a different page directory.

The linear address spaces of different tasks may map to completely distinct physical addresses. If the entries of different page directories point to different page tables and the page tables point to different pages of physical memory, then the tasks do not share any physical addresses.

The task state segments must lie in a space accessible to all tasks so that the mapping of TSS addresses does not change while the processor is reading and updating the TSSs during a task switch. The linear space mapped by the GDT also should be mapped to a shared physical space; otherwise, the purpose of the GDT is defeated. Figure 7-7 shows how the linear spaces of two tasks can overlap in the physical space by sharing page tables.

7.7.2 Task Logical Address Space

By itself, an overlapping linear-to-physical space mapping does not allow sharing of data among tasks. To share data, tasks must also have a common logical-to-linear space mapping; i.e., they also must have access to descriptors which point into a shared linear address space. There are three ways to create shared logical-to-physical address-space mappings:

1. Through the segment descriptors in the GDT. All tasks have access to the descriptors in the GDT. If those descriptors point into a linear-address space which is mapped to a common physical-address space for all tasks, then the tasks can share data and instructions.
2. Through shared LDTs. Two or more tasks can use the same LDT if the LDT selectors in their TSSs select the same LDT for use in address translation. Segment descriptors in the LDT addressing linear space mapped to overlapping physical space provide shared physical memory. This method of sharing is more selective than sharing by the GDT; the sharing can be limited to specific tasks. Other tasks in the system may have different LDTs which do not give them access to the shared areas.
3. Through segment descriptors in the LDTs which map to the same linear address space. If the linear address space is mapped to the same physical space by the page mapping of the tasks involved, these descriptors permit the tasks to share space. Such descriptors are commonly called "aliases." This method of sharing is even more selective than those listed above; other descriptors in the LDTs may point to independent linear addresses which are not shared.

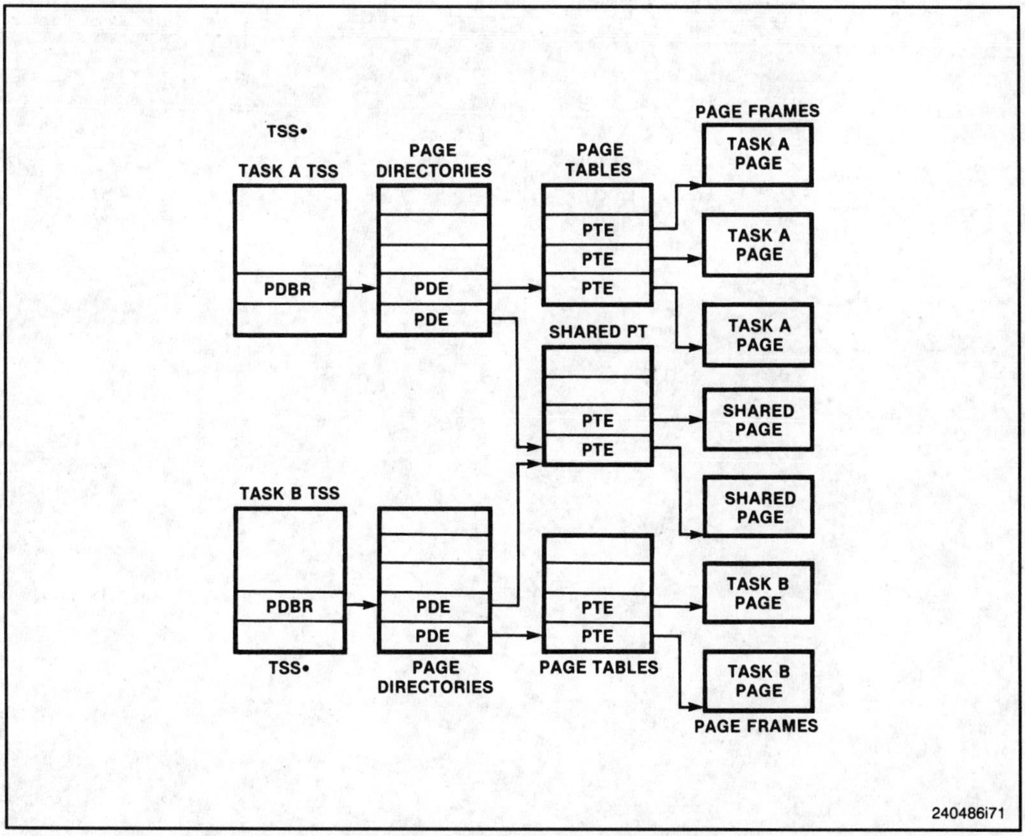

Figure 7-7. Overlapping Linear-to-Physical Mappings

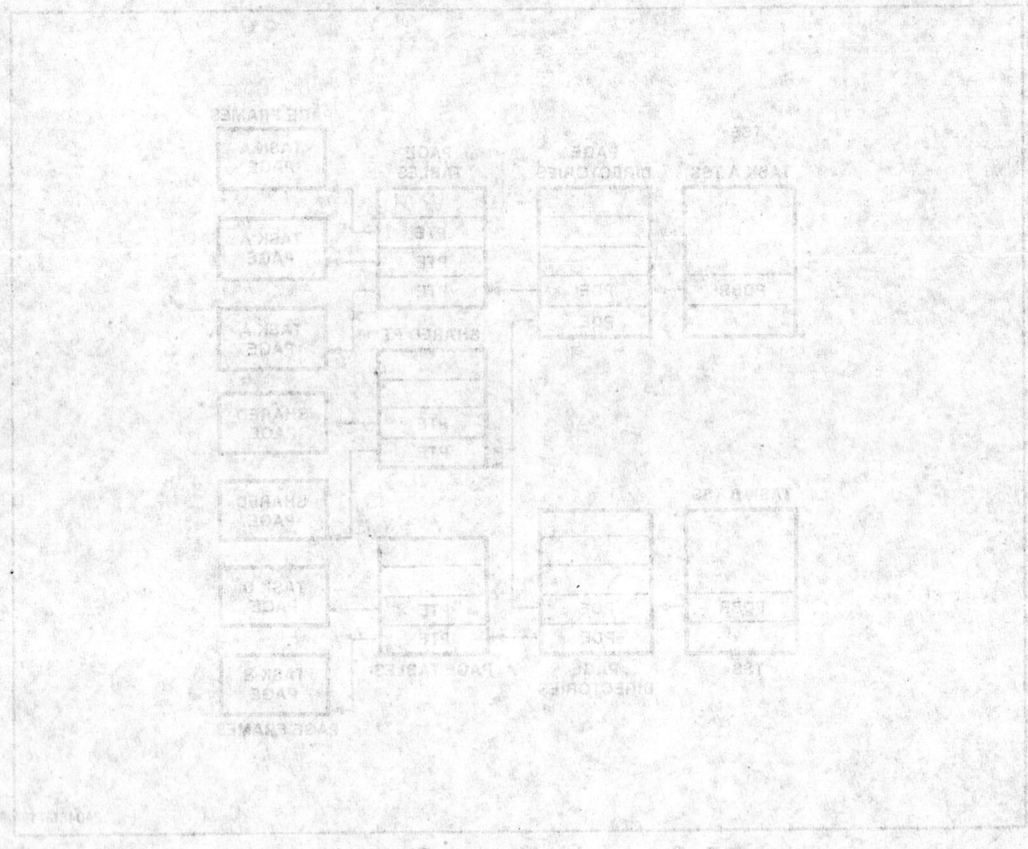

Input/Output 8

CHAPTER 8
INPUT/OUTPUT

This chapter explains the input/output architecture of the i486™ processor. Input/output is accomplished through I/O ports, which are registers connected to peripheral devices. An I/O port can be an input port, an output port, or a bidirectional port. Some I/O ports are used for carrying data, such as the transmit and receive registers of a serial interface. Other I/O ports are used to control peripheral devices, such as the control registers of a disk controller.

The i486 processor always synchronizes I/O instruction execution with external bus activity. All previous instructions are completed before an I/O operation begins. In particular, all writes held pending in the i486 CPU write buffers will be completed before an I/O read or write is performed.

The input/output architecture is the programmer's model of how these ports are accessed. The discussion of this model includes:

- Methods of addressing I/O ports.
- Instructions which perform I/O operations.
- The I/O protection mechanism.

8.1 I/O ADDRESSING

The i486 processor allows I/O ports to be addressed in either of two ways:

- Through a separate I/O address space accessed using I/O instructions.
- Through memory-mapped I/O, where I/O ports appear in the address space of physical memory.

The use of a separate I/O address space is supported by special instructions and a hardware protection mechanism. When memory-mapped I/O is used, the general-purpose instruction set can be used to access I/O ports, and protection is provided using segmentation or paging. Some system designers may prefer to use the I/O facilities built into the processor, while others may prefer the simplicity of a single physical address space.

If segmentation or paging is used for protection of the I/O address space, the AVL fields in segment descriptors or page table entries may be used to mark pages containing I/O as unrelocatable and unswappable. The AVL fields are provided for this kind of use, where a system programmer needs to make an extension to the address translation and protection mechanisms.

Hardware designers use these ways of mapping I/O ports into the address space when they design the address decoding circuits of a system. I/O ports can be mapped so that they appear in the I/O address space or the address space of physical memory (or both). System programmers may need to discuss with hardware designers the kind of I/O addressing they would like to have.

8.1.1 I/O Address Space

The i486 processor provides a separate I/O address space, distinct from the address space for physical memory, where I/O ports can be placed. The I/O address space consists of 2^{16} (64K) individually addressable 8-bit ports; any two consecutive 8-bit ports can be treated as a 16-bit port, and any four consecutive ports can be a 32-bit port. Extra bus cycles are required if a port crosses the boundary between two doublewords in physical memory.

The M/IO# pin on the i486 processor indicates when a bus cycle to the I/O address space occurs. When a separate I/O address space is used, it is the responsibility of the hardware designer to make use of this signal to select I/O ports rather than memory. In fact, the use of the separate I/O address space simplifies the hardware design because these ports can be selected by a single signal; unlike other processors, it is not necessary to decode a number of upper address lines in order to set up a separate I/O address space.

A program can specify the address of a port in two ways. With an immediate byte constant, the program can specify:

- 256 8-bit ports numbered 0 through 255.
- 128 16-bit ports numbered 0, 2, 4, . . . , 252, 254.
- 64 32-bit ports numbered 0, 4, 8, . . . , 248, 252.

Using a value in the DX register, the program can specify:

- 8-bit ports numbered 0 through 65535.
- 16-bit ports numbered 0, 2, 4, . . . , 65532, 65534.
- 32-bit ports numbered 0, 4, 8, . . . , 65528, 65532.

The i486 processor can transfer 8, 16, or 32 bits to a device in the I/O space. Like words in memory, 16-bit ports should be aligned to even addresses so that all 16 bits can be transferred in a single bus cycle. Like doublewords in memory, 32-bit ports should be aligned to addresses which are multiples of four. The processor supports data transfers to unaligned ports, but there is a performance penalty because an extra bus cycle must be used.

The IN and OUT instructions move data between a register and a port in the I/O address space. The instructions INS and OUTS move strings of data between the memory address space and ports in the I/O address space.

I/O port addresses 0F8H through 0FFH are reserved for use by Intel®. Do not assign I/O ports to these addresses.

The exact order of bus cycles used to access ports which require more than one bus cycle is undefined. For example, an OUT instruction which loads an unaligned doubleword port at location 2H accesses the word at 4H before accessing the word at 2H. This behavior is neither defined, nor guaranteed to remain the same in future Intel products.

If software needs to produce a particular order of bus cycles, this order must be specified explicitly. For example, to load a word-length port at 4H followed by loading a word port at 2H, two word-length instructions must be used, rather than a single doubleword instruction.

Note that although the i486 processor automatically masks parity errors for certain types of bus cycles, such as interrupt acknowledge cycles, it does not mask parity for bus cycles to the I/O address space. Programmers may need to be aware of this behavior as a possible source of spurious parity errors.

8.1.2 Memory-Mapped I/O

I/O devices may be placed in the address space for physical memory. This is called memory-mapped I/O. As long as the devices respond like memory components, they can be used with memory-mapped I/O.

Memory-mapped I/O provides additional programming flexibility. Any instruction which references memory may be used to access an I/O port located in the memory space. For example, the MOV instruction can transfer data between any register and a port. The AND, OR, and TEST instructions may be used to manipulate bits in the control and status registers of peripheral devices (see Figure 8-1). Memory-mapped I/O can use the full instruction set and the full complement of addressing modes to address I/O ports.

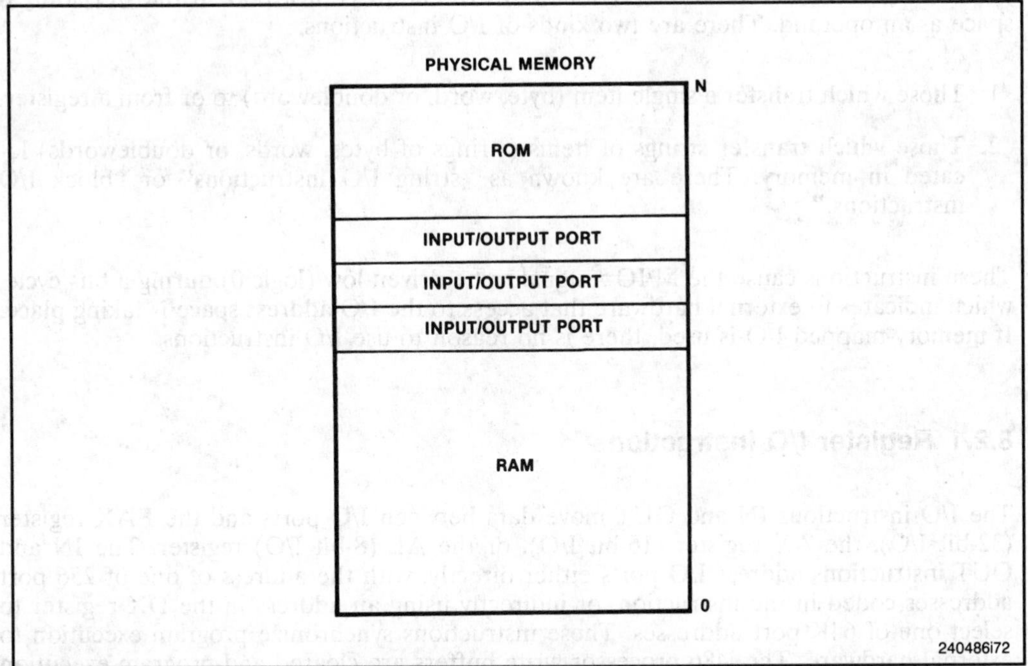

Figure 8-1. Memory-Mapped I/O

To optimize performance, the i486 CPU allows reads to be re-ordered ahead of buffered writes in certain precisely-defined circumstances. (See the *i486™ Processor Hardware Reference Manual* for further details about the operation of the write buffer.) Using memory-mapped I/O on the i486 CPU therefore creates the possibility that an I/O read will be performed before the memory write of a previous instruction. To eliminate this possibility, use an I/O instruction for the read.

Using an I/O instruction for an I/O write can also be advantageous because it guarantees that the write will be completed before the next instruction begins execution. If I/O writes are used to control system hardware, then this sequence of events is desirable, since it guarantees that the next instruction will be executed in the new state.

If caching is enabled, either external hardware or the paging mechanism (the PCD bit in the page table entry) must be used to prevent caching of I/O data.

Memory-mapped I/O, like any other memory reference, is subject to access protection and control. See Chapter 6 for a discussion of memory protection.

8.2 I/O INSTRUCTIONS

The I/O instructions of the i486 processor provide access to the processor's I/O ports for the transfer of data. These instructions have the address of a port in the I/O address space as an operand. There are two kinds of I/O instructions:

1. Those which transfer a single item (byte, word, or doubleword) to or from a register.
2. Those which transfer strings of items (strings of bytes, words, or doublewords) located in memory. These are known as "string I/O instructions" or "block I/O instructions."

These instructions cause the M/IO# signal to be driven low (logic 0) during a bus cycle, which indicates to external hardware that access to the I/O address space is taking place. If memory-mapped I/O is used, there is no reason to use I/O instructions.

8.2.1 Register I/O Instructions

The I/O instructions IN and OUT move data between I/O ports and the EAX register (32-bit I/O), the AX register (16-bit I/O), or the AL (8-bit I/O) register. The IN and OUT instructions address I/O ports either directly, with the address of one of 256 port addresses coded in the instruction, or indirectly using an address in the DX register to select one of 64K port addresses. These instructions synchronize program execution to external hardware. The i486 processor write buffers are cleared and program execution delayed until the last ready of the last bus cycle has been returned.

IN (Input from Port) transfers a byte, word, or doubleword from an input port to the AL, AX, or EAX registers. A byte IN instruction transfers 8 bits from the selected port to the AL register. A word IN instruction transfers 16 bits from the port to the AX register. A doubleword IN instruction transfers 32 bits from the port to the EAX register.

OUT (Output from Port) transfers a byte, word, or doubleword from the AL, AX, or EAX registers to an output port. A byte OUT instruction transfers 8 bits from the AL register to the selected port. A word OUT instruction transfers 16 bits from the AX register to the port. A doubleword OUT instruction transfers 32 bits from the EAX register to the port.

8.2.2 Block I/O Instructions

The INS and OUTS instructions move blocks of data between I/O ports and memory. Block I/O instructions use an address in the DX register to address a port in the I/O address space. These instructions use the DX register to specify:

- 8-bit ports numbered 0 through 65535.
- 16-bit ports numbered 0, 2, 4, . . . , 65532, 65534.
- 32-bit ports numbered 0, 4, 8, . . . , 65528, 65532.

Block I/O instructions use either the SI or DI register to address memory. For each transfer, the SI or DI register is incremented or decremented, as specified by the DF flag.

The INS and OUTS instructions, when used with repeat prefixes, perform block input or output operations. The repeat prefix REP modifies the INS and OUTS instructions to transfer blocks of data between an I/O port and memory. These block I/O instructions are string instructions (see Chapter 3 for more on string instructions). They simplify programming and increase the speed of data transfer by eliminating the need to use a separate LOOP instruction or an intermediate register to hold the data.

The string I/O instructions operate on byte strings, word strings, or doubleword strings. After each transfer, the memory address in the ESI or EDI registers is incremented or decremented by 1 for byte operands, by 2 for word operands, or by 4 for doubleword operands. The DF flag controls whether the register is incremented (the DF flag is clear) or decremented (the DF flag is set).

INS (Input String from Port) transfers a byte, word, or doubleword string element from an input port to memory. The INSB instruction transfers a byte from the selected port to the memory location addressed by the ES and EDI registers. The INSW instruction transfers a word. The INSD instruction transfers a doubleword. A segment override prefix cannot be used to specify an alternate destination segment. Combined with a REP prefix, an INS instruction makes repeated read cycles to the port, and puts the data into consecutive locations in memory.

OUTS (Output String from Port) transfers a byte, word, or doubleword string element from memory to an output port. The OUTSB instruction transfers a byte from the memory location addressed by the ES and EDI registers to the selected port. The OUTSW instruction transfers a word. The OUTSD instruction transfers a doubleword. A segment override prefix cannot be used to specify an alternate source segment. Combined with a REP prefix, an OUTS instruction reads consecutive locations in memory, and writes the data to an output port.

8.3 PROTECTION AND I/O

The I/O architecture has two protection mechanisms:

1. The IOPL field in the EFLAGS register controls access to the I/O instructions.
2. The I/O permission bit map of a TSS segment controls access to individual ports in the I/O address space.

These protection mechanisms are available only when a separate I/O address space is used. When memory-mapped I/O is used, protection is provided using segmentation or paging.

8.3.1 I/O Privilege Level

In systems where I/O protection is used, access to I/O instructions is controlled by the IOPL field in the EFLAGS register. This permits the operating system to adjust the privilege level needed to perform I/O. In a typical protection ring model, privilege levels 0 and 1 have access to the I/O instructions. This lets the operating system and the device drivers perform I/O, but keeps applications and less privileged device drivers from accessing the I/O address space. Applications access I/O through the operating system.

The following instructions can be executed only if CPL ≤ IOPL:

IN —Input
INS —Input String
OUT —Output
OUTS —Output String
CLI —Clear Interrupt-Enable Flag
STI —Set Interrupt-Enable Flag

These instructions are called "sensitive" instructions, because they are sensitive to the IOPL field. In virtual-8086 mode, IOPL is not used; only the I/O permission bit map limits access to I/O ports (see Chapter 23).

To use sensitive instructions, a procedure must run at a privilege level at least as privileged as that specified by the IOPL field. Any attempt by a less privileged procedure to use a sensitive instruction results in a general-protection exception. Because each task has its own copy of the EFLAGS register, each task can have a different IOPL.

A task can change IOPL only with the POPF instruction; however, such changes are privileged. No procedure may changer its IOPL unless it is running at privilege level 0. An attempt by a less privileged procedure to change the IOPL does not result in an exception; the IOPL simply remains unchanged.

The POPF instruction also may be used to change the state of the IF flag (as can the CLI and STI instructions); however, changes to the IF flag using the POPF instruction are IOPL-sensitive. A procedure may change the setting of the IF flag with a POPF instruction only if it runs with a CPL at least as privileged as the IOPL. An attempt by a less privileged procedure to change the IF flag does not result in an exception; the IF flag simply remains unchanged.

8.3.2 I/O Permission Bit Map

The i486 processor can generate exceptions for references to specific I/O addresses. These addresses are specified in the I/O permission bit map in the TSS (see Figure 8-2). The size of the map and its location in the TSS are variable. The processor finds the I/O

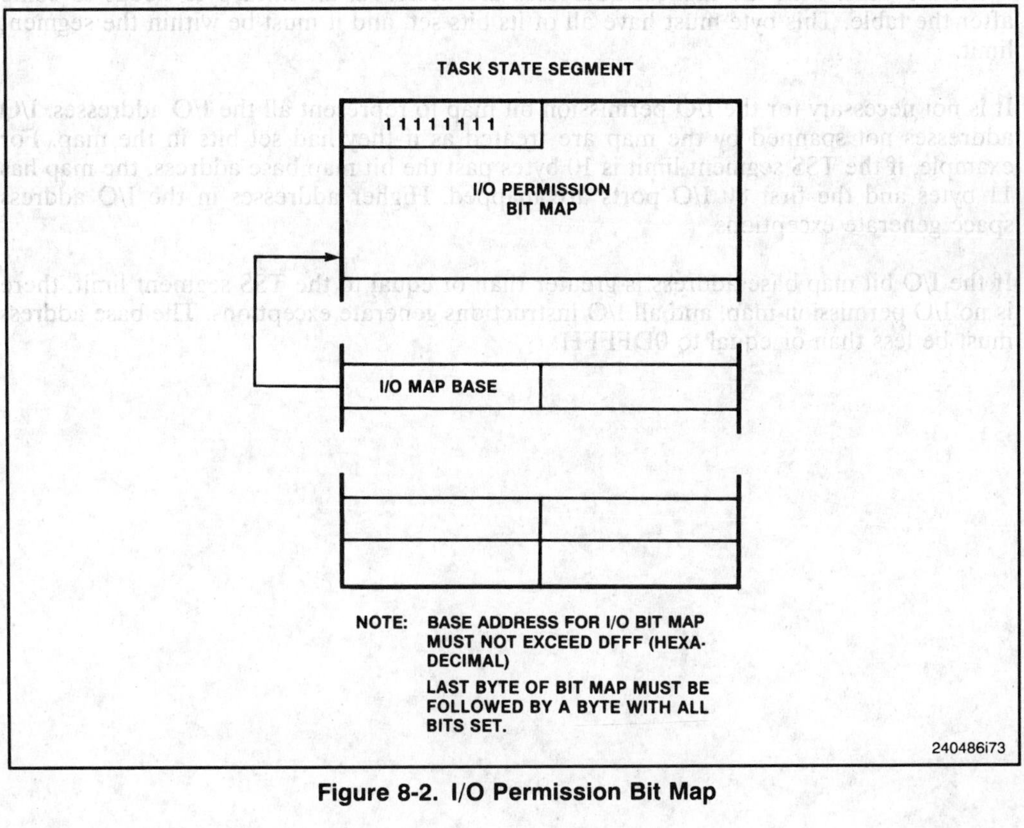

Figure 8-2. I/O Permission Bit Map

permission bit map with the I/O map base address in the TSS. The base address is a 16-bit offset into the TSS. This is an offset to the beginning of the bit map. The limit of the TSS is the limit on the size of the I/O permission bit map.

Because each task has its own TSS, each task has its own I/O permission bit map. Access to individual I/O ports can be granted to individual tasks.

If CPL ≤ IOPL in protected mode, then the processor allows I/O operations to proceed. If CPL >OPL, or if the processor is operating in virtual 8086 mode, then the processor checks the I/O permission map. Each bit in the map corresponds to an I/O port byte address; for example, the control bit for address 41 (decimal) in the I/O address space is found at bit position 1 of the sixth byte in the bit map. The processor tests all the bits corresponding to the I/O port being addressed; for example, a doubleword operation tests four bits corresponding to four adjacent byte addresses. If any tested bit is set, a general-protection exception is generated. If all tested bits are clear, the I/O operation proceeds.

Because I/O ports which are not aligned to word and doubleword boundaries are permitted, it is possible that the processor may need to access two bytes in the bit map when I/O permission is checked. For maximum speed, the processor has been designed to read two bytes for every access to an I/O port. To prevent exceptions from being generated when the ports with the highest addresses are accessed, an extra byte needs to come after the table. This byte must have all of its bits set, and it must be within the segment limit.

It is not necessary for the I/O permission bit map to represent all the I/O addresses. I/O addresses not spanned by the map are treated as if they had set bits in the map. For example, if the TSS segment limit is 10 bytes past the bit map base address, the map has 11 bytes and the first 80 I/O ports are mapped. Higher addresses in the I/O address space generate exceptions.

If the I/O bit map base address is greater than or equal to the TSS segment limit, there is no I/O permission map, and all I/O instructions generate exceptions. The base address must be less than or equal to 0DFFFH.

Exceptions and Interrupts 9

CHAPTER 9
EXCEPTIONS AND INTERRUPTS

Exceptions and interrupts are forced transfers of execution to a task or a procedure. The task or procedure is called a *handler*. Interrupts occur at random times during the execution of a program, in response to signals from hardware. Exceptions occur when instructions are executed which provoke exceptions. Usually, the servicing of interrupts and exceptions is performed in a manner transparent to application programs. Interrupts are used to handle events external to the processor, such as requests to service peripheral devices. Exceptions handle conditions detected by the processor in the course of executing instructions, such as division by 0.

There are two sources for interrupts and two sources for exceptions:

1. Interrupts
   - Maskable interrupts, which are received on the INTR input of the i486™ processor. Maskable interrupts do not occur unless the interrupt-enable flag (IF) is set.
   - Nonmaskable interrupts, which are received on the NMI (Non-Maskable Interrupt) input of the processor. The processor does not provide a mechanism to prevent nonmaskable interrupts.
2. Exceptions
   - Processor-detected exceptions. These are further classified as *faults*, *traps*, and *aborts*.
3. Programmed exceptions. The INTO, INT 3, INT *n*, and BOUND instructions may trigger exceptions. These instructions often are called "software interrupts," but the processor handles them as exceptions.

This chapter explains the features of the i486 processor which control and respond to interrupts.

9.1 EXCEPTION AND INTERRUPT VECTORS

The processor associates an identifying number with each different type of interrupt or exception. This number is called a *vector*.

The NMI interrupt and the exceptions are assigned vectors in the range 0 through 31. Not all of these vectors are currently used by the processor; unassigned vectors in this range are reserved for possible future uses. Do not use unassigned vectors.

The vectors for maskable interrupts are determined by hardware. External interrupt controllers (such as Intel®'s 8259A Programmable Interrupt Controller) put the vector on the bus of the i486 processor during its interrupt-acknowledge cycle. Any vectors in the range 32 through 255 can be used. Table 9-1 shows the assignment of exception and interrupt vectors.

Table 9-1. Exception and Interrupt Vectors

Vector Number	Description
0	Divide Error
1	Debug Exception
2	NMI Interrupt
3	Breakpoint
4	INTO-detected Overflow
5	BOUND Range Exceeded
6	Invalid Opcode
7	Device Not Available
8	Double Fault
9	(Intel® reserved. Do not use. Not used by i486™ CPU.)
10	Invalid Task State Segment
11	Segment Not Present
12	Stack Fault
13	General Protection
14	Page Fault
15	(Intel reserved. Do not use.)
16	Floating-Point Error
17	Alignment Check
18-31	(Intel reserved. Do not use.)
32-255	Maskable Interrupts

Exceptions are classified as *faults*, *traps*, or *aborts* depending on the way they are reported and whether restart of the instruction which caused the exception is supported.

Faults – A fault is an exception which is reported at the instruction boundary prior to the instruction in which the exception was detected. The fault is reported with the machine restored to a state which permits the instruction to be restarted. The return address for the fault handler points to the instruction which generated the fault, rather than the instruction following the faulting instruction.

Traps – A trap is an exception which is reported at the instruction boundary immediately after the instruction in which the exception was detected.

Aborts – An abort is an exception which does not always report the location of the instruction causing the exception and does not allow restart of the program which caused the exception. Aborts are used to report severe errors, such as hardware errors and inconsistent or illegal values in system tables.

9.2 INSTRUCTION RESTART

For most exceptions and interrupts, transfer of execution does not take place until the end of the current instruction. This leaves the EIP register pointing at the instruction which comes after the instruction which was being executed when the exception or interrupt occurred. If the instruction has a repeat prefix, transfer takes place at the end of the current iteration with the registers set to execute the next iteration. But if the exception is a fault, the processor registers are restored to the state they held before execution of the instruction began. This permits *instruction restart*.

Instruction restart is used to handle exceptions which block access to operands. For example, an application program could make reference to data in a segment which is not present in memory. When the exception occurs, the exception handler must load the segment (probably from a hard disk) and resume execution beginning with the instruction which caused the exception. At the time the exception occurs, the instruction may have altered the contents of some of the processor registers. If the instruction read an operand from the stack, it is necessary to restore the stack pointer to its previous value. All of these restoring operations are performed by the processor in a manner completely transparent to the application program.

When a fault occurs, the EIP register is restored to point to the instruction which received the exception. When the exception handler returns, execution resumes with this instruction.

9.3 ENABLING AND DISABLING INTERRUPTS

Certain conditions and flag settings cause the processor to inhibit certain kinds of interrupts and exceptions.

9.3.1 NMI Masks Further NMIs

While an NMI interrupt handler is executing, the processor disables additional calls to the procedure or task which handles the interrupt until the next IRET instruction is executed. This prevents stacking up calls to the interrupt handler. It is recommended that interrupt gates be used for NMI's in order to disable nested maskable interrupts, since an IRET instruction from the maskable-interrupt handler would re-enable NMI.

9.3.2 IF Masks INTR

The IF flag can turn off servicing of interrupts received on the INTR pin of the processor. When the IF flag is clear, INTR interrupts are ignored; when the IF flag is set, INTR interrupts are serviced. As with the other flag bits, the processor clears the IF flag in response to a RESET signal. The STI and CLI instructions set and clear the IF flag.

CLI (Clear Interrupt-Enable Flag) and **STI (Set Interrupt-Enable Flag)** put the IF flag (bit 9 in the EFLAGS register) in a known state. These instructions may be executed only if the CPL is an equal or more privileged level than the IOPL. A general-protection exception is generated if they are executed with a lesser privileged level.

The IF flag also is affected by the following operations:

- The PUSHF instruction stores all flags on the stack, where they can be examined and modified. The POPF instruction can be used to load the modified form back into the EFLAGS register.
- Task switches and the POPF and IRET instructions load the EFLAGS register; therefore, they can be used to modify the setting of the IF flag.
- Interrupts through interrupt gates automatically clear the IF flag, which disables interrupts. (Interrupt gates are explained later in this chapter).

9.3.3 RF Masks Debug Faults

The RF flag in the EFLAGS register can be used to turn off servicing of debug faults. If it is clear, debug faults are serviced; if it is set, they are ignored. This is used to suppress multiple calls to the debug exception handler when a breakpoint occurs.

For example, an instruction breakpoint may have been set for an instruction which references data in a segment which is not present in memory. When the instruction is executed for the first time, the breakpoint generates a debug exception. Before the debug handler returns, it should set the RF flag in the copy of the EFLAGS register saved on the stack. This allows the segment-not-present fault to be reported after the debug exception handler transfers execution back to the instruction. If the flag is not set, another debug exception occurs after the debug exception handler returns.

The processor sets the RF bit in the saved contents of the EFLAGS register when the other faults occur, so multiple debug exceptions are not generated when the instruction is restarted due to the segment-not-present fault. The processor clears its RF flag when the execution of the faulting instruction completes. This allows an instruction breakpoint to be generated for the following instruction. (See Chapter 11 for more information on debugging.)

9.3.4 MOV or POP to SS Masks Some Exceptions and Interrupts

Software which needs to change stack segments often uses a pair of instructions; for example:

```
MOV    SS, AX
MOV      ESP, StackTop
```

If an interrupt or exception occurs after the segment selector has been loaded but before the ESP register has been loaded, these two parts of the logical address into the stack space are inconsistent for the duration of the interrupt or exception handler.

To prevent this situation, the i486 processor inhibits interrupts, debug exceptions, and single-step trap exceptions after either a MOV to SS instruction or a POP to SS instruction, until the instruction boundary following the next instruction is reached. General-protection faults may still be generated. If the LSS instruction is used to modify the contents of the SS register, the problem does not occur.

9.4 PRIORITY AMONG SIMULTANEOUS EXCEPTIONS AND INTERRUPTS

If more than one exception or interrupt is pending at an instruction boundary, the processor services them in a predictable order. The priority among classes of exception and interrupt sources is shown in Table 9-2. The processor first services a pending exception or interrupt from the class which has the highest priority, transferring execution to the first instruction of the handler. Lower priority exceptions are discarded; lower priority interrupts are held pending. Discarded exceptions are re-issued when the interrupt handler returns execution to the point of interruption.

9.5 INTERRUPT DESCRIPTOR TABLE

The interrupt descriptor table (IDT) associates each exception or interrupt vector with a descriptor for the procedure or task which services the associated event. Like the GDT and LDTs, the IDT is an array of 8-byte descriptors. Unlike the GDT, the first entry of the IDT may contain a descriptor. To form an index into the IDT, the processor scales the exception or interrupt vector by eight, the number of bytes in a descriptor. Because

Table 9-2. Priority Among Simultaneous Exceptions and Interrupts

Priority	Descriptions
Highest	Debug Trap Exceptions from the last instruction (TF flag set, T bit in TSS set, or data breakpoint)
	Debug Fault Exceptions for the next instruction (code breakpoint)
	Non-Maskable Interrupt
	Maskable Interrupt
	Faults from fetching next instruction (Segment-Not-Present Fault or General-Protection Fault)
	Faults from instruction decoding (Illegal Opcode, instruction too long, or privilege violation) if WAIT instruction, Coprocessor-Not-Available
	Exception (TS and MP bits of CR0 set) if ESC instruction, Coprocessor-Not-Available
	Exception (EM or TS bits of CR0 set) if WAIT or ESC instruction, Coprocessor-Error
	Exception (Error# pin asserted)
	Segment-Not-Present Faults, Stack Faults, and General-Protection Faults for memory operands
	Alignment Faults for memory operands
Lowest	Page Faults for memory operands

there are only 256 vectors, the IDT need not contain more than 256 descriptors. It can contain fewer than 256 descriptors; descriptors are required only for the interrupt vectors which may occur.

The IDT may reside anywhere in physical memory. As Figure 9-1 shows, the processor locates the IDT using the IDTR register. This register holds both a 32-bit base address and 16-bit limit for the IDT. The LIDT and SIDT instructions load and store the contents of the IDTR register. Both instructions have one operand, which is the address of six bytes in memory.

If a vector references a descriptor beyond the limit, the processor enters shutdown mode. In this mode, the processor stops executing instructions until an NMI interrupt is received or reset initialization is invoked. The processor generates a special bus cycle to

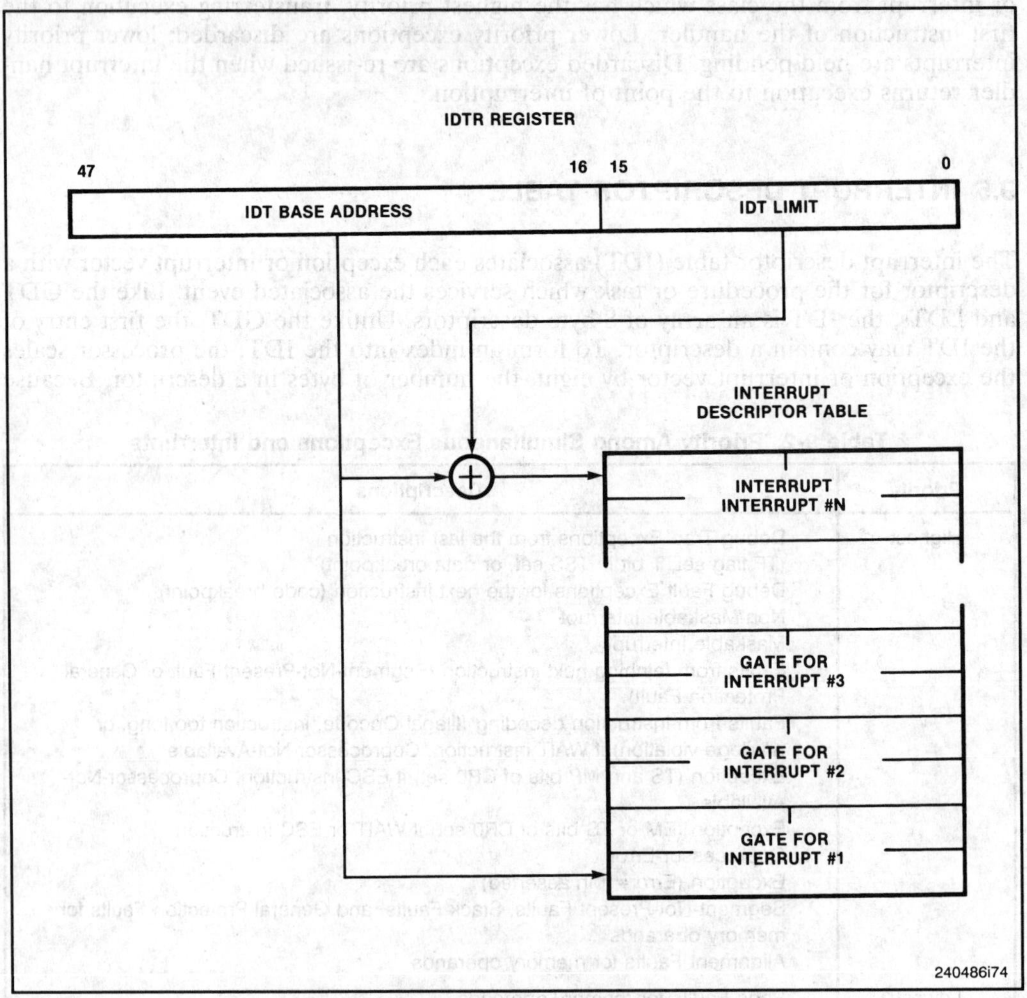

Figure 9-1. IDTR Register Locates IDT in Memory

indicate it has entered shutdown mode. Software designers may need to be aware of the response of hardware to receiving this signal. For example, hardware may turn on an indicator light on the front panel, generate an NMI interrupt to record diagnostic information, or invoke reset initialization.

LIDT (Load IDT register) loads the IDTR register with the base address and limit held in the memory operand. This instruction can be executed only when the CPL is 0. It normally is used by the initialization code of an operating system when creating an IDT. An operating system also may use it to change from one IDT to another.

SIDT (Store IDT register) copies the base and limit value stored in IDTR to memory. This instruction can be executed at any privilege level.

9.6 IDT DESCRIPTORS

The IDT may contain any of three kinds of descriptors:

- Task gates
- Interrupt gates
- Trap gates

Figure 9-2 shows the format of task gates, interrupt gates, and trap gates. (The task gate in an IDT is the same as the task gate in the GDT or an LDT already discussed in Chapter 7.)

9.7 INTERRUPT TASKS AND INTERRUPT PROCEDURES

Just as a CALL instruction can call either a procedure or a task, so an exception or interrupt can "call" an interrupt handler as either a procedure or a task. When responding to an exception or interrupt, the processor uses the exception or interrupt vector to index to a descriptor in the IDT. If the processor indexes to an interrupt gate or trap gate, it calls the handler in a manner similar to a CALL to a call gate. If the processor finds a task gate, it causes a task switch in a manner similar to a CALL to a task gate.

9.7.1 Interrupt Procedures

An interrupt gate or trap gate indirectly references a procedure which runs in the context of the currently executing task, as shown in Figure 9-3. The selector of the gate points to an executable-segment descriptor in either the GDT or the current LDT. The offset field of the gate descriptor points to the beginning of the exception or interrupt handling procedure.

The i486 processor calls an exception or interrupt handling procedure in much the same manner as a procedure call; the differences are explained in the following sections.

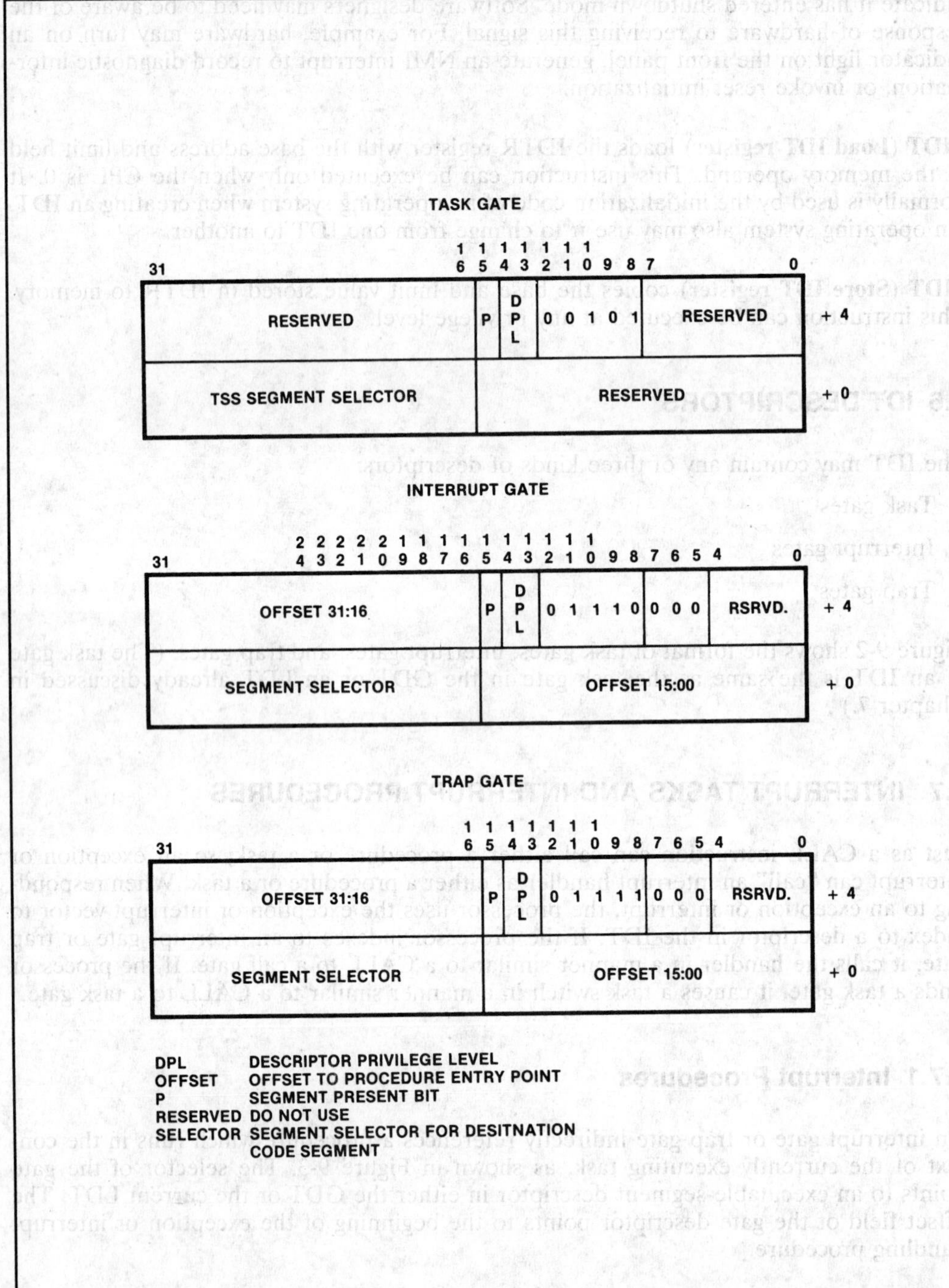

Figure 9-2. IDT Gate Descriptors

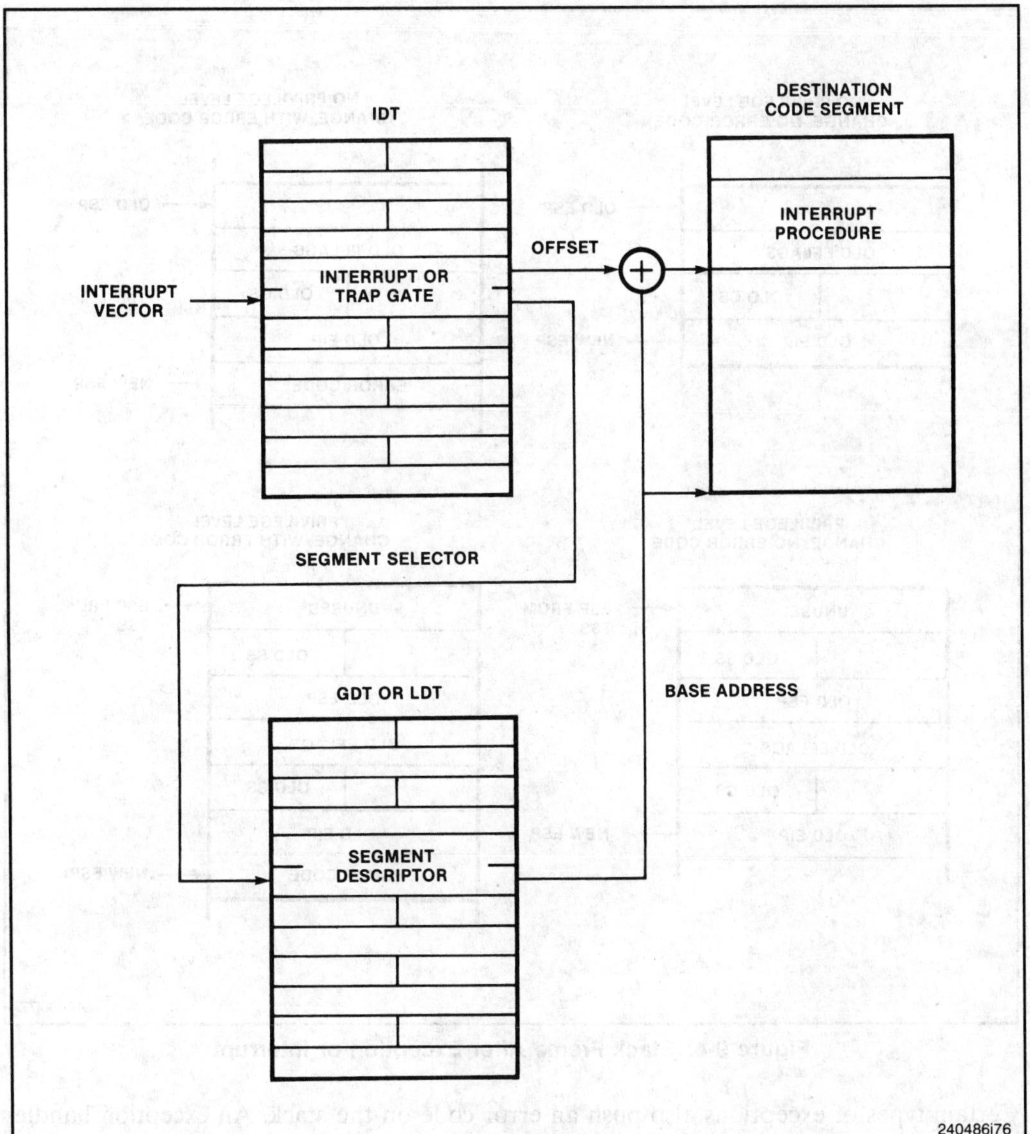

IDT

DESTINATION
CODE SEGMENT

INTERRUPT
PROCEDURE

OFFSET

INTERRUPT
VECTOR

INTERRUPT OR
TRAP GATE

SEGMENT SELECTOR

GDT OR LDT

BASE ADDRESS

SEGMENT
DESCRIPTOR

240486i76

Figure 9-3. Interrupt Procedure Call

9.7.1.1 STACK OF INTERRUPT PROCEDURE

Just as with a transfer of execution using a CALL instruction, a transfer to an exception or interrupt handling procedure uses the stack to store the processor state. As Figure 9-4 shows, an interrupt pushes the contents of the EFLAGS register onto the stack before pushing the address of the interrupted instruction.

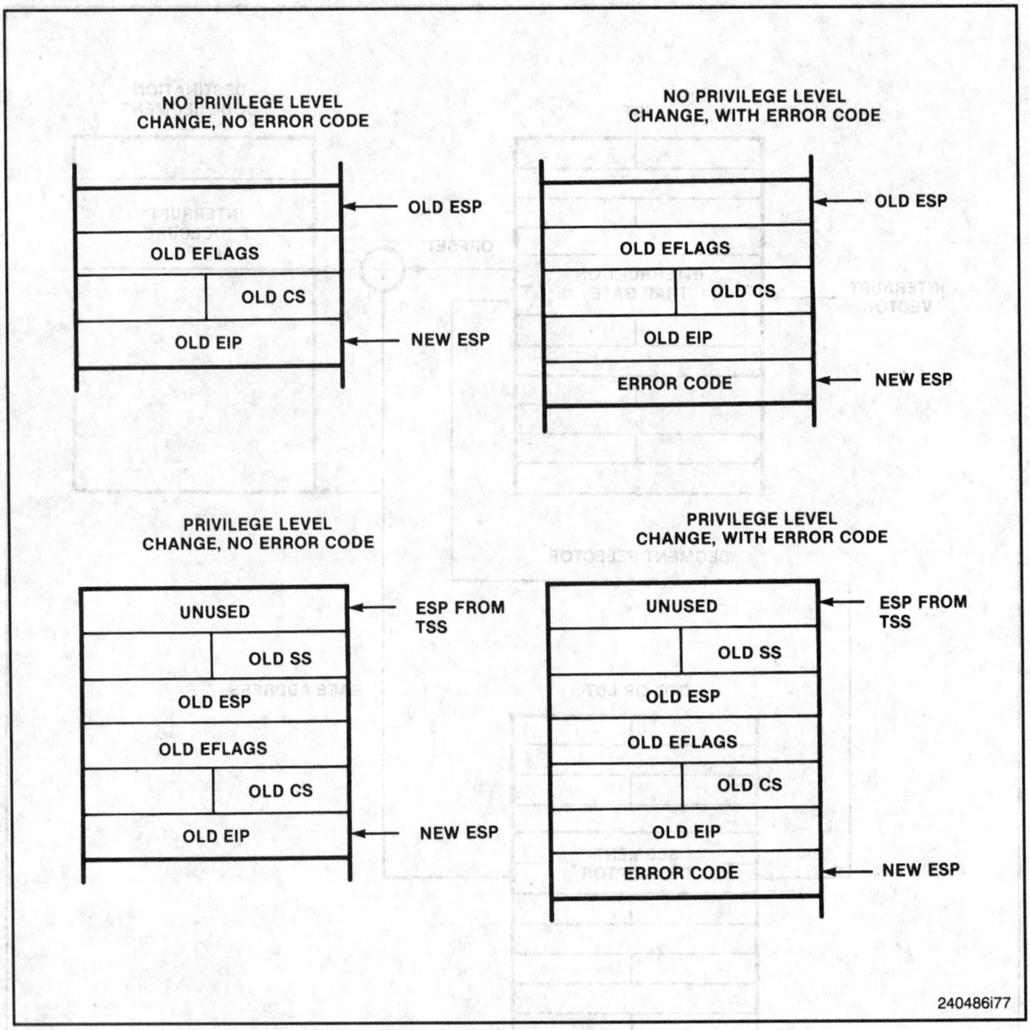

Figure 9-4. Stack Frame After Exception or Interrupt

Certain types of exceptions also push an error code on the stack. An exception handler can use the error code to help diagnose the exception.

9.7.1.2 RETURNING FROM AN INTERRUPT PROCEDURE

An interrupt procedure differs from a normal procedure in the method of leaving the procedure. The IRET instruction is used to exit from an interrupt procedure. The IRET instruction is similar to the RET instruction except that it increments the contents of the ESP register by an extra four bytes and restores the saved flags into the EFLAGS register. The IOPL field of the EFLAGS register is restored only if the CPL is 0. The IF flag is changed only if CPL $\leq$ IOPL.

9.7.1.3 FLAG USAGE BY INTERRUPT PROCEDURE

Interrupts using either interrupt gates or trap gates cause the TF flag to be cleared after its current value is saved on the stack as part of the saved contents of the EFLAGS register. In so doing, the processor prevents instruction tracing from affecting interrupt response. A subsequent IRET instruction restores the TF flag to the value in the saved contents of the EFLAGS register on the stack.

The difference between an interrupt gate and a trap gate is its effect on the IF flag. An interrupt which uses an interrupt gate clears the IF flag, which prevents other interrupts from interfering with the current interrupt handler. A subsequent IRET instruction restores the IF flag to the value in the saved contents of the EFLAGS register on the stack. An interrupt through a trap gate does not change the IF flag.

9.7.1.4 PROTECTION IN INTERRUPT PROCEDURES

The privilege rule which governs interrupt procedures is similar to that for procedure calls: the processor does not permit an interrupt to transfer execution to a procedure in a less privileged segment (numerically greater privilege level). An attempt to violate this rule results in a general-protection exception.

Because interrupts generally do not occur at predictable times, this privilege rule effectively imposes restrictions on the privilege levels at which exception and interrupt handling procedures can run. Either of the following techniques can be used to keep the privilege rule from being violated.

- The exception or interrupt handler can be placed in a conforming code segment. This technique can be used by handlers for certain exceptions (divide error, for example). These handlers must use only the data available on the stack. If the handler needs data from a data segment, the data segment would have to have privilege level 3, which would make it unprotected.
- The handler can be placed in a code segment with privilege level 0. This handler would always run, no matter what CPL the program has.

9.7.2 Interrupt Tasks

A task gate in the IDT indirectly references a task, as Figure 9-5 illustrates. The segment selector in the task gate addresses a TSS descriptor in the GDT.

When an exception or interrupt calls a task gate in the IDT, a task switch results. Handling an interrupt with a separate task offers two advantages:

- The entire context is saved automatically.
- The interrupt handler can be isolated from other tasks by giving it a separate address space. This is done by giving it a separate LDT.

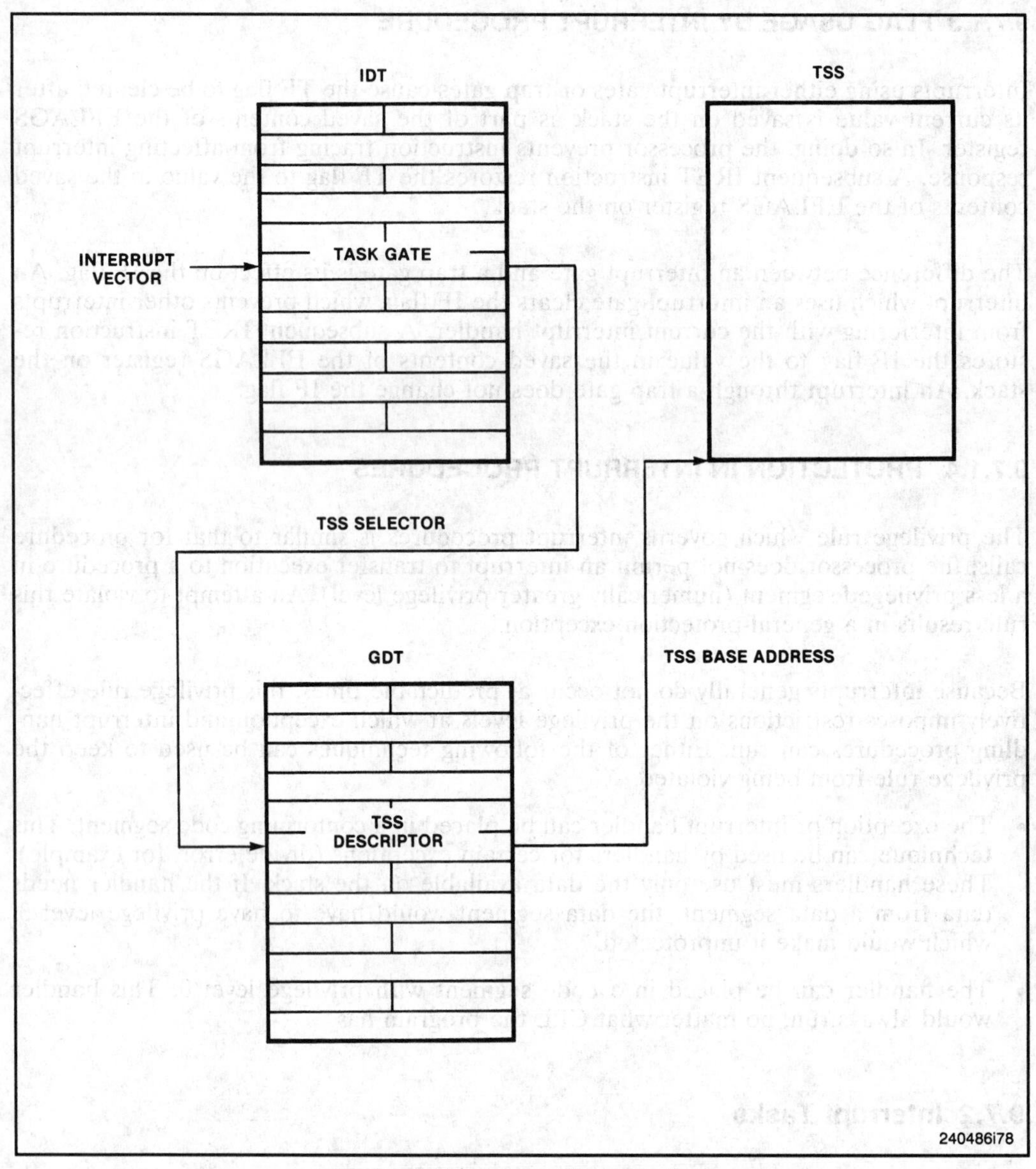

Figure 9-5. Interrupt Task Switch

A task switch caused by an interrupt operates in the same manner as the other task switches described in Chapter 7. The interrupt task returns to the interrupted task by executing an IRET instruction.

Some exceptions return an error code. If the task switch is caused by one of these, the processor pushes the code onto the stack corresponding to the privilege level of the interrupt handler.

When interrupt tasks are used in an operating system for the i486 processor, there are actually two mechanisms which can create new tasks: the software scheduler (part of the operating system) and the hardware scheduler (part of the processor's interrupt mechanism). The software scheduler needs to accommodate interrupt tasks which may be generated when interrupts are enabled.

9.8 ERROR CODE

With exceptions related to a specific segment, the processor pushes an error code onto the stack of the exception handler (whether it is a procedure or task). The error code has the format shown in Figure 9-6. The error code resembles a segment selector; however instead of an RPL field, the error code contains two one-bit fields:

1. The processor sets the EXT bit if an event external to the program caused the exception.
2. The processor sets the IDT bit if the index portion of the error code refers to a gate descriptor in the IDT.

If the IDT bit is not set, the TI bit indicates whether the error code refers to the GDT (TI bit clear) or to the LDT (TI bit set). The remaining 14 bits are the upper bits of the selector for the segment. In some cases the error code is *null* (i.e., all bits in the lower word are clear).

The error code is pushed on the stack as a doubleword. This is done to keep the stack aligned on addresses which are multiples of four. The upper half of the doubleword is reserved.

9.9 EXCEPTION CONDITIONS

The following sections describe conditions which generate exceptions. Each description classifies the exception as a *fault*, *trap*, or *abort*. This classification provides information needed by system programmers for restarting the procedure in which the exception occurred:

- Faults—The saved contents of the CS and EIP registers point to the instruction which generated the fault.

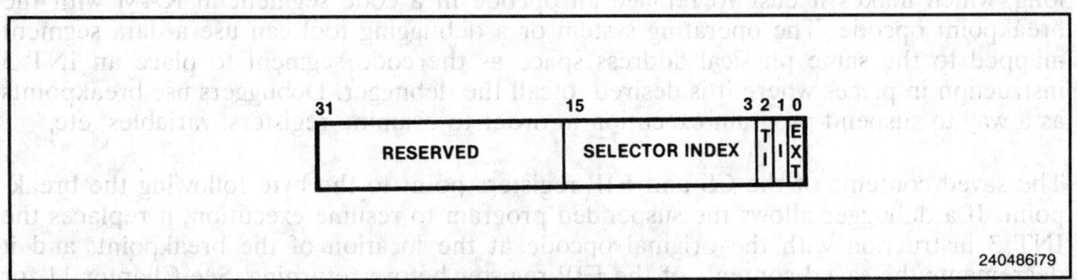

Figure 9-6. Error Code

- Traps—The saved contents of the CS and EIP registers stored when the trap occurs point to the instruction to be executed after the instruction which generated the trap. If a trap is detected during an instruction which transfers execution, the saved contents of the CS and EIP registers reflect the transfer. For example, if a trap is detected in a JMP instruction, the saved contents of the CS and EIP registers point to the destination of the JMP instruction, not to the instruction at the next address above the JMP instruction.
- Aborts—An abort is an exception which permits neither precise location of the instruction causing the exception nor restart of the program which caused the exception. Aborts are used to report severe errors, such as hardware errors and inconsistent or illegal values in system tables.

9.9.1 Interrupt 0—Divide Error

The divide-error fault occurs during a DIV or an IDIV instruction when the divisor is 0.

9.9.2 Interrupt 1—Debug Exceptions

The processor generates a debug exception for a number of conditions; whether the exception is a fault or a trap depends on the condition, as shown below:

- Instruction address breakpoint fault
- Data address breakpoint trap
- General detect fault
- Single-step trap
- Task-switch breakpoint trap

The processor does not push an error code for this exception. An exception handler can examine the debug registers to determine which condition caused the exception. See Chapter 11 for more detailed information about debugging and the debug registers.

9.9.3 Interrupt 3—Breakpoint

The INT 3 instruction generates a breakpoint trap. The INT 3 instruction is one byte long, which makes it easy to replace an opcode in a code segment in RAM with the breakpoint opcode. The operating system or a debugging tool can use a data segment mapped to the same physical address space as the code segment to place an INT 3 instruction in places where it is desired to call the debugger. Debuggers use breakpoints as a way to suspend program execution in order to examine registers, variables, etc.

The saved contents of the CS and EIP registers point to the byte following the breakpoint. If a debugger allows the suspended program to resume execution, it replaces the INT 3 instruction with the original opcode at the location of the breakpoint, and it decrements the saved contents of the EIP register before returning. See Chapter 11 for more information on debugging.

9.9.4 Interrupt 4 – Overflow

The overflow trap occurs when the processor executes an INTO instruction with the OF flag set. Because signed and unsigned arithmetic both use some of the same instructions, the processor cannot determine when overflow actually occurs. Instead, it sets the OF flag when the results, if interpreted as signed numbers, would be out of range. When doing arithmetic on signed operands, the OF flag can be tested directly or the INTO instruction can be used.

9.9.5 Interrupt 5 – Bounds Check

The bounds-check fault is generated when the processor, while executing a BOUND instruction, finds that the operand exceeds the specified limits. A program can use the BOUND instruction to check a signed array index against signed limits defined in a block of memory.

9.9.6 Interrupt 6 – Invalid Opcode

The invalid-opcode fault is generated when an invalid opcode is detected by the execution unit. (The exception is not detected until an attempt is made to execute the invalid opcode; i.e., prefetching an invalid opcode does not cause this exception.) No error code is pushed on the stack. The exception can be handled within the same task.

This exception also occurs when the type of operand is invalid for the given opcode. Examples include an intersegment JMP instruction using a register operand, or an LES instruction with a register source operand.

A third condition which generates this exception is the use of the LOCK prefix with an instruction which may not be locked. Only certain instructions may be used with bus locking, and only forms of these instructions which write to a destination in memory may be used. All other uses of the LOCK prefix generate an invalid-opcode exception.

NOTE

Table 9-3 is a list of undefined opcodes that are reserved by Intel. These opcodes do not generate interrupt 6.

9.9.7 Interrupt 7 – Device Not Available

The device-not-available fault is generated by either of two conditions:

- The processor executes an ESC instruction, and the EM bit of the CR0 register is set.
- The processor executes a WAIT or ESC instruction, and the TS bit of the CR0 register is set.

Table 9-3. Intel® Reserved Opcodes

Single Byte
82 D6 F1
Double Byte
0F 07 0F 10 0F 11 0F 12 0F 13 F6 XX F7 XX C0 XX C1 XX D0 XX D1 XX D2 XX D3 XX

Interrupt 7 thus occurs when the programmer wants ESC instructions to be handled by software (EM set), or when a WAIT or ESC instruction is encountered and the context of the floating-point unit is different from that of the current task.

On the 80286 and 386 processors, the MP bit in the CR0 register is used with the TS bit to determine if WAIT instructions should generate exceptions. For programs running on the i486 processor, the MP bit should always be set.

9.9.8 Interrupt 8 – Double Fault

Normally, when the processor detects an exception while trying to call the handler for a prior exception, the two exceptions can be handled serially. If, however, the processor cannot handle them serially, it signals the double-fault exception instead. To determine when two faults are to be signalled as a double fault, the i486 processor divides the exceptions into three classes: benign exceptions, contributory exceptions, and page faults. Table 9-4 shows this classification.

When two benign exceptions or interrupts occur, or one benign and one contributory, the two events can be handled in succession. When two contributory events occur, they cannot be handled, and a double-fault exception is generated.

If a benign or contributory exception is followed by a page fault, the two events can be handled in succession. This is also true if a page fault is followed by a benign exception. However if a page fault is followed by a contributory exception or another page fault, a double-fault abort is generated.

Table 9-4. Interrupt and Exception Classes

Class	Vector Number	Description
Benign Exceptions and Interrupts	1 2 3 4 5 6 7 16	Debug Exceptions NMI Interrupt Breakpoint Overflow Bounds Check Invalid Opcode Device Not Available Floating-Point Error
Contributory Exceptions	0 10 11 12 13	Divide Error Invalid TSS Segment Not Present Stack Fault General Protection
Page Faults	14	Page Fault

An initial segment of page fault encountered while prefetching instructions is outside the domain of Table 9-4. Any further faults generated while the processor is attempting to transfer control to the appropriate fault handler could still lead to a double-fault sequence.

The processor always pushes an error code onto the stack of the double-fault handler; however, the error code is always 0. The faulting instruction may not be restarted. If any other exception occurs while attempting to call the double-fault handler, the processor enters shutdown mode. This mode is similar to the state following execution of a HLT instruction. No instructions are executed until an NMI interrupt or a RESET signal is received. If the shutdown occurs while the processor is executing an NMI interrupt handler, then only a RESET can restart the processor. The processor generates a special bus cycle to indicate it has entered shutdown mode.

9.9.9 Interrupt 9 – (Intel® reserved. Do not use.)

Interrupt 9, the coprocessor-segment overrun abort, is generated in 386 CPU/387 math coprocessor systems when the 386 CPU detects a page or segment violation while transferring the middle portion of a 387 math coprocessor operand. This interrupt is not generated by the i486 processor; interrupt 13 occurs instead.

9.9.10 Interrupt 10 – Invalid TSS

An invalid-TSS fault is generated if a task switch to a segment with an invalid TSS is attempted. A TSS is invalid in the cases shown in Table 9-5. An error code is pushed

Table 9-5. Invalid TSS Conditions

Error Code Index	Description
TSS segment	TSS segment limit less than 67H
LDT segment	Invalid LDT or LDT not present
Stack segment	Stack segment selector exceeds descriptor table limit
Stack segment	Stack segment is not writable
Stack segment	Stack segment DPL not compatible with CPL
Stack segment	Stack segment selector RPL not compatible with CPL
Code segment	Code segment selector exceeds descriptor table limit
Code segment	Code segment is not executable
Code segment	Non-conforming code segment DPL not equal to CPL
Code segment	Conforming code segment DPL greater than CPL
Data segment	Data segment selector exceeds descriptor table limit
Data segment	Data segment not readable

onto the stack of the exception handler to help identify the cause of the fault. The EXT bit indicates whether the exception was caused by a condition outside the control of the program (e.g., if an external interrupt using a task gate attempted a task switch to an invalid TSS).

This fault can occur either in the context of the original task or in the context of the new task. Until the processor has completely verified the presence of the new TSS, the exception occurs in the context of the original task. Once the existence of the new TSS is verified, the task switch is considered complete; i.e., the TR register is loaded with a selector for the new TSS and, if the switch is due to a CALL or interrupt, the Link field of the new TSS references the old TSS. Any errors discovered by the processor after this point are handled in the context of the new task.

To ensure a TSS is available to process the exception, the handler for an invalid-TSS exception must be a task called using a task gate.

9.9.11 Interrupt 11 – Segment Not Present

The segment-not-present fault is generated when the processor detects that the present bit of a descriptor is clear. The processor can generate this fault in any of these cases:

- While attempting to load the CS, DS, ES, FS, or GS registers; loading the SS register, however, causes a stack fault.
- While attempting to load the LDT register using an LLDT instruction; loading the LDT register during a task switch operation, however, causes an invalid-TSS exception.
- While attempting to use a gate descriptor which is marked segment-not-present.

This fault is restartable. If the exception handler loads the segment and returns, the interrupted program resumes execution.

If a segment-not-present exception occurs during a task switch, not all the steps of the task switch are complete. During a task switch, the processor first loads all the segment registers, then checks their contents for validity. If a segment-not-present exception is discovered, the remaining segment registers have not been checked and therefore may not be usable for referencing memory. The segment-not-present handler should not rely on being able to use the segment selectors found in the CS, SS, DS, ES, FS, and GS registers without causing another exception. The exception handler should check all segment registers before trying to resume the new task; otherwise, general protection faults may result later under conditions which make diagnosis more difficult. There are three ways to handle this case:

1. Handle the segment-not-present fault with a task. The task switch back to the interrupted task causes the processor to check the registers as it loads them from the TSS.

2. Use the PUSH and POP instructions on all segment registers. Each POP instruction causes the processor to check the new contents of the segment register.

3. Check the saved contents of each segment register in the TSS, simulating the test which the processor makes when it loads a segment register.

This exception pushes an error code onto the stack. The EXT bit of the error code is set if an event external to the program caused an interrupt which subsequently referenced a not-present segment. The IDT bit is set if the error code refers to an IDT entry (e.g., an INT instruction referencing a not-present gate).

An operating system typically uses the segment-not-present exception to implement virtual memory at the segment level. A not-present indication in a gate descriptor, however, usually does not indicate that a segment is not present (because gates do not necessarily correspond to segments). Not-present gates may be used by an operating system to trigger exceptions of special significance to the operating system.

9.9.12 Interrupt 12 — Stack Exception

A stack fault is generated under two conditions:

- As a result of a limit violation in any operation which refers to the SS register. This includes stack-oriented instructions such as POP, PUSH, ENTER, and LEAVE, as well as other memory references which implicitly use the stack (for example, MOV AX, [BP+6]). The ENTER instruction generates this exception when there is too little space for allocating local variables.
- When attempting to load the SS register with a descriptor which is marked segment-not-present but is otherwise valid. This can occur in a task switch, a CALL instruction to a different privilege level, a return to a different privilege level, an LSS instruction, or a MOV or POP instruction to the SS register.

When the processor detects a stack exception, it pushes an error code onto the stack of the exception handler. If the exception is due to a not-present stack segment or to overflow of the new stack during an interlevel CALL, the error code contains a selector to the segment which caused the exception (the exception handler can test the present bit in the descriptor to determine which exception occurred); otherwise, the error code is 0.

An instruction generating this fault is restartable in all cases. The return address pushed onto the exception handler's stack points to the instruction which needs to be restarted. This instruction usually is the one which caused the exception; however, in the case of a stack exception from loading a not-present stack-segment descriptor during a task switch, the indicated instruction is the first instruction of the new task.

When a stack exception occurs during a task switch, the segment registers may not be usable for addressing memory. During a task switch, the selector values are loaded before the descriptors are checked. If a stack exception is generated, the remaining segment registers have not been checked and may cause exceptions if they are used. The stack fault handler should not expect to use the segment selectors found in the CS, SS, DS, ES, FS, and GS registers without causing another exception. The exception handler should check all segment registers before trying to resume the new task; otherwise, general protection faults may result later under conditions where diagnosis is more difficult.

9.9.13 Interrupt 13 – General Protection

All protection violations which do not cause another exception cause a general-protection exception. This includes (but is not limited to):

- Exceeding the segment limit when using the CS, DS, ES, FS, or GS segments.
- Exceeding the segment limit when referencing a descriptor table.
- Transferring execution to a segment which is not executable.
- Writing to a read-only data segment or a code segment.
- Reading from an execute-only code segment.
- Loading the SS register with a selector for a read-only segment (unless the selector comes from a TSS during a task switch, in which case an invalid-TSS exception occurs).
- Loading the SS, DS, ES, FS, or GS register with a selector for a system segment.
- Loading the DS, ES, FS, or GS register with a selector for an execute-only code segment.
- Loading the SS register with the selector of an executable segment.
- Accessing memory using the DS, ES, FS, or GS register when it contains a null selector.
- Switching to a busy task.
- Violating privilege rules.

- Exceeding the instruction length limit of 15 bytes (this only can occur when redundant prefixes are placed before an instruction).
- Loading the CR0 register with a set PG bit (paging enabled) and a clear PE bit (protection disabled).
- Interrupt or exception through an interrupt or trap gate from virtual-8086 mode to a handler at a privilege level other than 0.

The general-protection exception is a fault. In response to a general-protection exception, the processor pushes an error code onto the exception handler's stack. If loading a descriptor causes the exception, the error code contains a selector to the descriptor; otherwise, the error code is null. The source of the selector in an error code may be any of the following:

1. An operand of the instruction.
2. A selector from a gate which is the operand of the instruction.
3. A selector from a TSS involved in a task switch.

9.9.14 Interrupt 14—Page Fault

A page fault occurs when paging is enabled (the PG bit in the CR0 register is set) and the processor detects one of the following conditions while translating a linear address to a physical address:

- The page-directory or page-table entry needed for the address translation has a clear Present bit, which indicates that a page table or the page containing the operand is not present in physical memory.
- The procedure does not have sufficient privilege to access the indicated page.

The processor provides the page fault handler two items of information which aid in diagnosing the exception and recovering from it:

- An error code on the stack. The error code for a page fault has a format different from that for other exceptions (see Figure 9-7). The error code tells the exception handler three things:
    1. Whether the exception was due to a not-present page or to an access rights violation.
    2. Whether the processor was executing at user or supervisor level at the time of the exception.
    3. Whether the memory access which caused the exception was a read or write.
- The contents of the CR2 register. The processor loads the CR2 register with the 32-bit linear address which generated the exception. The exception handler can use this address to locate the corresponding page directory and page table entries. If another page fault can occur during execution of the page fault handler, the handler should push the contents of the CR2 register onto the stack.

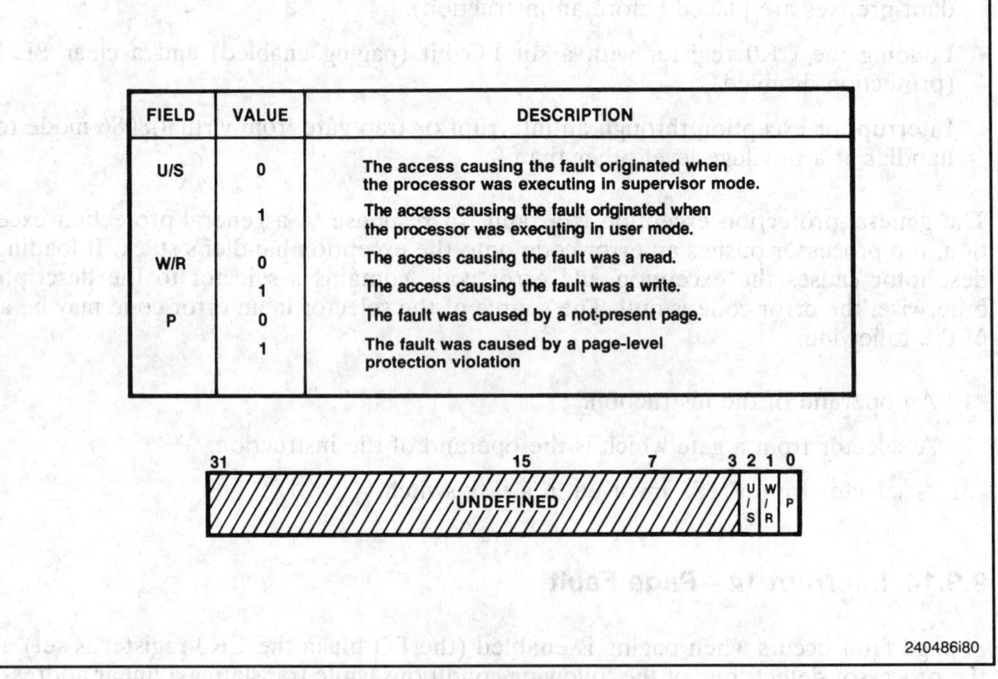

Figure 9-7. Page Fault Error Code

9.9.14.1 PAGE FAULT DURING TASK SWITCH

These operations during a task switch cause access to memory:

1. Write the state of the original task in the TSS of that task.
2. Read the GDT to locate the TSS descriptor of the new task.
3. Read the TSS of the new task to check the types of segment descriptors from the TSS.
4. May read the LDT of the new task in order to verify the segment registers stored in the new TSS.

A page fault can result from accessing any of these operations. In the last two cases the exception occurs in the context of the new task. The instruction pointer refers to the next instruction of the new task, not to the instruction which caused the task switch (or the last instruction to be executed, in the case of an interrupt). If the design of the operating system permits page faults to occur during task-switches, the page-fault handler should be called through a task gate.

9.9.14.2 PAGE FAULT WITH INCONSISTENT STACK POINTER

Special care should be taken to ensure that a page fault does not cause the processor to use an invalid stack pointer (SS:ESP). Software written for Intel 16-bit processors often uses a pair of instructions to change to a new stack; for example:

```
MOV SS, AX
MOV SP, StackTop
```

With the i486 processor, because the second instruction accesses memory, it is possible to get a page fault after the selector in the SS segment register has been changed but before the contents of the SP register have received the corresponding change. At this point, the two parts of the stack pointer SS:SP (or, for 32-bit programs, SS:ESP) are inconsistent. The new stack segment is being used with the old stack pointer.

The processor does not use the inconsistent stack pointer if the handling of the page fault causes a stack switch to a well defined stack (i.e., the handler is a task or a more privileged procedure). However, if the page fault occurs at the same privilege level and in the same task as the page fault handler, the processor will attempt to use the stack indicated by the inconsistent stack pointer.

In systems which use paging and handle page faults within the faulting task (with trap or interrupt gates), software executing at the same privilege level as the page fault handler should initialize a new stack by using the LSS instruction rather than an instruction pair shown above. When the page fault handler is running at privilege level 0 (the normal case), the problem is limited to programs which run at privilege level 0, typically the kernel of the operating system.

9.9.15 Interrupt 16—Floating-Point Error

A floating-point-error fault signals an error generated by a floating-point arithmetic instruction. Interrupt 16 can occur only if the NE bit in the CR0 register is set. See Chapter 16 for more information on floating-point error reporting.

9.9.16 Interrupt 17—Alignment Check

An alignment-check fault can be generated for access to unaligned operands. For example, a word stored at an odd byte address, or a doubleword stored at an address which is not an integer multiple of four. Table 9-6 lists the alignment requirements by data type. To enable alignment checking, the following conditions must be true:

- the AM bit in the CR0 register is set
- the AC flag is set
- CPL is 3 (user mode)

Table 9-6. Alignment Requirements by Data Type

Data Type	Address Must Be Divisible By
WORD	2
DWORD	4
Short REAL	4
Long REAL	8
TEMPREAL	8
Selector	2
48-bit Segmented Pointer	4
32-bit Flat Pointer	4
32-bit Segmented Pointer	2
48-bit "Pseudo-Descriptor"	4
FSTENV/FLDENV save area	4 or 2, depending on operand size
FSAVE/FRSTOR save area	4 or 2, depending on operand size
Bit String	4

Alignment checking is useful for programs which use the low two bits of pointers to identify the type of data structure they address. For example, a subroutine in a math library may accept pointers to numeric data structures. If the type of this structure is assigned a code of 10 (binary) in the lowest two bits of pointers to this type, math subroutines can correct for the type code by adding a displacement of −10 (binary). If the subroutine should ever receive the wrong pointer type, an unaligned reference would be produced, which would generate an exception.

Alignment-check faults are generated only in user mode (privilege level 3). Memory references which default to privilege level 0, such as segment descriptor loads, do not generate alignment-check faults, even when caused by a memory reference made in user mode.

Storing a 48-bit pseudo-descriptor (the memory image of the contents of a descriptor table base register) in user mode can generate an alignment-check fault. Although user-mode programs do not normally store pseudo-descriptors, the fault can be avoided by aligning the pseudo-descriptor to an odd word address (i.e., an address which is 2 MOD 4).

FSAVE and FRSTOR instructions generate unaligned references which can cause alignment-check faults. These instructions are rarely needed by application programs.

9.10 EXCEPTION SUMMARY

Table 9-7 summarizes the exceptions recognized by the i486 processor.

9.11 ERROR CODE SUMMARY

Table 9-8 summarizes the error information which is available with each exception.

Table 9-7. Exception Summary

Description	Vector Number	Return Address Points to Faulting Instruction?	Exception Type	Source of the Exception
Division by Zero	0	Yes	FAULT	DIV and IDIV instructions
Debug Exceptions	1	*1	*1	Any code or data reference
Breakpoint	3	No	TRAP	INT 3 instruction
Overflow	4	No	TRAP	INTO instruction
Bounds Check	5	Yes	FAULT	BOUND instruction
Invalid Opcode	6	Yes	FAULT	Reserved Opcodes
Device Not Available	7	Yes	FAULT	ESC and WAIT instructions
Double Fault	8	Yes	ABORT	Any instruction
Invalid TSS	10	Yes	FAULT[2]	JMP, CALL, IRET instructions, interrupts, and exceptions
Segment Not Present	11	Yes	FAULT	Any instruction which changes segments
Stack Fault	12	Yes	FAULT	Stack operations
General Protection	13	Yes	FAULT/TRAP[3]	Any code or data reference
Page Fault	14	Yes	FAULT	Any code or data reference
Floating-Point Error	16	Yes	FAULT[4]	ESC and WAIT instructions
Alignment Check	17	Yes	FAULT	Any data reference
Software Interrupt	0 to 255	No	TRAP	INT n instructions

1. Debug exceptions are either traps or faults. The exception handler can distinguish between traps and faults by examining the contents of the DR6 register.
2. An invalid-TSS exception cannot be restarted if it occurs during processing of an interrupt or exception.
3. All general-protection faults are restartable. If the fault occurs while attempting to call the handler, the interrupted program is restartable, but the interrupt may be lost.
4. Floating-point errors are not reported until the first ESC or WAIT instruction following the ESC instruction which generated the error.

Table 9-8. Error Code Summary

Description	Vector Number	Is an Error Code Generated?
Divide Error	0	No
Debug Exceptions	1	No
Breakpoint	3	No
Overflow	4	No
Bounds Check	5	No
Invalid Opcode	6	No
Device Not Available	7	No
Double Fault	8	Yes (always zero)
Invalid TSS	10	Yes
Segment Not Present	11	Yes
Stack Fault	12	Yes
General Protection	13	Yes
Page Fault	14	Yes
Floating-Point Error	16	No
Alignment Check	17	Yes (always zero)
Software Interrupt	0-255	No

Initialization 10

CHAPTER 10
INITIALIZATION

The i486™ processor has an input, called the RESET pin, which invokes reset initialization. After RESET is asserted, some registers of the i486 processor are set to known states. These known states, such as the contents of the EIP register, are sufficient to allow software to begin execution. Software then can build the data structures in memory, such as the GDT and IDT tables, which are used by system and application software.

Hardware asserts the RESET signal at power-up. Hardware may assert this signal at other times. For example, a button may be provided for manually invoking reset initialization. Reset also may be the response of hardware to receiving a halt or shutdown indication.

After reset initialization, the DH register holds a number which identifies the processor type. Binary object code can be made compatible with other Intel processors by using this number to select the correct initialization software. Note the i486 processor has several processing modes. It begins execution in a mode which emulates an 8086 processor, called real-address mode. If protected mode is to be used (the mode in which the 32-bit instruction set is available), the initialization software changes the setting of a mode bit in the CR0 register.

10.1 PROCESSOR STATE AFTER RESET

A self test may be requested at power-up. The self test is requested by asserting the AHOLD input during the falling edge of the RESET signal. It is the responsibility of the hardware designer to provide the request for self test, if desired. If the self test is selected, it takes about 2^{20} clock periods to complete. (Intel® reserves the right to change the exact number of periods without notification.)

The EAX register is clear if the i486 processor passed the test. A non-zero value in the EAX register after self test indicates the processor is faulty. If the self test is not requested, the contents of the EAX register after reset initialization are undefined (possibly non-zero). The DX register holds a component identifier and revision number after reset initialization, as shown in Figure 10-1. The DH register contains the value 4, which indicates an i486 processor. The DL register contains a unique identifier of the revision level.

The state of the CR0 register following power-up is shown in Figure 10-2. These states put the processor into real-address mode with paging disabled.

The state of the EBX, ECX, ESI, EDI, EBP, ESP, GDTR, LDTR, TR, debug registers (other than DR7), and floating-point operand stack is undefined following power-up. Software should not depend on any undefined states. The state of the flags and other registers following power-up is shown in Table 10-1.

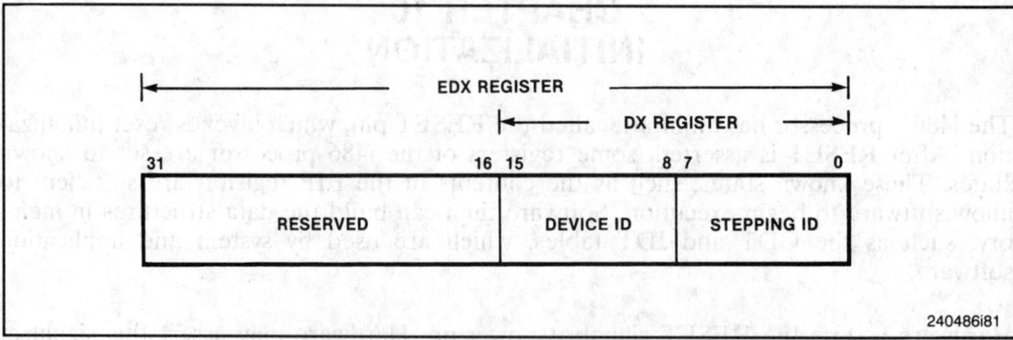

Figure 10-1. Contents of the EDX Register After Reset

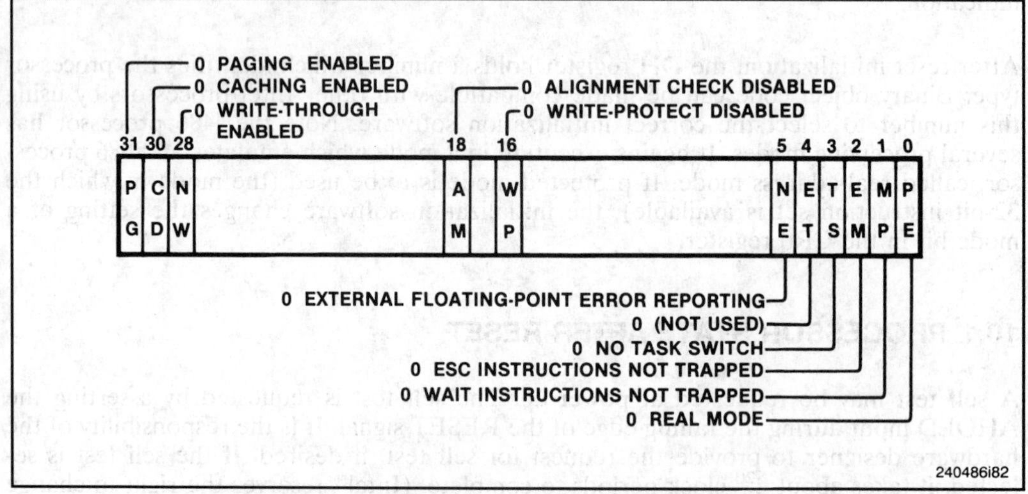

Figure 10-2. Contents of the CR0 Register After Reset

Note that the invisible parts of the CS and DS segment registers are initialized to values which allow execution to begin, even though segments have not been defined. The base address for the code segment is set to 64K below the top of the physical address space, which allows room for a ROM to hold the initialization software. The base address for the data segments are set to the bottom of the physical address space (address 0), where RAM is expected to be. To preserve these addresses, no instruction which loads the segment registers should be executed until a descriptor table has been defined and its base address and limit have been loaded into the GDTR register. If CS is reloaded while in real mode, it will point to the lowest 1 Megabyte of physical memory.

10.2 SOFTWARE INITIALIZATION IN REAL-ADDRESS MODE

After reset initialization, software sets up data structures needed for the processor to perform basic system functions, such as handling interrupts. If the processor remains in

Table 10-1. Processor State Following Power-Up

Register	State (hexadecimal)
EFLAGS	00000002H[1]
EIP	0000FFF0H
CS	0F000H[2]
DS	0000H[3]
SS	0000H
ES	0000H[3]
FS	0000H
GS	0000H
IDTR (base)	00000000H
IDTR (limit)	03FFH
DR7	0000H
Floating-Point Unit Registers[4]	
Control Word	037FH
Status Word	0000H
Tag Word	0FFFFH
IP Offset	00000000H
Data Operand Offset	00000000H
CS Selector	0000H
Operand Selector	0000H
Opcode	000H

NOTE: Undefined bits are reserved. Software should not depend on the states of any of these bits.
1. The high fourteen bits of the EFLAGS register are undefined following power-up. All of the flags are clear.
2. The invisible part of the CS register holds a base address of 0FFFF0000H and a limit of 0FFFFH.
3. The invisible parts of the DS and ES registers hold a base address of 0 and a limit of 0FFFFH.
4. The registers of the floating-point unit are not initialized unless the built-in self-test is invoked.

real-address mode, software sets up data structures in the form used by the 8086 processor. If the processor is going to operate in protected mode, software sets up data structures in the form used by the 80286 and i486 processors, then switches modes. See Section 10.7 for an example.

10.2.1 System Tables

In real-address mode, no descriptor tables are used. The interrupt vector table, which starts at address 0, needs to be loaded with pointers to exception and interrupt handlers before interrupts can be enabled. The NMI interrupt is always enabled. If the interrupt vector table and the NMI interrupt handler need to be loaded into RAM, there will be a period of time following reset initialization when an NMI interrupt cannot be handled.

10.2.2 NMI Interrupt

Hardware must provide a mechanism to prevent an NMI interrupt from being generated while software is unable to handle it. For example, the interrupt vector table and NMI interrupt handler can be provided in ROM. This allows an NMI interrupt to be handled immediately after reset initialization. Another solution would be to provide a mechanism which passes the NMI signal through an AND gate controlled by a bit in an I/O port. Hardware can clear the bit when the processor is reset, and software can set the bit when it is ready to handle NMI interrupts. System software designers should be aware of the mechanism used by hardware to protect software from NMI interrupts following reset.

10.2.3 First Instruction

Execution begins with the instruction addressed by the initial contents of the CS and IP registers. To allow the initialization software to be placed in a ROM at the top of the address space, the high 12 bits of addresses issued for the code segment are set, until the first instruction which loads the CS register, such as a far jump or call. As a result, instruction fetching begins from address 0FFFFFFF0H. Because the size of the ROM is unknown, the first instruction is intended to be a jump to the beginning of the initialization software. If protected mode will be used and the processor is still in real mode, then only near jumps should be performed within the ROM-based software. After a far jump is executed, addresses issued for the code segment are clear in their high 12 bits.

10.2.4 Enabling Caching

The cache is enabled by clearing the CD and NW bits in the CR0 register. This enables caching, write-through, and cache invalidation cycles. Because all cache lines are invalid following reset initialization, it is unnecessary to flush the cache before enabling caching.

Under circumstances where cache lines may be marked as valid, the cache may need to be flushed before enabling caching. This may occur as a result of using the test registers to run test patterns through the cache memory as part of confidence testing during software initialization.

10.3 SWITCHING TO PROTECTED MODE

Before switching to protected mode, a minimum set of system data structures must be created, and a minimum number of registers must be initialized.

10.3.1 System Tables

To allow protected mode software to access programs and data, at least one descriptor table, the GDT, and two descriptors must be created. Descriptors are needed for a code segment and a data segment. The stack can be be placed in a normal read/write data segment, so no descriptor for the stack is required. Before the GDT can be used, the base address and limit for the GDT must be loaded into the GDTR register using an LGDT instruction.

10.3.2 NMI Interrupt

If hardware allows NMI interrupts to be generated, the IDT and a gate for the NMI interrupt handler need to be created. Before the IDT can be used, the base address and limit for the IDT must be loaded into the IDTR register using an LIDT instruction.

10.3.3 PE Bit

Protected mode is entered by setting the PE bit in the CR0 register. Either an LMSW or MOV CR0 instruction may be used to set this bit (the MSW register is part of the CR0 register). Because the processor overlaps the interpretation of several instructions, it is necessary to discard the instructions which already have been read into the processor. A JMP instruction immediately after the LMSW instruction changes the flow of execution, so it has the effect of emptying the processor of instructions which have been fetched or decoded.

After entering protected mode, the segment registers continue to hold the contents they had in real address mode. Software should reload all the segment registers. Execution in protected mode begins with a CPL of 0.

10.4 SOFTWARE INITIALIZATION IN PROTECTED MODE

The data structures needed in protected mode are determined by the memory management features which are used. The processor supports segmentation models which range from a single, uniform address space (flat model) to a highly structured model with several independent, protected address spaces for each task (multi-segmented model). Paging can be enabled for allowing access to large data structures which are partly in memory and partly on disk. Both of these forms of address translation require data structures which are set up by the operating system and used by the memory management hardware.

10.4.1 Segmentation

A flat model without paging only requires a GDT with one code and one data segment descriptor. A flat model with paging requires code and data descriptors for supervisor mode and another set of code and data descriptors for user mode. In addition, it requires a page directory and at least one second-level page table.

A multi-segmented model may require additional segments for the operating system, as well as segments and LDTs for each application program. LDTs require segment descriptors in the GDT. Most operating systems, such as OS/2, allocate new segments and LDTs as they are needed. This provides maximum flexibility for handling a dynamic programming environment, such as an engineering workstation. An embedded system, such as a process controller, might pre-allocate a fixed number of segments and LDTs for a fixed number of application programs. This would be a simple and efficient way to structure the software environment of a system which requires fast real-time performance.

10.4.2 Paging

Unlike segmentation, paging is controlled by a mode bit. If the PG bit in the CR0 register is clear (its state following reset initialization), the paging mechanism is completely absent from the processor architecture seen by programmers.

If the PG bit is set, paging is enabled. The bit may be set using a MOV CR0 instruction. Before setting the PG bit, the following conditions must be true:

- Software has created at least two page tables, the page directory and at least one second-level page table.
- The PDBR register (same as the CR3 register) is loaded with the base address of the page directory.
- The processor is in protected mode (paging is not available in real-address mode). If all other restrictions are met, the PG and PE bits can be set at the same time.

As with the PE bit, setting the PG bit must be followed immediately with a JMP instruction. Also, the code which sets the PG bit must come from a page which has the same physical address after paging is enabled.

10.4.3 Tasks

If the multitasking mechanism is not used, it is unnecessary to initialize the TR register.

If the multitasking mechanism is used, a TSS and a TSS descriptor for the initialization software must be created. TSS descriptors must not be marked as busy when they are created; TSS descriptors should be marked as busy only as a side-effect of performing a task switch. As with descriptors for LDTs, TSS descriptors reside in the GDT. The LTR instruction is used to load a selector for the TSS descriptor of the initialization software into the TR register. This instruction marks the TSS descriptor as busy, but does not perform a task switch. The selector must be loaded before performing the first task switch, because a task switch copies the current task state into the TSS. After the LTR instruction has been used, further operations on the TR register are performed by task switching. As with segments and LDTs, TSSs and TSS descriptors can be either pre-allocated or allocated as needed.

10.5 TLB TESTING

The i486 processor provides a mechanism for testing the translation lookaside buffer (TLB), the cache used for translating linear addresses to physical addresses. Although failure of the TLB hardware is extremely unlikely, users may wish to include TLB confidence tests among other power-up tests for the i486 processor.

NOTE

This TLB testing mechanism is unique to the i486 processor and may not be continued in the same way in future processors. Software which uses this mechanism may be incompatible with future processors.

10.5.1 Structure of the TLB

The TLB is a four-way set-associative memory. Figure 10-3 illustrates its structure. In the data block, there are eight sets of four data entries each. A data entry in the TLB consists of the 20 high-order bits of a physical address. These 20 bits can be interpreted as the *base address* of a page, which is by definition clear in its 12 low-order bits.

The TLB translates a linear address into a physical address, and so is only concerned with the high-order 20 bits of either; the low-order 12 bits (these constitute the *offset* into the page) are the same in both the linear and the physical address.

Corresponding to the block of data entries is a block of valid, attribute and tag entries. The tag entry consists of the 17 high-order bits of a linear address. In translating addresses, the processor uses bits 12, 13, and 14 of the linear address to select one of the eight sets, and then checks the four tags of that set for a match with the high-order 17 bits of the linear address. If a match is found among the tags of the selected set, and the corresponding valid bit equals 1, then the linear address is translated by replacing its high-order 20 bits with the 20 bits of the corresponding data entry.

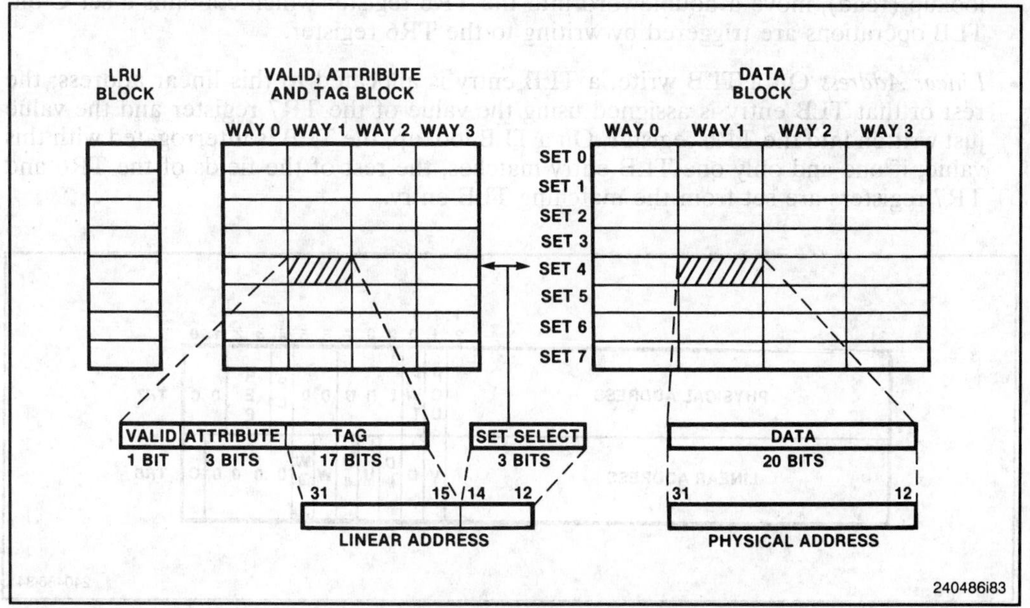

Figure 10-3. TLB Structure

Three LRU bits are provided with each set; they track the use of the data in the set, and are checked when a new entry is needed (and none of the entries in the set is invalid). A pseudo-LRU replacement algorithm is used.

10.5.2 Test Registers

Two test registers, shown in Figure 10-4, are provided for the purpose of testing. The TR6 register is the TLB test command register, and the TR7 register is the TLB test data register. These registers are accessed by forms of the MOV instruction. The MOV instructions are defined in both real-address mode and protected mode. The test registers are privileged resources; in protected mode, the MOV instructions which access them can be executed only at privilege level 0 (most privileged). An attempt to read or write the test registers from any other privilege level causes a general-protection exception.

Unlike the TLB of the 386 DX processor, the TLB of the i486 processor can be accessed without disabling paging. Also unlike the 386 DX processor, the TLB of the i486 processor uses a pseudo-LRU cache replacement algorithm to select entries for de-allocation when a new entry is needed and the TLB is full.

The TLB test command register (TR6) contains a command and an address tag:

- *C* This is the Command bit. There are two TLB testing commands: write entries into the TLB, and perform TLB lookups. To cause an write into the TLB entry, move a doubleword into the TR6 register which contains a clear C bit. To cause an TLB lookup (read), move a doubleword into the TR6 register which contains a set C bit. TLB operations are triggered by writing to the TR6 register.

- *Linear Address* On a TLB write, a TLB entry is allocated to this linear address; the rest of that TLB entry is assigned using the value of the TR7 register and the value just written into the TR6 register. On a TLB lookup, the TLB is interrogated with this value; if one and only one TLB entry matches, the rest of the fields of the TR6 and TR7 registers are set from the matching TLB entry.

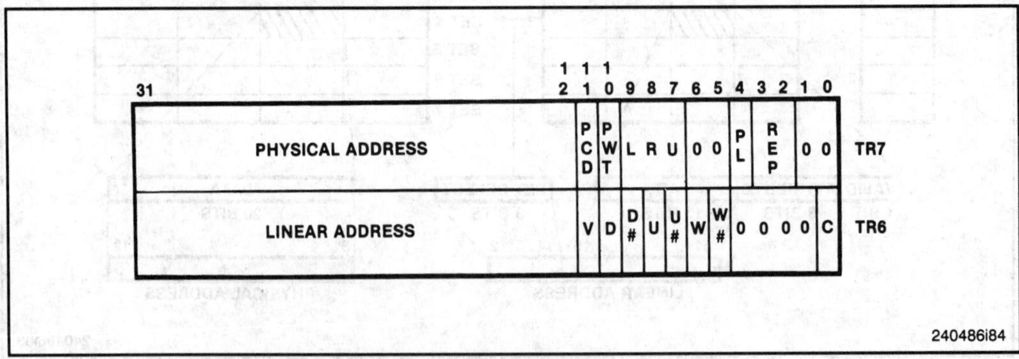

Figure 10-4. TLB Test Registers

- *V* This bit indicates the TLB entry contains valid data. Entries in the TLB which are not loaded with page table entries have a clear V bit. All V bits are cleared by writing to the CR3 register, which has the effect of emptying or "flushing" the TLB. The TLB must be flushed after modifying the page tables, because otherwise unmodified data might get used for address translation.
- *D, D#* The D bit (and its complement).
- *U, U#* The U/S bit (and its complement).
- *W, W#* The R/W bit (and its complement).

These bits are provided in both true and complement form for extra flexibility during TLB lookups. The meaning of these pairs of bits is given in Table 10-2.

The TLB test data register (TR7) holds data read from or data to be written to the TLB:

- *Physical Address* This is the data field of the TLB. On a write to the TLB, the TLB entry allocated to the linear address in the TR6 register is set to this value. On a TLB lookup (read), the data field (physical address) from the TLB is loaded into this field.
- *PCD* Corresponds to the PCD bit of a page table entry.
- *PWT* Corresponds to the PWT bit of a page table entry.
- *LRU* On a TLB read, corresponds to the bits used in the pseudo-LRU cache replacement algorithm. The states which are reported are the value of these bits before the TLB lookup. TLB lookups which result in hits and TLB writes can change these bits.
- *PL* On a TLB write, a set PL bit causes the REP field of the TR7 register to be used for selecting which of four associative blocks of the TLB entry is loaded. If the PL bit is clear, the internal pointer of the paging unit is used to select the block. The internal pointer is driven by the pseudo-LRU cache replacement algorithm. On a TLB lookup (read), the PL bit indicates whether the read was a hit (the PL bit is set) or a miss (the PL bit is clear).
- *REP* For a TLB write, selects which of four associative blocks of the TLB is to be written. For a TLB read, if the PL bit is set, REP reports in which of the four associative blocks the tag was found; if the PL bit is clear, the contents of this field are undefined.

Table 10-2. Meaning of Bit Pairs in the TR6 Register

Bit	Bit#	Effect on TLB Lookup	Effect on TLB Write
0	0	Do not match	undefined
0	1	Match if the bit is clear	Clear the bit
1	0	Match if the bit is set	Set the bit
1	1	Match if set or clear	undefined

10.5.3 Test Operations

To write a TLB entry:

1. Move a doubleword to the TR7 register which contains the desired physical address, PCD, PWT, PL, and REP values. If the PL bit is set, the REP field selects the associative block in which to place the entry. If the PL bit is clear, the internal pointer is used.
2. Move a doubleword to the TR6 register which contains the appropriate linear address, and values for the V, D, U, and W bits. The C bit must be clear.

Do not write duplicate tags; the results of doing so are undefined.

To lookup (read) a TLB entry:

1. Move a doubleword to the TR6 register which contains the appropriate linear address and attributes. The C bit must be set.
2. Read the TR7 register. If the PL bit in the TR7 register is set, then the rest of the register contents report the TLB contents. If the PL bit is clear, then the other values in the TR7 register, except the LRU bits, are undefined.

For the purposes of testing, the V bit functions as another bit of address. The V bit for a lookup request should usually be set, so that uninitialized tags do not match. Lookups with the V bit clear are unpredictable if any tags are uninitialized.

10.6 CACHE TESTING

The i486 processor provides a mechanism for testing the cache used for instructions and data. Although failure of the cache hardware is extremely unlikely, users may wish to include cache confidence tests among other power-up tests for the i486 processor.

NOTE

This cache testing mechanism is unique to the i486 processor and may not be continued in the same way in future processors. Software which uses this mechanism may be incompatible with future processors.

Caching must be disabled while performing cache testing.

10.6.1 Structure of the Cache

The cache is a *four-way set-associative* memory. This means that a data block from a given location in main memory can be stored in any of four locations in the cache. Four-way association is a compromise between the speed of direct-mapped cache on cache hits and the high hit ratio of fully associative cache. It permits rapid searches of the cache to find data while providing a high proportion of cache hits.

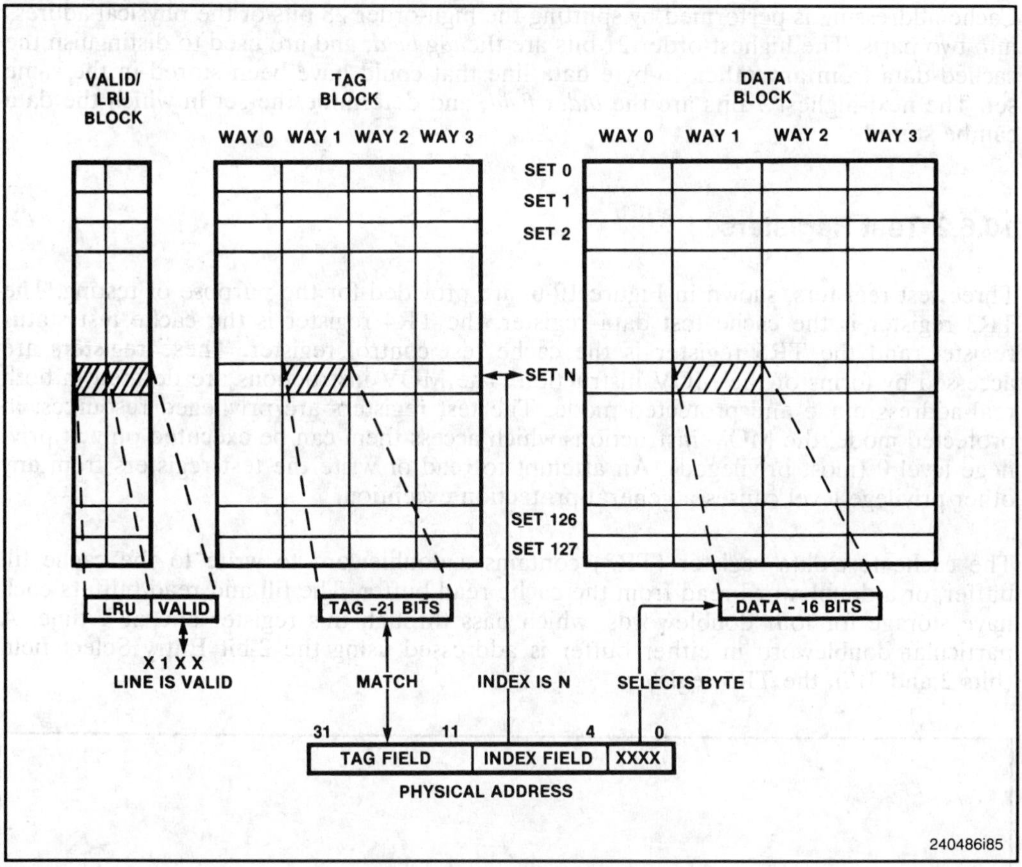

VALID/ LRU BLOCK
TAG BLOCK
DATA BLOCK
WAY 0 WAY 1 WAY 2 WAY 3
SET 0
SET 1
SET 2
SET N
SET 126
SET 127
LRU | VALID
X 1 X X
LINE IS VALID
TAG -21 BITS
DATA - 16 BITS
MATCH
INDEX IS N
SELECTS BYTE
31 11 4 0
TAG FIELD | INDEX FIELD | XXXX
PHYSICAL ADDRESS
240486i85

Figure 10-5. Cache Structure

The cache consists of three blocks:

- *Data Block*—contains up to 8K-bytes of data and instructions. The data block is divided into four arrays, each containing 128 *cache lines*. Each cache line holds data from 16 successive memory addresses, beginning with an address divisible by 16. To each 7-bit *index* into the arrays of the data block there correspond four cache lines, one from each array. Four cache lines with the same index are called a *set*.

- *Tag Block*—contains one 21-bit *tag* for each line of data in the cache. The tag block is therefore also divided into four arrays, each containing 128 tags. The tag consists of the high-order 21 bits of the physical address of the data stored in the corresponding cache line.

- *Valid and LRU Block*—contains one 7-bit quantity for each of the 128 sets of cache lines. Four bits are used to mark the cache lines in the set individually as valid or invalid. The other three bits track the use of the data in the set, and are checked when a cache line-fill is needed (and none of the lines in the set is invalid). As in the TLB, a pseudo-LRU cache replacement algorithm is used.

Cache addressing is performed by splitting the high-order 28 bits of the physical address into two parts. The highest-order 21 bits are the *tag field*, and are used to distinguish the cached data from any other 16-byte data line that could have been stored in the same set. The next-highest 7 bits are the *index field*, and determine the set in which the data can be stored.

10.6.2 Test Registers

Three test registers, shown in Figure 10-6, are provided for the purpose of testing. The TR3 register is the cache test data register, the TR4 register is the cache test status register, and the TR5 register is the cache test control register. These registers are accessed by forms of the MOV instruction. The MOV instructions are defined in both real-address mode and protected mode. The test registers are privileged resources; in protected mode, the MOV instructions which access them can be executed only at privilege level 0 (most privileged). An attempt to read or write the test registers from any other privilege level causes a general-protection exception.

The cache test data register (TR3) contains a doubleword to write to the cache fill buffer, or a doubleword read from the cache read buffer. The fill and read buffers each have storage for four doublewords, which pass through this register one at a time. A particular doubleword in either buffer is addressed using the 2-bit Entry Select field (bits 2 and 3) in the TR5 register.

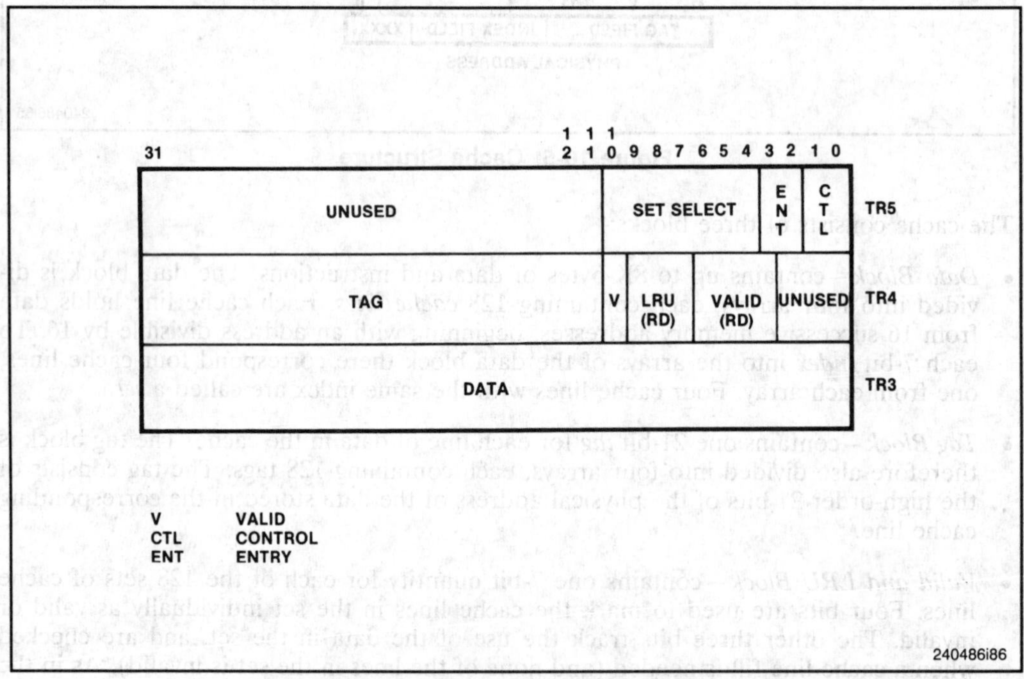

Figure 10-6. Cache Test Registers

The cache test status register (TR4) contains Valid and LRU bits, and a tag:

- *Valid (bits 3..6)* On a cache lookup, these are the four Valid bits of the set which was accessed.
- *LRU* On a cache lookup, these are the three LRU bits of the set which was accessed. On a cache write, these bits are ignored; the LRU bits in the cache are updated by the pseudo-LRU cache replacement algorithm.
- *Valid (bit 10)* This is the Valid bit for the particular entry which was accessed. On a cache lookup, it is a copy of one of the bits reported in bits 3..6. On a cache write, it becomes the new valid bit for the entry and set selected.
- *Tag Address* On a cache write, this is the address which becomes the tag.

  The cache test control register (TR5) contains the 7-bit set select, 2-bit entry select, and a 2-bit control field:

  – Control The functions encoded by these bits are shown in Table 10-3.
- *Entry Select* During a cache read or write, selects one of the four entries in the set addressed by the Set Select; during cache-fill-buffer writes or read-buffer reads, selects one of the four doublewords in a line.
- *Set Select* Selects one of the 128 sets.

Writing to TR5 with either bit 0 or bit 1 set causes a cache access. TR5 cannot be read.

10.6.3 Test Operations

Before cache testing:

1. Disable caching by setting the CD bit in the CR0 register.

To write to the cache fill buffer:

1. Load the TR5 register with a value in the Entry Select field which addresses one of the four doublewords in the cache fill buffer. The value of the Control field must be 00 (binary).
2. Load the TR3 register with the data to be written to the cache fill buffer. The write to the buffer is triggered by loading this register.
3. Repeat steps 1 and 2 above for each of the remaining three doublewords in the cache fill buffer.

Table 10-3. Encoding of Cache Test Control Bits

Control Bits Bit 1 Bit 0	Description
00	Write to cache fill buffer, or read from cache read buffer.
01	Perform cache write.
10	Perform cache read.
11	Flush the cache (mark all entries as invalid).

To write to the cache:

1. Load the cache fill buffer, as described above.
2. Load the TR4 register with the tag (bits 11..31) and a valid bit (bit 10). The other bits of the TR4 register (bits 0..9) have no effect on the cache write.
3. Load the TR5 register with Control, Entry Select, and Set Select values. The value in the Control field must be 01 (binary). The cache write is triggered by loading this register.

To read from the cache:

1. Load the TR5 register with Control, Entry Select, and Set Select values. The value in the Control field must be 10 (binary). The cache read is triggered by loading this register. The cache read loads the TR4 register with the tag for the entry which was read, and the LRU and Valid bits for the entire set which was read. The cache read loads the cache read buffer with 128 bits of data. The buffer can be read using the following procedure.

To read from the cache read buffer:

1. Load the TR5 register with Control and Entry Select values. The Entry Select value addresses one of the four doublewords in the cache read buffer. The value in the Control field must be 00 (binary).
2. Read a doubleword from the cache read buffer by unloading the TR3 register. The read from the buffer is triggered by unloading this register.
3. Repeat steps 1 and 2 above for each of the remaining three doublewords in the cache read buffer.

To flush the cache:

1. Load the TR5 register with a Control value. The value in the Control field must be 11 (binary). None of the other fields have any meaning in this case. The cache flush is triggered by loading this register. All of the LRU bits and Valid bits are cleared.

10.7 INITIALIZATION EXAMPLE

The following program templates are provided by Intel for your benefit in developing software for the i486 processor.

```
;  simpinit.asm
;  Initialization code for simple flat (linear) model example
;
;  *********************************************************************
;
;  Version 2.0
;  Copyright Intel Corp., 1988
;  This template is intended for your benefit in developing applications/
```

```
;  systems using Intel i486(TM) or Intel386(TM) family microprocessors.
;  Intel hereby grants you permission to modify and incorporate it as
;  needed.
;
;  ***********************************************************************
;
;  This is an example of initialization code to put either the i486(TM)
;  processor, 386(TM) DX processor, 386(TM) SX processor or 376(TM) processor
;  into flat mode. All of memory is treated as simple linear RAM.
;  There are no interrupt routines. The builder creates the GDT
;  alias and IDT alias and places them, by default, in GDT[1] and GDT[2].
;  After entering protected mode, this code jumps to an ASM386/486 startup
;  routine for a C application. You can change this JMP address to that of
;  your code, or make the label of your code C_STARTUP.

NAME simpstart              ; name of object module
EXTRN c_startup:near        ; this is the label jmped to after init_code

pe_flag         equ 1       ; for setting PE bit
data_selc       equ 20H     ; offset of _phantom_data_ in GDT (GDT[4])
CODEMACRO       opprefx     ; macro to change default operand size
                db 66H
ENDM

init_code       SEGMENT ER PUBLIC
;  GDT_DESC is a public symbol referred to in the build file. The LOCATION
;  definition in the TABLE section of the build file points to this label;
;  the builder stores the base and limit for the named table at this
;  location in memory.

PUBLIC          gdt_desc
gdt_desc        dp ?
;  START is a label that points to the true beginning of our executable
;  code. The BOOTSTRAP control causes the builder to place a short jump
;  to the named label in this case, START) at the component reset vector.
PUBLIC          start
;  Since this code initializes either an i486, 386 DX, 386 SX or 376 processor
;  into protected mode, the first instructions at START test for component
;  type. The i486 or 386 DX or 386 SX processor at reset is in real or
;  compatibility mode: the PE bit is off and the D bit for CS is not set.
;  Instructions execute in their 16-bit form. The 376 processor at reset
;  has the PE bit on as well as the D bit, so instructions execute in their
;  32-bit form.
    nop                         ; NOPs are for initializing a i486 or 386 DX
    nop                         ; or 386 SX processor
start:
    cld                         ; clear direction flag
    smsw bx                     ; check for processor type at reset
    test bl,1                   ; use SMSW rather than MOV for speed
    jnz pestart
```

```
; Loading the GDTR at REALSTART or PESTART depends on user hardware
; returning a READY after a write to ROM.
realstart:                    ; is an i486 or 386 DX or 386 SX processor and in
    opprefix                  ;  16-bit real mode, use operand prefix to
    mov eax,offset gdt_desc   ;  get 32-bit address of GDT pointer
    opprefix                  ; use operand prefix to
    and eax,0ffffh            ;  make address relative to reset area
    lgdtw cs:[eax]            ; load 24 bits of base into GDTR

    mov ax,bx                 ; copy machine status word
    or al,pe_flag             ; set PE bit
    lmsw ax                   ; load machine status word with PE bit set
    jmp next                  ; flush prefetch queue

pestart:                      ; is a 376 processor and in 32-bit protected
mode
    mov eax,offset gdt_desc   ; get 32-bit address of GDT pointer
    and eax,0ffffh            ; make address relative to reset area
    lgdt cs:[eax]             ; load 32 bits of base into GDTR
next:
    xor eax,eax               ; initialize data selectors
    mov al,data_selc          ; GDT[4] is _phantom_data_
    mov ds,ax
    mov ss,ax
    mov es,ax
    mov fs,ax
    mov gs,ax
    test bl,1
    jnz pejump

    opprefix                  ; use operand prefix for i486 or 386 DX or 386 SX
pejump:                       ; processor jump
    jmp far ptr c_startup     ; first far jump causes A31-20 to drop low
init_code ENDS

END
; cstart.asm
; An ASM386/486 module to initialize the stack and call a C application
;
; ************************************************************************
;
; Version 2.0
; Copyright Intel Corp., 1988
; This template is intended for your benefit in developing applications/
; systems using Intel i486(TM) or Intel386(TM) family microprocessors.
; Intel hereby grants you permission to modify and incorporate it as
; needed.
;
; ************************************************************************
```

```
;
NAME cstart                  ; name of the object module
EXTRN main:near              ; label of the C application to be called
PUBLIC c_startup             ; public symbol used in processor initialization
                               code

stack STACKSEG 1024

data SEGMENT RW PUBLIC
data ENDS
code32 SEGMENT ER PUBLIC

c_startup:
   mov esp,stackstart stack ; initialize stack pointer
   call main                ; call C application
   hlt                      ; halt processor

code32 ENDS
/* simple.c
C386/486(TM) application code for simple flat model example
*****************************************************************************

Version 2.0
Copyright Intel Corp., 1988
This template is intended for your benefit in developing applications/
systems using Intel i486(TM) or Intel386(TM) family microprocessors. Intel
hereby grants you permission to modify and incorporate it as needed.

*****************************************************************************

*/
char message[]="IT WORKS" ;

main ()
{
int array_count[10];
aray_count[1] = 1;
aray_count[2] = 2;
aray_count[3] = 3;
aray_count[4] = 4;
aray_count[5] = 5;
aray_count[6] = 6;
aray_count[7] = 7;
aray_count[8] = 8;
}
-- simple.bld
-- Build file for input to BLD386/486 to create simple flat model example
--
-- *****************************************************************************
```

```
--
-- Version 2.0
-- Copyright Intel Corp., 1988
-- This template is intended for your benefit in developing applications/
-- systems using Intel i486(TM) or Intel386(TM) family microprocessors.
-- Intel hereby grants you permission to modify and incorporate it as
-- needed.
--
-- **********************************************************************
--
simple; -- build program id
SEGMENT
    *segments       (DPL = 0),      -- Give all user segments a DPL of 0.
    _phantom_code_ (DPL = 0),       -- These two segments are created by
    _phantom_data_ (DPL = 0),       -- the builder when the FLAT control is
                                    -- used.
                                    -- Their default DPL is 0; they are listed
                                    -- here for reference only.
    init_code                       -- Put initialization code at reset area.
                (BASE = 0ffff0300H);


TABLE
        -- create GDT
    GDT                             -- GDT_DESC is a public symbol in the
-- "simpstart" initialization module.
        (LOCATION = gdt_desc,       -- In a buffer starting at GDT_DESC,
                                    -- BLD386/486 places the GDT base and
                                    -- GDT limit values. Buffer must be
                                    -- 6 bytes long. The base and limit
                                    -- values are places in this buffer
                                    -- as two bytes of limit plus
                                    -- four bytes of base in the format
                                    -- required for use by the LGDT
                                    -- instruction.
         BASE = 0ffff0100H
        );  -- end GDT
TASK                                -- Task is for *ICD(TM)-486 or ICE(TM)-386
    main_task                       -- or ICE(TM)-376 emulator initialization.
        (BASE = 0ffff0200H,
         DATA = data,               -- Points to a segment that
                                    -- indicates initial DS value.
         CODE = main,               -- Entry point is main, which
                                    -- must be a public id.
         STACKS = (stack),          -- Segment id points to stack
                                    -- segment. Sets the initial SS:ESP.
         NO INTENABLED              -- Disable interrupts.
);
TABLE
```

```
    ldt1 (NOT CREATED);                -- Builder does not place LDT in object
                                       -- module, but contents appear in listing.
END


--
-- Note: ICD-486 is an in-circuit debugger for the i486 CPU. This product
-- is scheduled for availability in the fourth quarter of 1989.
--
echo off
echo simple.bat
echo A DOS batch file for generating a bootloadable simple flat model
echo ********************************************************************
echo *                                                                  *
echo * Version 2.0                                                      *
echo * Copyright Intel Corp., 1988                                      *
echo * This template is intended for your benefit in developing         *
echo * applications/systems using Intel i486(TM) or Intel386(TM) family *
echo * microprocessors. Intel hereby grants you permission to modify    *
echo * and incorporate it as needed.                                    *
echo *                                                                  *
echo ********************************************************************
REM
REM The following two invocations of ASM386/486 create object modules
REM "simpinit.obj" and "cstart.obj". The assembler issues warnings with
REM each invocation due to the use of privileged instructions in the files.
REM The "debug" control directs ASM386/486 to include extra information
REM useful in symbolic debugging. The listing files are "simpinit.lst" and
REM "cstart.lst".
echo *echo asm386 simpinit.asm debug mod486
asm386 simpinit.asm debug mod486
echo (1 warning due to use of privileged instructions)
echo *
echo asm386 cstart.asm debug mod486
asm386 cstart.asm debug mod486
echo (1 warning due to use of privileged instructions)
REM
REM The invocation of C-386/486 creates an object module "simple.obj". The
REM "regallocate" control directs the compiler to optimize the allocation of
REM register variables. The "code" control causes placement of a pseudo-
REM assembly language listing at the end of the listing file. "Debug"
REM directs C-386/486 to include extra information useful in symbolic
REM debugging. The listing file is "simple.lst".
echo *
echo c386 simple.c debug regallocate code mod486
c386 simple.c debug regallocate code mod486
REM
REM BND386/486 combines the input segments and resolves symbolic addressing.
REM The "noload" control directs the binder to create a linkable (rather
REM than loadable) file. The "debug" control indicates that the binder does
```

```
REM not purge debug information. "Object" directs the output file to be
REM named "simple.bnd". The listing file is "simple.mp1".
echo *
echo bnd386 simple.obj,simpinit.obj,cstart.obj noload debug object
(simple.bnd) mod486
bnd386 simple.obj,simpinit.obj,cstart.obj noload debug object (simple.bnd) mod486
REM
REM The goal is an absolute bootloadable file (all addresses fixed in
REM memory) suitable for loading into an ICD-486(TM) in-circuit debugger or an ICE-386(TM)
REM or ICE-376(TM) in-circuit emulator. BLD386/486 creates such an absolute module,
REM necessary descriptor tables, and a task for initializing the emulator. The
REM "buildfile" control identifies "simple.bld" as the build file. The
REM "bootstrap" control identifies the symbol "start" as the label of the
REM instruction to be jumped to by the bootstrap jump placed at 0fffffff0H.
REM The "flat" control directs the builder to configure the file in a flat
REM model, where all code resides in the _phantom_code_ segment and all data
REM resides in the _phantom_data_ segment. The "mod486" control causes the
REM builder to issue messages to guide creation of the object module for an
REM i486(TM) processor. The "mod376" control causes the builder to issue
REM messages to guide creation of the object module for a 376(TM)
REM processor. You can remove either control to create an object module for
REM a 386(TM) DX processor. The listing file is "simple.mp2". The final system
REM is "simple".
echo *
echo bld386 simple.bnd buildfile (simple.bld) bootstrap (start) flat mod486
bld386 simple.bnd buildfile (simple.bld) bootstrap (start) flat mod486
```

11 Debugging

CHAPTER 11
DEBUGGING

The i486™ processor has advanced debugging facilities which are particularly important for sophisticated software systems, such as multitasking operating systems. The failure conditions for these software systems can be very complex and time-dependent. The debugging features of the i486 processor give the system programmer valuable tools for looking at the dynamic state of the processor.

The debugging support is accessed through the debug registers. They hold the addresses of memory locations, called *breakpoints*, which invoke debugging software. An exception is generated when a memory operation is made to one of these addresses. A breakpoint is specified for a particular form of memory access, such as an instruction fetch or a doubleword write operation. The debug registers support both instruction breakpoints and data breakpoints.

With other processors, instruction breakpoints are set by replacing normal instructions with breakpoint instructions. When the breakpoint instruction is executed, the debugger is called. But with the debug registers of the i486 processor, this is not necessary. By eliminating the need to write into the code space, the debugging process is simplified (there is no need to set up a data segment mapped to the same memory as the code segment) and breakpoints can be set in ROM-based software. In addition, breakpoints can be set on reads and writes to data which allows real-time monitoring of variables.

11.1 DEBUGGING SUPPORT

The features of the architecture which support debugging are:

- **Reserved debug interrupt vector** – Specifies a procedure or task to be called when an event for the debugger occurs.
- **Debug address registers** – Specifies the addresses of up to four breakpoints.
- **Debug control register** – Specifies the forms of memory access for the breakpoints.
- **Debug status register** – Reports conditions which were in effect at the time of the exception.
- **Trap bit of TSS (T-bit)** – Generates a debug exception when an attempt is made to perform a task switch to a task with this bit set in its TSS.
- **Resume flag (RF)** – Suppresses multiple exceptions to the same instruction.
- **Trap flag (TF)** – Generates a debug exception after every execution of an instruction.
- **Breakpoint instruction** – Calls the debugger (generates a debug exception). This instruction is an alternative way to set code breakpoints. It is especially useful when more than four breakpoints are desired, or when breakpoints are being placed in the source code.
- **Reserved interrupt vector for breakpoint exception** – Calls a procedure or task when a breakpoint instruction is executed.

These features allow a debugger to be called either as a separate task or as a procedure in the context of the current task. The following conditions can be used to call the debugger:

- Task switch to a specific task.
- Execution of the breakpoint instruction.
- Execution of any instruction.
- Execution of an instruction at a specified address.
- Read or write of a byte, word, or doubleword at a specified address.
- Write to a byte, word, or doubleword at a specified address.
- Attempt to change the contents of a debug register.

11.2 DEBUG REGISTERS

Six registers are used to control debugging. These registers are accessed by forms of the MOV instruction. A debug register may be the source or destination operand for one of these instructions. The debug registers are privileged resources; the MOV instructions which access them may be executed only at privilege level 0. An attempt to read or write the debug registers from any other privilege level generates a general-protection exception. Figure 11-1 shows the format of the debug registers.

11.2.1 Debug Address Registers (DR0-DR3)

Each of these registers holds the linear address for one of the four breakpoints. If paging is enabled, these addresses are translated to physical addresses by the paging algorithm. Each breakpoint condition is specified further by the contents of the DR7 register.

11.2.2 Debug Control Register (DR7)

The debug control register shown in Figure 11-1 specifies the sort of memory access associated with each breakpoint. Each address in registers DR0 to DR3 corresponds to a field R/W0 to R/W3 in the DR7 register. The processor interprets these bits as follows:

00 – Break on instruction execution only
01 – Break on data writes only
10 – *undefined*
11 – Break on data reads or writes but not instruction fetches

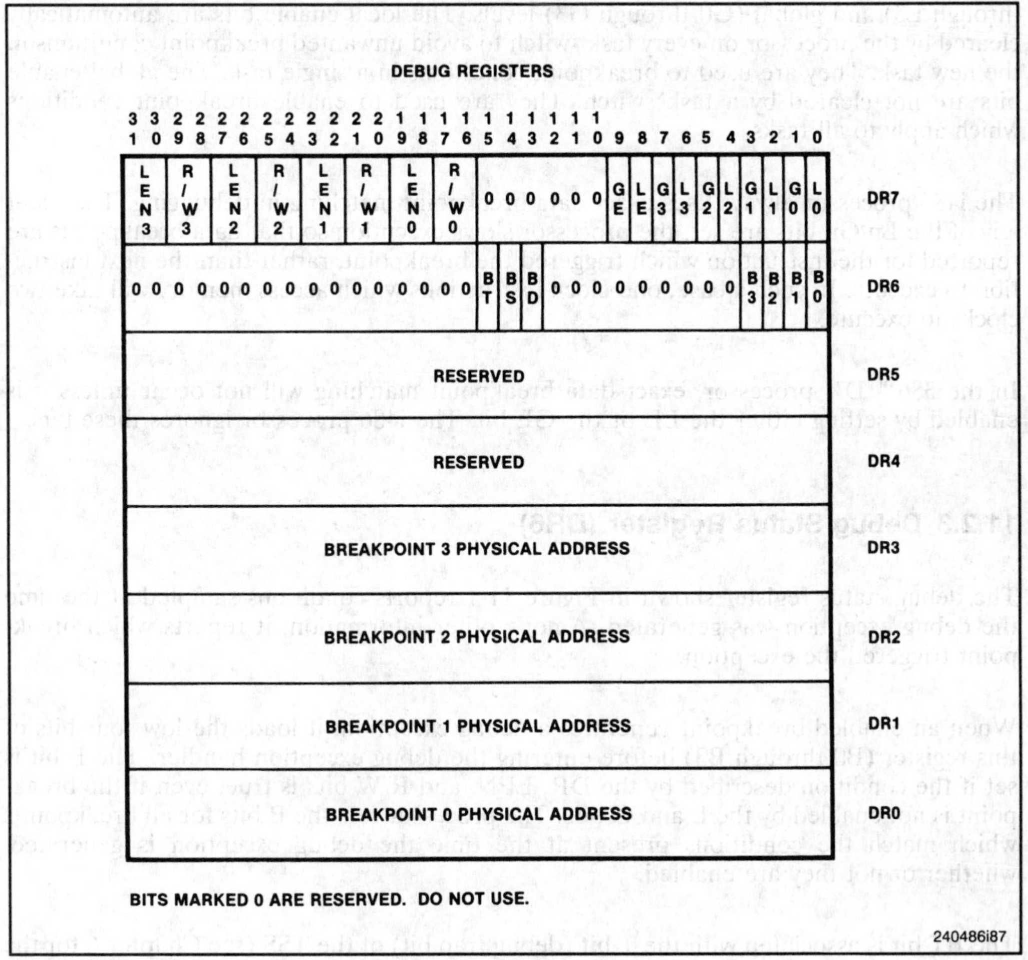

Figure 11-1. Debug Registers

The LEN0 to LEN3 fields in the DR7 register specify the size of the breakpointed location in memory. A size of 1, 2, or 4 bytes may be specified. The length fields are interpreted as follows:

00 – one-byte length
01 – two-byte length
10 – *undefined*
11 – four-byte length

If RW*n* is 00 (instruction execution), then LEN*n* should also be 00. The effect of using any other length is undefined.

The low eight bits of the DR7 register (fields L0 to L3 and G0 to G3) individually enable the four address breakpoint conditions. There are two levels of enabling: the local (L0 through L3) and global (G0 through G3) levels. The local enable bits are automatically cleared by the processor on every task switch to avoid unwanted breakpoint conditions in the new task. They are used to breakpoint conditions in a single task. The global enable bits are not cleared by a task switch. They are used to enable breakpoint conditions which apply to all tasks.

The i486 processor always uses exact data breakpoint matching in debugging. That is, if any of the Ln/Gn bits are set, the processor slows execution so that data breakpoints are reported for the instruction which triggered the breakpoint, rather than the next instruction to execute. In such a case, one-clock instructions which access memory will take two clocks to execute.

In the 386™ DX processor, exact data breakpoint matching will not occur unless it is enabled by setting either the LE or the GE bit. The i486 processor ignores these bits.

11.2.3 Debug Status Register (DR6)

The debug status register shown in Figure 11-1 reports conditions sampled at the time the debug exception was generated. Among other information, it reports which breakpoint triggered the exception.

When an enabled breakpoint generates a debug exception, it loads the low four bits of this register (B0 through B3) before entering the debug exception handler. The B bit is set if the condition described by the DR, LEN, and R/W bits is true, even if the breakpoint is not enabled by the L and G bits. The processor sets the B bits for all breakpoints which match the conditions present at the time the debug exception is generated, whether or not they are enabled.

The BT bit is associated with the T bit (debug trap bit) of the TSS (see Chapter 6 for the format of a TSS). The processor sets the BT bit before entering the debug handler if a task switch has occurred to a task with a set T bit in its TSS. There is no bit in the DR7 register to enable or disable this exception; the T bit of the TSS is the only enabling bit.

The BS bit is associated with the TF flag. The BS bit is set if the debug exception was triggered by the single-step execution mode (TF flag set). The single-step mode is the highest-priority debug exception; when the BS bit is set, any of the other debug status bits also may be set.

The BD bit is set if the next instruction will read or write one of the eight debug registers while they are being used by in-circuit emulation.

Note that the contents of the DR6 register are never cleared by the processor. To avoid any confusion in identifying debug exceptions, the debug handler should clear the register before returning.

11.2.4 Breakpoint Field Recognition

The address and LEN bits for each of the four breakpoint conditions define a range of sequential byte addresses for a data breakpoint. The LEN bits permit specification of a one-, two-, or four-byte range. Two-byte ranges must be aligned on word boundaries (addresses which are multiples of two) and four-byte ranges must be aligned on doubleword boundaries (addresses which are multiples of four). These requirements are enforced by the processor; it uses the LEN bits to mask the lower address bits in the debug registers. Unaligned code or data breakpoint addresses do not yield the expected results.

A data breakpoint for reading or writing is triggered if any of the bytes participating in a memory access is within the range defined by a breakpoint address register and its LEN bits. Table 11-1 gives some examples of combinations of addresses and fields with memory references which do and do not cause traps.

A data breakpoint for an unaligned operand can be made from two sets of entries in the breakpoint registers where each entry is byte-aligned, and the two entries together cover the operand. This breakpoint generates exceptions only for the operand, not for any neighboring bytes.

Instruction breakpoint addresses must have a length specification of one byte (LEN = 00); the behavior of code breakpoints for other operand sizes is undefined. The processor recognizes an instruction breakpoint address only when it points to the first byte of an instruction. If the instruction has any prefixes, the breakpoint address must point to the first prefix.

Table 11-1. Breakpointing Examples

Comment		Address (hex)	Length (in bytes)
Register Contents	**DR0**	**A0001**	**1 (LEN0 = 00)**
Register Contents	**DR1**	**A0002**	**1 (LEN0 = 00)**
Register Contents	**DR2**	**B0002**	**2 (LEN0 = 01)**
Register Contents	**DR3**	**C0000**	**4 (LEN0 = 11)**
Memory Operations Which Trap		A0001	1
		A0002	1
		A0001	2
		A0002	2
		B0002	2
		B0001	4
		C0000	4
		C0001	2
		C0003	1
Memory Operations Which Don't Trap		A0000	1
		A0003	4
		B0000	2
		C0004	4

11.3 DEBUG EXCEPTIONS

Two of the interrupt vectors of the i486 processor are reserved for debug exceptions. The debug exception is the usual way to invoke debuggers designed for the i486 processor; the breakpoint exception is intended for putting breakpoints in debuggers.

11.3.1 Interrupt 1 – Debug Exceptions

The handler for this exception usually is a debugger or part of a debugging system. The processor generates a debug exception for any of several conditions. The debugger can check flags in the DR6 and DR7 registers to determine which condition caused the exception and which other conditions also might apply. Table 11-2 shows the states of these bits for each kind of breakpoint condition.

Instruction breakpoints are faults; other debug exceptions are traps. The debug exception may report either or both at one time. The following sections present details for each class of debug exception.

11.3.1.1 INSTRUCTION-BREAKPOINT FAULT

The processor reports an instruction breakpoint before it executes the breakpointed instruction (i.e., a debug exception caused by an instruction breakpoint is a fault).

The RF flag permits the debug exception handler to restart instructions which cause faults other than debug faults. When one of these faults occurs, the system software writer must set the RF bit in the copy of the EFLAGS register which is pushed on the stack in the debug exception handler routine. This bit is set in preparation of resuming the program's execution at the breakpoint address without generating another breakpoint fault on the same instruction. (Note: The RF bit does not cause breakpoint traps to be ignored, nor other kinds of faults.)

Table 11-2. Debug Exception Conditions

Flags Tested	Description
BS = 1	Single-step trap
B0 = 1 and (GE0 = 1 or LE0 = 1)	Breakpoint defined by DR0, LEN0, and R/W0
B1 = 1 and (GE1 = 1 or LE1 = 1)	Breakpoint defined by DR1, LEN1, and R/W1
B2 = 1 and (GE2 = 1 or LE2 = 1)	Breakpoint defined by DR2, LEN2, and R/W2
B3 = 1 and (GE3 = 1 or LE3 = 1)	Breakpoint defined by DR3, LEN3, and R/W3
BD = 1	Debug registers in use for in-circuit emulation
BT = 1	Task switch

The processor clears the RF flag at the successful completion of every instruction except after the IRET instruction, the POPF instruction, and JMP, CALL, or INT instructions which cause a task switch. These instructions set the RF flag to the value specified by the the saved copy of the EFLAGS register.

The processor sets the RF flag in the copy of the EFLAGS register pushed on the stack before entry into any fault handler. When the fault handler is entered for instruction breakpoints, for example, the RF flag is set in the copy of the EFLAGS register pushed on the stack; therefore, the IRET instruction which returns control from the exception handler will set the RF flag in the EFLAGS register, and execution will resume at the breakpointed instruction without generating another breakpoint for the same instruction.

If, after a debug fault, the RF flag is set and the debug handler retries the faulting instruction, it is possible that retrying the instruction will generate other faults. The restart of the instruction after these faults also occurs with the RF flag set, so repeated debug faults continue to be suppressed. The processor clears the RF flag only after *successful* completion of the instruction.

11.3.1.2 DATA-BREAKPOINT TRAP

A data-breakpoint exception is a trap; i.e., the processor generates an exception for a data breakpoint after executing the instruction which accesses the breakpointed memory location.

When using data breakpoints, it is recommended either the LE or GE bits of the DR7 register also be set. If either the LE or GE bits are set, any data breakpoint trap is reported immediately after completion of the instruction which accessed the breakpointed memory location. This immediate reporting is done by forcing the i486 processor execution unit to wait for completion of data operand transfers before beginning execution of the next instruction. If neither bit is set, data breakpoints may not be generated until one instruction after the data is accessed, or they may not be generated at all. This is because instruction execution normally is overlapped with memory transfers. Execution of the next instruction may begin before the memory operations of the previous instruction are completed.

If a debugger needs to save the contents of a write breakpoint location, it should save the original contents before setting the breakpoint. Because data breakpoints are traps, the original data is overwritten before the trap exception is generated. The handler can report the saved value after the breakpoint is triggered. The data in the debug registers can be used to address the new value stored by the instruction which triggered the breakpoint.

11.3.1.3 GENERAL-DETECT FAULT

The general-detect fault occurs when an attempt is made to use the debug registers at the same time they are being used by in-circuit emulation. This additional protection feature is provided to guarantee emulators can have full control over the debug registers when required. The exception handler can detect this condition by checking the state of the BD bit of the DR6 register.

11.3.1.4 SINGLE-STEP TRAP

This trap occurs after an instruction is executed if the TF flag was set before the instruction was executed. Note the exception does not occur after an instruction which sets the TF flag. For example, if the POPF instruction is used to set the TF flag, a single-step trap does not occur until after the instruction following the POPF instruction.

The processor clears the TF flag before calling the exception handler. If the TF flag was set in a TSS at the time of a task switch, the exception occurs after the first instruction is executed in the new task.

The single-step flag normally is not cleared by privilege changes inside a task. The INT instructions, however, do clear the TF flag. Therefore, software debuggers which single-step code must recognize and emulate INT *n* or INTO instructions rather than executing them directly.

To maintain protection, the operating system should check the current execution privilege level after any single-step trap to see if single stepping should continue at the current privilege level.

The interrupt priorities guarantee that if an external interrupt occurs, single stepping stops. When both an external interrupt and a single step interrupt occur together, the single step interrupt is processed first. This clears the TF flag. After saving the return address or switching tasks, the external interrupt input is examined before the first instruction of the single step handler executes. If the external interrupt is still pending, then it is serviced. The external interrupt handler does not run in single-step mode. To single step an interrupt handler, single step an INTn instruction which calls the interrupt handler.

11.3.1.5 TASK-SWITCH TRAP

The debug exception also occurs after a task switch if the T bit of the new task's TSS is set. The exception occurs after control has passed to the new task, but before the first instruction of that task is executed. The exception handler can detect this condition by examining the BT bit of the DR6 register.

Note that if the debug exception handler is a task, the T bit of its TSS should not be set. Failure to observe this rule will put the processor in a loop.

11.3.2 Interrupt 3 — Breakpoint Instruction

The breakpoint trap is caused by execution of the INT 3 instruction. Typically, a debugger prepares a breakpoint by replacing the first opcode byte of an instruction with the opcode for the breakpoint instruction. When execution of the INT 3 instruction calls the exception handler, the return address points to the first byte of the instruction following the INT 3 instruction.

With older processors, this feature is used extensively for setting instruction breakpoints. With the i486 processor, this use is more easily handled using the debug registers. However, the breakpoint exception still is useful for breakpointing debuggers, because the breakpoint exception can call an exception handler other than itself. The breakpoint exception also can be useful when it is necessary to set a greater number of breakpoints than permitted by the debug registers, or when breakpoints are being placed in the source code of a program under development.

Caching 12

CHAPTER 12
CACHING

The i486™ processor has an on-chip internal cache for storing 8K bytes of instructions and data. The cache raises system performance by satisfying an internal read request more quickly than a bus cycle to memory. This also reduces the processor's use of the external bus. The internal cache is transparent to program operation.

The i486 processor can use an external second-level cache outside of the processor chip. An external cache normally improves performance and reduces bus bandwidth required by the i486 processor.

Caches require special consideration in multiprocessor systems. When one processor accesses data cached in another processor, it must not receive incorrect data. If it modifies data, all other processors which access that data must receive the modified data. This property is called *cache consistency*. The i486 processor provides mechanisms which maintain cache consistency in the presence of multiple processors and external caches.

The operation of internal and external caches is transparent to application software, but knowledge of the behavior of these caches may be useful in optimizing software performance. In multiprocessor systems, maintenance of cache consistency may require intervention by system software.

The cache is available in all execution modes: real mode, protected mode, and virtual-8086 mode. For properly designed single-processor systems, the cache can be initially enabled and not require further control.

12.1 INTRODUCTION TO CACHING

Caches are often implemented as associative memories. An associative memory has extra storage for each unit of memory, called a *tag*. When an address is applied to an associative memory, each tag simultaneously compares itself against the address. If a tag matches the address, access is provided to the unit of memory associated with the tag. This is called a *cache hit*. If no match occurs, the cache signals a *cache miss*. A cache miss requires a bus cycle to access main memory.

To gain efficiency in the implementation of the internal cache, storage is allocated in chunks of 128-bits, called *cache lines*. External caches are not likely to use cache lines smaller than those of the internal cache.

The cache of the i486 processor does not support partially-filled cache lines, so caching a single doubleword requires caching four doublewords. This would be an inefficient use of the cache if it were not for the fact that the processor rarely makes access to random locations in memory. Over any small span of time, the processor usually accesses a small number of areas in memory, such as the code segment or the stack, and it usually accesses many neighboring addresses in these areas.

To simplify the hardware implementation, cache lines can only be mapped to aligned 128-bit blocks of main memory. (An aligned 128-bit block begins at an address which is clear in its low four bits.) When a new cache line is allocated, the processor loads a block from main memory into the cache line. This operation is called a *cache line fill*. Allocated cache lines are said to be *valid*. Unallocated cache lines are *invalid*.

Caching can be *write-through* or *write-back*. On reads, both forms of caching operate as described above. On writes, write-through caching updates both cache memory and main memory; write-back caching updates only the cache memory. Write-back caching updates main memory when a write-back operation is performed. Write-back operations are triggered when cache lines need to be de-allocated, such as when new cache lines are being allocated in a cache which is already full. Write-back operations also are triggered by the mechanisms used to maintain cache consistency.

The internal cache of the i486 processor is a write-through cache. It can be used with external caches which are write-through, write-back, or a mixture of both.

12.2 OPERATION OF THE INTERNAL CACHE

Software controls the operating mode of the cache. Caching can be enabled (its state following reset initialization), caching can be disabled while valid cache lines exist (a mode in which the cache acts like a fast, internal RAM), or caching can be fully disabled.

Precautions must be followed when disabling the cache. Whenever CD is set to 1, the i486 processor will not read external memory if a copy is still in the cache. Whenever NW is set to 1, the i486 processor will not write to external memory if the data is in the cache. This means stale data can develop in the i486 CPU cache. This stale data will not be written to external memory if NW is later set to 0 or that cache line is later overwritten as a result of a cache miss. In general, the cache should be flushed when disabled.

It is possible to freeze data in the cache by loading it using test registers while CD and NW are set. This is useful to provide guaranteed cache hits for time critical interrupt code and data.

Note that all segments should start on 16 byte boundaries to allow programs to align code/data in cache lines.

12.2.1 Cache Disabling Bits

Table 12-1 summarizes the modes enabled by the CD and NW bits.

Table 2-1. Cache Operating Modes

CD	NW	Description
1	1	Caching is disabled, but valid cache lines continue to respond. To completely disable the cache, enter this mode and perform a cache flush. To use the cache as a fast internal RAM, preload the cache with valid cache lines by careful choice of memory operations or by using the test registers. In this mode, writes to valid cache lines update the cache, but do not update main memory.
1	0	No new cache lines are allocated, but valid cache lines continue to respond.
0	1	Invalid setting. A general-protection exception with an error code of zero is generated.
0	0	Caching is enabled.

12.2.2 Cache Management Instructions

The INVD and WBINVD instructions are used to invalidate the contents of the internal and external caches. The INVD instruction flushes the internal cache and generates a special bus cycle which indicates that external caches also should be flushed. (The response of hardware to receiving a cache flush bus cycle is implementation dependent; hardware might use some other mechanism for maintaining cache consistency.)

There is only one difference between the WBINVD and INVD instructions. The WBINVD instruction generates a special bus cycle which indicates external, write-back caches should write-back modified data to main memory. This cycle is produced immediately before the cycle to flush the cache.

12.2.3 Self-modifying Code

A write to an instruction in the cache will modify it in both cache and memory, but if the instruction was prefetched before the write, the old version of the instruction could be the one executed. To prevent this, flush the instruction prefetch unit by coding a jump instruction immediately after any write that modifies an instruction.

12.3 PAGE-LEVEL CACHE MANAGEMENT

The i486 processor defines two bits in entries in the page directory and second-level page tables which are reserved on 386 processors. These bits are used to drive processor output pins. These bits are used to manage the caching of pages.

12.3.1 Cache Management Bits

The PCD and PWT bits control caching on a page-by-page basis. The PCD bit (page-level cache disable) affects the operation of the internal cache. Both the PCD bit and the PWT bit (page-level write-through) drive processor output pins for controlling external caches. The treatment of these signals by external hardware is implementation-dependent; for example, some hardware systems may control the caching of pages by decoding some of the high address bits.

There are three potential sources of the bits used to drive the PCD and PWT outputs of the processor: the CR3 register, the page directory, and the second-level page tables. The processor outputs are driven by the CR3 register for bus cycles where paging is not used to generate the address, such as the loading of an entry in the page directory. The outputs are driven by a page directory entry when an entry from a second-level page table is accessed. The outputs are driven by a second-level page table entry when instructions or data in memory are accessed.

12.3.1.1 PCD BIT

When a page table entry has a set PCD bit (bit position 4), caching of the page is disabled, even if hardware is requesting caching by asserting the KEN# input. When the PCD bit is clear, caching may be requested by hardware on a cycle-by-cycle basis.

Disabling caching is necessary for pages which contain memory-mapped I/O ports. It also is useful for pages which do not provide a performance benefit when cached, such as initialization software.

Regardless of the page-table entries, the i486 processor will force the PCD output HIGH whenever the CD (Cache Disable) bit in CR0 is set.

12.3.1.2 PWT BIT

When a page table entry has a set PWT bit (bit position 3), a write-through caching policy is specified for data in the corresponding page. Clearing the PWT bit allows the possibility of using a write-back policy for the page. Since the internal cache of the i486 processor is a write-through cache, it is not affected by the state of the PWT bit. External caches however may use write-back caching, and so can use the output signal driven by the PWT bit to control caching policy on a page-by-page basis.

In multiprocessor systems, enabling write-through may be advantageous for shared memory, particularly for memory locations written infrequently by one processor, but read often by many processors.

Multiprocessing 13

CHAPTER 13
MULTIPROCESSING

The i486™ processor supports multiprocessing on the system bus. Processors on the system bus can have different bus widths.

Multiprocessors can increase particular aspects of system performance. For example, a computer graphics system may use an i860™ CPU for fast rendering of raster images, while an i486 processor is used to support a standard operating system, such as UNIX or OS/2. Multiprocessing systems are sensitive to two design issues:

- *Maintaining cache consistency*—When one processor accesses data cached in another processor, it must not receive incorrect data. If it modifies data, all other processors which access that data must receive the modified data.
- *Reliable communication*—Processors need to be able to communicate with each other in a way which eliminates interference when more than one processor simultaneously accesses the same area in memory.

Cache consistency was discussed earlier, in Chapter 12. Reliable communication is discussed in the following section, which describes the mechanism used to "lock" the bus.

13.1 LOCKED AND PSEUDO-LOCKED BUS CYCLES

While the system architecture of multiprocessor systems varies greatly, they generally have a need for reliable communication with memory. A processor in the act of updating the Accessed bit of a segment descriptor, for example, should reject other attempts to update the descriptor until the operation is complete.

It also is necessary to have reliable communication with other processors. Bus masters need to exchange data in a reliable way. For example, a bit in memory may be shared by several bus masters for use as a signal that some resource, such as a peripheral device, is idle. A bus master may test this bit, see that the resource is free, and change the state of the bit. The state would indicate to other potential bus masters that the resource is in use. A problem could arise if another bus master reads the bit between the time the first bus master reads the bit and the time the state of the bit is changed. This condition would indicate to both potential bus masters that the resource is free. They may interfere with each other as they both attempt to use the resource. The processor prevents this problem through support of locked bus cycles; requests for control of the bus are ignored during locked cycles.

The i486 processor protects the integrity of certain critical memory operations by asserting an output signal called LOCK#. Reads and writes of aligned 64-bit operands and (128-bit) instruction prefetches are protected by an output called PLOCK#. It is the responsibility of the hardware designer to use these signals to control memory access among processors.

The processor automatically asserts one of these signals during certain critical memory operations. Software can specify which other memory operations need to have LOCK# asserted.

The features of the general-purpose multiprocessing interface include:

- The LOCK# signal, which appears on a pin of the processor.
- The PLOCK# signal, which appears on a pin of the processor.
- The LOCK instruction prefix, which allows software to assert LOCK#.
- Automatic assertion of LOCK# for some kinds of memory operations.
- Automatic assertion of PLOCK# for some other kinds of memory operations.

13.1.1 LOCK Prefix and the LOCK# Signal

The LOCK prefix and its bus signal only should be used to prevent other bus masters from interrupting a data movement operation. The LOCK prefix can be used with the following i486 CPU instructions when they modify memory. An invalid-opcode exception results from using the LOCK prefix before any other instruction, or with these instructions when no write operation is made to memory (i.e., when the destination operand is in a register).

- Bit test and change: the BTS, BTR, and BTC instructions.
- Exchange: the XCHG, XADD, and CMPXCHG instructions (no LOCK prefix is needed for the XCHG instruction).
- One-operand arithmetic and logical: the INC, DEC, NOT, NEG instructions.
- Two-operand arithmetic and logical: the ADD, ADC, SUB, SBB, AND, OR, and XOR instructions.

A locked instruction is *guaranteed* to lock only the area of memory defined by the destination operand, but may lock a larger memory area. For example, typical 8086 and 80286 configurations lock the entire physical memory space.

Semaphores (shared memory used for signalling between multiple processors) should be accessed using identical address and length. For example, if one processor accesses a semaphore using word access, other processors should not access the semaphore using byte access.

The integrity of the lock is not affected by the alignment of the memory field. The LOCK# signal is asserted for as many bus cycles as necessary to update the entire operand.

13.1.2 Automatic Locking

There are some critical memory operations for which the processor automatically asserts the LOCK# signal. These operations are:

- Acknowledging interrupts.

  After an interrupt request, the interrupt controller uses the data bus to send the interrupt vector of the source of the interrupt to the processor. The processor asserts LOCK# to ensure no other data appears on the data bus during this time.

- Setting the Busy bit of a TSS descriptor.

  The processor tests and sets the Busy bit in the Type field of the TSS descriptor when switching to a task. To ensure two different processors do not switch to the same task simultaneously, the processor asserts the LOCK# signal while testing and setting this bit.

- Updating segment descriptors.

  When loading a segment descriptor, the processor will set the Accessed bit if the bit is clear. During this operation, the processor asserts LOCK# so the descriptor will not be modified by another processor while it is being updated. For this action to be effective, operating-system procedures which update descriptors should use the following steps:

  - Use a locked operation when updating the access-rights byte to mark the descriptor not-present, and specify a value for the Type field which indicates the descriptor is being updated.
  - Update the fields of the descriptor. (This may require several memory accesses; therefore, LOCK cannot be used.)
  - Use a locked operation when updating the access-rights byte to mark the descriptor as valid and present.

  Note that the 386 DX processor always updates the Accessed bit, whether it is clear or not. The i486 processor only updates the Accessed bit if it is not already set.

- Updating page-directory and page-table entries.

  When updating page-directory and page-table entries, the processor uses locked cycles to set the Accessed and Dirty bits.

- Executing an XCHG instruction.

  The i486 processor always asserts LOCK# during an XCHG instruction which references memory (even if the LOCK prefix is not used).

13.1.3 Pseudo-Locking

The PLOCK# pin indicates that the current bus cycle and the following one should be treated as an atomic transfer. By implementing the pseudo-lock mechanism, system hardware can guarantee atomic reads and writes of 64-bit operands. The operand must be aligned to a doubleword boundary, so that the read or write requires no more than two bus cycles to be completed.

The pseudo-lock mechanism can also be used to protect instruction prefetches and other transfers of more than 32 bits. For a detailed discussion of the PLOCK# signal, its timing and its various uses, see the *i486™ Processor Hardware Reference Manual*.

Part III
Numeric Processing

14

Introduction to Numeric Applications

CHAPTER 14
INTRODUCTION TO NUMERIC APPLICATIONS

The i486™ processor contains a high-performance numerics processing element that provides significant numeric capabilities and direct support for floating-point, extended-integer, and BCD data types. The i486 Floating Point Unit (FPU) easily supports powerful and accurate numeric applications through its implementation, with radix 2, of the IEEE Standard 854 for Floating-Point Arithmetic. The i486 processor provides floating-point performance comparable to that of large minicomputers while offering compatibility with object code for 8087, 80287, 387™ DX and 387 SX math coprocessors.

14.1 HISTORY

The i486 FPU is compatible with its predecessors, the earlier Intel® 8087, 80287 and 387 DX. Programs designed to use the 8087, 80287 or 387 math coprocessor should run unchanged on the i486 processor.

The 8087 NPX was designed for use in 8086-family systems. The 8086 was the first microprocessor family to partition the processing unit to permit high-performance numeric capabilities. The 8087 NPX for this processor family implemented a complete numeric processing environment in compliance with an early proposal for IEEE Standard 754 for Binary Floating-Point Arithmetic.

With the 80287 Numeric Processor Extension, high-speed numeric computations were extended to 80286 high-performance multitasking and multiuser systems. Multiple tasks using the numeric processor extension were afforded the full protection of the 80286 memory management and protection features.

The 387 DX and SX math coprocessors are Intel's third generation numerics processors. They implement the final IEEE Std 754, adds new trigonometric instructions, and uses a new design and CHMOS-III process to allow higher clock rates and require fewer clocks per instruction. Together, the 387 math coprocessor with additional instructions and the improved standard brought even more convenience and reliability to numerics programming and made this convenience and reliability available to applications that need the high-speed and large memory capacity of the 32-bit environment of the 386™ microprocessor.

The FPU of the i486 processor is an on-chip equivalent of the 387 DX conforming to both IEEE Std 754 and the more recent, generalized IEEE Std 854. Having the FPU on chip results in a considerable performance improvement in numerics-intensive computation. Figure 14-1 illustrates the relative performance of 5-MHz 8086 CPU/8087 NPX, 8-MHz 80286 CPU/80287 NPX, 20-MHz 386 DX CPU/387 DX systems, and a 33-MHz i486 processor, in executing numerics-oriented applications.

14.2 PERFORMANCE

Table 14-1 compares the execution times of several i486 CPU numeric instructions with the equivalent operations executed on a 16-MHz 387 DX math coprocessor. As

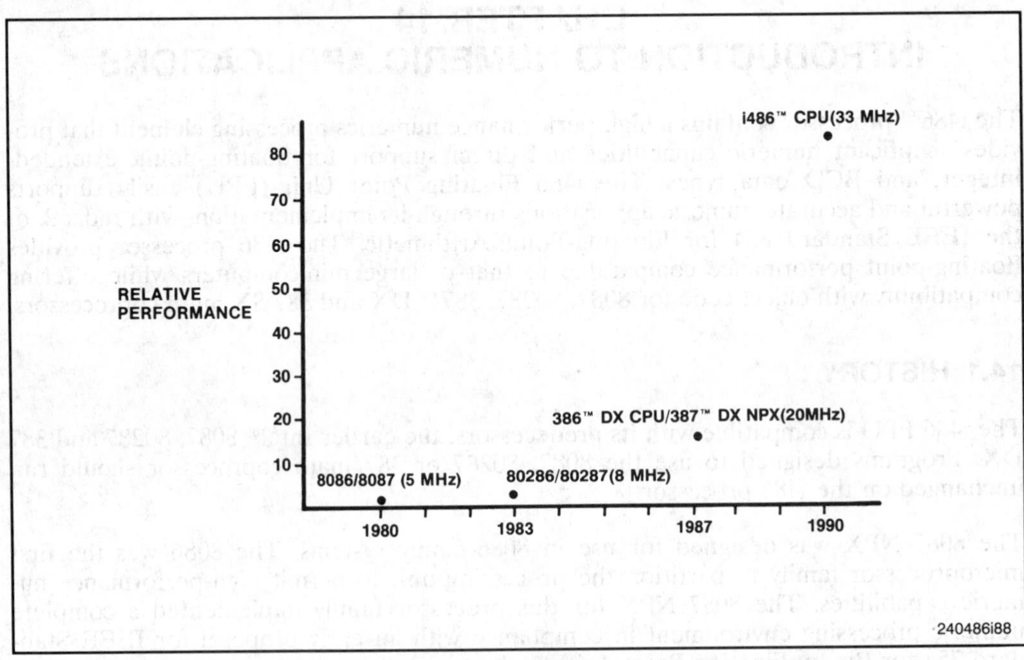

Figure 14-1. Evolution and Performance of Numeric Processors

Table 14-1. Numeric Processing Speed Comparisons

Floating-Point Instruction			Approximate Performance Ratio: 33 MHz i486™ ÷ 16 MHz 386™ DX/387™ DX
FADD	ST, ST(i)	Addition	4.2
FDIV	dword_var	Division	2.0
FYL2X	stack(0),(1) assumed	Logarithm	2.5
FPATAN	stack(0) assumed	Arctangent	2.2
F2XMI	stack(0) assumed	Exponentiation	2.2
FLD	ST(0), ST(i)	Data Transfer	5.5

indicated in the table, the 33-MHz i486 floating-point processor provides about 5 times the performance of a 16-MHz 387 DX math coprocessor. A 33-MHz i486 processor multiplies 32-bit and 64-bit floating-point numbers in about .33 and .42 microseconds, respectively. Of course, the actual performance of the processor in a given system depends on the characteristics of the individual application.

The i486 Integer Unit (IU) and FPU coordinate their activities in a manner transparent to software. Moreover, built-in coordination facilities allow the IU to proceed with other instructions while the FPU is simultaneously executing numeric instructions. Programs can exploit this concurrency of execution to further increase system performance and throughput.

14.3 EASE OF USE

The i486 FPU provides more than raw execution speed for computation-intensive tasks; it brings the functionality and power of accurate numeric computation into the hands of the general user. These features are available in most high-level languages available for the i486 processor.

Like the 8087, 80287 and 387 DX that preceded it, the i486 FPU is explicitly designed to deliver stable, accurate results when programmed using straightforward "pencil and paper" algorithms. IEEE Std 754 specifically addresses this issue, recognizing the fundamental importance of making numeric computations both easy and safe to use.

For example, most computers can overflow when two single-precision floating-point numbers are multiplied together and then divided by a third, even if the final result is a perfectly valid 32-bit number. The i486 FPU delivers the correctly rounded result. Other typical examples of undesirable machine behavior in straightforward calculations occur when computing financial rate of return, which involves the expression $(1 + i)^n$ or when solving for roots of a quadratic equation:

$$\frac{-b \pm \sqrt{b^2 - 4ac}}{2a}$$

If a does not equal 0, the formula is numerically unstable when the roots are nearly coincident or when their magnitudes are wildly different. The formula is also vulnerable to spurious over/underflows when the coefficients a, b, and c are all very big or all very tiny. When single-precision (4-byte) floating-point coefficients are given as data and the formula is evaluated in the i486 FPU's normal way, keeping all intermediate results in its stack, the FPU produces impeccable single-precision roots. This happens because, by default and with no effort on the programmer's part, the FPU evaluates all those subexpressions with so much extra precision and range as to overwhelm any threat to numerical integrity.

If double-precision data and results were at issue, a better formula would have to be used, and once again the i486 FPU's default evaluation of that formula would provide substantially enhanced numerical integrity over mere double-precision evaluation.

On most machines, straightforward algorithms will not deliver consistently correct results (and will not indicate when they are incorrect). To obtain correct results on traditional machines under all conditions usually requires sophisticated numerical techniques that are foreign to most programmers. General application programmers using straightforward algorithms will produce much more reliable programs using the i486 processor. This simple fact greatly reduces the software investment required to develop safe, accurate computation-based products.

Beyond traditional numerics support for scientific applications, the i486 processor has built-in facilities for commercial computing. It can process decimal numbers of up to 18 digits without round-off errors, performing *exact arithmetic* on integers as large as 2^{64} or 10^{18}. Exact arithmetic is vital in accounting applications where rounding errors may introduce monetary losses that cannot be reconciled.

The i486 processor contains a number of optional numerical facilities that can be invoked by sophisticated users. These advanced features include directed rounding, gradual underflow, and programmed exception-handling facilities.

These automatic exception-handling facilities permit a high degree of flexibility in numeric processing software, without burdening the programmer. While performing numeric calculations, the i486 processor automatically detects exception conditions that can potentially damage a calculation (for example, $X \div 0$ or $\sqrt{X}$ when $X < 0$). By default, on-chip exception logic handles these exceptions so that a reasonable result is produced and execution may proceed without program interruption. Alternatively, the processor can invoke a software exception handler to provide special results whenever various types of exceptions are detected.

14.4 APPLICATIONS

The i486 processor's versatility and performance make it appropriate to a broad array of numeric applications. In general, applications that exhibit any of the following characteristics can benefit by implementing numeric processing on the i486 processor:

- Numeric data vary over a wide range of values, or include nonintegral values.
- Algorithms produce very large or very small intermediate results.
- Computations must be very precise; i.e., a large number of significant digits must be maintained.
- Performance requirements exceed the capacity of traditional microprocessors.
- Consistently safe, reliable results must be delivered using a programming staff that is not expert in numerical techniques.

Note also that the i486 processor can reduce software development costs and improve the performance of systems that use not only real numbers, but operate on multiprecision binary or decimal integer values as well.

A few examples, which show how the i486 processor might be used in specific numerics applications, are described below. In many cases, these types of systems have been implemented in the past with minicomputers or small mainframe computers.

- Business data processing—The i486 FPU's ability to accept decimal operands and produce *exact* decimal results of up to 18 digits greatly simplifies accounting programming. Financial calculations that use power functions can take advantage of the i486 processor's exponentiation and logarithmic instructions. Many business software packages can benefit from the speed and accuracy of the i486 FPU.

- Simulation – The large (32-bit) memory space and raw speed of the i486 processor make it suitable for attacking large simulation problems, which heretofore could only be executed on expensive mini and mainframe computers. For example, complex electronic circuit simulations using SPICE can be performed on an i486 processor. Simulation of mechanical systems using finite element analysis can employ more elements, resulting in more detailed analysis or simulation of larger systems.
- Graphics transformations – The i486 processor can be used in graphics applications, with the FPU performing many functions concurrently with the operation of the IU; these functions include rotation, scaling, and interpolation. By also using an 82786 Graphics Display Controller to perform high-speed drawing and window management, very powerful and highly self-sufficient terminals can be built from a small number of parts.
- Process control – The i486 FPU solves dynamic range problems automatically, and its extended precision allows control functions to be fine-tuned for more accurate and efficient performance. Using the i486 processor to implement control algorithms also contributes to improved reliability and safety, while the processor's speed can be exploited in real-time operations.
- Computer numerical control (CNC) – The i486 processor can move and position machine tool heads with accuracy in real-time. Axis positioning also benefits from the hardware trigonometric support provided by the FPU.
- Robotics – Coupling small size and modest power requirements with powerful computational abilities, the i486 processor is ideal for on-board six-axis positioning.
- Navigation – Very small, lightweight, and accurate inertial guidance systems can be implemented with the i486 processor. Its built-in trigonometric functions can speed and simplify the calculation of position from bearing data.
- Data acquisition – The i486 processor can be used to scan, scale, and reduce large quantities of data as it is collected, thereby lowering storage requirements and time required to process the data for analysis.

The preceding examples are oriented toward *traditional* numerics applications. There are, in addition, many other types of systems that do not appear to the end user as *computational*, but can employ the i486 processor's numerical capabilities to advantage. The imaginative system designer has an opportunity similar to that created by the introduction of the microprocessor itself. Many applications can be viewed as numerically-based if sufficient computational power is available to support this view (e.g., character generation for a laser printer). This is analogous to the thousands of successful products that have been built around "buried" microprocessors, even though the products themselves bear little resemblance to computers.

14.5 PROGRAMMING INTERFACE

The i486 processor has a class of instructions known as ESCAPE instructions, all having a common format. These ESC instructions are numeric instructions for the FPU. These numeric instructions are part of a single integrated instruction set.

Numeric processing in the i486 processor centers around the floating-point register stack. Programmers can treat these eight 80-bit registers either as a fixed register set, with instructions operating on explicitly-designated registers, or as a classical stack, with instructions operating on the top one or two stack elements.

Internally, the i486 FPU holds all numbers in a uniform 80-bit extended format. Operands that may be represented in memory as 16-, 32-, or 64-bit integers, 32-, 64-, or 80-bit floating-point numbers, or 18-digit packed BCD numbers, are automatically converted into extended format as they are loaded into the FPU registers. Computation results are subsequently converted back into one of these destination data formats when they are stored into memory from the FPU registers.

Table 14-2 lists each of the seven numeric data types supported by the i486 FPU, showing the data format for each type. The table also shows the approximate range of normalized values that can be represented with each type. Denormal values are also supported in each of the real types, as required by IEEE Std 854. Denormals are discussed in Chapter 16.

All operands are stored in memory with the least significant digits starting at the initial (lowest) memory address. Numeric instructions access and store memory operands using only this initial address. For maximum system performance, every operand should start at a memory address divisible by the smallest power of two greater than the operand's length (in bytes).

Table 14-3 lists the numeric instructions by class. No special programming tools are necessary to use the numerical capabilities of the i486 processor, because all of the numeric instructions and data types are directly supported by the ASM386/486 Assembler, by high-level languages from Intel, and by assemblers and compilers produced by many independent software vendors. Numeric routines for the i486 processor can be written in ASM386/486 Assembler or any of the following higher-level languages from Intel:

PL/M−386/486
C−386/486
FORTRAN−386/486
ADA−386/486

Table 14-2. Numeric Data Types

Data Type	Bits	Significant Digits (Decimal)	Approximate Normalized Range (Decimal)
Word integer	16	4	$-32{,}768 \le x \le +32{,}767$
Short integer	32	9	$-2 \times 10^{9} \le x \le +2 \times 10^{9}$
Long integer	64	18	$-9 \times 10^{18} \le x \le +9 \times 10^{18}$
Packed decimal	80	18	$-99...99 \le x \le +99...99$ (18 digits)
Single real	32	7	$1.18 \times 10^{-38} < \lvert x \rvert < 3.40 \times 10^{38}$
Double real	64	15-16	$2.23 \times 10^{-308} < \lvert x \rvert < 1.79 \times 10^{308}$
Extended real*	80	19	$3.37 \times 10^{-4932} < \lvert x \rvert < 1.18 \times 10^{4932}$

*Equivalent to *double extended* format of IEEE Std 854.

Table 14-3. Principal Numeric Instructions

Class	Instruction Types
Data Transfer	Load (all data types), Store (all data types), Exchange
Arithmetic	Add, Subtract, Multiply, Divide, Subtract Reversed, Divide Reversed, Square Root, Scale, Extract, Remainder, Integer Part, Change Sign, Absolute Value
Comparison	Compare, Examine, Test
Transcendental	Tangent, Arctangent, Sine, Cosine, Sine and Cosine, $2^x - 1$, $Y \cdot Log_2(X)$, $Y \cdot Log_2(X+1)$
Constants	0, 1, π, $Log_{10}2$, Log_e2, $Log_2 10$, $Log_2 e$
Processor Control	Load Control Word, Store Control Word, Store Status Word, Load Environment, Store Environment, Save, Restore, Clear Exceptions, Initialize

In addition, all of the development tools supporting the 8086/8087, 80286/80287 and 386 DX CPU/387 DX NPX can also be used to develop numerical software for the i486 processor.

All of these high-level languages provide programmers with access to the computational power and speed of the i486 processor without requiring an understanding of its architecture. Such architectural considerations as concurrency and synchronization are handled automatically by these high-level languages. For the ASM386/486 programmer, specific rules for handling these issues are discussed in a later section of this manual.

15 Architecture of the Floating-Point Unit

CHAPTER 15
ARCHITECTURE OF THE FLOATING-POINT UNIT

To the programmer, the i486™ FPU appears as a set of additional registers, data types, and instructions. Refer to Chapter 26 for detailed explanations of the numerical instruction set. This chapter explains the numerical registers and data types of the i486 architecture.

15.1 NUMERICAL REGISTERS

The i486 numerical registers consist of

- Eight individually-addressable 80-bit numeric registers, organized as a register stack.
- Three 16-bit registers containing:

  The FPU status word.
  The FPU control word.
  The tag word.
- Error pointers, consisting of:

  Two 16-bit registers containing selectors for the last instruction and operand.
  Two 32-bit registers containing offsets for the last instruction and operand.
  One 11-bit register containing the opcode of the last non-control FPU instruction.

All of the i486 numeric instructions focus on the contents of these FPU registers.

15.1.1 The FPU Register Stack

The i486 FPU register stack is shown in Figure 15-1. Each of the eight numeric registers in the stack is 80 bits wide and is divided into fields corresponding to the i486 processor's extended real data type.

Numeric instructions address the data registers relative to the register on the top of the stack. At any point in time, this top-of-stack register is indicated by the TOP (stack TOP) field in the FPU status word. Load or push operations decrement TOP by one and load a value into the new top register. A store-and-pop operation stores the value from the current TOP register and then increments TOP by one. Like stacks in memory, the FPU register stack grows *down* toward lower-addressed registers.

Many numeric instructions have several addressing modes that permit the programmer to implicitly operate on the top of the stack, or to explicitly operate on specific registers relative to the TOP. The ASM386/486 Assembler supports these register addressing modes, using the expression ST(0), or simply ST, to represent the current Stack Top and ST(*i*) to specify the *i*th register from TOP in the stack ($0 \leq i \leq 7$). For example, if TOP contains 011B (register 3 is the top of the stack), the following statement would add the contents of two registers in the stack (registers 3 and 5):

```
FADD   ST, ST(2)
```

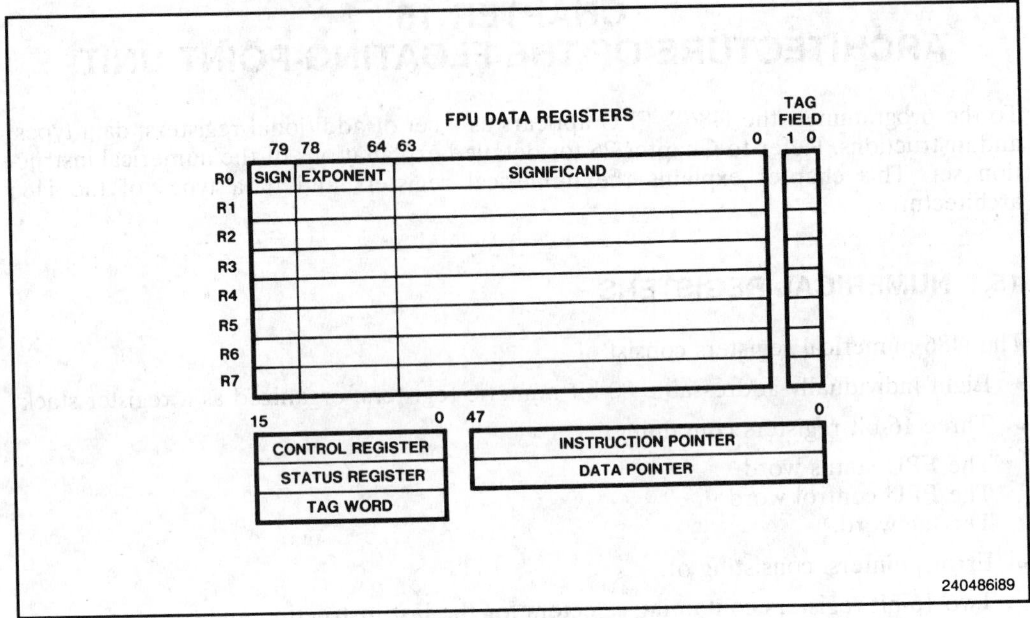

Figure 15-1. i486™ FPU Register Set

The stack organization and top-relative addressing of the numeric registers simplify subroutine programming by allowing routines to pass parameters on the register stack. By using the stack to pass parameters rather than using "dedicated" registers, calling routines gain more flexibility in how they use the stack. As long as the stack is not full, each routine simply loads the parameters onto the stack before calling a particular subroutine to perform a numeric calculation. The subroutine then addresses its parameters as ST, ST(1), etc., even though TOP may, for example, refer to physical register 3 in one invocation and physical register 5 in another.

15.1.2 The FPU Status Word

The 16-bit status word shown in Figure 15-2 reflects the overall state of the FPU. This status word may be stored into memory using the FSTSW/FNSTSW, FSTENV/FNSTENV, and FSAVE/FNSAVE instructions, and can be transferred into the AX register with the FSTSW AX/FNSTSW AX instructions, allowing the FPU status to be inspected by the Integer Unit.

The B-bit (bit 15) is included for 8087 compatibility only. It reflects the contents of the ES bit (bit 7 of the status word).

The four FPU condition code bits (C_3-C_0) are similar to the flags in a CPU: the i486 processor updates these bits to reflect the outcome of arithmetic operations. The effect of these instructions on the condition code bits is summarized in Table 15-1. These condition code bits are used principally for conditional branching. The FSTSW AX instruction stores the FPU status word directly into the AX register, allowing these

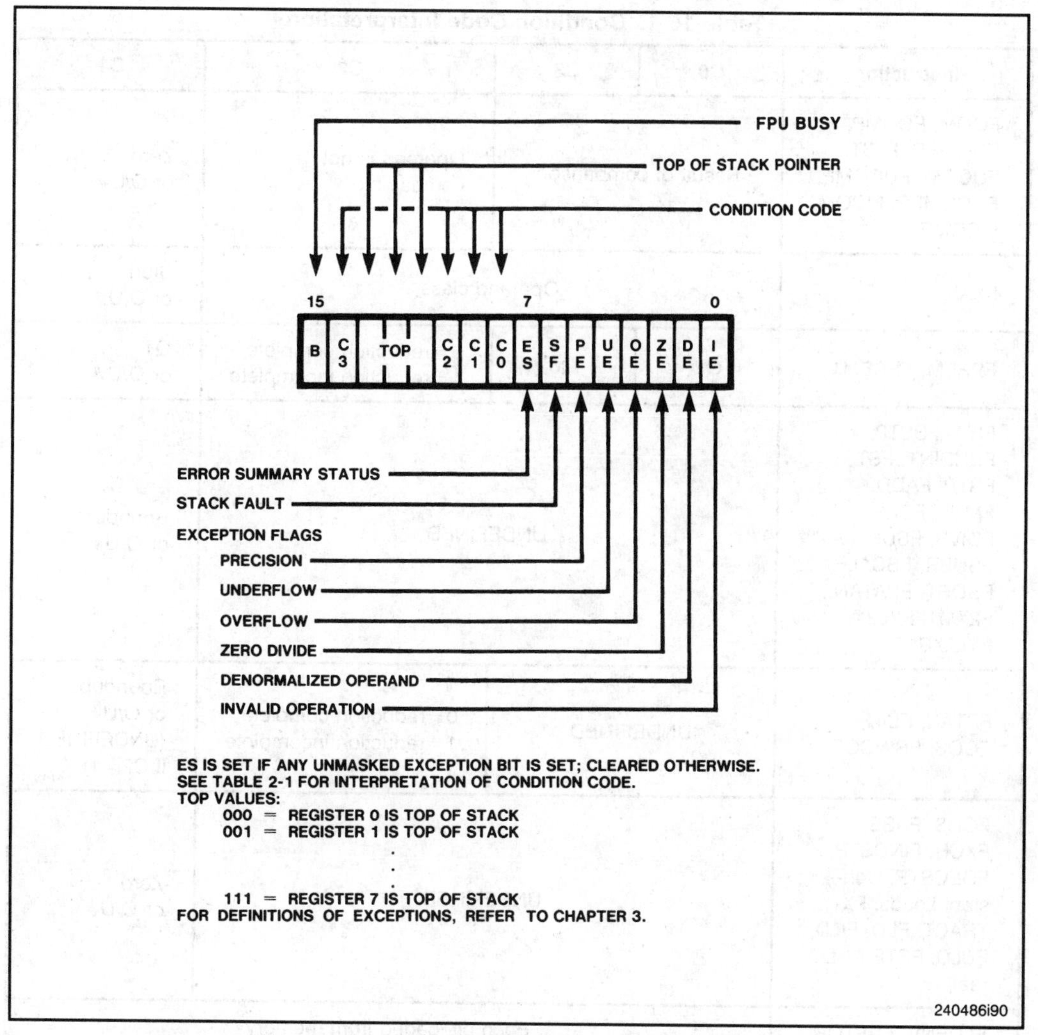

Figure 15-2. i486™ FPU Status Word

condition codes to be inspected efficiently by i486 code. The SAHF instruction can copy C_3-C_0 directly to i486 flag bits to simplify conditional branching. Table 15-2 shows the mapping of these bits to the i486 flag bits.

Bits 12-14 of the status word point to the FPU register that is the current Top of Stack (TOP). The significance of the stack top has been described in the prior section on the register stack.

Figure 15-2 shows the six exception flags in bits 0-5 of the status word. Bit 7 is the exception summary status (ES) bit. ES is set if any unmasked exception bits are set, and is cleared otherwise. Bits 0-5 indicate whether the FPU has detected one of six possible

Table 15-1. Condition Code Interpretation

<table>
<tr><th>Instruction</th><th>C0</th><th>C3</th><th>C2</th><th>C1</th></tr>
<tr><td>FCOM, FCOMP, FCOMPP, FTST, FUCOM, FUCOMP, FUCOMPP, FICOM, FICOMP</td><td colspan="2">Result of comparison</td><td>Operand is not comparable</td><td>Zero or O/U#</td></tr>
<tr><td>FXAM</td><td colspan="3">Operand class</td><td>Sign or O/U#</td></tr>
<tr><td>FPREM, FRREM1</td><td>Q2</td><td>Q0</td><td>0 = reduction complete
1 = reduction incomplete</td><td>Q1 or O/U#</td></tr>
<tr><td>FIST, FBSTP, FRNDINT, FST, FSTP, FADD, FMUL, FDIV, FDIVR, FSUB, FSUBR, FSCALE, FSQRT, FPATAN, F2XM1, FYL2X, FYL2XP1</td><td colspan="3">UNDEFINED</td><td>Roundup or O/U#</td></tr>
<tr><td>FPTAN, FSIN, FCOS, FSINCOS</td><td colspan="2">UNDEFINED</td><td>0 = reduction complete
1 = reduction incomplete</td><td>Roundup or O/U# (UNDEFINED if C2 = 1)</td></tr>
<tr><td>FCHS, FABS, FXCH, FINCSTP, FDECSTP, Constant Loads, FXTRACT, FLD, FILD, FBLD, FSTP (ext. real)</td><td colspan="3">UNDEFINED</td><td>Zero or O/U#</td></tr>
<tr><td>FLDENV, FRSTOR</td><td colspan="4">Each bit loaded from memory</td></tr>
<tr><td>FLDCW, FSTENV, FSTCW, FSTSW, FCLEX</td><td colspan="4">UNDEFINED</td></tr>
<tr><td>FINIT, FSAVE</td><td>Zero</td><td>Zero</td><td>Zero</td><td>Zero</td></tr>
</table>

O/U# — When both IE and SF bits of status word are set, indicating a stack exception, this bit distinguishes between stack overflow (C1 = 1) and underflow (C1 = 0).

Reduction — If FPREM and FPREM1 produces a remainder that is less than the modulus, reduction is complete. When reduction is incomplete the value at the top of the stack is a partial remainder, which can be used as input to further reduction. For FPTAN, FSIN, FCOS, and FSINCOS, the reduction bit is set if the operand at the top of the stack is too large. In this case the original operand remains at the top of the stack.

Roundup — When the PE bit of the status word is set, this bit indicates whether the last rounding in the instruction was upward.

UNDEFINED — Do not rely on finding any specific value in these bits.

Table 15-2. Correspondence Between FPU and IU Flag Bits

FPU Flag	IU Flag
C_0	CF
C_1	(none)
C_2	PF
C_3	ZF

exception conditions since these status bits were last cleared or reset. They are "sticky" bits, and can only be cleared by the instructions FINIT, FCLEX, FLDENV, FSAVE, and FRSTOR.

Bit 6 is the stack fault (SF) bit. This bit distinguishes invalid operations due to stack overflow or underflow from other kinds of invalid operations. When SF is set, bit 9 (C_1) distinguishes between stack overflow ($C_1 = 1$) and underflow ($C_1 = 0$).

15.1.3 Control Word

The FPU provides the programmer with several processing options, which are selected by loading a word from memory into the control word. Figure 15-3 shows the format and encoding of the fields in the control word.

The low-order byte of this control word configures the numerical exception masking. Bits 0–5 of the control word contain individual masks for each of the six floating-point exception conditions recognized by the i486 processor. The high-order byte of the control word configures the FPU processing options, including

- Precision control
- Rounding control

The precision-control bits (bits 8–9) can be used to set the FPU internal operating precision at less than the default precision (64-bit significand). These control bits can be used to provide compatibility with the earlier-generation arithmetic processors having less precision than the i486 processor or 387 math coprocessor. The precision-control bits affect the results of only the following five arithmetic instructions: ADD, SUB(R), MUL, DIV(R), and SQRT. No other operations are affected by PC.

The rounding-control bits (bits 10–11) provide for the common round-to-nearest mode, as well as directed rounding and true chop. Rounding control affects only the arithmetic instructions (refer to Chapter 16 for lists of arithmetic and nonarithmetic instructions).

15.1.4 The FPU Tag Word

The tag word indicates the contents of each register in the register stack, as shown in Figure 15-4. The tag word is used by the FPU itself to distinguish between empty and

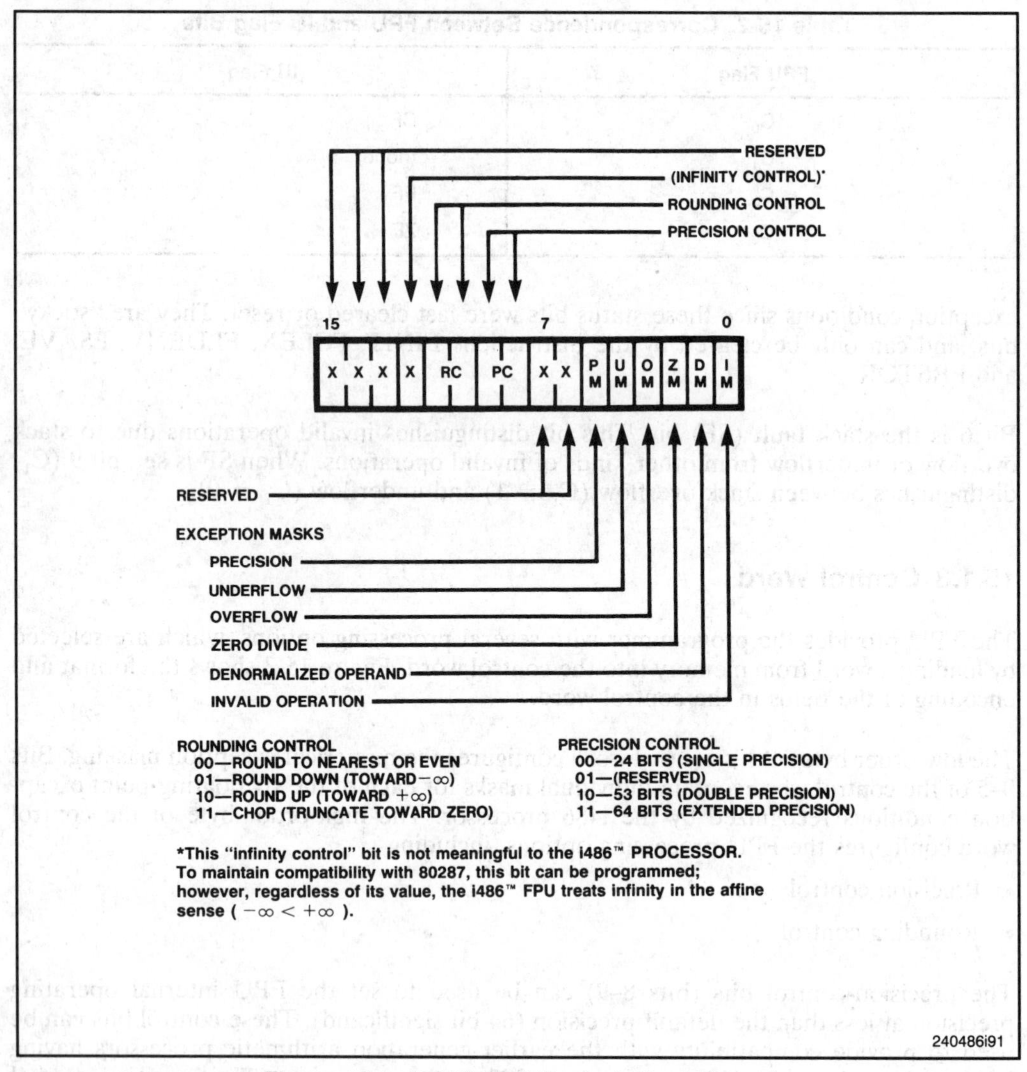

Figure 15-3. i486™ FPU Control Word Format

nonempty register locations. Programmers of exception handlers may use this tag information to check the contents of a numeric register without performing complex decoding of the actual data in the register. The tag values from the tag word correspond to physical registers 0–7. Programmers must use the current top-of-stack (TOP) pointer stored in the FPU status word to associate these tag values with the relative stack registers ST(0) through ST(7).

The exact values of the tags are generated during execution of the FSTENV and FSAVE instructions according to the actual contents of the nonempty stack locations. During execution of other instructions, the i486 processor updates the TW only to indicate whether a stack location is empty or nonempty.

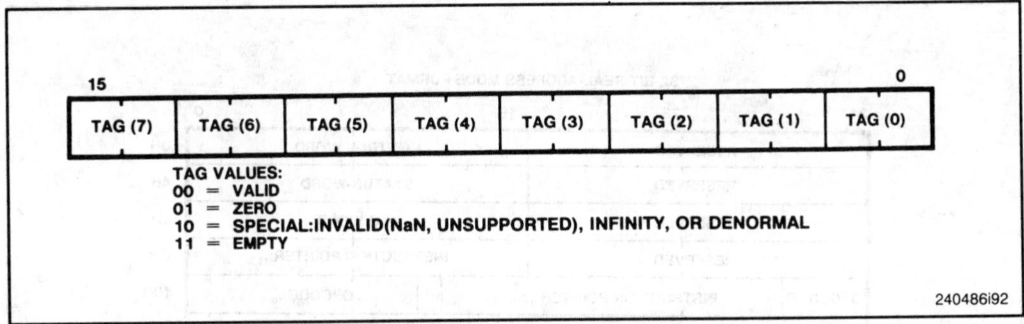

Figure 15-4. Tag Word Format

15.1.5 The Numeric Instruction and Data Pointers

The instruction and data pointers provide support for programmed exception-handlers. These registers are accessed by the ESC instructions FLDENV, FSTENV, FSAVE, and FRSTOR. Whenever the i486 processor decodes an ESC instruction, it saves the instruction address, the operand address (if present), and the instruction opcode.

When stored in memory, the instruction and data pointers appear in one of four formats, depending on the operating mode of the processor (protected mode or real-address mode) and depending on the operand-size attribute in effect (32-bit operand or 16-bit operand). In virtual-8086 mode, the real-address mode formats are used.

Figures 15-5 through 15-8 show these pointers as they are stored following an FSTENV instruction.

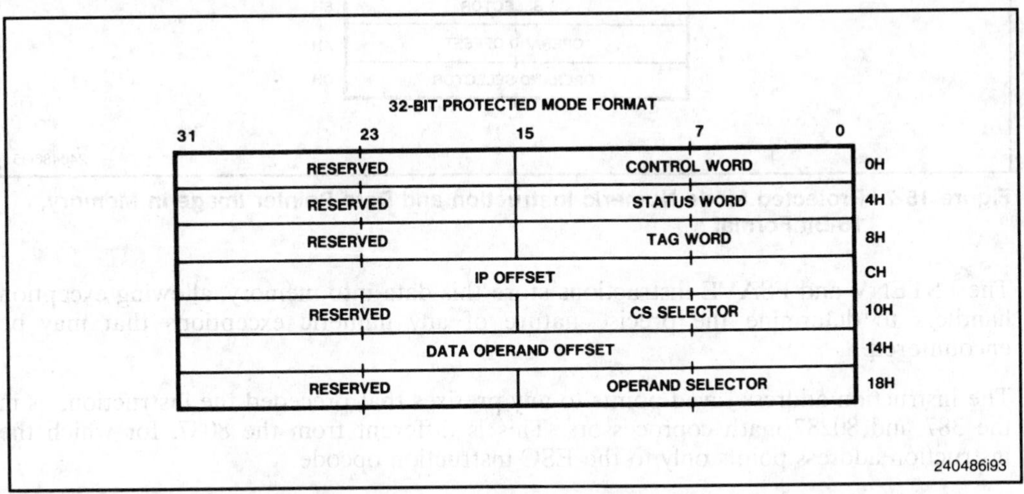

Figure 15-5. Protected Mode Numeric Instruction and Data Pointer Image in Memory, 32-Bit Format

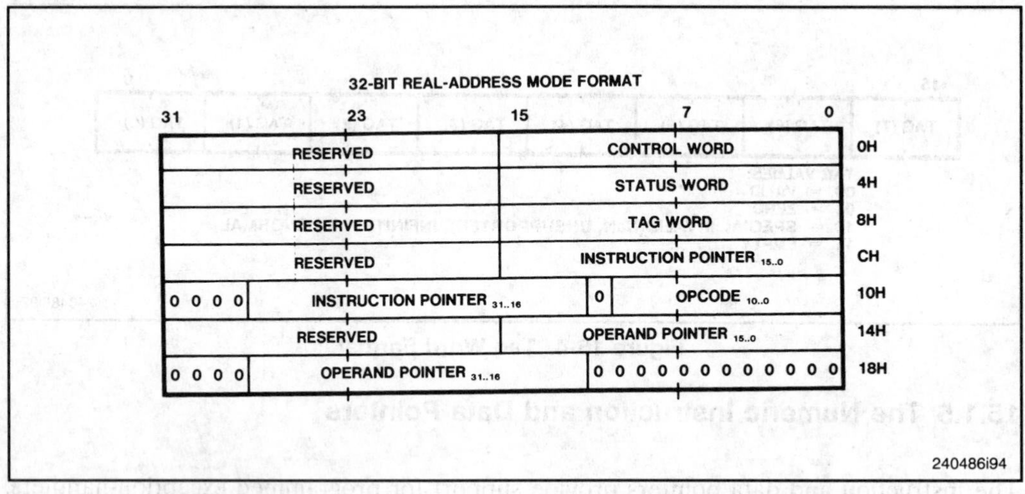

Figure 15-6. Real Mode Numeric Instruction and Data Pointer Image in Memory, 32-Bit Format

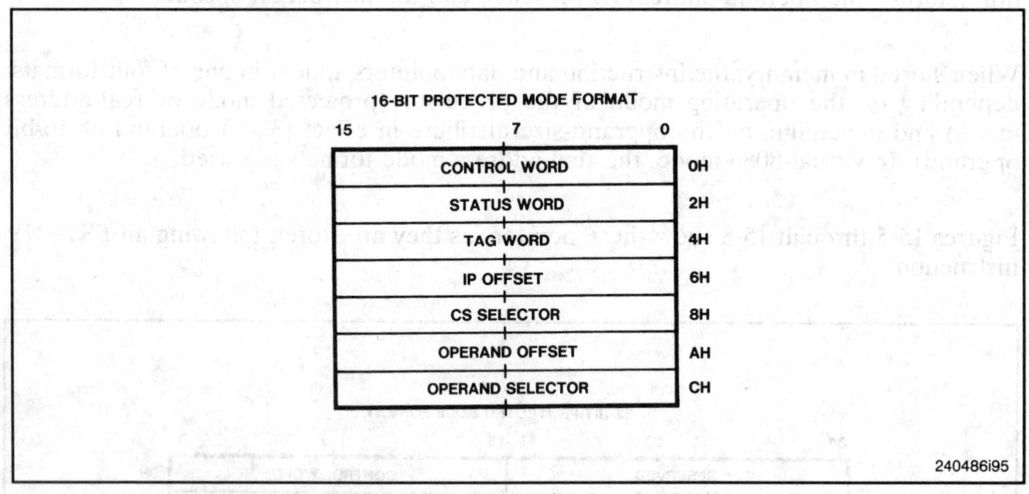

Figure 15-7. Protected Mode Numeric Instruction and Data Pointer Image in Memory, 16-Bit Format

The FSTENV and FSAVE instructions store this data into memory, allowing exception handlers to determine the precise nature of any numeric exceptions that may be encountered.

The instruction address saved points to any prefixes that preceded the instruction, as in the 387 and 80287 math coprocessors. This is different from the 8087, for which the instruction address points only to the ESC instruction opcode.

Note that the processor control instructions FINIT, FLDCW, FSTCW, FSTSW, FCLEX, FSTENV, FLDENV, FSAVE, and FRSTOR do not affect the data pointer.

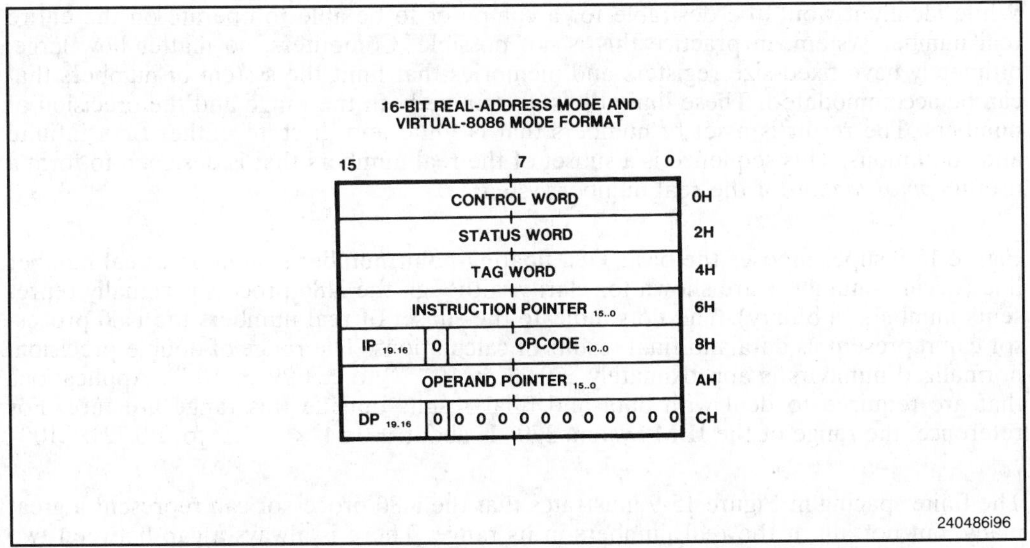

Figure 15-8. Real Mode Numeric Instruction and Data Pointer Image in Memory, 16-Bit Format

Note also that, except for the instructions just mentioned, the value of the data pointer is *undefined* if the prior ESC instruction did not have a memory operand.

15.2 COMPUTATION FUNDAMENTALS

This section covers numeric programming concepts that are common to all applications. It describes the i486 FPU's internal number system and the various types of numbers that can be employed in numeric programs. The most commonly used options for rounding and precision (selected by fields in the control word) are described, with exhaustive coverage of less frequently used facilities deferred to later sections. Exception conditions that may arise during execution of floating-point instructions are also described along with the options that are available for responding to these exceptions.

15.2.1 Number System

The system of real numbers that people use for pencil and paper calculations is conceptually infinite and continuous. There is no upper or lower limit to the magnitude of the numbers one can employ in a calculation, or to the precision (number of significant digits) that may be required to represent them. For any given real number, there are always arbitrarily many numbers both larger and smaller. There are also arbitrarily many numbers between any two real numbers. For example, between 2.5 and 2.6 are 2.51, 2.5897, 2.500001, etc.

While ideally it would be desirable for a computer to be able to operate on the entire real number system, in practice this is not possible. Computers, no matter how large, ultimately have fixed-size registers and memories that limit the system of numbers that can be accommodated. These limitations determine both the range and the precision of numbers. The result is a set of numbers that is finite and discrete, rather than infinite and continuous. This sequence is a subset of the real numbers that is designed to form a useful *approximation* of the real number system.

Figure 15-9 superimposes the basic i486 floating-point number system on a real number line (decimal numbers are shown for clarity, although the i486 processor actually represents numbers in binary). The dots indicate the subset of real numbers the i486 processor can represent as data and final results of calculations. The range of double-precision, normalized numbers is approximately $\pm 2.23 \times 10^{-308}$ to $\pm 1.79 \times 10^{308}$. Applications that are required to deal with data and final results outside this range are rare. For reference, the range of the IBM System 370* is about $\pm 0.54 \times 10^{-78}$ to $\pm 0.72 \times 10^{76}$.

The finite spacing in Figure 15-9 illustrates that the i486 processor can represent a great many, but not all, of the real numbers in its range. There is always a gap between two adjacent floating-point numbers, and it is possible for the result of a calculation to fall in this space. When this occurs, the FPU rounds the true result to a number that it can represent. Thus, a real number that requires more digits than the FPU can accommodate (e.g., a 20-digit number) is represented with some loss of accuracy. Notice also that the representable numbers are not distributed evenly along the real number line. In fact,

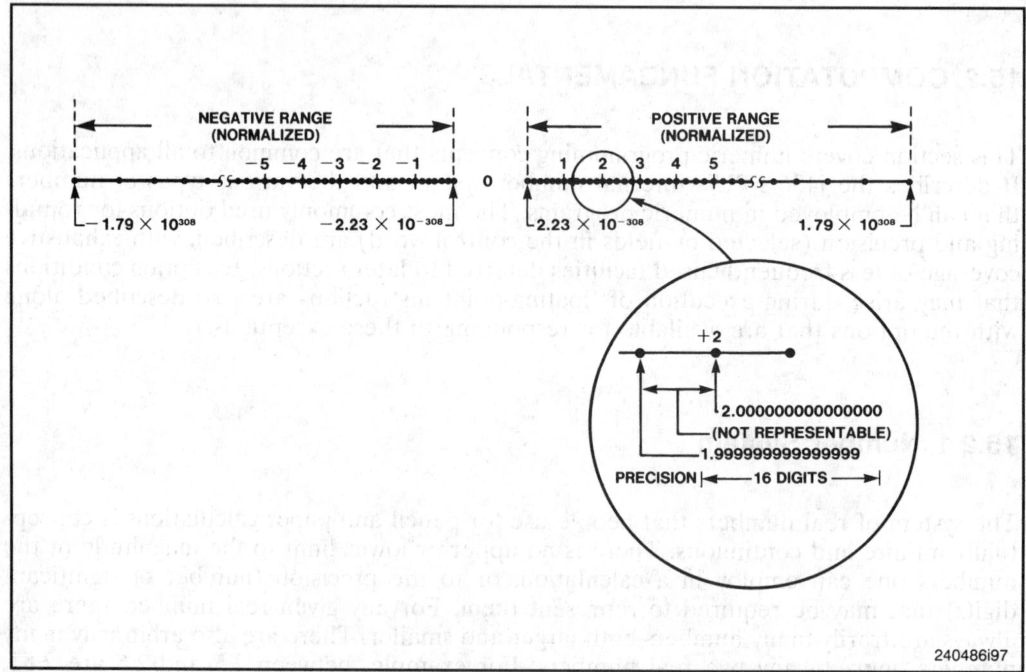

Figure 15-9. Double-Precision Number System

the same number of representable numbers exists between any two successive powers of 2 (i.e., as many representable numbers exist between 2 and 4 as between 65,536 and 131,072). Therefore, the gaps between representable numbers are larger as the numbers increase in magnitude. All integers in the range $\pm 2^{64}$ (approximately $\pm 10^{19}$), however, are exactly representable.

In its internal operations, the FPU actually employs a number system that is a substantial superset of that shown in Figure 15-9. The internal format (called extended real) extends the representable (normalized) range to about $\pm 3.37 \times 10^{-4932}$ to $\pm 1.18 \times 10^{4932}$, and its precision to about 19 (equivalent decimal) digits. This format is designed to provide extra range and precision for constants and intermediate results, and is not normally intended for data or final results.

From a practical standpoint, the i486 processor's set of real numbers is sufficiently large and dense so as not to limit the vast majority of applications. Compared to most computers, including mainframes, the i486 processor provides a very good approximation of the real number system. It is important to remember, however, that it is not an exact representation, and that computer arithmetic on real numbers is inherently approximate.

15.2.2 Data Types and Formats

The i486 processor recognizes seven numeric data types for memory-based values, divided into three classes: binary integers, packed decimal integers, and binary reals. A later section describes how these formats are stored in memory (the sign is always located in the highest-addressed byte).

Figure 15-10 summarizes the format of each data type. In the figure, the most significant digits of all numbers (and fields within numbers) are the leftmost digits.

15.2.2.1 BINARY INTEGERS

The three binary integer formats are identical except for length, which governs the range that can be accommodated in each format. The leftmost bit is interpreted as the number's sign: 0 = positive and 1 = negative. Negative numbers are represented in standard two's complement notation (the binary integers are the only i486 processor format to use two's complement). The quantity zero is represented with a positive sign (all bits are 0). The i486 processor word integer format is identical to the 16-bit signed integer data type; the short integer format is identical to the 32-bit signed integer data type.

The binary integer formats exist in memory only. When used by the i486 FPU, they are automatically converted to the 80-bit extended real format. All binary integers are exactly representable in the extended real format.

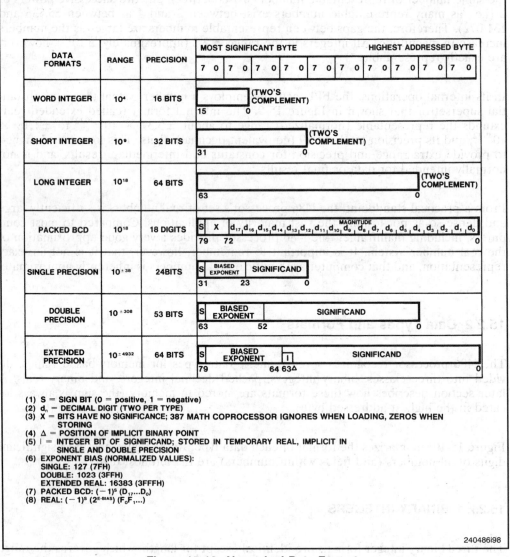

DATA FORMATS	RANGE	PRECISION	MOST SIGNIFICANT BYTE … HIGHEST ADDRESSED BYTE (7 0 | 7 0 | 7 0 | 7 0 | 7 0 | 7 0 | 7 0 | 7 0 | 7 0 | 7 0)
WORD INTEGER	10^4	16 BITS	(TWO'S COMPLEMENT) 15 … 0
SHORT INTEGER	10^9	32 BITS	(TWO'S COMPLEMENT) 31 … 0
LONG INTEGER	10^{18}	64 BITS	(TWO'S COMPLEMENT) 63 … 0
PACKED BCD	10^{18}	18 DIGITS	S | X | MAGNITUDE: d_{17} d_{16} d_{15} d_{14} d_{13} d_{12} d_{11} d_{10} d_9 d_8 d_7 d_6 d_5 d_4 d_3 d_2 d_1 d_0; 79 72 … 0
SINGLE PRECISION	$10^{\pm 38}$	24BITS	S | BIASED EXPONENT | SIGNIFICAND; 31 23 0
DOUBLE PRECISION	$10^{\pm 308}$	53 BITS	S | BIASED EXPONENT | SIGNIFICAND; 63 52 0
EXTENDED PRECISION	$10^{\pm 4932}$	64 BITS	S | BIASED EXPONENT | I | SIGNIFICAND; 79 64 63Δ 0

(1) S = SIGN BIT (0 = positive, 1 = negative)
(2) d_n = DECIMAL DIGIT (TWO PER TYPE)
(3) X = BITS HAVE NO SIGNIFICANCE; 387 MATH COPROCESSOR IGNORES WHEN LOADING, ZEROS WHEN STORING
(4) Δ = POSITION OF IMPLICIT BINARY POINT
(5) I = INTEGER BIT OF SIGNIFICAND; STORED IN TEMPORARY REAL, IMPLICIT IN SINGLE AND DOUBLE PRECISION
(6) EXPONENT BIAS (NORMALIZED VALUES):
SINGLE: 127 (7FH)
DOUBLE: 1023 (3FFH)
EXTENDED REAL: 16383 (3FFFH)
(7) PACKED BCD: $(-1)^S (D_{17} \ldots D_0)$
(8) REAL: $(-1)^S (2^{E-BIAS}) (F_0 F_1 \ldots)$

240486i98

Figure 15-10. Numerical Data Formats

15.2.2.2 DECIMAL INTEGERS

Decimal integers are stored in packed decimal notation, with two decimal digits "packed" into each byte, except the leftmost byte, which carries the sign bit (0 = positive, 1 = negative). Negative numbers are not stored in two's complement form and are distinguished from positive numbers only by the sign bit. The most significant digit of the number is the leftmost digit. All digits must be in the range 0–9.

The decimal integer format exists in memory only. When used by the i486 FPU, it is automatically converted to the 80-bit extended real format. All decimal integers are exactly representable in the extended real format.

15.2.2.3 REAL NUMBERS

The i486 processor represents real numbers of the form:

$$(-1)^s 2^E (b_0{}_\Delta b_1 b_2 b_3 .. b_{p-1})$$

where:

s	= 0 or 1
E	= any integer between Emin and Emax, inclusive
b_i	= 0 or 1
p	= number of bits of precision

Table 15-3 summarizes the parameters for each of the three real-number formats.

The i486 processor stores real numbers in a three-field binary format that resembles scientific, or exponential, notation. The format consists of the following fields:

- The number's significant digits are held in the *significand* field, $b_0{}_\Delta b_1 b_2 b_3 .. b_{p-1}$. (The term "significand" is analogous to the term "mantissa" used to describe floating point numbers on some computers.)
- The *exponent* field, e = E+bias, locates the binary point within the significant digits (and therefore determines the number's magnitude). (The term "exponent" is analogous to the term "characteristic" used to describe floating point numbers on some computers.)
- The 1-bit *sign* field indicates whether the number is positive or negative. Negative numbers differ from positive numbers only in the sign bits of their significands.

Table 15-3. Summary of Format Parameters

Parameter	Format		
	Single	Double	Extended
Format width in bits	32	64	80
p (bits of precision)	24	53	64
Exponent width in bits	8	11	15
Emax	+127	+1023	+16383
Emin	−126	−1022	−16382
Exponent bias	+127	+1023	+16383

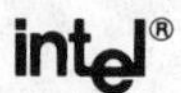

Table 15-4 shows how the real number 178.125 (decimal) is stored in the single real format. The table lists a progression of equivalent notations that express the same value to show how a number can be converted from one form to another. (The ASM386/486 and PL/M-386/486 language translators perform a similar process when they encounter programmer-defined real number constants.) Note that not every decimal fraction has an exact binary equivalent. The decimal number 1/10, for example, cannot be expressed exactly in binary (just as the number 1/3 cannot be expressed exactly in decimal). When a translator encounters such a value, it produces a rounded binary approximation of the decimal value.

The i486 processor usually carries the digits of the significand in normalized form. This means that, except for the value zero, the significand contains an *integer bit* and *fraction bits* as follows:

1_Δfff...ff

where $_\Delta$ indicates an assumed binary point. The number of fraction bits varies according to the real format: 23 for single, 52 for double, and 63 for extended real. By normalizing real numbers so that their integer bit is always a 1, the i486 processor eliminates leading zeros in small values ($|X| < 1$). This technique maximizes the number of significant digits that can be accommodated in a significand of a given width. Note that, in the single and double formats, the integer bit is *implicit* and is not actually stored; the integer bit is physically present in the extended format only.

If one were to examine only the significand with its assumed binary point, all normalized real numbers would have values greater than or equal to 1 and less than 2. The exponent field locates the *actual* binary point in the significant digits. Just as in decimal scientific notation, a positive exponent has the effect of moving the binary point to the right, and a negative exponent effectively moves the binary point to the left, inserting leading zeros as necessary. An unbiased exponent of zero indicates that the position of the assumed binary point is also the position of the actual binary point. The exponent field, then, determines a real number's magnitude.

Table 15-4. Real Number Notation

Notation	Value		
Ordinary Decimal	178.125		
Scientific Decimal	1_Δ78125E2		
Scientific Binary	1_Δ0110010001E111		
Scientific Binary (Biased Exponent)	1_Δ0110010001E10000110		
Single Format (Normalized)	Sign	Biased Exponent	Significand
	0	10000110	01100100010000000000000 1_Δ(implicit)

In order to simplify comparing real numbers (e.g., for sorting), the i486 processor stores exponents in a biased form. This means that a constant is added to the *true exponent* described above. As Table 15-3 shows, the value of this *bias* is different for each real format. It has been chosen so as to force the *biased exponent* to be a positive value. This allows two real numbers (of the same format and sign) to be compared as if they are unsigned binary integers. That is, when comparing them bitwise from left to right (beginning with the leftmost exponent bit), the first bit position that differs orders the numbers; there is no need to proceed further with the comparison. A number's true exponent can be determined simply by subtracting the bias value of its format.

The single and double real formats exist in memory only. If a number in one of these formats is loaded into an FPU register, it is automatically converted to extended format, the format used for all internal operations. Likewise, data in registers can be converted to single or double real for storage in memory. The extended real format may be used in memory also, typically to store intermediate results that cannot be held in registers.

Most applications should use the double format to store real-number data and results; it provides sufficient range and precision to return correct results with a minimum of programmer attention. The single real format is appropriate for applications that are constrained by memory, but it should be recognized that this format provides a smaller margin of safety. It is also useful for the debugging of algorithms, because roundoff problems will manifest themselves more quickly in this format. The extended real format should normally be reserved for holding intermediate results, loop accumulations, and constants. Its extra length is designed to shield final results from the effects of rounding and overflow/underflow in intermediate calculations. However, the range and precision of the double format are adequate for most microcomputer applications.

15.2.3 Rounding Control

Internally, the i486 FPU employs three extra bits (guard, round, and sticky bits) that enable it to round numbers in accord with the infinitely precise true result of a computation; these bits are not accessible to programmers. Whenever the destination can represent the infinitely precise true result, the FPU delivers it. Rounding occurs in arithmetic and store operations when the format of the destination cannot exactly represent the infinitely precise true result. For example, a real number may be rounded if it is stored in a shorter real format, or in an integer format. Or, the infinitely precise true result may be rounded when it is returned to a register.

The i486 FPU has four rounding modes, selectable by the RC field in the control word (see Figure 15-3). Given a true result b that cannot be represented by the target data type, the FPU determines the two representable numbers a and c that most closely bracket b in value ($a < b < c$). The processor then rounds (changes) b to a or to c according to the mode selected by the RC field as shown in Table 15-5. Rounding

Table 15-5. Rounding Modes

RC Field	Rounding Mode	Rounding Action
00	Round to nearest	Closer to *b* of *a* or *c*; if equally close, select even number (the one whose least significant bit is zero).
01	Round down (toward $-\infty$)	*a*
10	Round up (toward $+\infty$)	*c*
11	Chop (toward 0)	Smaller in magnitude of *a* or *c*.

NOTE: $a < b < c$; *a* and *c* are successive representable numbers; *b* is not representable.

introduces an error in a result that is less than one unit in the last place to which the result is rounded.

- "Round to nearest" is the default mode and is suitable for most applications; it provides the most accurate and statistically unbiased estimate of the true result.
- The "chop" or "round toward zero" mode is provided for integer arithmetic applications.
- "Round up" and "round down" are termed *directed rounding* and can be used to implement interval arithmetic. Interval arithmetic is used to determine upper and lower bounds for the true result of a multi-step computation, when the intermediate results of the computation are subject to rounding.

Rounding control affects only the arithmetic instructions (refer to Chapter 16 for lists of arithmetic and nonarithmetic instructions).

15.2.4 Precision Control

The i486 FPU allows results to be calculated with either 64, 53, or 24 bits of precision in the significand as selected by the precision control (PC) field of the control word. The default setting, and the one that is best suited for most applications, is the full 64 bits of significance provided by the extended real format. The other settings are required by the IEEE standard and are provided to obtain compatibility with the specifications of certain existing programming languages. Specifying less precision nullifies the advantages of the extended format's extended fraction length. When reduced precision is specified, the rounding of the fractional value clears the unused bits on the right to zeros. Precision Control affects only the instructions FADD, FSUB, FMUL, FDIV, and FSQRT.

16 Special Computational Situations

CHAPTER 16
SPECIAL COMPUTATIONAL SITUATIONS

Besides being able to represent positive and negative numbers, the numerical data formats may be used to describe other entities. These special values provide extra flexibility, but most users will not need to understand them in order to use the numerics capabilities of the i486™ processor successfully. This section describes the special values that may occur in certain cases and the significance of each. The numeric exceptions are also described, for writers of exception handlers and for those interested in probing the limits of numeric computation using the i486 processor.

The material presented in this section is mainly of interest to programmers concerned with writing exception handlers. Many readers will only need to skim this section.

When discussing these special computational situations, it is useful to distinguish between *arithmetic instructions* and *nonarithmetic instructions*. Nonarithmetic instructions are those that have no operands or transfer their operands without substantial change; arithmetic instructions are those that make significant changes to their operands. Table 16-1 defines these two classes of instructions.

16.1 SPECIAL NUMERIC VALUES

The numerical data formats of the i486 processor encompass encodings for a variety of special values in addition to the typical real or integer data values that result from normal calculations. These special values have significance and can express relevant information about the computations or operations that produced them. The various types of special values are

- Denormal real numbers
- Zeros
- Positive and negative infinity
- NaN (Not-a-Number)
- Indefinite
- Unsupported formats

The following sections explain the origins and significance of each of these special values. Tables 16-6 through 16-9 at the end of this section show how each of these special values is encoded for each of the numeric data types.

16.1.1 Denormal Real Numbers

The i486 processor generally stores nonzero real numbers in normalized floating-point form; that is, the integer (leading) bit of the significand is always a one. (Refer to Chapter 15 for a review of operand formats.) This bit is explicitly stored in the extended

Table 16-1. Arithmetic and Nonarithmetic Instructions

Nonarithmetic Instructions	Arithmetic Instructions
FABS	F2XM1
FCHS	FADD (P)
FCLEX	FBLD
FDECSTP	FBSTP
FFREE	FCOMP(P)(P)
FINCSTP	FCOS
FINIT	FDIV(R)(P)
FLD (register-to-register)	FIADD
FLD (extended format from memory)	FICOM(P)
FLD constant	FIDIV(R)
FLDCW	FILD
FLDENV	FIMUL
FNOP	FIST(P)
FRSTOR	FISUB(R)
FSAVE	FLD (conversion)
FST(P) (register-to-register)	FMUL(P)
FSTP (extended format to memory)	FPATAN
FSTCW	FPREM
FSTENV	FPREM1
FSTSW	FPTAN
FWAIT	FRNDINT
FXAM	FSCALE
FXCH	FSIN
	FSINCOS
	FSQRT
	FST(P) (conversion)
	FSUB(R)(P)
	FTST
	FUCOM(P)(P)
	FXTRACT
	FYL2X
	FYL2XP1

format, and is implicitly assumed to be a one (1_Δ) in the single and double formats. Since leading zeros are eliminated, normalized storage allows the maximum number of significant digits to be held in a significand of a given width.

When a numeric value becomes very close to zero, normalized floating-point storage cannot be used to express the value accurately. The term *tiny* is used here to precisely define what values require special handling. A number R is said to be *tiny* when $-2^{Emin} < R < 0$ or $0 < R < +2^{Emin}$. (As defined in Chapter 15, Emin is -126 for single format, -1022 for double format, and -16382 for extended format.) In other words, a nonzero number is *tiny* if its exponent would be too negative to store in the destination format.

To accommodate these instances, the i486 processor can store and operate on reals that are not normalized, i.e., whose significands contain one or more leading zeros. Denormals typically arise when the result of a calculation yields a value that is *tiny*.

Denormal values have the following properties:

- The biased floating-point exponent is stored at its smallest value (zero)
- The integer bit of the significand (whether explicit or implicit) is zero

The leading zeros of denormals permit smaller numbers to be represented, at the possible cost of some lost precision (the number of significant bits is reduced by the leading zeros). In typical algorithms, extremely small values are most likely to be generated as intermediate, rather than final, results. By using the extended real format for holding intermediate values, quantities as small as $\pm 3.37 \times 10^{-4932}$ can be represented; this makes the occurrence of denormal numbers a rare phenomenon in i486 numerical applications. Nevertheless, the i486 processor can load, store, and operate on denormalized real numbers when they do occur.

Denormals receive special treatment by the i486 processor in three respects:

- The i486 processor avoids creating denormals whenever possible. In other words, it always normalizes real numbers except in the case of tiny numbers.
- The i486 processor provides the unmasked underflow exception to permit programmers to detect cases when denormals would be created.
- The i486 processor provides the denormal exception to permit programmers to detect cases when denormals enter into further calculations.

Denormalizing means incrementing the true result's exponent and inserting a corresponding leading zero in the significand, shifting the rest of the significand one place to the right. Denormal values may occur in any of the single, double, or extended formats. Table 16-2 shows the range of denormalized values in each format.

Denormalization produces either a denormal or a zero. Denormals are readily identified by their exponents, which are always the minimum for their formats; in biased form, this is always the bit string: 00..00. This same exponent value is also assigned to the zeros, but a denormal has a nonzero significand. A denormal in a register is tagged *special*. Tables 16-8 and 16-9 later in this chapter show how denormal values are encoded in each of the real data formats.

Table 16-2. Denormalized Values

Format	Smallest Magnitude		Largest Magnitude	
	(Exact)	(Approx.)	(Exact)	(Approx.)
Single Precision	2^{-150}	10^{-46}	$2^{-126}-2^{-150}$	10^{-38}
Double Precision	2^{-1075}	10^{-324}	$2^{-1022}-2^{-1075}$	10^{-308}
Extended	2^{-16461}	10^{-4956}	$2^{-16382}-2^{-16461}$	10^{-4932}

The denormalization process causes loss of significance if low-order one-bits bits are shifted off the right of the significand. In a severe case, *all* the significand bits of the true result are shifted out and replaced by the leading zeros. In this case, the result of denormalization is a true zero, and, if the value is in a register, it is tagged as a zero.

Denormals are rarely encountered in most applications. Typical debugged algorithms generate extremely small results during the evaluation of intermediate subexpressions; the final result is usually of an appropriate magnitude for its single or double format real destination. If intermediate results are held in temporary real, as is recommended, the great range of this format makes underflow very unlikely. Denormals are likely to arise only when an application generates a great many intermediates, so many that they cannot be held on the register stack or in extended format memory variables. If storage limitations force the use of single or double format reals for intermediates, and small values are produced, underflow may occur, and, if masked, may generate denormals.

When a denormal number is single or double format is used as a source operand and the denormal exception is masked, the i486 FPU automatically *normalizes* the number when it is converted to extended format.

16.1.1.1 DENORMALS AND GRADUAL UNDERFLOW

Floating-pont arithmetic cannot carry out all operations exactly for all operands; approximation is unavoidable when the exact result is not representable as a floating-point variable. To keep the approximation mathematically tractable, the hardware is made to conform to accuracy standards that can be modeled by certain inequalities instead of equations. Let the assignment

$$X \leftarrow Y @ Z \qquad \text{(where @ is some operation)}$$

represent a typical operation. In the default rounding mode (round to nearest), each operation is carried out with an absolute error no larger than half the separation between the two floating-point numbers closest to the exact results. Let x be the value stored for the variable whose name in the program is X, and similarly y for Y, and z for Z. Normally y and z will differ by accumulated errors from what is desired and from what would have been obtained in the absence of error. For the calculation of x we assume that y and z are the best approximations available, and we seek to compute x as well as we can. If $y@z$ is representable exactly, then we expect $x = y@z$, and that is what we get for every algebraic operation on the i486 processor FPU (i.e., when $y@z$ is one of $y+z$, $y-z$, $y\times z$, $y\div z$, *sqrt* z). But if $y@z$ must be approximated, as is usually the case, then x must differ from $y@z$ by no more than half the difference between the two representable numbers that straddle $y@z$. That difference depends on two factors:

1. The precision to which the calculation is carried out, as determined either by the precision control bits or by the format used in memory. On the i486 processor, the precisions are single (24 significant bits), double (53 significant bits), and extended (64 significant bits).

2. How close *y@z* is to zero. In this respect the existence of denormal numbers on the i486 processor provides a distinct advantage over systems that do not admit denormal numbers.

In any floating-point number system, the density of representable numbers is greater near zero than near the largest representable magnitudes. However, machines that do not use denormal numbers suffer from an enormous gap between zero and its closest neighbors. Figures 16-1 and 16-2 show what happens near zero in two kinds of floating-point number systems.

Figure 16-1 shows a floating-point number system that (like the i486 processor) admits denormal numbers. For simplicity, only the non-negative numbers appear and the figure illustrates a number system that carries just four significant bits instead of the 24, 53, or 64 significant bits that the i486 processor offers.

Each vertical tick mark stands for a number representable in four significant bits, and the longer verticals stand for powers of 2. The horizontal marks are evenly spaced; those uncrossed by vertical tick marks stand for numbers unrepresentable at this precision. The denormal numbers lie between 0 and the nearest normal power of 2. They are no less dense than the remaining nonzero numbers.

Figure 16-2 shows a floating-point number system that (unlike the i486 or 387 FPUs) does not admit denormal numbers. There are two large gaps, one on the positive side of zero (as illustrated) and one on the negative side of zero (not illustrated). The gap between zero and the nearest neighbor of zero differs from the gap between that neighbor and the next bigger number by a factor of about 8.4×10^6 for single, 4.5×10^{15} for double, and 9.2×10^{18} for extended format. Those gaps would complicate error analysis.

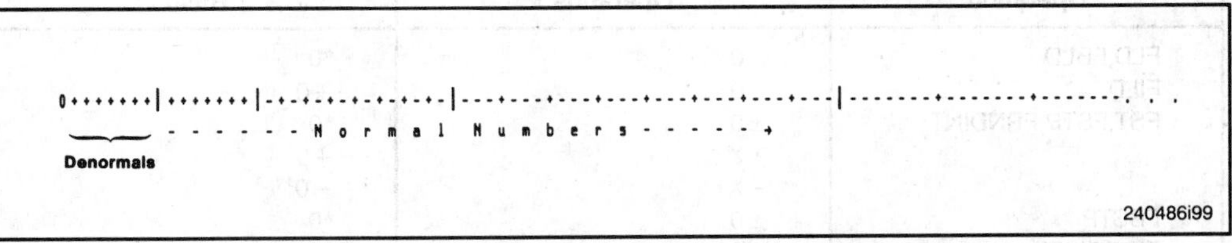

Figure 16-1. Floating-Point System with Denormals

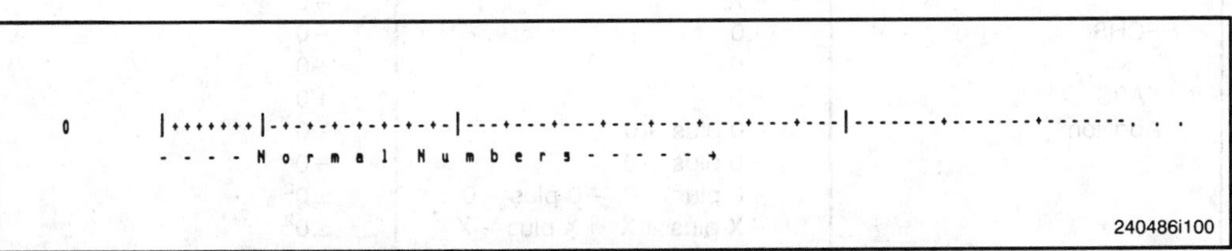

Figure 16-2. Floating-Point System without Denormals

The advantage of denormal numbers is apparent when one considers what happens in either case when the underflow exception is masked and *y@z* falls into the space between zero and the smallest normal magnitude. The i486 processor returns the nearest denormal number. This action might be called "gradual underflow." The effect is no different from the rounding that can occur when *y@z* falls in the normal range.

On the other hand, the system that does not have denormal numbers returns zero as the result, an action that can be much more inaccurate than rounding. This action could be called "abrupt underflow." The i486 FPU and 387 math coprocessor handle denormal values differently values differently than the 8087/80287 math coprocessors. See Section 16.2.4 for more details.

16.1.2 Zeros

The value *zero* in the real and decimal integer formats may be signed either positive or negative, although the sign of a binary integer zero is always positive. For computational purposes, the value of zero always behaves identically, regardless of sign, and typically the fact that a zero may be signed is transparent to the programmer. If necessary, the FXAM instruction may be used to determine a zero's sign.

A programmer can code a zero, or it can be created by the FPU as its masked response to an underflow exception. If a zero is loaded or generated in a register, the register is tagged *zero*. Table 16-3 lists the results of instructions executed with zero operands and also shows how a zero may be created from nonzero operands.

Table 16-3. Zero Operands and Results

Operation	Operands	Result
FLD,FBLD	±0	*0
FILD	+0	+0
FST,FSTP,FRNDINT	±0	*0
	+X	+0[1]
	−X	−0[1]
FBSTP	±0	*0
FIST,FISTP	±0	*0
	+X	+0[3]
	−X	−0[4]
FCHS	+0	−0
	−0	+0
FABS	±0	+0
Addition	+0 plus +0	+0
	−0 plus −0	−0
	+0 plus −0, −0 plus +0	±0[2]
	−X plus +X, +X plus −X	±0[2]
	±0 plus ±X, ±X plus ±0	#X

Table 16-3. Zero Operands and Results

Operation	Operands	Result
Subtraction	+0 minus −0	+0
	−0 minus +0	−0
	+0 minus +0, −0 minus −0	±0[2]
	+X minus +X, −X minus −X	−#X
		#X
	±0 minus ±X	
	±X minus ±0	
Multiplication	±0 × ±0	⊕0
	±0 × ±X, ±X × ±0	⊕0
	+X × +Y, −X × −Y	+0[1]
	+x × −Y, −X × +Y	−0[1]
Division	±0 ÷ ±0	Invalid Operation
	±X ÷ ±0	⊕∞ (Zero Divide)
	±X ÷ ±∞	⊕0
	+0 ÷ +X, −0 ÷ −X	+0
	+0 ÷ −X, −0 ÷ +X	−0
	−X ÷ −Y, +X ÷ +Y	+0[1]
	−X ÷ +Y, +X ÷ −Y	−0[1]
FPREM, FPREM1	±0 rem ±0	Invalid Operation
	±X rem ±0	Invalid Operation
	+0 rem ±X	+0
	−0 rem ±X	−0
	+X rem ±Y	+0 Y exactly divides X
	−X rem ±Y	−0 Y exactly divides X
FSQRT	±0	*0
Compare	±0 : +X	±0 < +X
	±0 : ±0	±0 = ±0
	±0 : −X	±0 >−X
FTST	±0	±0 = 0
FXAM	+0	$C_3=1$; $C_2=C_1=C_0=0$
	−0	$C_3=C_1=1$; $C_2=C_0=0$
FSCALE	±0 scaled by −∞	*0
	±0 scaled by +∞	Invalid Operation
	±0 scaled by X	*0
FXTRACT	+0	ST= +0,ST(1) = −∞, Zero divide
	−0	ST= −0,ST(1) = −∞, Zero divide
FPTAN	±0	*0
FSIN (or SIN result of FSINCOS)	±0	*0
FCOS (or COS result of FSINCOS)	±0	+1

Table 16-3. Zero Operands and Results

Operation	Operands	Result
FPATAN	±0 ÷ +X	*0
	±0 ÷ −X	*π
	±X ÷ ±0	#π/2
	±0 ÷ +0	*0
	±0 ÷ −0	*π
	+∞ ÷ ±0	+π/2
	−∞ ÷ ±0	−π/2
	±0 ÷ +∞	*0
	±0 ÷ −∞	*π
F2XM1	+0	+0
	−0	−0
FYL2X	±Y × log(±0)	Zero Divide
	±0 × log(±0)	Invalid Operation
FYL2XP1	+Y × log(±0+1)	*0
	−Y × log(±0+1)	−*0

X and Y denote nonzero positive operands.
1 When extreme underflow denormalizes the result to zero.
2 Sign determined by rounding mode: + for nearest, up, or chop, − for down.
3 When 0 < X < 1 and rounding mode is not *up*.
4 When −1 < x < 0 and rounding mode is not *down*.
* Sign of original zero operand.
# Sign of original X operand.
−# Complement of sign of original X operand.
⊕ Exclusive OR of the signs of the operands.

16.1.3 Infinity

The real formats support signed representations of infinities. These values are encoded with a biased exponent of all ones and a significand of $1_{\Delta}00..00$; if the infinity is in a register, it is tagged *special*.

A programmer can code an infinity, or it can be created by the FPU as its masked response to an overflow or a zero divide exception. Note that depending on rounding mode, the masked response may create the largest valid value representable in the destination rather than infinity.

The signs of the infinities are observed, and comparisons are possible. Infinities are always interpreted in the affine sense; that is, $-\infty$ < (any finite number) < $+\infty$. Arithmetic on infinities is always exact and, therefore, signals no exceptions, except for the invalid operations specified in Table 16-4.

16.1.4 NaN (Not-a-Number)

A NaN (Not a Number) is a member of a class of special values that exists in the real formats only. A NaN has an exponent of 11..11B, may have either sign, and may have any significand except $1_{\Delta}00..00$B, which is assigned to the infinities. A NaN in a register is tagged *special*.

Table 16-4. Infinity Operands and Results

Operation	Operands	Result
FLD,FBLD	± ∞	* ∞
FST,FSTP,FRNDINT	± ∞	* ∞
FCHS	+ ∞	− ∞
	− ∞	+ ∞
FABS	± ∞	+ ∞
Addition	+ ∞ plus + ∞	+ ∞
	− ∞ plus − ∞	− ∞
	+ ∞ plus − ∞	Invalid Operation
	− ∞ plus + ∞	Invalid Operation
	± ∞ plus ±X	* ∞
	±X plus ± ∞	* ∞
Subtraction	+ ∞ minus − ∞	+ ∞
	− ∞ minus + ∞	− ∞
	+ ∞ minus + ∞	Invalid Operation
	− ∞ minus − ∞	Invalid Operation
	± ∞ minus ±X	* ∞
	±X minus ± ∞	− * ∞
Multiplication	± ∞ × ± ∞	⊕ ∞
	± ∞ × ±Y, ±Y × ± ∞	⊕ ∞
	±0 × ± ∞, ± ∞ × ±0	Invalid Operation
Division	± ∞ ÷ ± ∞	Invalid Operation
	± ∞ ÷ ±X	⊕ ∞
	±X ÷ ± ∞	⊕0
	± ∞ ÷ ±0	⊕ ∞
FPREM,FPREM1	± ∞ rem ± ∞	Invalid Operation
	± ∞ rem ±X	Invalid Operation
	±X rem ± ∞	$X, Q = 0
FSQRT	− ∞	Invalid Operation
	+ ∞	+ ∞
Compare	+ ∞ : + ∞	+ ∞ = + ∞
	− ∞ : − ∞	− ∞ = − ∞
	+ ∞ : − ∞	+ ∞ > − ∞
	− ∞ : + ∞	− ∞ < + ∞
	+ ∞ : ±X	+ ∞ > X
	− ∞ : ±X	− ∞ < X
	±X : + ∞	X < + ∞
	±X : − ∞	X > + ∞
	+ ∞	+ ∞ >0
FTST	− ∞	− ∞ <0
FSCALE	± ∞ scaled by − ∞	Invalid Operation
	± ∞ scaled by + ∞	* ∞
	± ∞ scaled by ±X	* ∞
	±0 scaled by − ∞	±0_1
	±0 scaled by ∞	Invalid Operation
	±Y scaled by + ∞	# ∞
	±Y scaled by − ∞	#0
FXTRACT	± ∞	ST = * ∞, ST(1) = + ∞
FXAM	+ ∞	C0=C2=1;C1=C3=0
	− ∞	C0=C1=C2=1; C3=0

Table 16-4. Infinity Operands and Results

Operation	Operands	Result
FPATAN	± ∞ ÷ ±X	*π/2
	±Y ÷ + ∞	#0
	±Y ÷ − ∞	#π
	± ∞ ÷ + ∞	*π/4
	± ∞ ÷ − ∞	*3π/4
	± ∞ ÷ ±0	*π/2
	+0 ÷ + ∞	+0
	+0 ÷ − ∞	+π
	−0 ÷ + ∞	−0
	−0 ÷ − ∞	−π
F2XM1	+ ∞	+ ∞
	− ∞	−1
FYL2X	± ∞ × log (1)	Invalid Operation
	± ∞ × log (X>1)	* ∞
	± ∞ × log (0<X<1)	−* ∞
	±Y × log (+ ∞)	# ∞
	±0 × log (+ ∞)	Invalid Operation
	±Y × log (− ∞)	Invalid Operation
FYL2XP1	± ∞ × log (1)	Invalid Operation
	± ∞ × log (X>0)	* ∞
	± ∞ × log (−1<X<0)	−* ∞
	±Y × log (+ ∞)	# ∞
	±0 × log (+ ∞)	Invalid Operation
	±Y × log (− ∞)	Invalid Operation

X Zero or nonzero positive operand.
Y Nonzero positive operand.
* Sign of original infinity operand.
−* Complement of sign of original infinity operand.
$ Sign of original operand.
⊕ Exclusive OR of signs of operands.
Sign of the original Y operand.
1 Sign of original zero operand.

There are two classes of NaNs: signaling (SNaN) and quiet (QNaN). Among the QNaNs, the value *real indefinite* is of special interest.

16.1.4.1 SIGNALING NaNs

A signaling NaN is a NaN that has a zero as the most significant bit of its significand. The rest of the significand may be set to any value. The FPU never generates a signaling NaN as a result; however, it recognizes signaling NaNs when they appear as operands. Arithmetic operations (as defined at the beginning of this chapter) on a signaling NaN cause an invalid-operation exception (except for load operations from the stack, FXCH, FCHS, and FABS).

By unmasking the invalid operation exception, the programmer can use signaling NaNs to trap to the exception handler. The generality of this approach and the large number of NaN values that are available provide the sophisticated programmer with a tool that can be applied to a variety of special situations.

For example, a compiler could use signaling NaNs as references to uninitialized (real) array elements. The compiler could preinitialize each array element with a signaling NaN whose significand contained the index (relative position) of the element. If an application program attempted to access an element that it had not initialized, it would use the NaN placed there by the compiler. If the invalid operation exception were unmasked, an interrupt would occur, and the exception handler would be invoked. The exception handler could determine which element had been accessed, since the operand address field of the exception pointers would point to the NaN, and the NaN would contain the index number of the array element.

16.1.4.2 QUIET NaNs

A quiet NaN is a NaN that has a one as the most significant bit of its significand. The i486 processor creates the quiet NaN *real indefinite* (defined below) as its default response to certain exceptional conditions. The i486 processor may derive other QNaNs by converting an SNaN. The i486 processor converts a SNaN by setting the most significant bit of its significand to one, thereby generating an QNaN. The remaining bits of the significand are not changed; therefore, diagnostic information that may be stored in these bits of the SNaN is propagated into the QNaN.

The i486 processor will generate the special QNaN, *real indefinite*, as its masked response to an invalid operation exception. This NaN is signed negative; its significand is encoded $1_{\Delta}100..00$. All other NaNs represent values created by programmers or derived from values created by programmers.

Both quiet and signaling NaNs are supported in all operations. A QNaN is generated as the masked response for invalid-operation exceptions and as the result of an operation in which at least one of the operands is a QNaN. The i486 processor applies the rules shown in Table 16-5 when generating a QNaN.

Note that handling of a QNaN operand has greater priority than all exceptions except certain invalid-operation exceptions (refer to the section "Exception Priority" in this chapter).

Table 16-5. Rules for Generating QNaNs

Operation	Action
Real operation on an SNaN and a QNaN.	Deliver the QNaN operand.
Real operation on two SNaNs.	Deliver the QNaN that results from converting the SNaN that has the larger significand.
Real operation on two QNaNs.	Deliver the QNaN that has the larger significand.
Real operation on an SNaN and another number.	Deliver the QNaN that results from converting the SNaN.
Real operation on a QNaN and another number.	Deliver the QNaN.
Invalid operation that does not involve NaNs.	Deliver the default QNaN *real indefinite.*

Quiet NaNs could be used, for example, to speed up debugging. In its early testing phase, a program often contains multiple errors. An exception handler could be written to save diagnostic information in memory whenever it was invoked. After storing the diagnostic data, it could supply a quiet NaN as the result of the erroneous instruction, and that NaN could point to its associated diagnostic area in memory. The program would then continue, creating a different NaN for each error. When the program ended, the NaN results could be used to access the diagnostic data saved at the time the errors occurred. Many errors could thus be diagnosed and corrected in one test run.

In embedded applications which use computed results in further computations, an undetected QNaN can invalidate all subsequent results. Such applications should therefore periodically check for QNaNs and provide a recovery mechanism to be used if a QNaN result is detected.

16.1.5 Indefinite

For each numeric data type, one unique encoding is reserved for representing the special value *indefinite*. The i486 processor produces this encoding as its response to a masked invalid-operation exception.

In the case of reals, the *indefinite* value is a QNaN as discussed in the prior section.

Packed decimal *indefinite* may be stored with a FBSTP instruction; attempting to use this encoding in a FBLD instruction, however, will have an undefined result; thus *indefinite* cannot be loaded from a packed decimal integer.

In the binary integers, the same encoding may represent either *indefinite* or the largest negative number supported by the format (-2^{15}, -2^{31}, or -2^{63}). The i486 processor will store this encoding as its masked response to an invalid operation, or when the value in a source register represents or rounds to the largest negative integer representable by the destination. In situations where its origin may be ambiguous, the invalid-operation exception flag can be examined to see if the value was produced by an exception response. When this encoding is loaded or used by an integer arithmetic or compare operation, it is always interpreted as a negative number; thus *indefinite* cannot be loaded from a binary integer.

16.1.6 Encoding of Data Types

Tables 16-6 through 16-9 show how each of the special values just described is encoded for each of the numeric data types. In these tables, the least-significant bits are shown to the right and are stored in the lowest memory addresses. The sign bit is always the left-most bit of the highest-addressed byte.

16.1.7 Unsupported Formats

The extended format permits many bit patterns that do not fall into any of the previously mentioned categories. Table 16-10 shows these unsupported formats. Some of these encodings were supported by the 80287 math coprocessor; however, most of them are not supported by the 387 and i486 FPUs. These changes are required due to changes made in the final version of IEEE Std 754 that eliminated these data types.

The categories of encodings formerly known as pseudo-NaNs, pseudoinfinities, and unnormal numbers are not supported. The i486 processor raises the invalid-operation exception when they are encountered as operands.

The encodings formerly known as pseudodenormal numbers are not generated by the i486 processor; however, they are correctly utilized when encountered as operands. The exponent is treated as if it were 00..01 and the mantissa is unchanged. The denormal exception is raised.

Table 16-6. Binary Integer Encodings

Class		Sign	Magnitude
Positives	(Largest)	0	11..11
	⋮	⋮	⋮
	(Smallest)	0	00..01
Zero		0	00..00
Negatives	(Smallest)	1	11..11
	⋮	⋮	⋮
	(Largest/Indefinite*)	1	00..00
		Word: Short: Long:	15 bits 31 bits 63 bits

*If this encoding is used as a source operand (as in an integer load or integer arithmetic instruction), the FPU interprets it as thelargest negative number representable in the format... -2^{15}, -2^{31}, or -2^{63}. The FPU delivers this encoding to an integer destination in two cases:

1. If the result is the largest negative number.
2. As the response to a masked invalid operation exception, in which case it represents the special value *integer indefinite*.

Table 16-7. Packed Decimal Encodings

Class		Sign		Magnitude					
				digit	digit	digit	digit	...	digit
Positives	(Largest)	0	0000000	1 0 0 1	1 0 0 1	1 0 0 1	1 0 0 1	...	1 0 0 1
	.	.	.			.			
	(Smallest)	0	0000000	0 0 0 0	0 0 0 0	0 0 0 0	0 0 0 0	...	0 0 0 1
	Zero	0	0000000	0 0 0 0	0 0 0 0	0 0 0 0	0 0 0 0	...	0 0 0 0
Negatives	Zero	1	0000000	0 0 0 0	0 0 0 0	0 0 0 0	0 0 0 0	...	0 0 0 0
	(Smallest)	1	0000000	0 0 0 0	0 0 0 0	0 0 0 0	0 0 0 0	...	0 0 0 0
	.	.	.			.			
	(Largest)	1	0000000	1 0 0 1	1 0 0 1	1 0 0 1	1 0 0 1	...	1 0 0 1
Indefinite*		1	1111111	1 1 1 1	1 1 1 1	U U U U**	U U U U	...	U U U U
		— 1 byte —		— 9 bytes —					

*The *packed decimal indefinite* is stored by FBSTP in response to a masked invalid operation exception. Attempting to load this value via FBLD produces an undefined result.

**UUUU means bit values are undefined and may contain any value.

Table 16-8. Single and Double Real Encodings

Class				Sign	Biased Exponent	Significand ff-ff*
Positives	NaNs	Quiet		0 0	11..11 . . 11..11	11..11 . . 10..00
		Signaling		0 0	11..11 . . 11..11	01..11 . . 00..01
	Infinity			0	11..11	00..00
	Reals	Normals		0 0	11..10 . . 00..01	11..11 . . 00..00
		Denormals		0 0	00..00 . . 00..00	11..11 . . 00..01
		Zero		0	00..00	00..00
Negatives	Reals	Zero		1	00..00	00.00
		Denormals		1 1	00..00 . . 00..00	00..01 . . 11..11
		Normals		1 1	00..01 . . 11..10	00..00 . . 11..11
	Infinity			1	11..11	00..00
	NaNs	Signaling		1 1	11..11 . . 11..11	00..01 . . 01..11
		Quiet	Indefinite	1 1	11..11 . . 11..11	10..00 . . 11..11
				Single:	– 8 bits –	– 23 bits –
				Double:	– 11 bits –	– 52 bits –

*Integer bit is implied and not stored.

Table 16-9. Extended Real Encodings

		Class		Sign	Biased Exponent	Significand I.ff-ff
Positives	NaNs	Quiet		0 . . 0	11..11 . . 11..11	1 11..11 . . 1 10..00
		Signaling		0 . . 0	11..11 . . 11..11	1 01..11 . . 1 00..01
	Infinity			0	11..11	1 00..00
	Reals	Normals		0 . . 0	11..10 . . 00..01	1 11..11 . . 1 00..00
		Denormals		0 . . 0	00..00 . . 00..00	0 11..11 . . 1 00..01
		Zero		0	00..00	0 00..00
Negatives	Reals	Zero		1	00..00	0 00..00
		Denormals		1 . . 1	00..00 . . 00..00	0 00..01 . . 0 11..11
		Normals		1 . . 1	00..01 . . 11..10	1 00..00 . . 1 11..11
	Infinity			1	11..11	1 00..00
	NaNs	Signaling		1 . . 1	11..11 . . 11..11	1 00..01 . . 1 01..11
		Quiet	Indefinite	1 . . 1	11..11 . . 11..11	1 10..00 . . 1 11..11
					— 15 bits —	— 64 bits —

Table 16-10. Unsupported Formats

Class			Sign	Biased Exponent	Significand f.ff--ff
Positives	Pseudo NaNs	Quiet	0 . 0	11..11 . 11..11	0 11..11 . 0 10..00
		Signaling	0 . 0	11..11 . 11..11	0 01..11 . 0 00..01
	Pseudoinfinity		0	11..11	0 00..00
	Reals	Unnormals	0 . 0	11..10 . 00..01	0 11..11 . 0 00..00
		Pseudodenormals	0 . 0	00..00 . 00..00	1 11..11 . 1 00..00
Negatives	Reals	Pseudodenormals	1 . 1	00..00 . 00..00	1 11..11 . 1 00..00
		Unnormals	1 . 1	11..10 . 00..01	0 11..11 . 0 00..00
	Pseudoinfinity		1	11..11	0 00..00
	Pseudo NaNs	Signaling	1 . 1	11..11 . 11..11	0 01..11 . 0 00..01
		Quiet	1 . 1	11..11 . 11..11	0 11..11 . 0 10..00
				— 15 bits —	— 64 bits —

16.2 NUMERIC EXCEPTIONS

The i486 processor can recognize six classes of numeric exception conditions while executing numeric instructions:

1. I — Invalid operation
   - Stack fault
   - IEEE standard invalid operation
2. Z — Divide-by-zero
3. D — Denormalized operand
4. O — Numeric overflow

5. U– Numeric underflow
6. P– Inexact result (precision)

16.2.1 Handling Numeric Exceptions

When numeric exceptions occur, the i486 processor takes one of two possible courses of action:

- The FPU can itself handle the exception, producing the most reasonable result and allowing numeric program execution to continue undisturbed.
- A software exception handler can be invoked to handle the exception.

Each of the six exception conditions described above has a corresponding flag bit in the FPU status word and a mask bit in the FPU control word. If an exception is masked (the corresponding mask bit in the control word = 1), the i486 processor takes an appropriate default action and continues with the computation. If the exception is unmasked (mask = 0), a software exception handler is invoked immediately before execution of the next WAIT or non-control floating-point instruction. Depending on the value of the NE bit of the CR0 control register, the exception handler is invoked either (NE = 1) through interrupt vector 16 or (NE = 0) through an external interrupt.

Note that when exceptions are masked, the FPU may detect multiple exceptions in a single instruction, because it continues executing the instruction after performing its masked response. For example, the FPU could detect a denormalized operand, perform its masked response to this exception, and then detect an underflow.

16.2.1.1 AUTOMATIC EXCEPTION HANDLING

The i486 processor has a default fix-up activity for every possible exception condition it may encounter. These masked-exception responses are designed to be safe and are generally acceptable for most numeric applications.

As an example of how even severe exceptions can be handled safely and automatically using the default exception responses, consider a calculation of the parallel resistance of several values using only the standard formula (Figure 16-3). If R1 becomes zero, the circuit resistance becomes zero. With the divide-by-zero and precision exceptions masked, the i486 processor will produce the correct result.

By masking or unmasking specific numeric exceptions in the FPU control word, programmers can delegate responsibility for most exceptions to the i486 processor, reserving the most severe exceptions for programmed exception handlers. Exception-handling software is often difficult to write, and the masked responses have been tailored to deliver the most reasonable result for each condition. For the majority of applications, masking all exceptions yields satisfactory results with the least programming effort. Certain exceptions can usefully be left unmasked during the debugging phase of software development, and then masked when the clean software is actually run. An invalid-operation exception for example, typically indicates a program error that must be corrected.

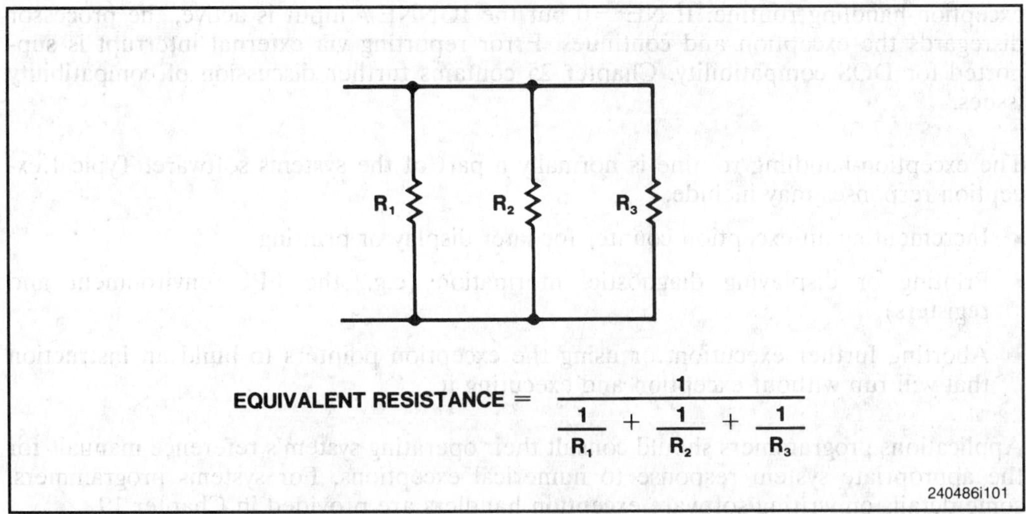

Figure 16-3. Arithmetic Example Using Infinity

The exception flags in the FPU status word provide a cumulative record of exceptions that have occurred since these flags were last cleared. Once set, these flags can be cleared only by executing the FCLEX (clear exceptions) instruction, by reinitializing the FPU, or by overwriting the flags with an FRSTOR or FLDENV instruction. This allows a programmer to mask all exceptions, run a calculation, and then inspect the status word to see if any exceptions were detected at any point in the calculation.

16.2.1.2 SOFTWARE EXCEPTION HANDLING

If the FPU encounters an unmasked exception condition, a software exception handler is invoked immediately before execution of the next WAIT or non-control floating-point instruction. The exception handler is invoked either through interrupt vector 16 or through an external interrupt, depending on the value of the NE bit of the CR0 control register.

If NE = 1, an unmasked floating-point exception results in interrupt 16, immediately before the execution of the next non-control floating-point or WAIT instruction. Interrupt 16 is an operating-system call that invokes the exception handler. Chapter 9 contains a general discussion of exceptions and interrupts on the i486 processor.

If NE = 0 (and the IGNNE# input is inactive), an unmasked floating-point exception causes the processor to freeze immediately before executing the next non-control floating-point or WAIT instruction. The frozen processor waits for an external interrupt, which must be supplied by external hardware in response to the FERR# output of the processor. (Regardless of the value of NE, an unmasked numerical exception causes the FERR# output to be activated.) In this case, the external interrupt invokes the exception-handling routine. If NE =0 but the IGNNE# input is active, the processor disregards the exception and continues. Error reporting via external interrupt is supported for DOS compatibility. Chapter 25 contains further discussion of compatibility issues.

The exception-handling routine is normally a part of the systems software. Typical exception responses may include:

- Incrementing an exception counter for later display or printing
- Printing or displaying diagnostic information (e.g., the FPU environment and registers)
- Aborting further execution, or using the exception pointers to build an instruction that will run without exception and executing it

Applications programmers should consult their operating system's reference manuals for the appropriate system response to numerical exceptions. For systems programmers, some details on writing software exception handlers are provided in Chapter 19.

16.2.2 Invalid Operation

This exception may occur in response to two general classes of operations:

1. Stack operations
2. Arithmetic operations

The stack flag (SF) of the status word indicates which class of operation caused the exception. When SF is 1 a stack operation has resulted in stack overflow or underflow; when SF is 0, an arithmetic instruction has encountered an invalid operand.

16.2.2.1 STACK EXCEPTION

When SF is 1, indicating a stack operation, the O/U# bit of the condition code (bit C1) distinguishes between stack overflow and underflow as follows:

O/U# = 1 Stack overflow—an instruction attempted to push down a nonempty stack location.

O/U# = 0 Stack underflow—an instruction attempted to read an operand from an empty stack location.

When the invalid-operation exception is masked, the FPU returns the QNaN *indefinite*. This value overwrites the destination register, destroying its original contents.

When the invalid-operation exception is not masked, an exception handler is invoked. TOP is not changed, and the source operands remain unaffected.

16.2.2.2 INVALID ARITHMETIC OPERATION

This class includes the invalid operations defined in IEEE Std 854. The FPU reports an invalid operation in any of the cases shown in Table 16-11. Also shown in this table are the FPU's responses when the invalid exception is masked. When unmasked, an exception handler is invoked, and the operands remain unaltered. An invalid operation generally indicates a program error.

16.2.3 Division by Zero

If an instruction attempts to divide a finite nonzero operand by zero, the FPU will report a zero-divide exception. This is possible for F(I)DIV(R)(P) as well as the other instructions that perform division internally: FYL2X and FXTRACT. The masked response for FDIV and FYL2X is to return an infinity signed with the exclusive OR of the signs of

Table 16-11. Masked Responses to Invalid Operations

Condition	Masked Response
Any arithmetic operationon an unsupported format.	Return the QNaN *indefinite*.
Any arithmetic operation on a signaling NaN.	Return a QNaN (refer to the section "Rules for Generating QNaNs").
Compare and test operations: one or both operands is a NaN.	Set condition codes "not comparable."
Addition of opposite-signed infinities or subtraction of like-signed infinities.	Return the QNaN *indefinite*.
Multiplication: $\infty \times 0$; or $0 \times \infty$.	Return theQNaN *indefinite*.
Division: $\infty \div \infty$; or $0 \div 0$.	Return the QNaN *indefinite*.
Remainder instructions FPREM, FPREM1 when modulus (divisor) is zero or dividend is ∞.	Return the QNaN *indefinite*; set C_2.
Trigonometric instructions FCOS, FPTAN, FSIN, FSINCOS when argument is ∞.	Return theQNaN *indefinite*; set C_2.
FSQRT of negative operand (except FSQRT $(-0) = -0$), FYL2X of negative operand (except FYL2X $(-0) = -\infty$), FYL2XP1 of operand more negative than -1.	Return the QNaN *indefinite*.
FIST(P) instructions when source register is empty, a NaN, ∞, or exceeds representable range of destination.	Store integer *indefinite*.
FBSTP instruction when source register is empty, a NaN, ∞, or exceeds 18 decimal digits.	Store packed decimal *indefinite*.
FXCH instruction when one or both registers are tagged empty.	Change empty registers to the QNaN *indefinite* and then perform exchange.

the operands. For FXTRACT, ST(1) is set to $-\infty$; ST is set to zero with the same sign as the original operand. If the divide-by-zero exception is unmasked, an exception handler is invoked; the operands remain unaltered.

16.2.4 Denormal Operand

If an arithmetic instruction attempts to operate on a denormal operand, the FPU reports the denormal-operand exception. Denormal operands may have reduced significance due to lost low-order bits, therefore it may be advisable in certain applications to preclude operations on these operands. This can be accomplished by an exception handler that responds to unmasked denormal exceptions. Most users will mask this exception so that computation may proceed; any loss of accuracy will be analyzed by the user when the final result is delivered.

When this exception is masked, the FPU sets the D-bit in the status word, then proceeds with the instruction. Gradual underflow and denormal numbers as handled on the i486 processor will produce results at least as good as, and often better than what could be obtained from a machine that flushes underflows to zero. In fact, a denormal operand in single- or double-precision format will be normalized to the extended-real format when loaded into the FPU. Subsequent operations will benefit from the additional precision of the extended-real format used internally.

When this exception is not masked, the D-bit is set and the exception handler is invoked. The operands are not changed by the instruction and are available for inspection by the exception handler.

The i486 FPU and 387 math coprocessors handle denormal values differently than the 8087 and 80287. This change is due to revisions in the IEEE standard before being approved. The difference in operation occurs when the denormal exception is masked. The i486 FPU and 387 math coprocessors will automatically normalize denormals. The 8087 and 80287 math coprocessors will generate a denormal result.

The difference in denormal handling is usually not an issue. The denormal exception is normally masked for the 387 and i486 FPUs. For programs that also run on a 80287 math coprocessor, the denormal exception is often unmasked and an exception handler is provided to normalize any denormal values. Such an exception handler is redundant for the i486 and 387 DX FPUs. The default exception handler should be used.

A program can detect at run-time whether it is running on a 387 or i486 FPU or the older 8087/80287 math coprocessors. The code sequence in Figure 16-4 is recommended to recognize an 8087/80287. The example in Figure 16-4 can be used to selectively mask the denormal exception for a 387 DX or i486 FPU. A denormal exception handler should also be provided to support an 8087/80287 math coprocessor. This code example can also be used to set a flag to allow use of new instructions added to the 387 and i486 FPUs beyond the instructions of the 8087/80287 math coprocessors.

```
FINIT                ; Use default infinity mode:
                     ;  projective for 8087/80287,
                     ;  affine for 387 DX and i486 FPU
FLD1                 ; Generate infinity
FLDZ
FDIV
FLD    ST            ; Form negative infinity
FCHS
FCOMPP               ; Compare +infinity with -infinity
FSTSW  temp          ; 8087/80287 will say they are equal
MOV    AX, temp
SAHF
JZ     Using_8087
```

Figure 16-4. Coprocessor Detection Code

16.2.5 Numeric Overflow and Underflow

If the exponent of a numeric result is too large for the destination real format, the FPU signals a numeric overflow. Conversely, if the exponent of a result is too small to be represented in the destination format, a numeric underflow is signaled. If either of these exceptions occur, the result of the operation is outside the range of the destination real format.

Typical algorithms are most likely to produce extremely large and small numbers in the calculation of intermediate, rather than final, results. Because of the great range of the extended-precision format, overflow and underflow are relatively rare events in most numerical applications for the i486 processor.

16.2.5.1 OVERFLOW

The overflow exception can occur whenever the rounded true result would exceed in magnitude the largest finite number in the destination format. The exception can occur in the execution of most of the arithmetic instructions and in some of the conversion instructions; namely, FST(P), F(I)ADD(P), F(I)SUB(R)(P), F(I)MUL(P), FDIV(R)(P), FSCALE, FYL2X, and FYL2XP1.

The response to an overflow condition depends on whether the overflow exception is masked:

- Overflow exception masked. The value returned depends on the rounding mode as Table 16-12 illustrates.

- Overflow exception not masked. The unmasked response depends on whether the instruction is supposed to store the result on the stack or in memory:

  - If the destination is the stack, then true result is divided by $2^{24,576}$ and rounded. (The bias 24,576 is equal to 3×2^{13}.) The significand is rounded to the appropriate precision (according to the precision control (PC) bit of the control word, for those instructions controlled by PC, otherwise to extended precision). The roundup bit (C1) of the status word is set if the significand was rounded upward.

    The biasing of the exponent by 24,576 normally translates the number as nearly as possible to the middle of the exponent range so that, if desired, it can be used in subsequent scaled operations with less risk of causing further exceptions. With the instruction FSCALE, however, it can happen that the result is too large and overflows even after biasing. In this case, the unmasked response is exactly the same as the masked round-to-nearest response, namely ± infinity. The intention of this feature is to ensure the trap handler will discover that a translation of the exponent by −24574 would not work correctly without obliging the programmer of Decimal-to-Binary or Exponential functions to determine which trap handler, if any, should be invoked.

  - If the destination is memory (this can occur only with the store instructions), then no result is stored in memory. Instead, the operand is left intact in the stack. Because the data in the stack is in extended-precision format, the exception handler has the option either of reexecuting the store instruction after proper adjustment of the operand or of rounding the significand on the stack to the destination's precision as the standard requires. The exception handler should ultimately store a value into the destination location in memory if the program is to continue.

Table 16-12. Masked Overflow Results

Rounding Mode	Sign of True Result	Result
To nearest	+ −	+ ∞ − ∞
Toward − ∞	+ −	Largest finite positive number − ∞
Toward + ∞	+ −	+ ∞ Largest finite negative number
Toward zero	+ −	Largest finite positive number Largest finite negative number

16.2.5.2 UNDERFLOW

Underflow can occur in the execution of the instructions FST(P), FADD(P), FSUB(RP), FMUL(P), F(I)DIV(RP), FSCALE, FPREM(1), FPTAN, FSIN, FCOS, FSINCOS, FPATAN, F2XM1, FYL2X, and FYL2XP1.

Two related events contribute to underflow:

1. Creation of a tiny result which, because it is so small, may cause some other exception later (such as overflow upon division).
2. Creation of an inexact result; i.e. the delivered result differs from what would have been computed were both the exponent range and precision unbounded.

Which of these events triggers the underflow exception depends on whether the underflow exception is masked:

1. Underflow exception masked. The underflow exception is signaled when the result is both tiny and inexact.
2. Underflow exception not masked. The underflow exception is signaled when the result is tiny, regardless of inexactness.

The response to an underflow exception also depends on whether the exception is masked:

1. Masked response. The result is denormal or zero. The precision exception is also triggered.
2. Unmasked response. The unmasked response depends on whether the instruction is supposed to store the result on the stack or in memory:
   - If the destination is the stack, then the true result is multiplied by $2^{24,576}$ and rounded. (The bias 24,576 is equal to 3×2^{13}.) The significand is rounded to the appropriate precision (according to the precision control (PC) bit of the control word, for those instructions controlled by PC, otherwise to extended precision). The roundup bit (C_1) of the status word is set if the significand was rounded upward.

     The biasing of the exponent by 24,576 normally translates the number as nearly as possible to the middle of the exponent range so that, if desired, it can be used in subsequent scaled operations with less risk of causing further exceptions. With the instruction FSCALE, however, it can happen that the result is too tiny and underflows even after biasing. In this case, the unmasked response is exactly the same as the masked round-to-nearest response, namely ± 0. The intention of this feature is to ensure the trap handler will discover that a translation by $+24576$ would not work correctly without obliging the programmer of Decimal-to-Binary or Exponential functions to determine which trap handler, if any, should be invoked.
   - If the destination is memory (this can occur only with the store instructions), then no result is stored in memory. Instead, the operand is left intact in the stack.

Because the data in the stack is in extended-precision format, the exception handler has the option either of reexecuting the store instruction after proper adjustment of the operand or of rounding the significand on the stack to the destination's precision as the standard requires. The exception handler should ultimately store a value into the destination location in memory if the program is to continue.

16.2.6 Inexact (Precision)

This exception condition occurs if the result of an operation is not exactly representable in the destination format. For example, the fraction 1/3 cannot be precisely represented in binary form. This exception occurs frequently and indicates that some (generally acceptable) accuracy has been lost.

By their nature, the transcendental instructions typically cause the inexact exception.

The C1 (roundup) bit of the status word indicates whether the inexact result was rounded up (C1 = 1) or chopped (C1 = 0).

The inexact exception accompanies the underflow exception when there is also a loss of accuracy. When underflow is masked, the underflow exception is signaled only when there is a loss of accuracy; therefore the precision flag is always set as well. When underflow is unmasked, there may or may not have been a loss of accuracy; the precision bit indicates which is the case.

This exception is provided for applications that need to perform exact arithmetic only. Most applications will mask this exception. The FPU delivers the rounded or over/underflowed result to the destination, regardless of whether a trap occurs.

16.2.7 Exception Priority

The i486 processor deals with exceptions according to a predetermined precedence. Precedence in exception handling means that higher-priority exceptions are flagged and results are delivered according to the requirements of that exception. Lower-priority exceptions may not be flagged even if they occur. For example, dividing an SNaN by zero causes an invalid-operand exception (due to the SNaN) and not a zero-divide exception; the masked result is the QNaN *real indefinite*, not ∞. A denormal or inexact (precision) exception, however, can accompany a numeric underflow or overflow exception.

The precedence among numeric exceptions is as follows:

1. Invalid operation exception, subdivided as follows:
   a. Stack underflow.
   b. Stack overflow.
   c. Operand of unsupported format.
   d. SNaN operand.

2. QNaN operand. Though this is not an exception, if one operand is a QNaN, dealing with it has precedence over lower-priority exceptions. For example, a QNaN divided by zero results in a QNaN, not a zero-divide exception.
3. Any other invalid-operation exception not mentioned above or zero divide.
4. Denormal operand. If masked, then instruction execution continues, and a lower-priority exception can occur as well.
5. Numeric overflow and underflow. Inexact result (precision) can be flagged as well.
6. Inexact result (precision).

16.2.8 Standard Underflow/Overflow Exception Handler

As long as the underflow and overflow exceptions are masked, no additional software is required to cause the output of the i486 processor to conform to the requirements of IEEE Std 854. When unmasked, these exceptions give the exception handler an additional option in the case of store instructions. No result is stored in memory; instead, the operand is left intact on the stack. The handler may round the significand of the operand on the stack to the destination's precision as the standard requires, or it may adjust the operand and reexecute the faulting instruction.

Floating-Point Instruction Set 17

CHAPTER 17
FLOATING-POINT INSTRUCTION SET

The floating-point instructions available on the i486™ processor can be grouped into six functional classes:

- Data Transfer Instructions
- Nontranscendental Instructions
- Comparison Instructions
- Transcendental Instructions
- Constant Instructions
- Control Instructions

In this chapter, the instruction classes are described as a collection of resources available to ASM386/486 programmers. For details of format, encoding, and execution times, see the instruction reference pages in Chapter 26.

The 387™ math coprocessors and i486 FPU have more instructions than the 8087/80287 math coprocessors. Some 386 DX microprocessor systems use an 80287 math coprocessor. See Figure 16-4 for an example of how to detect whether an 8087/80287 math coprocessor is present to use the new instructions when available.

17.1 SOURCE AND DESTINATION OPERANDS

The typical floating-point instruction takes one or two operands, which can come from the FPU register stack or from memory. Many instructions, such as FSIN, automatically operate on the top FPU stack element. Others allow, or require, the programmer to code the operand(s) explicitly along with the instruction mnemonic. Still others accept one explicit operand and one implicit operand (usually the top FPU stack element).

Whether specified by the programmer or supplied by default, floating-point operands are of two basic types, *sources* and *destinations*. A source operand provides an input to an instruction, but is not altered by its execution. Even when an instruction converts the source operand from one format to another (e.g., real to integer), the conversion is performed in an internal work area to avoid altering the source operand. A destination operand may also provide an input to an instruction; on execution, however, the instruction returns a result to the destination, overwriting its previous contents.

Many instructions allow their operands to be coded in more than one way. For example, FADD (add real) may be written without operands, with only a source, or with a destination and a source. When both destination and source operands are specified, the destination must precede the source on the command line, and both must come from the FPU stack.

Memory operands can be coded with any of the memory-addressing methods provided by the ModR/M byte. To review these methods (BASE + (INDEX X SCALE) + DISPLACEMENT), refer to Chapter 2. Floating-point instructions with memory operands either read from memory or write to it; no floating-point instruction does both.For a detailed description of each instruction, including its range of possible encodings, see the reference pages in Chapter 26.

17.2 DATA TRANSFER INSTRUCTIONS

These instructions (summarized in Table 17-1) move operands among elements of the register stack, and between the stack top and memory. Any of the seven data types can be converted to extended-real and loaded (pushed) onto the stack in a single operation; they can be stored to memory in the same manner. The data transfer instructions automatically update the FPU tag word to reflect whether the register is empty or full following the instruction.

17.3 NONTRANSCENDENTAL INSTRUCTIONS

The nontranscendental instruction set provides a wealth of variations on the basic add, subtract, multiply, and divide operations, and a number of other useful functions. These range from a simple absolute value instruction to instructions which perform exact modulo division, round real numbers to integers, and scale values by powers of two. Table 17-2 shows the nontranscendental operations provided, apart from basic arithmetic.

The basic arithmetic instructions (addition, subtraction, multiplication and division) are designed to encourage the development of very efficient algorithms. In particular, they allow the programmer to reference memory as easily as the FPU register stack. Table 17-3 summarizes the available operation/operand forms that are provided for basic arithmetic. In addition to the four normal operations, there are "reversed" subtraction

Table 17-1. Data Transfer Instructions

Real		Integer		Packed Decimal	
FLD	Load Real	FILD	Load Integer	FBLD	Load Packed Decimal
FST	Store Real	FIST	Store Integer		
FSTP	Store Real and Pop	FISTP	Store Integer and Pop	FBSTP	Load Packed Decimal and Pop
FXCH	Exchange registers				

Table 17-2. Nontranscendental Instructions (Besides Basic Arithmetic)

Mnemonic	Operation
FSQRT	Square Root
FSCALE	Scale
FXTRACT	Extract Exponent and Significand
FPREM	Partial Remainder
FPREM1*	IEEE Standard Partial Remainder
FRNDINT	Round to Integer
FABS	Absolute Value
FCHS	Change Sign

*Not available on 8087/80287 math coprocessor.

Table 17-3. Basic Arithmetic Instructions and Opernads

Instruction Form	Mnemonic Form	Operand Forms: Destination, Source
Classical Stack	F*op*	{ST(1), ST}
Classical Stack, extra pop	F*op*P	{ST(1), ST}
Register	F*op*	ST(i), ST or ST, ST(i)
Register, pop	F*op*P	ST(i), ST
Real Memory	F*op*	{ST} single-real/double-real
Integer Memory	FI*op*	{ST} word-integer/short-integer

NOTES:

Braces ({ }) surround implicit operands; these are not coded, but are supplied by the assembler.

op=	ADD	DEST ← DEST + SRC
	SUB	DEST ← ST − Other Operand
	SUBR	DEST ← Other Operand − ST
	MUL	DEST ← DEST × SRC
	DIV	DEST ← ST ÷ Other Operand
	DIVR	DEST ← Other Operand ÷ ST

and division instructions which eliminate the need for many exchanges between ST(0) and ST(1). The variety of instruction and operand forms give the programmer unusual flexibility:

- Operands can be located in registers or memory.
- Results can be deposited in a choice of registers.
- Operands can be a variety of numerical data types: extended real, double real, single real, short integer or word integer, with automatic conversion to extended real performed by the FPU.

Five basic instruction forms can be used across all six operations, as shown in Table 17-3. The classical stack form can be used to make the FPU operate like a classical stack machine. No operands are coded in this form, only the instruction mnemonic. The FPU picks the source operand from the stack top (ST) and the destination from the next stack element (ST(1)). After performing its calculation, it returns the result to ST(1) and then pops ST, effectively replacing the operands by the result.

The register form is a generalization of the classical stack form; the programmer specifies the stack top as one operand and any register on the stack as the other operand. Coding the stack top as the destination provides a convenient way to access a constant, held elsewhere in the stack, from the top stack. The destination need not always be ST, however. The basic two-operand instructions allow the use of another register as the destination. Using ST as the source allows, for example, adding the stack top into a register used as an accumulator.

Often the operand in the stack top is needed for one operation but then is of no further use in the computation. The register pop form can be used to pick up the stack top as the source operand, and then discard it by popping the stack. Coding operands of ST(1), ST with a register pop mnemonic is equivalent to a classical stack operation: the top is popped and the result is left at the new top.

The two memory forms increase the flexibility of the nontranscendental instructions. They permit a real number or a binary integer in memory to be used directly as a source operand. This is useful in situations where operands are not used frequently enough to justify holding them in registers. Note that any memory-addressing method can be used to define these operands, so they can be elements in arrays, structures, or other data organizations, as well as simple scalars.

17.4 COMPARISON INSTRUCTIONS

The instructions of this class allow numbers of all supported real and integer data types to be compared. Each of these instructions (Table 17-4) analyzes the top stack element, often in relationship to another operand, and reports the result as a condition code (flags C0, C2, and C3) in the status word.

The basic operations are compare, test (compare with zero), and examine (report type, sign, and normalization). Special forms of the compare operation are provided to optimize algorithms by allowing direct comparisons with binary integers and real numbers in memory, as well as popping the stack after a comparison.

Table 17-4. Comparison Instructions

Mnemonic	Operation
FCOM	Compare Real
FCOMP	Compare Real and Pop
FCOMPP	Compare Real and Pop Twice
FICOM	Compare Integer
FICOMP	Compare Integer and Pop
FTST	Test
FUCOM*	Unordered Compare Real
FUCOMP*	Unordered Compare Realand Pop
FUCOMPP*	Unordered Compare Real and Pop Twice
FXAM	Examine

*Not available on 8087/80287 math coprocessor.

The FSTSW AX (store status word) instruction can be used after a comparison to transfer the condition code to the AX register for inspection. The TEST instruction is recommended for using the FPU flags (once they are in the AX register) to control conditional branching. First check to see if the comparison resulted in *unordered*. This can happen, for instance, if one of the operands is a NaN. TEST the contents of the AX register against the constant 0400H; this will clear ZF (the Zero Flag of the EFLAGS register) if the original comparison was unordered, and set ZF otherwise. The JNZ instruction can now be used to transfer control (if necessary) to code which handles the case of unordered operands. With the unordered case now filtered out, TEST the contents of the AX register against the appropriate constant from Table 17-5, and then use the corresponding conditional branch.

It is not always necessary to filter out the unordered case when using this algorithm for conditional jumps. If the software has been thoroughly tested, and incorporates periodic checks for QNaN results (as recommended in Chapter 16), then it is not necessary to check for *unordered* every time a comparison is made.

Instructions other than those in the comparison group can update the condition code. To ensure that the status word is not altered inadvertently, store it immediately following a comparison operation.

17.5 TRANSCENDENTAL INSTRUCTIONS

The instructions in this group (Table 17-6) perform the time-consuming core calculations for all common trigonometric, inverse trigonometric, hyperbolic, inverse hyperbolic, logarithmic, and exponential functions. The transcendentals operate on the top one or two stack elements, and they return their results to the stack. The trigonometric operations assume their arguments are expressed in radians. The logarithmic and exponential operations work in base 2.

The results of transcendental instructions are highly accurate. The absolute value of the relative error of the transcendental instructions is guaranteed to be less than 2^{-62}. (Relative error is the ratio between the absolute error and the exact value.)

The trigonometric functions accept a practically unrestricted range of operands, whereas the other transcendental instructions require that arguments be more restricted in range. FPREM or FPREM1 can be used to bring the otherwise valid operand of a periodic function into range. Prologue and epilogue software can be used to reduce arguments

Table 17-5. TEST Constants for Conditional Branching

Order	Constant	Branch
ST > Operand	4500H	JZ
ST < Operand	0100H	JNZ
ST = Operand	4000H	JNZ
Unordered	0400H	JNZ

Table 17-6. Transcendental Instructions

Mnemonic	Operation
FSIN*	Sine
FCOS*	Cosine
FSINCOS*	Sine and Cosine
FPTAN**	Tangent
FPATAN	Arctangent of ST(1) ÷ ST
F2XM1**	$2^X - 1$; X is in ST
FYL2X	Y x $\log_2 X$; Y is in ST(1), X is in ST
FYL2XP1	Y x $\log_2(X + 1)$; Y is in ST(1), X is in ST

*Not available on 80287/8087 math coprocessor.
**Operand range extended over 80287/8087 math coprocessor.

for other instructions to the expected range and to adjust the result to correspond to the original arguments if necessary. The instruction descriptions in the reference pages of Chapter 26 document the allowed operand range for each instruction.

When the argument of a trigonometric function is in range, it is automatically reduced by the appropriate multiple of 2π (in 66-bit precision), by means of the same mechanism used in the FPREM and FPREM1 instructions. The value of π used in the automatic reduction has been chosen so as to guarantee no loss of significance in the operand, provided it is within the specified range. The internal value of π is:

4 * 0.C90FDAA2 2168C234 C H

A program may use an explicit value for π in computations whose results later appear as arguments to trigonometric functions. In such a case (in explicit reduction of a trigonometric operand outside the specified range, for example), the value used for π should be the same as the full 66-bit internal π. This will insure that the results are consistent with the automatic argument reduction performed by the trigonometric functions. The 66-bit π cannot be represented as an extended-real value, so it must be encoded as two or more numbers. A common solution is to represent π as the sum of a highπ which contains the 33 most-significant bits and a lowπ which contains the 33 least-significant bits. When using this two-part π, all computations should be performed separately on each part, with the results added only at the end.

The complications of maintaining a consistent value of π for argument reduction can be avoided, either by applying the trigonometric functions only to arguments within the range of the automatic reduction mechanism, or by performing all argument reductions (down to a magnitude less than π/4) explicitly in software.

17.6 CONSTANT INSTRUCTIONS

Each of these instructions (Table 17-7) pushes a commonly used constant onto the stack. (ST(7) must be empty to avoid an invalid exception.) The values have full extended real precision (64 bits) and are accurate to approximately 19 decimal digits. Because an

Table 17-7. Constant Instructions

Mnemonic	Operation
FLDZ	Load +0.0
FLD1	Load +1.0
FLDPI	Load π
FLDL2T	Load $\log_2 10$
FLDL2E	Load $\log_2 e$
FLDLG2	Load $\log_{10} 2$
FLDLN2	Load $\log_e 2$

external real constant occupies 10 memory bytes, the constant instructions, which are only two bytes long, save storage and improve execution speed, in addition to simplifying programming.

The constants used by these instructions are stored internally in a format more precise than extended real. When loading the constant, the FPU rounds the more precise internal constant according the RC (rounding control) bit of the control word. However, in spite of this rounding, the precision exception is not raised (to maintain compatibility). When the rounding control is set to round to nearest, the FPU produces the same constant that is produced by the 8087 and 80287 numeric coprocessors.

17.7 CONTROL INSTRUCTIONS

The FPU control instructions are shown in Table 17-8. The FSTSW instruction is commonly used for conditional branching. The remaining instructions are not typically used in calculations; they provide control over the FPU for system-level activities. These activities include initialization of the FPU, numeric exception handling, and task switching.

Table 17-8. Control Instructions

Mnemonic	Operation
FINIT / FNINIT	Initialize FPU
FLDCW	Load Control Word
FSTCW / FNSTCW	Store Control Word
FSTSW / FNSTSW	Store Status Word
FSTSW AX / FNSTSW AX*	Store Status Word to AX Register
FCLEX / FNCLEX	Clear Exceptions
FSTENV / FNSTENV	Store Environment
FLDENV	Load Environment
FSAVE / FNSAVE	Save State
FRSTOR	Restore State
FINCSTP	Increment Stack-Top Pointer
FDECSTP	Decrement Stack-Top Pointer
FFREE	Free Register
FNOP	No Operation
FWAIT	Report FPU Error

*Not available on 8087 math coprocessor.

As shown in Table 17-8, certain instructions have alternative mnemonics. The instructions which initialize the FPU, clear exceptions, or store (all or part of) the FPU environment come in two forms:

- *Wait* – the mnemonic is prefixed only with an F, such as FSTSW. This form checks for unmasked numeric exceptions.
- *No-wait* – the mnemonic is prefixed with an FN, such as FNSTSW. This form ignores unmasked numeric exceptions.

When the control instruction is coded using the no-wait form of the mnemonic, the ASM386/486 assembler does not precede the ESC instruction with a WAIT instruction, and the processor does not test for a floating-point error condition before executing the control instruction.

The only no-wait instructions are those shown in Table 17-8. All other floating-point instructions are automatically synchronized by the processor; all operands are transferred before the next instruction is initiated. Because of this automatic synchronization, non-control floating-point instructions need not be preceded by a WAIT instruction in order to execute correctly.

Exception synchronization relies on the WAIT instruction. Since the Integer Unit and the FPU operate in parallel, it is possible in the case of a floating-point exception for the processor to disturb information vital to exception recovery before the exception-handler can be invoked. Coding a WAIT or FWAIT instruction in the proper place can prevent this. See Chapter 18 for details.

It should also be noted that the 8087 instructions FENI and FDISI and the 80287 instruction FSETPM perform no function in the i486 processor. If these opcodes are detected in the instruction stream, the i486 processor performs no specific operation and no internal states are affected. Chapter 25 contain a more complete description of the differences between floating-point operations on the i486 processor and on 8087, 80287, and 387 DX numeric coprocessors.

Numeric Applications 18

CHAPTER 18
NUMERIC APPLICATIONS

18.1 PROGRAMMING FACILITIES

This section describes how programmers in ASM386/486 and in a variety of higher-level languages can make use of the i486™ processor's numerics capabilities.

The level of detail in this section is intended to give programmers a basic understanding of the software tools that can be used for numeric programming, but this information does not document the full capabilities of these facilities. Complete documentation is available with each program development product.

18.1.1 High-Level Languages

A variety of Intel® high-level languages are available that automatically make use of the numeric instruction set when appropriate. These languages include C-386/486 and PL/M-386/486. In addition many high-level language compilers are available from independent software vendors.

Each of these high-level languages has special numeric libraries allowing programs to take advantage of the capabilities of the FPU. No special programming conventions are necessary to make use of the FPU when programming numeric applications in any of these languages.

Programmers in PL/M-386/486 and ASM386/486 can also make use of many of these library routines by using routines contained in the Support Library. These libraries implement many of the functions provided by higher-level languages, including exception handlers, ASCII-to-floating-point conversions, and a more complete set of transcendental functions than that provided by the i486 numeric instruction set.

18.1.2 C Programs

C programmers automatically cause the C compiler to generate i486 numeric instructions when they use the **double** and **float** data types. The **float** type corresponds to the single real format; the **double** type corresponds to the double real format. The statement **#include ⟨math.h⟩** causes mathematical functions such as **sin** and **sqrt** to return values of type **double**. Figure 18-1 illustrates the ease with which C programs can make use of the i486 processor's numerics capabilities.

```
/*********************************************************
*                                                        *
*                  SAMPLE C PROGRAM                      *
*                                                        *
*********************************************************/

/** Include /usr/include/stdio.h if necessary **/
/** Include math declarations for transcendenatals and others **/

#include </usr/include/math.h>
#define PI 3.1415926535897943

main()
{
double        sin_result, cos_result;
double        angle_deg = 0.0, angle_rad;
int           i, no_of_trial = 4;

    for( i = 1; i <= no_of_trial; i++){
        angle_rad = angle_deg * PI / 180.0;
        sin_result = sin (angle_rad);
        cos_result = cos (angle_rad);
        printf("sine of %f degrees equals %f\n", angle_deg, sin_result);
        printf("cosine of %f degrees equals %f\n\n", angle_deg, cos_result);
        angle_deg = angle_deg + 30.0;
        }
  /** etc. **/
  }
```

Figure 18-1. Sample C-386/486 Program

18.1.3 PL/M-386/486

Programmers in PL/M-386/486 can access a very useful subset of the i486 processor's numeric capabilities. The PL/M-386/486 REAL data type corresponds to the single real (32-bit) format. This data type provides a range of about $8.43 \times 10^{-37} \leq |X| \leq 3.38 \times 10^{38}$, with about seven significant decimal digits. This representation is adequate for the data manipulated by many microcomputer applications.

The utility of the REAL data type is extended by the PL/M-386/486 compiler's practice of holding intermediate results in the extended real format. This means that the full range and precision of the processor are utilized for intermediate results. Underflow, overflow, and rounding exceptions are most likely to occur during intermediate computations rather than during calculation of an expression's final result. Holding intermediate results in extended-precision real format greatly reduces the likelihood of overflow and underflow and eliminates roundoff as a serious source of error until the final assignment of the result is performed.

The compiler generates floating-point instructions to evaluate expressions that contain REAL data types, whether variables or constants or both. This means that addition, subtraction, multiplication, division, comparison, and assignment of REALs will be performed by the FPU. INTEGER expressions, on the other hand, are evaluated by the Integer Unit.

Five built-in procedures (Table 18-1) give the PL/M-386/486 programmer access to FPU control instructions. Prior to any arithmetic operations, a typical PL/M-386/486 program will set up the FPU using the INIT$REAL$MATH$UNIT procedure and then issue SET$REAL$MODE to configure the FPU. SET$REAL$MODE loads the FPU control word, and its 16-bit parameter has the format shown for the control word in Chapter 14. The recommended value of this parameter is 033EH (round to nearest, 64-bit precision, all exceptions masked except invalid operation). Other settings may be used at the programmer's discretion.

If any exceptions are unmasked, an exception handler must be provided in the form of an interrupt procedure that is designated to be invoked via interrupt vector number 16. The exception handler can use the GET$REAL$ERROR procedure to obtain the low-order byte of the FPU status word and to then clear the exception flags. The byte returned by GET$REAL$ERROR contains the exception flags; these can be examined to determine the source of the exception.

The SAVE$REAL$STATUS and RESTORE$REAL$STATUS procedures are provided for multitasking environments where a running task that uses the FPU may be preempted by another task that also uses the FPU. It is the responsibility of the operating system to issue SAVE$REAL$STATUS before it executes any statements that affect the FPU; these include the INIT$REAL$MATH$UNIT and SET$REAL$MODE procedures as well as arithmetic expressions. SAVE$REAL$STATUS saves the FPU state (registers, status, and control words, etc.) on the memory stack. RESTORE$REAL$STATUS reloads the state information; the preempting task must invoke this procedure before terminating in order to restore the FPU to its state at the time the running task was preempted. This enables the preempted task to resume execution from the point of its preemption.

Table 18-1. PL/M-386/486 Built-In Procedures

Procedure	FPU Control Instruction	Description
INIT$REAL$MATH$UNIT	FINIT	Initialize FPU
SET$REAL$MODE	FLDCW	Set exception masks, rounding precision, and infinity controls.
GET$REAL$ERROR	FNSTSW & FNCLEX	Store, then clear, exception flags.
SAVE$REAL$STATUS	FNSAVE	Save FPU state.
RESTORE$REAL$STATUS	FRSTOR	Restore FPU state.

18.1.4 ASM386/486

The ASM386/486 assembly language provides programmers with complete access to all of the facilities of the processor.

18.1.4.1 DEFINING DATA

The ASM386/486 directives shown in Table 18-2 allocate storage for numeric variables and constants. As with other storage allocation directives, the assembler associates a type with any variable defined with these directives. The type value is equal to the length of the storage unit in bytes (10 for DT, 8 for DQ, etc.). The assembler checks the type of any variable coded in an instruction to be certain that it is compatible with the instruction. For example, the coding FIADD ALPHA will be flagged as an error if ALPHA's type is not 2 or 4, because integer addition is only available for word and short integer (doubleword) data types. The operand's type also tells the assembler which machine instruction to produce; although to the programmer there is only an FIADD instruction, a different machine instruction is required for each operand type.

On occasion it is desirable to use an instruction with an operand that has no declared type. For example, if register BX points to a short integer variable, a programmer may want to code FIADD [BX]. This can be done by informing the assembler of the operand's type in the instruction, coding FIADD DWORD PTR [BX]. The corresponding overrides for the other storage allocations are WORD PTR, QWORD PTR, and TBYTE PTR.

The assembler does not, however, check the types of operands used in processor control instructions. Coding FRSTOR [BP] implies that the programmer has set up register BP to point to the location (probably in the stack) where the processor's 94-byte state record has been previously saved.

The initial values for numeric constants may be coded in several different ways. Binary integer constants may be specified as bit strings, decimal integers, octal integers, or hexadecimal strings. Packed decimal values are normally written as decimal integers, although the assembler will accept and convert other representations of integers. Real values may be written as ordinary decimal real numbers (decimal point required), as decimal numbers in scientific notation, or as hexadecimal strings. Using hexadecimal strings is primarily intended for defining special values such as infinities, NaNs, and denormalized numbers. Most programmers will find that ordinary decimal and scientific decimal provide the simplest way to initialize numeric constants. Figure 18-2 compares several ways of setting the various numeric data types to the same initial value.

Table 18-2. ASM386/486 Storage Allocation Directives

Directives	Interpretation	Data Types
DW	Define Word	Word integer
DD	Define Doubleword	Short integer, short real
DQ	Define Quadword	Long integer, long real
DT	Define Tenbyte	Packed decimal, temporary real

```
; THE FOLLOWING ALL ALLOCATE THE CONSTANT: -126
; NOTE TWO'S COMPLETE STORAGE OF NEGATIVE BINARY INTEGERS.
;
; EVEN                                         ; FORCE WORD ALIGNMENT
WORD_INTEGER     DW   1111111110000010B        ; BIT STRING
SHORT_INTEGER    DD   0FFFFFF82H               ; HEX STRING MUST START
                                               ; WITH DIGIT
LONG_INTEGER     DQ   -126                     ; ORDINARY DECIMAL
SINGLE_REAL      DD   -126.0                   ; NOTE PRESENCE OF '.'
DOUBLE_REAL      DD   -1.26E2                  ; "SCIENTIFIC"
PACKED_DECIMAL   DT   -126                     ; ORDINARY DECIMAL INTEGER
;
; IN THE FOLLOWING, SIGN AND EXPONENT IS 'C005'
;     SIGNIFICAND IS '7E00...00', 'R' INFORMS ASSEMBLER THAT
;     THE STRING REPRESENTS A REAL DATA TYPE.
;
EXTENDED_REAL    DT   0C0057E00000000000000R   ; HEX STRING
```

Figure 18-2. Sample Numeric Constants

Note that preceding numeric variables and constants with the ASM386/486 EVEN directive ensures that the operands will be word-aligned in memory. The best performance is obtained when data transfers are double-word aligned. All numeric data types occupy integral numbers of words so that no storage is "wasted" if blocks of variables are defined together and preceded by a single EVEN declarative.

18.1.4.2 RECORDS AND STRUCTURES

The ASM386/486 RECORD and STRUC (structure) declaratives can be very useful in numeric programming. The record facility can be used to define the bit fields of the control, status, and tag words. Figure 18-3 shows one definition of the status word and how it might be used in a routine that polls the FPU until it has completed an instruction.

Because structures allow different but related data types to be grouped together, they often provide a natural way to represent "real world" data organizations. The fact that the structure template may be "moved" about in memory adds to its flexibility. Figure 18-4 shows a simple structure that might be used to represent data consisting of a series of test score samples. This sample structure can be reorganized, if necessary, for the sake of more efficient execution. If the two double real fields were listed before the integer fields, then (provided that the structure is instantiated only at addresses divisible by eight) all the fields would be optimally aligned for efficient memory access and caching. A structure could also be used to define the organization of the information stored and loaded by the FSTENV and FLDENV instructions.

```
; RESERVE SPACE FOR STATUS WORD
STATUS_WORD
; LAY OUT STATUS WORD FIELDS
STATUS RECORD
&    BUSY:           1,
&    COND_CODE3:     1,
&    STACK_TOP:      3,
&    COND_CODE2:     1,
&    COND_CODE1:     1,
&    COND_CODE0:     1,
&    INT_REQ:        1,
&    S_FLAG:         1,
&    P_FLAG:         1,
&    U_FLAG:         1,
&    O_FLAG:         1,
&    Z_FLAG:         1,
&    D_FLAG:         1,
&    I_FLAG:         1
; REDUCE UNTIL COMPLETE
REDUCE: FPREM1
        FNSTSW  STATUS_WORD
        TEST    STATUS_WORD, MASK_COND_CODE2
        JNZ     REDUCE
```

Figure 18-3. Status Word Record Definition

```
SAMPLE       STRUC
    N_OBS    DD  ?   ; SHORT INTEGER
    MEAN     DQ  ?   ; DOUBLE REAL
    MODE     DW  ?   ; WORD INTEGER
    STD_DEV  DQ  ?   ; DOUBLE REAL
    ; ARRAY OF OBSERVATIONS -- WORD INTEGER
    TEST_SCORES DW 1000 DUP (?)
SAMPLE       ENDS
```

Figure 18-4. Structure Definition

18.1.4.3 Addressing Methods

Numeric data in memory can be accessed with any of the memory addressing methods provided by the ModR/M byte and (optionally) the SIB byte. This means that numeric data types can be incorporated in data aggregates ranging from simple to complex according to the needs of the application. The addressing methods and the ASM386/486 notation used to specify them in instructions make the accessing of structures, arrays, arrays of structures, and other organizations direct and straightforward. Table 18-3 gives several examples of numeric instructions coded with operands that illustrate different addressing methods.

Table 18-3. Addressing Method Examples

Coding	Interpretation
FIADD ALPHA	ALPHA is a simple scalar (mode is direct).
FDIVR ALPHA.BETA	BETA is a field in a structure that is "overlaid" on ALPHA (mode is direct).
FMUL QWORD PTR [BX]	BX contains the address of a long real variable (mode is register indirect).
FSUB ALPHA [SI]	ALPHA is an array and SI contains the offset of an array element from the start of the array (mode is indexed).
FILD [BP].BETA	BP contains the address of a structure on the CPU stack and BETA is a field in the structure (mode is based).
FBLD TBYTE PTR [BX] [DI]	BX contains the address of a packed decimal array and DI contains the offset of an array element (mode is based indexed).

18.1.5 Comparative Programming Example

Figures 18-5 and 18-6 show the PL/M-386/486 and ASM386/486 code for a simple numeric program, called ARRSUM. The program references an array (X$ARRAY), which contains 0–100 single real values; the integer variable NOFX indicates the number of array elements the program is to consider. ARRSUM steps through X$ARRAY accumulating three sums:

- SUM$X, the sum of the array values
- SUM$INDEXES, the sum of each array value times its index, where the index of the first element is 1, the second is 2, etc.
- SUM$SQUARES, the sum of each array element squared

(A true program, of course, would go beyond these steps to store and use the results of these calculations.) The control word is set with the recommended values: round to nearest, 64-bit precision, interrupts enabled, and all exceptions masked except invalid operation. It is assumed that an exception handler has been written to field the invalid operation if it occurs, and that it is invoked by interrupt pointer 16.

The PL/M-386/486 version of ARRSUM (Figure 18-5) is very straightforward and illustrates how easily the numerics capabilities of the i486 processor can be used in this language. After declaring variables, the program calls built-in procedures to initialize the FPU and to load to the control word. The program clears the sum variables and then steps through X$ARRAY with a DO-loop. The loop control takes into account PL/M-386/486's practice of considering the index of the first element of an array to be 0. In the computation of SUM$INDEXES, the built-in procedure FLOAT converts I+1 from integer to real because the language does not support "mixed mode" arithmetic. One of the strengths of the i486 FPU, of course, is that it *does* support arithmetic on mixed data types (because all values are converted internally to the 80-bit extended-precision real format).

```
/****************************************************************
*                                                               *
*                     ARRAYSUM  MODDULE                         *
*                                                               *
****************************************************************/

array$sum:      do;

        declare (sum$x, sum$indexes, sum$squares) real;
        declare x$array(100) real;
        declare (n$of$x, i) integer;
        declare control $ FPU literally '033eh';

            /*  Assume x$array and n$of$x are initialized */
            call init$real$math$unit;
            call set$real$mode(control $ FPU);

            /* Clear sums */
            sum$x, sum$indexes, sum$squares = 0.0;

            /* Loop through array, accumulating sums */
            do i = 0 to n$of$x - 1;
                sum$x = sum$x + x$array(i);
                sum$indexes = sum$indexes + (x$array(i)*float(i+1));
                sum$squares = sum$squares + (x$array(i)*x$array(i));
            end;

            /* etc. */

        end array$sum;
```

Figure 18-5. Sample PL/M-386/486 Program

The ASM386/486 version (Figure 18-6) defines the external procedure INITFPU, which makes the different initialization requirements of the processor and its emulator transparent to the source code. After defining the data and setting up the segment registers and stack pointer, the program calls INITFPU and loads the control word. The computation begins with the next three instructions, which clear three registers by loading (pushing) zeros onto the stack. As shown in Figure 18-7, these registers remain at the bottom of the stack throughout the computation while temporary values are pushed on and popped off the stack above them.

The program uses the LOOP instruction to control its iteration through X_ARRAY; register ECX, which LOOP automatically decrements, is loaded with N_OF_X, the number of array elements to be summed. Register ESI is used to select (index) the array elements. The program steps through X_ARRAY from back to front, so ESI is initialized to point at the element just beyond the first element to be processed. The ASM386/486

```
name        arraysum

; Define initialization routine

extrn       initFPU:far

; Allocate space for data

data        segment rw public
control_FPU           dw 033eh
n_of_x                dd ?
x_array               dd 100 dup (?)


sum_squares           dd ?
sum_indexes           dd ?
sum_x                 dd ?
data        ends

; Allocate CPU stack space

stack       stackseg  400

; Begin code

code        segment er public

assume  ds:data, ss:stack

start:
     mov     ax, data
     mov     ds, ax
     mov     ax, stack
     mov     eax, 0h
     mov     ss, ax
     mov     esp, stackstart stack

 ; Assume x_array and n_of_x have
 ; been initialized

 ; Prepare the FPU or its emulator

     call    initFPU
     fldcw   control_FPU

 ; Clear three registers to hold
 ; running sums

     fldz
     fldz
     fldz
```

Figure 18-6. Sample ASM386/486 Program

```
; Setup ECX as loop counter and ESI
; as index into x_array

    mov     ecx, n_of_x
    imul    ecx
    mov     esi, eax

; ESI now contains index of last
; element + 1
; Loop through x_array and
; accumulate sum

sum_next:
; backup one element and push on
; the stack

    sub     esi, type x_array
    fld     x_array[esi]

; add to the sum and duplicate x
; on the stack

    fadd    st(3), st
    fld     st

; square it and add into the sum of
; (index+1) and discard

    fmul    st, st
    faddp   st(2), st

; reduce index for next iteration

    dec     n_of_x
    loop    sum_next

; Pop sums into memory

pop_results:
    fstp    sum_squares
    fstp    sum_indexes
    fstp    sum_x
    fwait

;
; Etc.
;
code        ends
end     start, ds:data, ss:stack
```

Figure 18-6. Sample ASM386/486 Program (Contd.)

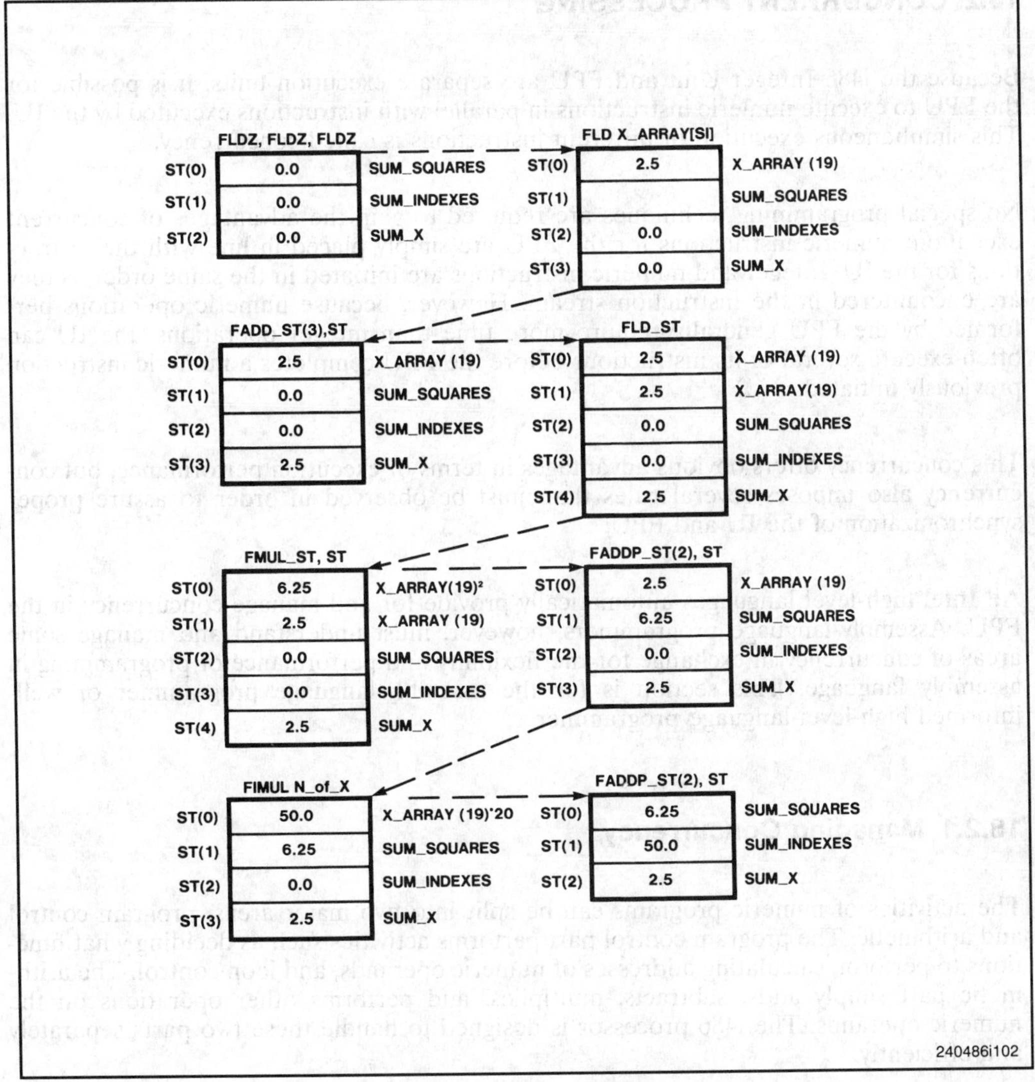

Figure 18-7. Instructions and Register Stack

TYPE operator is used to determine the number of bytes in each array element. This permits changing X_ARRAY to a double-precision real array by simply changing its definition (DD to DQ) and reassembling.

Figure 18-7 shows the effect of the instructions in the program loop on the FPU register stack. The figure assumes that the program is in its first iteration, that N_OF_X is 20, and that X_ARRAY(19) (the 20th element) contains the value 2.5. When the loop terminates, the three sums are left as the top stack elements so that the program ends by simply popping them into memory variables.

18.2 CONCURRENT PROCESSING

Because the i486 Integer Unit and FPU are separate execution units, it is possible for the FPU to execute numeric instructions in parallel with instructions executed by the IU. This simultaneous execution of different instructions is called concurrency.

No special programming techniques are required to gain the advantages of concurrent execution; numeric instructions for the FPU are simply placed in line with the instructions for the IU. Integer and numeric instructions are initiated in the same order as they are encountered in the instruction stream. However, because numeric operations performed by the FPU generally require more time than integer operations, the IU can often execute several of its instructions before the FPU completes a numeric instruction previously initiated.

This concurrency offers obvious advantages in terms of execution performance, but concurrency also imposes several rules that must be observed in order to assure proper synchronization of the IU and FPU.

All Intel high-level languages automatically provide for and manage concurrency in the FPU. Assembly-language programmers, however, must understand and manage some areas of concurrency in exchange for the flexibility and performance of programming in assembly language. This section is for the assembly-language programmer or well-informed high-level-language programmer.

18.2.1 Managing Concurrency

The activities of numeric programs can be split into two major areas: program control and arithmetic. The program control part performs activities such as deciding what functions to perform, calculating addresses of numeric operands, and loop control. The arithmetic part simply adds, subtracts, multiplies, and performs other operations on the numeric operands. The i486 processor is designed to handle these two parts separately and efficiently.

Concurrency management is required to check for an exception before letting the processor change a value just used by the FPU. Almost any numeric instruction can, under the wrong circumstances, produce a numeric exception. For programmers in higher-level languages, all required synchronization is automatically provided by the appropriate compiler. For assembly-language programmers exception synchronization remains the responsibility of the programmer.

A complication is that a programmer may not expect his numeric program to cause numeric exceptions, but in some systems, they may regularly happen. To better understand these points, consider what can happen when the FPU detects an exception.

Depending on options determined by the software system designer, the i486 processor can perform one of two things when a numeric exception occurs:

- The FPU can provide a default fix-up for selected numeric exceptions. Programs can mask individual exception types to indicate that the FPU should generate a safe, reasonable result whenever that exception occurs. The default exception fix-up activity is treated by the FPU as part of the instruction causing the exception; no external indication of the exception is given. When exceptions are detected, a flag is set in the numeric status register, but no information regarding where or when is available. If the FPU performs its default action for all exceptions, then the need for exception synchronization is not manifest. However, as will be shown later, this is not sufficient reason to ignore exception synchronization when designing programs that use the FPU.
- As an alternative to the default fix-up of numeric exceptions, the IU can be notified whenever an exception occurs. When a numeric exception is unmasked and the exception occurs, the FPU stops further execution of the numeric instruction and signals this event. On the next occurrence of an ESC or WAIT instruction, the processor traps to a software exception handler. The exception handler can then implement any sort of recovery procedures desired for any numeric exception detectable by the FPU. Some ESC instructions do not check for exceptions. These are the nonwaiting forms FNINIT, FNSTENV, FNSAVE, FNSTSW, FNSTCW, and FNCLEX.

When the FPU signals an unmasked exception condition, it is requesting help. The fact that the exception was unmasked indicates that further numeric program execution under the arithmetic and programming rules of the FPU is unreasonable.

If concurrent execution is allowed, the state of the processor when it recognizes the exception is undefined. It may have changed many of its internal registers and be executing a totally different program by the time the exception occurs. To handle this situation, the FPU has special registers updated at the start of each numeric instruction to describe the state of the numeric program when the failed instruction was attempted.

Exception synchronization ensures that the FPU is in a well-defined state after an unmasked numeric exception occurs. Without a well-defined state, it would be impossible for exception recovery routines to determine why the numeric exception occurred, or to recover successfully from the exception.

The following two sections illustrate the need to always consider exception synchronization when writing numeric code, even when the code is initially intended for execution with exceptions masked. If the code is later moved to an environment where exceptions are unmasked, the same code may not work correctly. An example of how some instructions written without exception synchronization will work initially, but fail when moved into a new environment, is shown in Figure 18-8.

18.2.1.1 INCORRECT EXCEPTION SYNCHRONIZATION

In Figure 18-8, three instructions are shown to load an integer, calculate its square root, then increment the integer. The synchronous execution of the FPU will allow this program to execute correctly when no exceptions occur on the FILD instruction.

INCORRECT ERROR SYNCHRONIZATION

```
FILD    COUNT   ; FPU instruction
INC     COUNT   ; integer instruction alters operand
FSQRT           ; subsequent FPU instruction -- error from
                ;     previous FPU instruction detected here
```

PROPER ERROR SYNCHRONIZATION

```
FILD    COUNT   ; FPU instruction
FSQRT           ; subsequent FPU instruction -- error from
                ;     previous FPU instruction detected here
INC     COUNT   ; integer instruction alters operand
```

Figure 18-8. Exception Synchronization Examples

This situation changes if the numeric register stack is extended to memory. To extend the FPU stack to memory, the invalid exception is unmasked. A push to a full register or pop from an empty register sets SF and causes an invalid exception.

The recovery routine for the exception must recognize this situation, fix up the stack, then perform the original operation. The recovery routine will not work correctly in the first example shown in the figure. The problem is that the value of COUNT is incremented before the exception handler is invoked, so that the recovery routine will load an incorrect value of COUNT, causing the program to fail or behave unreliably.

18.2.1.2 PROPER EXCEPTION SYNCHRONIZATION

Exception synchronization relies on the WAIT instruction. Whenever an unmasked numerical exception occurs, the FPU asserts an error-condition signal internal to the processor. When the next WAIT instruction (or non-control ESC instruction) is encountered, the error-condition signal is acknowledged and a software exception handler is invoked. (See Chapter 16 for a more detailed discussion of the various floating-point error-reporting mechanisms.) If this WAIT or ESC instruction is properly placed, the processor will not yet have disturbed any information vital to recovery from the exception.

System-Level Considerations 19

CHAPTER 19
SYSTEM-LEVEL CONSIDERATIONS

System programming for i486™ processor systems requires a more detailed understanding of the FPU than does application programming. Such things as initialization, exception handling, and data and error synchronization are all the responsibility of the systems programmer. These topics are covered in detail in the sections that follow.

19.1 ARCHITECTURE

On a software level, the FPU appears as an extension of the Integer Unit. On the hardware level, however, the mechanisms by which the FPU and IU interact are more complex. This section describes this interaction and points out features that are of interest to systems programmers.

19.1.1 Independent of Addressing Mode

Unlike the 80287 NPX (but like the 387™ NPX), the FPU of the i486 processor operates the same regardless of whether the processor is operating in real-address mode, in protected mode, or in virtual 8086 mode.

Numeric instructions can utilize any memory location accessible by the task currently executing. When operating in protected mode, all references to memory operands are automatically verified by the memory management and protection mechanisms as for any other memory references by the currently-executing task. Protection violations associated with numeric instructions automatically cause the processor to trap to an appropriate exception handler.

To the numerics programmer, the operating mode affects only the manner in which the FPU instruction and data pointers are represented in memory following an FSAVE or FSTENV instruction. Each of these instructions produces one of four formats depending on both the operating mode and on the operand-size attribute in effect for the instruction. The differences are detailed in the discussion of the FSAVE and FSTENV instructions in Chapter 26.

19.2 PROCESSOR INITIALIZATION AND CONTROL

One of the principal responsibilities of systems software is the initialization, monitoring, and control of the hardware and software resources of the system, including the FPU. In this section, issues related to system initialization and control are described, including the handling of exceptions that may occur during the execution of numeric instructions.

19.2.1 System Initialization

During initialization of an i486 processor system, systems software must initialize the FPU and set flags in CR0 to reflect the state of the numeric environment. These activities can be quickly and easily performed as part of the overall system initialization.

19.2.2 Configuring the Numerics Environment

System software must load the appropriate values into the MP, EM, and NE bits of the CR0 control register.

The MP (Monitor coProcessor) bit determines whether WAIT instructions trap when the con-text of the FPU is different from that of the currently executing task. If MP = 1 and TS = 1, then a WAIT instruction will cause a Device Not Available fault (interrupt vector 7). The MP bit was used on the 80286 and 386™ DX microprocessors to support the use of a WAIT instruction to wait on a device other than a numeric coprocessor. The device would report its status through the BUSY# pin. Since the i486 processor does not have such a pin, the MP bit has no relevant use, and should be set to 1 for normal operation.

The EM (EMulate coprocessor) bit determines whether ESC instructions are executed by the FPU (EM = 0) or trap via interrupt vector 7 to be handled by software (EM = 1). The EM bit was used on the 386 DX microprocessor so that numeric applications written for a 386 DX CPU/387 DX system could be run in the absence of a 387 DX coprocessor with a software 387 DX emulator. For normal operation of the i486 processor, the EM bit should be cleared to 0.

The NE (Numeric Exception) bit determines whether unmasked floating-point exceptions are handled through interrupt vector 16 (NE = 1) or through external interrupt (NE =0). In systems using an external interrupt controller to invoke numeric exception handlers, the NE bit should be cleared to 0. Other systems can make use of the automatic error reporting through interrupt 16, and should set the NE bit to 1. See section 19.2.5 below for a discussion of numeric exception handling.

19.2.3 Initializing the FPU

Initializing the FPU simply means placing the FPU in a known state unaffected by any activity performed earlier. A single FNINIT instruction performs this initialization. All the error masks are set, all registers are tagged empty, TOP is set to zero, and default rounding and precision controls are set. Table 19-1 shows the state of the FPU following FINIT or FNINIT.

The FNINIT instruction leaves the FPU in the same state as that which results from a hardware RESET signal with Built-In Self-Test. When the Built-In Self-Test is not requested, a hardware RESET leaves the FPU state unchanged. An FNINIT instruction should be executed after reset.

Table 19-1. FPU State Following Initialization

Field	Value	Interpretation
Control Word	037FH	
(Infinity Control)*	0	Affine
Rounding Control	00	Round to nearest
Precision Control	11	64 bits
Exception Masks	111111	All exceptions masked
Status Word	0000H	
(Busy)	0	—
Condition Code	0000	—
Stack Top	000	Register 0 is stack top
Exception Summary	0	No exceptions
Stack Flag	0	—
Exception Flags	000000	No exceptions
Tag Word	FFFFH	
Tags	11	Empty
Registers	N.C.	Not changed
Exception Pointers		
Instruction Code		Cleared
Instruction Address		Cleared
Operand Address		Cleared

*The i486™ processor does not have infinity control. This value is listed to emphasize that programs written for the 80287 may not behave the same on the i486 processor if they depend on this bit.

19.2.4 Emulation

Setting the EM bit to 1 will cause the i486 processor to trap via interrupt vector 7 (Device Not Available) to a software exception handler whenever it encounters an ESC instruction. The EM bit was used to run numeric applications on a 386 processor with a software 387 emulator. Numeric applications designed to be run with a non-standard 387 emulator may not run successfully on the i486 processor without the emulator. Setting the EM bit to 1 makes it possible to run such applications, or programs which use non-standard floating-point arithmetic, on the i486 processor.

19.2.5 Handling Numerics Exceptions

Once the FPU has been initialized and normal execution of applications has been commenced, the FPU may occasionally require attention in order to recover from numeric processing exceptions. This section provides details for writing software exception handlers for numeric exceptions. Numeric processing exceptions have already been introduced in Chapter 16.

If the FPU encounters an unmasked exception condition, a software exception handler is invoked immediately before execution of the next WAIT or non-control floating-point instruction. The exception handler is invoked either through interrupt vector 16 or through an external interrupt, depending on the value of the NE bit of the CR0 control register.

If NE = 1, an unmasked floating-point exception results in interrupt 16, immediately before the exception of the next non-control floating-point or WAIT instruction. Interrupt 16 is an operating-system call that invokes the exception handler. Chapter 9 contains a general discussion of exceptions and interrupts on the i486 processor.

If NE = 0 (and the IGNNE# input is inactive), an unmasked floating-point exception causes the processor to freeze immediately before executing the next non-control floating-point or WAIT instruction. The frozen processor waits for an external interrupt, which must be supplied by external hardware in response to the FERR# output of the processor. (Regardless of the value of NE, an unmasked numerical exception causes the FERR# output to be activated.) In this case, the external interrupt invokes the exception-handling routine. If NE = 0 but the IGNNE# input is active, the processor disregards the exception and continues. Error reporting via external interrupt is supported for DOS compatibility. Chapter 25 contains further discussion of compatibility issues.

When handling numeric errors, the processor has two responsibilities:

- It must not disturb the numeric context when an error is detected.
- It must clear the error and attempt recovery from the error.

Although the manner in which programmers may treat these responsibilities varies from one implementation to the next, most exception handlers will include these basic steps:

- Store the FPU environment (control, status, and tag words, operand and instruction pointers) as it existed at the time of the exception.
- Clear the exception bits in the status word.
- Enable interrupts.
- Identify the exception by examining the status and control words in the saved environment.
- Take some system-dependent action to rectify the exception.
- Return to the interrupted program and resume normal execution.

19.2.6 Simultaneous Exception Response

In cases where multiple exceptions arise simultaneously, the FPU signals one exception according to the precedence shown at the end of Chapter 16. This means, for example, that an SNaN divided by zero results in an invalid operation, not in a zero divide exception.

19.2.7 Exception Recovery Examples

Recovery routines for numeric exceptions can take a variety of forms. They can change the arithmetic and programming rules of the FPU. These changes may redefine the default fix-up for an error, change the appearance of the FPU to the programmer, or change how arithmetic is defined on the FPU.

A change to an exception response might be to perform denormal arithmetic on denormals loaded from memory. A change in appearance might be extending the register stack into memory to provide an "infinite" number of numeric registers. The arithmetic of the FPU can be changed to automatically extend the precision and range of variables when exceeded. All these functions can be implemented on the i486 processor via numeric exceptions and associated recovery routines in a manner transparent to the application programmer.

Some other possible application-dependent actions might include:

- Incrementing an exception counter for later display or printing
- Printing or displaying diagnostic information (e.g., the FPU environment and registers)
- Aborting further execution
- Storing a diagnostic value (a NaN) in the result and continuing with the computation

Notice that an exception may or may not constitute an error, depending on the application. Once the exception handler corrects the condition causing the exception, the floating-point instruction that caused the exception can be restarted, if appropriate. This cannot be accomplished using the IRET instruction, however, because the trap occurs at the ESC or WAIT instruction following the offending ESC instruction. The exception handler must obtain (using FSAVE or FSTENV) the address of the offending instruction in the task that initiated it, make a copy of it, execute the copy in the context of the offending task, and then return via IRET to the current instruction stream.

In order to correct the condition causing the numeric exception, exception handlers must recognize the precise state of the FPU at the time the exception handler was invoked, and be able to reconstruct the state of the FPU when the exception initially occurred. To reconstruct the state of the FPU, programmers must understand when, during the execution of a numeric instruction, exceptions are actually recognized.

Invalid operation, zero divide, and denormalized exceptions are detected before an operation begins, whereas overflow, underflow, and precision exceptions are not raised until a true result has been computed. When a *before* exception is detected, the FPU register stack and memory have not yet been updated, and appear as if the offending instructions has not been executed.

When an *after* exception is detected, the register stack and memory appear as if the instruction has run to completion; i.e., they may be updated. (However, in a store or store-and-pop operation, unmasked over/underflow is handled like a *before* exception; memory is not updated and the stack is not popped.) The programming examples contained in Chapter 20 include an outline of several exception handlers to process numeric exceptions.

20 Numeric Programming Examples

CHAPTER 20
NUMERIC PROGRAMMING EXAMPLES

The following sections contain examples of numeric programs for the i486™ processor written in ASM386/486. These examples are intended to illustrate some of the techniques useful for programming i486 processor systems for numeric applications.

20.1 CONDITIONAL BRANCHING EXAMPLE

As discussed in Chapter 15, several numeric instructions post their results to the condition code bits of the FPU status word. Although there are many ways to implement conditional branching following a comparison, the basic approach is as follows:

- Execute the comparison.
- Store the status word. (The FPU status word can be stored directly into AX register.)
- Inspect the condition code bits.
- Jump on the result.

Figure 20-1 is a code fragment that illustrates how two memory-resident double-format real numbers might be compared (similar code could be used with the FTST instruction). The numbers are called A and B, and the comparison is A to B.

The comparison itself requires loading A onto the top of the FPU register stack and then comparing it to B, while popping the stack with the same instruction. The status word is then written into the AX register.

A and B have four possible orderings, and bits C3, C2, and C0 of the condition code indicate which ordering holds. These bits are positioned in the upper byte of the FPU status word so as to correspond to the zero, parity, and carry flags (ZF, PF, and CF), when the byte is written into the flags. The code fragment sets ZF, PF, and CF of the EFLAGS register to the values of C3, C2, and C0 of the FPU status word, and then uses the conditional jump instructions to test the flags. The resulting code is extremely compact, requiring only seven instructions.

The FXAM instruction updates all four condition code bits. Figure 20-2 shows how a jump table can be used to determine the characteristics of the value examined. The jump table (FXAM_TBL) is initialized to contain the 32-bit displacement of 16 labels, one for each possible condition code setting. Note that four of the table entries contain the same value, "EMPTY." The first two condition code settings correspond to "EMPTY." The two other table entries that contain "EMPTY" will never be used on the i486 processor or the 387™ math coprocessors, but may be used if the code is executed with an 80287.

The program fragment performs the FXAM and stores the status word. It then manipulates the condition code bits to finally produce a number in register AX that equals the condition code times 2. This involves zeroing the unused bits in the byte that contains the code, shifting C3 to the right so that it is adjacent to C2, and then shifting the code

```
        .
        .
        .
A       DQ  ?
B       DQ  ?
        .
        .
        .
        FLD     A  ; LOAD A ONTO TOP OF FPU STACK
        FCOMP   B  ; COMPARE A:B, POP A
        FSTSW   AX ; STORE RESULT TO AX REGISTER
;
; CPU AX REGISTER CONTAINS CONDITION CODES
; (RESULTS OF COMPARE)
; LOAD CONDITION CODES INTO FLAGS
;
        SAHF
;
; USE CONDITIONAL JUMPS TO DETERMINE ORDERING OF A TO B
;
        JP A_B_UNORDERED                ; TEST C2 (PF)
        JB A_LESS               ; TEST C0 (CF)
        JE A_EQUAL              ; TEST C3 (ZF)
A_GREATER:                      ; C0 (CF) = 0, C3 (ZF) = 0
        .
A_EQUAL:                        ; C0 (CF) = 0, C3 (ZF) = 1
        .
        .
A_LESS:                         ; C0 (CF) = 1, C3 (ZF) = 0
        .
        .
A_B_UNORDERED:                  ; C2 (PF) = 1
        .
        .
```

Figure 20-1. Conditional Branching for Compares

to multiply it by 2. The resulting value is used as an index that selects one of the displacements from FXAM_TBL (the multiplication of the condition code is required because of the 2-byte length of each value in FXAM_TBL). The unconditional JMP instruction effectively vectors through the jump table to the labeled routine that contains code (not shown in the example) to process each possible result of the FXAM instruction.

20.2 EXCEPTION HANDLING EXAMPLES

There are many approaches to writing exception handlers. One useful technique is to consider the exception handler procedure as consisting of "prologue," "body," and "epilogue" sections of code. This procedure is invoked via interrupt number 16.

```
; JUMP TABLE FOR EXAMINE ROUTINE
;
FXAM_TBL  DD POS_UNNORM, POS_NAN, NEG_UNNORM, NEG_NAN,
&            POS_NORM, POS_INFINITY, NEG_NORM,
&            NEG_INFINITY, POS_ZERO, EMPTY, NEG_ZERO,
&            EMPTY, POS_DENORM, EMPTY, NEG_DENORM, EMPTY
          .
          .
; EXAMINE ST AND STORE RESULT (CONDITION CODES)
          FXAM
          XOR EAX,EAX ; CLEAR EAX
          FSTSW AX
; CALCULATE OFFSET INTO JUMP TABLE
          AND AX,0100011100000000B ; CLEAR ALL BITS EXCEPT C3, C2-C0
          SHR EAX,6     ;  SHIFT C2-C0 INTO PLACE     (000XXX00)
          SAL AH,5      ;  POSITION C3                (00X00000)
          OR  AL,AH     ;  DROP C3 IN ADJACENT TO C2  (00XXXX00)
          XOR AH,AH     ;  CLEAR OUT THE OLD COPY OF C3

; JUMP TO THE ROUTINE 'ADDRESSED' BY CONDITION CODE

          JMP FXAM_TBL[EAX]

; HERE ARE THE JUMP TARGETS, ONE TO HANDLE
;    EACH POSSIBLE RESULT OF FXAM

POS_UNNORM:
          .
POS_NAN:
          .
NEG_UNNORM:
          .
NEG_NAN:
          .
POS_NORM:
          .
POS_INFINITY:
          .
NEG_NORM:
          .
NEG_INFINITY:
          .
POS_ZERO:
          .
EMPTY:
          .
NEG_ZERO:
          .
POS_DENORM:
          .
NEG_DENORM:
```

Figure 20-2. Conditional Branching for FXAM

In the transfer of control to the exception handler, interrupts have been disabled by hardware. The prologue performs all functions that must be protected from possible interruption by higher-priority sources. Typically, this involves saving registers and transferring diagnostic information from the FPU to memory. When the critical processing has been completed, the prologue may re-enable interrupts to allow higher-priority interrupt handlers to preempt the exception handler.

The body of the exception handler examines the diagnostic information and makes a response that is necessarily application-dependent. This response may range from halting execution, to displaying a message, to attempting to repair the problem and proceed with normal execution.

The epilogue essentially reverses the actions of the prologue, restoring the processor so that normal execution can be resumed. The epilogue must *not* load an unmasked exception flag into the FPU or another exception will be requested immediately.

Figures 20-3 through 20-5 show the ASM386/486 coding of three skeleton exception handlers. They show how prologues and epilogues can be written for various situations, but provide comments indicating only where the application dependent exception handling body should be placed.

```
SAVE_ALL            PROC
;
; SAVE REGISTERS, ALLOCATE STACK SPACE
; FOR FPU STATE IMAGE
    PUSH EBP
    MOV  EBP,ESP
    SUB  ESP,108
; SAVE FULL FPU STATE, ENABLE INTERRUPTS
    FNSAVE  [EBP-108]
    STI
;
; APPLICATION-DEPENDENT EXCEPTION HANDLING
; CODE GOES HERE
;
; CLEAR EXCEPTION FLAGS IN STATUS WORD
;  (WHICH IS IN MEMORY)
; RESTORE MODIFIED STATE IMAGE
    MOV BYTE PTR [EBP-104], 0H
    FRSTOR  [EBP-108]
; DEALLOCATE STACK SPACE, RESTORE REGISTERS
    MOVE ESP,EBP
      .
      .
    POP EBP
;
; RETURN TO INTERRUPTED CALCULATION
    IRET
SAVE_ALL            ENDP
```

Figure 20-3. Full-State Exception Handler

```
SAVE_ENVIRONMENT PROC
;
; SAVE REGISTERS, ALLOCATE STACK SPACE
; FOR FPU ENVIRONMENT
    PUSH      EBP

    MOV       EBP,ESP
    SUB       ESP,28
; SAVE ENVIRONMENT, ENABLE INTERRUPTS
    FNSTENV [EBP-28]
    STI
;
; APPLICATION EXCEPTION-HANDLING CODE GOES HERE
;
; CLEAR EXCEPTION FLAGS IN STATUS WORD
;  (WHICH IS IN MEMORY)
; RESTORE MODIFIED ENVIRONMENT IMAGE
    MOV       BYTE PTR [EBP-24], 0H
    FLDENV  [EBP-28]
; DE-ALLOCATE STACK SPACE, RESTORE REGISTERS
    MOV       ESP,EBP
    POP       EBP
;
; RETURN TO INTERRUPTED CALCULATION
    IRET
SAVE_ENVIRONMENT ENDP
```

Figure 20-4. Reduced-Latency Exception Handler

Figures 20-3 and 20-4 are very similar; their only substantial difference is their choice of instructions to save and restore the FPU. The tradeoff here is between the increased diagnostic information provided by FNSAVE and the faster execution of FNSTENV. For applications that are sensitive to interrupt latency or that do not need to examine register contents, FNSTENV reduces the duration of the "critical region," during which the processor does not recognize another interrupt request.

After the exception handler body, the epilogues prepare the processor to resume execution from the point of interruption (i.e., the instruction following the one that generated the unmasked exception). Notice that the exception flags in the memory image that is loaded into the FPU are cleared to zero prior to reloading (in fact, in these examples, the entire status word image is cleared).

The examples in Figures 20-3 and 20-4 assume that the exception handler itself will not cause an unmasked exception. Where this is a possibility, the general approach shown in Figure 20-5 can be employed. The basic technique is to save the full FPU state and then

```
          .
          .
          .
    LOCAL CONTROL  DW  ?  ; ASSUME INITIALIZED
          .
          .
          .
REENTRANT          PROC
;
; SAVE REGISTERS, ALLOCATE STACK SPACE FOR
; FPU STATE IMAGE
    PUSH    EBP
          .
          .
          .
    MOV     EBP,ESP
    SUB     ESP,108
; SAVE STATE, LOAD NEW CONTROL WORD,
; ENABLE INTERRUPTS
    FNSAVE  [EBP-108]
    FLDCW   LOCAL_CONTROL
    STI
          .
          .
          .
; APPLICATION EXCEPTION HANDLING CODE GOES HERE.
; AN UNMASKED EXCEPTION GENERATED HERE WILL
; CAUSE THE EXCEPTION HANDLER TO BE REENTERED.
; IF LOCAL STORAGE IS NEEDED, IT MUST BE
; ALLOCATED ON THE STACK.
          .
          .
          .
; CLEAR EXCEPTION FLAGS IN STATUS WORD
; (WHICH IS IN MEMORY)
; RESTORE MODIFIED STATE IMAGE
    MOV     BYTE PTR [EBP-104], 0H
    FRSTOR  [EBP-108]
; DE-ALLOCATE STACK SPACE, RESTORE REGISTERS
    MOV     ESP,EBP
          .
          .
          .
    POP     EBP
; RETURN TO POINT OF INTERRUPTION
    IRET
REENTRANT          ENDP
```

Figure 20-5. Reentrant Exception Handler

to load a new control word in the prologue. Note that considerable care should be taken when designing an exception handler of this type to prevent the handler from being reentered endlessly.

20.3 FLOATING-POINT TO ASCII CONVERSION EXAMPLES

Numeric programs must typically format their results at some point for presentation and inspection by the program user. In many cases, numeric results are formatted as ASCII strings for printing or display. This example shows how floating-point values can be converted to decimal ASCII character strings. The function shown in Figure 20-6 can be invoked from PL/M-386/486, Pascal-386/486, FORTRAN-386/486, or ASM386/486 routines.

Shortness, speed, and accuracy were chosen rather than providing the maximum number of significant digits possible. An attempt is made to keep integers in their own domain to avoid unnecessary conversion errors.

Using the extended precision real number format, this routine achieves a worst case accuracy of three units in the 16th decimal position for a noninteger value or integers greater than 10^{18}. This is double precision accuracy. With values having decimal exponents less than 100 in magnitude, the accuracy is one unit in the 17th decimal position.

Higher precision can be achieved with greater care in programming, larger program size, and lower performance.

20.3.1 Function Partitioning

Three separate modules implement the conversion. Most of the work of the conversion is done in the module FLOATING_TO_ASCII. The other modules are provided separately, because they have a more general use. One of them, GET_POWER_10, is also used by the ASCII to floating-point conversion routine. The other small module, TOS_STATUS, identifies what, if anything, is in the top of the numeric register stack.

20.3.2 Exception Considerations

Care is taken inside the function to avoid generating exceptions. Any possible numeric value is accepted. The only possible exception is insufficient space on the numeric register stack.

The value passed in the numeric stack is checked for existence, type (NaN or infinity), and status (denormal, zero, sign). The string size is tested for a minimum and maximum value. If the top of the register stack is empty, or the string size is too small, the function returns with an error code.

Overflow and underflow is avoided inside the function for very large or very small numbers.

```
SOURCE

+1 $title('Convert a floating point number to ASCII')

                name    floating_to_ascii

                public  floating_to_ascii
                extrn   get_power_10:near,tos_status:near
;
; This subroutine will convert the floating point
; number in the top of the NPX stack to an ASCII
; string and separate power of 10 scaling value
; (in binary).  The maximum width of the ASCII string
; formed is controlled by a parameter which must be
; > 1.  Unnormal values, denormal values, and psuedo
; zeroes will be correctly converted. However, unnormals
; and pseudo zeros are no longer supported formats on the i486 processor
; ( in conformance with the IEEE floating point
; standard) and hence not generated internally. A
; returned value will indicate how many binary bits
; of precision were lost in an unnormal or denormal
; value.  The magnitude (in terms of binary power)
; of a pseudo zero will also be indicated. Integers
; less than 10**18 in magnitude are accurately converted
; if the destination ASCII string field is wide enough
; to hold all the digits. Otherwise the value is converted
; to scientific notation.
;
; The status of the conversion is identified by the
; return value, it can be:
;
;           0        conversion complete, string_size is defined
;           1        invalid arguments
;           2        exact integer conversion, string_size is defined
;           3        indefinite
;           4        + NAN (Not A Number)
;           5        - NAN
;           6        + Infinity
;           7        - Infinity
;           8        pseudo zero found, string_size is defined
;
;           The PLM-386/486 calling convention is:
;
; floating_to_ascii:
;           procedure (number,denormal_ptr,string_ptr,size_ptr,
;           field_size, power_ptr) word external;
;           declare (denormal_ptr,string_ptr,power_ptr,size_ptr)
;           pointer;
;           declare field_size word,
;           string_size based size_ptr word;
;           declare number real;
;           declare denormal integer based denormal_ptr;
```

Figure 20-6. Floating-Point to ASCII Conversion Routine

```
;       declare power integer based power_ptr;
;       end floating_to_ascii;
;
;           The floating point value is expected to be
;   on the top of the  FPU stack.  This subroutine
;   expects 3 free entries on the FPU stack and
;   will pop the passed value off when done.  The
;   generated ASCII string will have a leading
;   character either '-' or '+' indicating the sign
;   of the value.  The ASCII decimal digits will
;   immediately follow. The numeric value of the
;   ASCII string is (ASCII STRING.)*10**POWER. If
;   the given number was zero, the ASCII string will
;   contain a sign and a single zero chacter.  The
;   value string_size indicates the total length of
;   the ASCII string including the sign character.
;   String(0) will always hold the sign.  It is
;   possible for string_size to be less than
;   field_size. This occurs for zeroes or integer
;   values.  A pseudo zero will return a special
;   return code.  The denormal count will indicate
;       the power of two originally associated with the
;   value.  The power of ten and ASCII string will
;   be as if the value was an ordinary zero.
;
;   This subroutine is accurate up to a maximum of
;   18 decimal digits for integers.  Integer values
;   will have a decimal power of zero associated
;   with them.  For non integers, the result will be
;   accurate to within 2 decimal digits of the 16th
;   decimal place(double precision).  The exponentiate
;   instruction is also used for scaling the value into
;   the range acceptable for the BCD data  type.  The
;   rounding mode in effect on entry to the
;   subroutine is used for the conversion.
;
;           The following registers are not transparent:
;
;                   eax ebx ecx edx esi edi eflags
;
;
;
;           Define the stack layout.
;
ebp_save        equ     dword ptr [ebp]
es_save         equ     ebp_save + size ebp_save
return_ptr      equ     es_save + size es_save
power_ptr       equ     return_ptr + size return_ptr
field_size      equ     power_ptr + size power_ptr
size_ptr        equ     field_size + size field_size
string_ptr      equ     size_ptr + size size_ptr
denormal_ptr    equ     string_ptr + size string_ptr

parms_size      equ     size power_ptr + size field_size +
&               size size_ptr + size string_ptr +
&               size denormal_ptr
```

Figure 20-6. Floating-Point to ASCII Conversion Routine (Contd.)

```
;
;              Define constants used
;
BCD_DIGITS          equ     18      ; Number of digits in bcd_value
WORD_SIZE           equ     4
BCD_SIZE            equ     10
MINUS               equ     1       ; Define return values
NAN                 equ     4       ; The exact values chosen
INFINITY            equ     6       ; here are important.  They must
INDEFINITE          equ     3       ; correspond to the possible return
PSEUDO_ZERO         equ     8       ; values and be in the same numeric
INVALID             equ     -2      ; order as tested by the program.
ZERO                equ     -4
DENORMAL            equ     -6
UNNORMAL            equ     -8
NORMAL              equ     0
EXACT               equ     2
;
;              Define layout of temporary storage area.
;
power_two           equ     word ptr [ebp - WORD_SIZE]
bcd_value           equ     tbyte ptr power_two - BCD_SIZE
bcd_byte            equ     byte ptr bcd_value
fraction            equ     bcd_value

local_size          equ     size power_two + size bcd_value
;
;              Allocate stack space for the temporaries so
;       the stack will be big enough
;
stack  stackseg (local_size+6) ; Allocate stack
                               ; space for locals
+1 $eject
```

Figure 20-6. Floating-Point to ASCII Conversion Routine (Contd.)

```
code            segment public er
                extrn   power_table:qword
;
;       Constants used by this function.
;
                even                        ; Optimize for 16 bits
const10         dw      10                  ; Adjustment value for
;                       ; too big BCD
;
; Convert the C3,C2,C1,C0 encoding from tos_status
; into meaningful bit flags and values.
;
status_table    db      UNNORMAL, NAN, UNNORMAL + MINUS,
&       NAN + MINUS, NORMAL, INFINITY,
&       NORMAL + MINUS, INFINITY + MINUS,
&               ZERO, INVALID, ZERO + MINUS, INVALID,
&               DENORMAL, INVALID, DENORMAL + MINUS, INVALID
floating_to_ascii proc

        call    tos_status          ; Look at status of ST(0)

; Get descriptor from table
        movzx   eax, status_table[eax]
        cmp     al,INVALID                  ; Look for empty ST(0)
        jne     not_empty
;
;         ST(0) is empty!  Return the status value.
;
        ret     parms_size
;
;         Remove infinity from stack and exit.
;
found_infinity:
        fstp    st(0)               ; OK to leave fstp running
        jmp     short exit_proc
;
;         String space is too small!
;       Return invalid code.
;
small_string:
        mov     al,INVALID
exit_proc:
        leave           ; Restore stack setup
```

Figure 20-6. Floating-Point to ASCII Conversion Routine (Contd.)

```
        pop     es
        ret     parms_size
;
; ST(0) is NAN or indefinite.  Store the
; value in memory and look at the fraction
; field to separate indefinite from an ordinary NAN.
;
NAN_or_indefinite:
        fstp    fraction        ; Remove value from stack
                                ; for examination
        test    al,MINUS        ; Look at sign bit
        fwait                           ; Insure store is done
        jz      exit_proc               ; Can't be indefinite if
                                ; positive

        mov     ebx,0C0000000H  ; Match against upper 32
                                ;bits of fraction

; Compare bits 63-32
        sub     ebx, dword ptr fraction + 4

; Bits 31-0 must be zero
        or      ebx, dword ptr fraction
        jnz     exit_proc

; Set return value for indefinite value
     mov al,INDEFINITE
        jmp     exit_proc
;
;          Allocate stack space for local variables
;       and establish parameter addressibility.
;
not_empty:
        push    es                      ; Save working register
        enter local_size, 0             ; Setup stack addressing


; Check for enough string space
        mov     ecx,field_size
        cmp     ecx,2
        jl      small_string

        dec     ecx                     ; Adjust for sign character

; See if string is too large for BCD
        cmp     ecx,BCD_DIGITS
        jbe     size_ok

; Else set maximum string size
        mov     ecx,BCD_DIGITS
size_ok:
        cmp     al,INFINITY             ; Look for infinity

; Return status value for + or - inf
        jge     found_infinity
```

Figure 20-6. Floating-Point to ASCII Conversion Routine (Contd.)

```
        cmp     al,NAN          ; Look for NAN or INDEFINITE
        jge     NAN_or_indefinite
;
;   Set default return values and check that
;   the number is normalized.
;
        fabs    ; Use positive value only
                  ; sign bit in al has true sign of value
        xor     edx,edx             ; Form 0 constant
        mov     edi,denormal_ptr; Zero denormal count
        mov     [edi], dx
        mov     ebx,power_ptr   ; Zero power of ten value
        mov     [ebx], dx
        mov dl, al
        and dl, 1
    add dl, EXACT
        cmp     al,ZERO             ; Test for zero
        jae     convert_integer ; Skip power code if value
                                            ; is zero
    fstp   fraction
    fwait
    mov    al, bcd_byte + 7
    or     byte ptr bcd_byte + 7, 80h
    fld    fraction
    fxtract
    test   al, 80h
    jnz    normal_value

    fld1
    fsub
    ftst
    fstsw  ax
    sahf
    jnz    set_unnormal_count
;
;   Found a pseudo zero
;
    fldlg2              ; Develop power of ten estimate
    add    dl, PSEUDO_ZERO - EXACT
    fmulp  st(2), st
    fxch                ; Get power of ten
    fistp  word ptr [ebx] ; Set power of ten
    jmp    convert_integer

set_unnormal_count:
    fxtract             ; Get original fraction,
                        ; now normalized
    fxch                ; Get unnormal count
    fchs
    fistp  word ptr [edi] ; Set unnormal count


;  Calculate the decimal magnitude associated
;  with this number to within one order.  This
```

Figure 20-6. Floating-Point to ASCII Conversion Routine (Contd.)

```
;  error will always be inevitable due to
;  rounding and lost precision.  As a result,
;  we will deliberately  fail to consider the
;  LOG10 of the fraction value in calculating
;  the order. Since the fraction will always
;  be 1 <= F < 2, its  LOG10 will not change
;  the basic accuracy of the function.  To
;  get the decimal order of magnitude, simply
;  multiply the power of two by LOG10(2) and
;  truncate the result to an integer.
;
normal_value:
        fstp    fraction        ; Save the fraction field
                                ; for later use
        fist    power_two       ; Save power of two
        fldlg2                          ; Get LOG10(2)
                                        ; Power_two is now safe to use
        fmul            ; Form LOG10(of exponent of number)
        fistp   word ptr [ebx]  ; Any rounding mode
                                                ; will work here
;
;       Check if the magnitude of the number rules
;    out treating it as an integer.
;
;       CX has the maximum number of decimal digits
;  allowed.
;
        fwait           ; Wait for power_ten to be valid

; Get power of ten of value
        movsx si, word ptr [ebx]
        sub     esi,ecx                 ; Form scaling factor
                                ; necessary in ax
        ja      adjust_result   ; Jump if number will not fit
;
;       The number is between 1 and 10**(field_size).
;       Test if it is an integer.
;
        fild    power_two       ; Restore original number
        sub     dl,NORMAL-EXACT ; Convert to exact return
                                ; value
        fld     fraction
        fscale                          ; Form full value, this
                                ; is safe here
        fst     st(1)                   ; Copy value for compare
        frndint                         ; Test if its an integer
        fcomp                           ; Compare values
        fstsw   ax                      ; Save status
        sahf                            ; C3=1 implies it was
                                ; an integer
        jnz     convert_integer

        fstp    st(0)           ; Remove non integer value
        add     dl,NORMAL-EXACT ; Restore original return value
```

Figure 20-6. Floating-Point to ASCII Conversion Routine (Contd.)

```
; Scale the number to within the range allowed
; by the BCD format.The scaling operation should
; produce a number within one decimal order of
; magnitude of the largest decimal number
; representable within the given string width.
;
; The scaling power of ten value is in si.
;
adjust_result:
        mov     eax,esi             ; Setup for pow10
        mov     word ptr [ebx],ax   ; Set initial power
                                    ; of ten return value
        neg     eax                 ; Subtract one for each order of
                                    ; magnitude the value is scaled by
        call    get_power_10        ; Scaling factor is
                                    ; returned as
                                    ; exponent and fraction
        fld     fraction            ; Get fraction
        fmul                        ; Combine fractions
        mov     esi,ecx             ; Form power of ten of
                                    ;the maximum
        shl     esi,3               ; BCD value to fit in
                                    ; the string
        fild    power_two           ; Combine powers of two
        faddp   st(2),st
        fscale                      ; Form full value,
                                    ; exponent was safe
        fstp    st(1)               ; Remove exponent
;
;       Test the adjusted value against a table
;     of exact powers of ten. The combined errors
;     of the magnitude estimate and power function
;     can result in a value one order of magnitude
;     too small or too large to fit correctly in
;     the BCD field. To handle this problem, pretest
;     the adjusted value, if it is too small or
;     large, then adjust it by ten and adjust the
;     power of ten value.
;
test_power:

; Compare against exact power entry. Use the next
; entry since cx has been decremented by one
        fcom    power_table[esi]+type power_table
        fstsw   ax                  ; No wait is necessary
        sahf                        ; If C3 = C0 = 0 then
        jb      test_for_small      ; too big

        fidiv   const10             ; Else adjust value
        and     dl,not EXACT        ; Remove exact flag
        inc     word ptr [ebx]      ; Adjust power of ten value
        jmp     short in_range      ; Convert the value to a BCD
                                    ; integer
test_for_small:
        fcom    power_table[esi]    ; Test relative size
```

Figure 20-6. Floating-Point to ASCII Conversion Routine (Contd.)

```
        fstsw   ax                          ; No wait is necess
ary
        sahf                                ; If C0 = 0 then
                                    ; st(0) >= lower bound
        jc      in_range                    ; Convert the value
 to a
                                    ; BCD integer

        fimul   const10             ; Adjust value into range
        dec     word ptr [ebx]      ; Adjust power of ten value
in_range:
        frndint                     ; Form integer value
;
;       Assert: 0 <= TOS <= 999,999,999,999,999,999
;       The TOS number will be exactly representable
;   in 18 digit BCD format.
;
convert_integer:
        fbstp   bcd_value           ; Store as BCD format number
;
;         While the store BCD runs, setup registers
;     for the conversion to ASCII.
;
        mov     esi,BCD_SIZE-2  ; Initial BCD index value
        mov     cx,0f04h                ; Set shift count and mask
        mov     ebx,1                   ; Set initial size of ASCII
                                ; field for sign
        mov     edi,string_ptr  ; Get address of start of
                                ; ASCII string
        mov     ax,ds                   ; Copy ds to es
        mov     es,ax
        cld                                     ; Set autoincrement mode
        mov     al,'+'                  ; Clear sign field
        test    dl,MINUS        ; Look for negative value
        jz      positive_result

        mov     al,'-'
positive_result:
        stosb                                   ; Bump string pointer
                                ; past sign
        and     dl,not MINUS    ; Turn off sign bit
        fwait                                   ; Wait for fbstp to finish
;
;         Register usage:
;                                       ah:     BCD byte value in use
;                                       al:     ASCII character value
;                                       dx:     Return value
;                                       ch:     BCD mask = 0fh
;                                       cl:     BCD shift count = 4
;                                       bx:     ASCII string field width
;                                       esi:    BCD field index
;                                       di:     ASCII string field pointer
;                                       ds,es:  ASCII string segment base
;
;         Remove leading zeroes from the number.
```

Figure 20-6. Floating-Point to ASCII Conversion Routine (Contd.)

```
;
skip_leading_zeroes:
        mov     ah,bcd_byte[esi]                ; Get BCD byte
        mov     al,ah                   ; Copy value
        shr     al,cl                   ; Get high order digit
        and     al,0fh                  ; Set zero flag
        jnz     enter_odd               ; Exit loop if leading
                            ; non zero found

        mov     al,ah                   ; Get BCD byte again
        and     al,0fh                  ; Get low order digit
        jnz     enter_even              ; Exit loop if non zero
                            ; digit found

        dec     esi                             ; Decrement BCD index
        jns     skip_leading_zeroes
;
;         The significand was all zeroes.
;
        mov     al,'0'                  ; Set initial zero
        stosb
        inc     ebx                             ; Bump string length
        jmp     short exit_with_value
;
;         Now expand the BCD string into digit
;       per byte values 0-9.
;
digit_loop:
        mov     ah,bcd_byte[esi]        ; Get BCD byte
        mov     al,ah
        shr     al,cl                   ; Get high order digit
enter_odd:
        add     al,'0'                  ; Convert to ASCII
        stosb                           ; Put digit into ASCII
                            ; string area
        mov     al,ah                   ; Get low order digit
        and     al,0fh
        inc     ebx                     ; Bump field size counter
enter_even:
        add     al,'0'          ; Convert to ASCII
        stosb                   ; Put digit into ASCII area
        inc     ebx                     ; Bump field size counter
        dec     esi                     ; Go to next BCD byte
        jns     digit_loop
;
;         Conversion complete.  Set the string
;       size and remainder.
;
exit_with_value:
        mov     edi,size_ptr
        mov     word ptr [edi],bx
        mov     eax,edx                 ; Set return value
        jmp     exit_proc

floating_to_ascii       endp
                        code                    ends
                                                end
```

Figure 20-6. Floating-Point to ASCII Conversion Routine (Contd.)

```
+1 $title(Calculate the value of 10**ax)
   ;
   ;        This subroutine will calculate the
   ;    value of 10**eax. For values of
   ;    0 <= eax < 19, the result will exact.
   ;    All registers are transparent
   ;    and the value is returned on the TOS
   ;    as two numbers, exponent in ST(1) and
   ;    fraction in ST(0). The exponent value
   ;    can be larger than the largest
   ;    exponent of an extended real format
   ;    number.  Three stack entries are used.
   ;

                   name    get_power_10
                   public  get_power_10,power_table

   stack           stackseg    8

   code            segment public er
   ;
   ;        Use exact values from 1.0 to 1e18.
   ;
                   even             ; Optimize 16 bit access
   power_table     dq      1.0,1e1,1e2,1e3

                   dq      1e4,1e5,1e6,1e7

                   dq      1e8,1e9,1e10,1e11

                   dq      1e12,1e13,1e14,1e15

                   dq      1e16,1e17,1e18


   get_power_10    proc

         cmp       eax,18           ; Test for 0 <= ax < 19
         ja        out_of_range

         fld       power_table[eax*8]; Get exact value
         fxtract                    ; Separate power
```

Figure 20-6. Floating-Point to ASCII Conversion Routine (Contd.)

```
                                ; and fraction
        ret                 ; OK to leave fxtract running
;
;         Calculate the value using the
;       exponentiate instruction. The following
;       relations are used:
;               10**x = 2**(log2(10)*x)
;               2**(I+F) = 2**I * 2**F
;         if st(1) = I and st(0) = 2**F then
;         fscale produces 2**(I+F)
;
out_of_range:

        fldl2t                          ; TOS = LOG2(10)
        enter   4,0

      ; save power of 10 value, P
      mov      [ebp-4],eax

      ; TOS,X = LOG2(10)*P = LOG2(10**P)
         fimul   dword ptr [ebp-4]
         fld1                ; Set TOS = -1.0
         fchs
         fld     st(1)       ; Copy power value
                             ; in base two
         frndint             ; TOS = I: -inf < I <= X
                             ; where I is an integer
                             ; Rounding mode does
                             ; not matter
         fxch    st(2)       ; TOS = X, ST(1) = -1.0
                                ; ST(2) = I
         fsub    st,st(2)       ; TOS,F = X-I:
                                ; -1.0 < TOS <= 1.0

         ; Restore orignal rounding control
         pop     eax
         f2xm1                          ; TOS = 2**(F) - 1.0
         leave                          ; Restore stack
         fsubr                          ; Form 2**(F)
         ret                            ; OK to leave fsubr running

get_power_10    endp

code            ends
                end
```

Figure 20-6. Floating-Point to ASCII Conversion Routine (Contd.)

```
+1 $title(Determine TOS register contents)
   ;
   ;        This subroutine will return a value
   ;    from 0-15 in eax corresponding
   ;        to the contents of FPU TOS.  All
   ;    registers are transparent and no
   ;        errors are possible.  The return
   ;    value corresponds to c3,c2,c1,c0
   ;        of FXAM instruction.
   ;

        name     tos_status
        public   tos_status

   stack         stackseg    6

   code          segment public er

   tos_status    proc

        fxam                      ; Get status of TOS register
        fstsw  ax        ; Get current status
        mov      al,ah            ; Put bit 10-8 into bits 2-0
        and      eax,4007h        ; Mask out bits c3,c2,c1,c0
        shr      ah, 3            ; Put bit c3 into bit 11
        or       al,ah            ; Put c3 into bit 3
        mov      ah,0             ; Clear return value
        ret

   tos_status    endp

   code          ends
                 end
```

Figure 20-6. Floating-Point to ASCII Conversion Routine (Contd.)

20.3.3 Special Instructions

The functions demonstrate the operation of several numeric instructions, different data types, and precision control. Shown are instructions for automatic conversion to BCD, calculating the value of 10 raised to an integer value, establishing and maintaining concurrency, data synchronization, and use of directed rounding on the FPU.

Without the extended precision data type and built-in exponential function, the double precision accuracy of this function could not be attained with the size and speed of the shown example.

The function relies on the numeric BCD data type for conversion from binary floating-point to decimal. It is not difficult to unpack the BCD digits into separate ASCII decimal digits. The major work involves scaling the floating-point value to the comparatively limited range of BCD values. To print a 9-digit result requires accurately scaling the given value to an integer between 10^8 and 10^9. For example, the number +0.123456789 requires a scaling factor of 10^9 to produce the value +123456789.0, which can be stored in 9 BCD digits. The scale factor must be an exact power of 10 to avoid changing any of the printed digit values.

These routines should exactly convert all values exactly representable in decimal in the field size given. Integer values that fit in the given string size are not be scaled, but directly stored into the BCD form. Noninteger values exactly representable in decimal within the string size limits are also exactly converted. For example, 0.125 is exactly representable in binary or decimal. To convert this floating-point value to decimal, the scaling factor is 1000, resulting in 125. When scaling a value, the function must keep track of where the decimal point lies in the final decimal value.

20.3.4 Description of Operation

Converting a floating-point number to decimal ASCII takes three major steps: identifying the magnitude of the number, scaling it for the BCD data type, and converting the BCD data type to a decimal ASCII string.

Identifying the magnitude of the result requires finding the value X such that the number is represented by $I \times 10^X$, where $1.0 \leq I < 10.0$. Scaling the number requires multiplying it by a scaling factor 10^S, so that the result is an integer requiring no more decimal digits than provided for in the ASCII string.

Once scaled, the numeric rounding modes and BCD conversion put the number in a form easy to convert to decimal ASCII by host software.

Implementing each of these three steps requires attention to detail. To begin with, not all floating-point values have a numeric meaning. Values such as infinity, indefinite, or NaN may be encountered by the conversion routine. The conversion routine should recognize these values and identify them uniquely.

Special cases of numeric values also exist. Denormals have numeric values, but should be recognized because they indicate that precision was lost during some earlier calculations.

Once it has been determined that the number has a numeric value, and it is normalized (setting appropriate denormal flags, if necessary, to indicate this to the calling program), the value must be scaled to the BCD range.

20.3.5 Scaling the Value

To scale the number, its magnitude must be determined. It is sufficient to calculate the magnitude to an accuracy of 1 unit, or within a factor of 10 of the required value. After scaling the number, a check is made to see if the result falls in the range expected. If not, the result can be adjusted one decimal order of magnitude up or down. The adjustment test after the scaling is necessary due to inevitable inaccuracies in the scaling value.

Because the magnitude estimate for the scale factor need only be close, a fast technique is used. The magnitude is estimated by multiplying the power of 2, the unbiased floating-point exponent, associated with the number by $\log_{10}2$. Rounding the result to an integer produces an estimate of sufficient accuracy. Ignoring the fraction value can introduce a maximum error of 0.32 in the result.

Using the magnitude of the value and size of the number string, the scaling factor can be calculated. Calculating the scaling factor is the most inaccurate operation of the conversion process. The relation $10^X = 2^{(X*\log_2 10)}$ is used for this function. The exponentiate instruction F2XM1 is used.

Due to restrictions on the range of values allowed by the F2XM1 instruction, the power of 2 value is split into integer and fraction components. The relation $2^{(I + F)} = 2^I \times 2^F$ allows using the FSCALE instruction to recombine the 2^F value, calculated through F2XM1, and the 2^I part.

20.3.5.1 INACCURACY IN SCALING

The inaccuracy in calculating the scale factor arises because of the trailing zeros placed into the fraction value of the power of two when stripping off the integer valued bits. For each integer valued bit in the power of 2 value separated from the fraction bits, one bit of precision is lost in the fraction field due to the zero fill occurring in the least significant bits.

Up to 14 bits may be lost in the fraction because the largest allowed floating point exponent value is $2^{14}-1$. These bits directly reduce the accuracy of the calculated scale factor, thereby reducing the accuracy of the scaled value. For numbers in the range of $10^{\pm 30}$, a maximum of 8 bits of precision are lost in the scaling process.

20.3.5.2 AVOIDING UNDERFLOW AND OVERFLOW

The fraction and exponent fields of the number are separated to avoid underflow and overflow in calculating the scaling values. For example, to scale 10^{-4932} to 10^8 requires a scaling factor of 10^{4950}, which cannot be represented by the i486 processor.

By separating the exponent and fraction, the scaling operation involves adding the exponents separate from multiplying the fractions. The exponent arithmetic involves small integers, all easily represented by the i486 processor.

20.3.5.3 FINAL ADJUSTMENTS

It is possible that the power function (Get_Power_10) could produce a scaling value such that it forms a scaled result larger than the ASCII field could allow. For example, scaling $9.9999999999999999 \times 10^{4900}$ by $1.00000000000000010 \times 10^{-4883}$ produces $1.00000000000000009 \times 10^{18}$. The scale factor is within the accuracy of the FPU and the result is within the conversion accuracy, but it cannot be represented in BCD format. This is why there is a post-scaling test on the magnitude of the result. The result can be multiplied or divided by 10, depending on whether the result was too small or too large, respectively.

20.3.6 Output Format

For maximum flexibility in output formats, the position of the decimal point is indicated by a binary integer called the power value. If the power value is zero, then the decimal point is assumed to be at the right of the rightmost digit. Power values greater than zero indicate how many trailing zeros are not shown. For each unit below zero, move the decimal point to the left in the string.

The last step of the conversion is storing the result in BCD and indicating where the decimal point lies. The BCD string is then unpacked into ASCII decimal characters. The ASCII sign is set corresponding to the sign of the original value.

20.4 TRIGONOMETRIC CALCULATION EXAMPLES

In this example, the kinematics of a robot arm is modeled with the 4 × 4 homogeneous transformation matrices proposed by Denavit and Hartenberg[1,2]. The translational and rotational relationships between adjacent links are described with these matrices using the D-H matrix method. For each link, there is a 4 × 4 homogeneous transformation

1. **J. Denavit and R.S. Hartenberg, "A Kinematic Notation for Lower-Pair Mechanisms Based on Matrices," *J. Applied Mechanics*, June 1955, pp. 215-221.**
2. **C.S. George Lee, "Robert Arm Kinematics, Dynamics, and Control," *IEEE Computer*, Dec. 1982.**

matrix that represents the link's coordinate system (L_i) at the joint (J_i) with respect to the previous link's coordinate system (J_{i-1}, L_{i-1}). The following four geometric quantities completely describe the motion of any rigid joint/link pair (J_i, L_i), as Figure 20-7 illustrates.

θ_i = The angular displacement of the $\mathbf{x}_i$ axis from the $\mathbf{x}_{i-1}$ axis by rotating around the $\mathbf{z}_{i-1}$ axis (anticlockwise).

d_i = The distance from the origin of the (i-1)th coordinate system along the $\mathbf{z}_{i-1}$ axis to the $\mathbf{x}_i$ axis.

a_i = The distance of the origin of the ith coordinate system from the $\mathbf{z}_{i-1}$ axis along the $-\mathbf{x}_i$ axis.

α_i = The angular displacement of the $\mathbf{z}_i$ axis from the $\mathbf{z}_{i-1}$ about the $\mathbf{x}_i$ axis (anticlockwise).

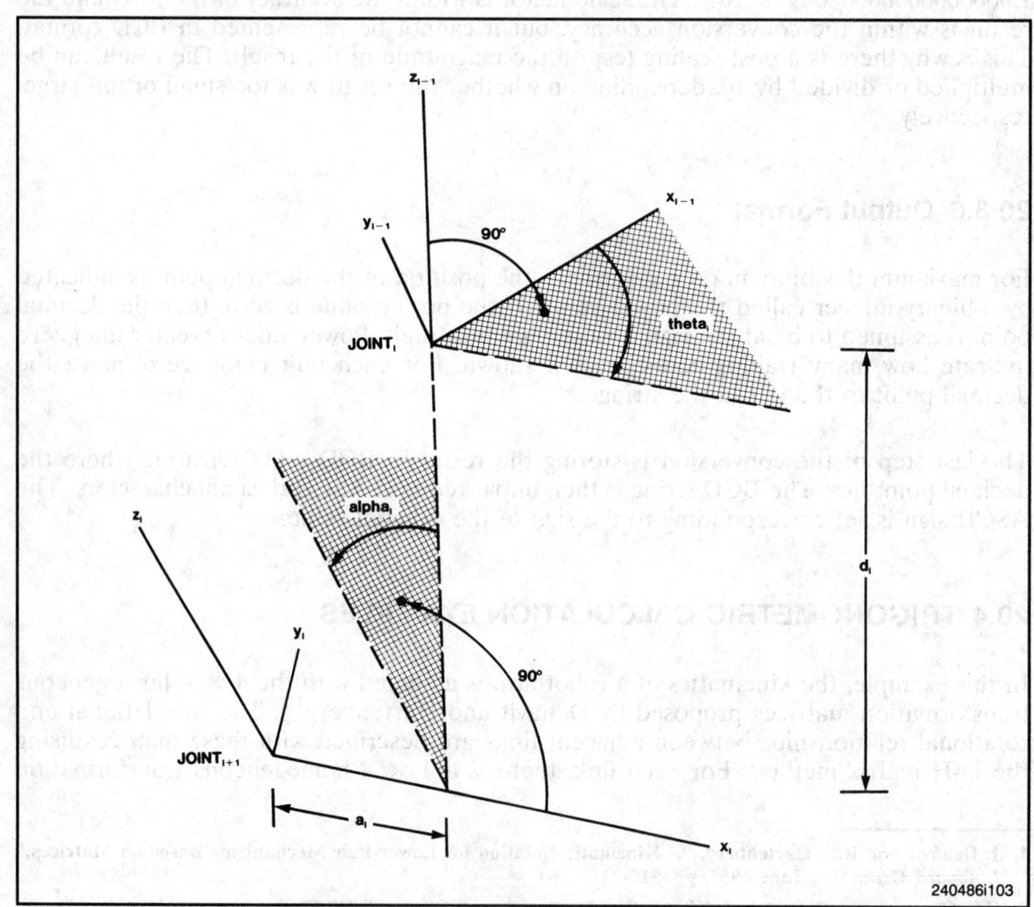

Figure 20-7. Relationships Between Adjacent Joints

The D-H transformation matrix $\mathbf{A}^{i}_{i-1}$ for adjacent coordinate frames (from joint_{i-1} to joint_i is calculated as follows:

$$\mathbf{A}^{i}_{i-1} = \mathbf{T}_{z,d} \times \mathbf{T}_{z,\theta} \times \mathbf{T}_{x,a} \times \mathbf{T}_{x,\alpha}$$

where:

$\mathbf{T}_{z,d}$ represents a translation along the $\mathbf{z}_{i-1}$ axis

$\mathbf{T}_{z,\theta}$ represents a rotation of angle θ about the $\mathbf{z}_{i-1}$ axis

$\mathbf{T}_{x,a}$ represents a translation along the $\mathbf{x}_i$ axis

$\mathbf{T}_{x,\alpha}$ represents a rotation of angle α about the $\mathbf{x}_i$ axis

$$A^{i}_{i-1} = \begin{vmatrix} \text{COS } \theta_i & -\text{COS } \alpha_i \text{ SIN } \theta_i & \text{SIN } \alpha_i \text{ SIN } \theta_i & \text{COS } \theta_i \\ \text{SIN } \theta_i & \text{COS } \alpha_i \text{ COS } \theta_i & -\text{SIN } \alpha_i \text{ COS } \theta_i & \text{SIN } \theta_i \\ 0 & \text{SIN } \alpha_i & \text{COS } \alpha_i & d_i \\ 0 & 0 & 0 & 1 \end{vmatrix}$$

The composite homogeneous matrix **T** which represents the position and orientation of the joint/link pair with respect to the base system is obtained by successively multiplying the D-H transformation matrices for adjacent coordinate frames.

$$\mathbf{T}^{i}_{o} = \mathbf{A}^{1}_{0} \times \mathbf{A}^{2}_{1} \times \ldots \times \mathbf{A}^{i}_{i-1}$$

This example in Figure 20-8 illustrates how the transformation process can be accomplished using the floating-point capabilities of the i486 processor. The program consists of two major procedures. The first procedure TRANS_PROC is used to calculate the elements in each D-H matrix, $\mathbf{A}^{i}_{i-1}$. The second procedure MATRIXMUL_PROC finds the product of two successive D-H matrices.

```
Name ROT_MATRIX_CAL
; This example illustrates the use
; of the i486 floating point
; instructions, in particular, the
; FSINCOS function which  gives both
; the SIN and COS values.
; The program calculates the
; composite matrix for base to end-
; effector transformation.
;
; Only the kinematics is considered in
; this example.
;
; If the composite matrix mentioned above
; is given by:
; T1n = A1 x A2 x ... x An
; T1n is found by successively calling
; trans_proc and matrixmul_pro until
; all matrices have been exhausted.
;
; trans_proc calculates entries in each
; A(A1,...,An) while matrixmul_proc
; performs the matrix multiplication for
; Ai and Ai+1. matrixmul_proc in turn
; calls matrix_row and matrix_elem to
; do the multiplication.


; Define stack space

trans_stack stackseg 400

; Define the matrix structure for
; 4X4 transformational matrices

  a_matrix struc
          a11     dq     ?
          a12     dq     ?
          a13     dq     ?
          a14     dq     ?
          a21     dq     ?
          a22     dq     ?
          a23     dq     ?
          a24     dq     ?
          a31     dq     0h
          a32     dq     ?
          a33     dq     ?
          a34     dq     ?
          a41     dq     0h
          a42     dq     0h
          a43     dq     0h
          a44     dq     1h
```

Figure 20-8. Robot Arm Kinematics Example

```
    a_matrix ends

; Assume One joint in the storage
; allocation and hence for
; two sets of parameters; however,
; more joints are possible
;
    alp_deg struc
            alpha_deg1 dd  ?
            alpha_deg2 dd  ?
    alp_deg ends

    tht_deg struc
            theta_deg1 dd  ?
            theta_deg2 dd  ?
    tht_deg ends

    A_array struc
            A1          dq  ?
            A2          dq  ?
    A_array ends

    D_array struc
            D1          dq  ?
            D2          dq  ?
    D_array ends

; trans_data is the data segment
;

trans_data          segment rw public

        Amx             a_matrix<>
        Bmx             a_matrix<>

        Tmx             a_matrix<>

        ALPHA_DEG       alp_deg<>

        THETA_DEG       tht_deg<>

        A_VECTOR        A_array<>

        D_VECTOR        D_array<>

        ZERO            dd          0
        d180            dd          180
        NUM_JOINT       equ         1
        NUM_ROW         equ         4
        NUM_COL         equ         4
        REVERSE         db          1h
trans_data ends

assume    ds:trans_data, es:trans_data
```

Figure 20-8. Robot Arm Kinematics Example (Contd.)

```
; trans_code contains the procedures
; for calculating matrix elements and
; matrix multiplications

trans_code      segment   er public
trans_proc proc far

    ; Calculate alpha and theta in radians
    ; from their values in degrees

      fldpi
      fdiv     d180

    ; Duplicate pi/180
      fld      st

      fmul     qword ptr ALPHA_DEG[ecx*8]
      fxch     st(1)
      fmul     qword ptr THETA_DEG[ecx*8]

    ; theta(radians) in ST and
    ; alpha(radians) in ST(1)

    ; Calculate matrix elements
    ; a11 = cos theta
    ; a12 = - cos alpha * sin thet
    ; a13 = sin alpha * sin theta
    ; a14 = A * cos theta
    ; a21 = sin theta
    ; a22 = cos alpha * cos theta
    ; a23 = -sin alpha * cos theta
    ; a24 = A * sin theta
    ; a32 = sin alpha
    ; a33 = cos alpha
    ; a34 = D
    ; a31 = a41 = a42 = a43 = 0.0
    ; a44 =1

    ; ebx contains the offset for the matrix

      fsincos              ;cos theta in ST
                           ;sin theta in ST(1)
      fld      st          ;duplicate cos theta
      fst      [ebx].a11 ;cos theta in a11
      fmul     qword ptr A_VECTOR[ecx*8]
      fstp     [ebx].a14 ;A * cos thetain a14
      fxch     st(1)       ;sin theta in ST
      fst      [ebx].a21 ;sin theta in a21
      fld      st          ;duplicate sin theta
      fmul     qword ptr A_VECTOR[ecx*8]
      fstp     [ebx].a24 ;A * sin theta in a24
      fld      st(2)       ;alpha in ST
      fsincos              ;cos alpha in ST
```

Figure 20-8. Robot Arm Kinematics Example (Contd.)

```
                        ;sin alpha in ST(1)
                        ;sin theta in ST(2)
                        ;cos theta in ST(3)
    fst     [ebx].a33 ;cos alpha in a33
    fxch    st(1)     ;sin alpha in ST
    fst     [ebx].a32 ;sin alpha in a32
    fld     ST(2)     ;sin theta in ST
                      ;sin alpha in ST(1)
    fmul    st,st(1)  ;sin alpha * sin theta
    fstp    [ebx].a13 ;stored in a13
    fmul    st,st(3)  ;cos theta * sin alpha
    fchs              ;-cos theta * sin alpha
    fstp    [ebx].a23 ;stored in a23
    fld     st(2)     ;cos theta in ST
                      ;cos alpha in ST(1)
                      ;sin theta in ST(2)
                      ;cos theta in ST(3)
    fmul    st,st(1)  ;cos theta * cos alpha
    fstp    [ebx].a22 ;stored in a22
    fmul    st,st(1)  ;cos alpha * sin theta
   ;
   ; To take advantage of parallel operations
   ; between the IU and FPU
   ;
    push    eax  ; save eax
   ;
   ; also move D into a34 in a faster way
    mov     eax, dword ptr D_VECTOR[ecx*8]
    mov     dword ptr [ebx + 88], eax
    mov     eax, dword ptr D_VECTOR[ecx*8 + 4]
    mov     dword ptr [ebx + 92], eax
    pop     eax  ; restore eax
    fchs              ;-cos alpha * sin theta
    fstp    [ebx].a12 ;stored in a12
                      ;and all nonzero elements
                      ;have been calculated
    ret

trans_proc endp


matrix_elem proc far

    ; This procedure calculate the dot product
    ; of the ith row of the first matrix and
    ; the jth column of the second matrix:
    ;
    ; Tij where Tij = sum of Aik x Bkj over k
    ;
    ; parameters passed from the calling routine,
    ; matrix_row:
    ; ESI = (i-1)*8
    ; EDI = (j-1)*8
    ; local register, EBP = (k-1)*8
    ;
```

Figure 20-8. Robot Arm Kinematics Example (Contd.)

```
        push    ebp     ; save ebp
        push    ecx     ; ecx to be used as a tmp reg
        mov     ecx, esi; save it for later indexing

      ; locating the element in the first matrix, A
        imul    ecx, NUM_COL    ; ecx contains offset due
                                ; to preceding rows; the
                                ; offset is from the
                                ; beginning of the matrix

        xor     ebp, ebp; clear ebp, which will be
                        ; used a temp reg to index( k)
                        ; across the ith row of the first
                        ; matrix as well as down the jth
                        ; column of the second matrix

      ; clear Tij for accumulating Aik*Bkj
        mov      dword ptr [edx][edi],ebp
        mov      dword ptr [edx][edi+4], ebp

        push    ecx     ; save on stack: esi * num_col =
                        ; the offset of the beginnging
                        ; of the ith row from the
                        ; beginning of the A matrix

NXT_k:
        add     ecx, ebp ; get to the kth column entry
                         ; of the ith row of the A matrix

      ; load Aik into FPU
        fld     qword ptr [eax][ecx]

      ; locating  Bkj
        mov     ecx, ebp
        imul    ecx, NUM_ROW ; ecx contains the offset
                             ; of the beginning of the
                             ; kth row from the
                             ; beginning of the B matrix
        add     ecx, edi     ; get to the jth column

                             ; of the kth row of the B
                             ; matrix
        fmul    qword ptr [ebx][ecx]; Aik * Bkj
        pop     ecx         ; esi * num_col
                            ; in ecx again
        push    ecx         ; also at top of program
                            ; stack

      ; add to the result in the output matrix,Tij
        add     ecx, edi

      ; accumulating the sum of Aik * Bkj
        fadd    qword ptr [edx][ecx]
        fstp    qword ptr [edx][ecx]
      ; increment k by 1, i.e., ebp by 8
        add     ebp, 8
```

Figure 20-8. Robot Arm Kinematics Example (Contd.)

```
    ; Has k reached the width of the matrix yet?
      cmp     ebp, NUM_COL*8
      jl      NXT_k

    ; Restore registers
      pop     ecx      ; clear esi*num_col from stack
      pop     ecx      ; restore ecx
      pop     ebp      ; restore ebp
      ret

matrix_elem endp


matrix_row proc far

      xor     edi, edi
    ; scan across a row

NXT_COL:
      call    matrix_elem
      add     edi, 8
      cmp     edi, NUM_COL*8
      jl      NXT_COL
      ret

matrix_row endp


matrixmul_proc proc far

    ; This procedure does the matrix
    ; multiplication by calling matrix_row
    ; to calculate entries in each row
    ;
    ; The matrix multiplication is
    ; performed in the following manner,
    ;    Tij = Aik x Bkj
    ; where i and j denote the row and column
    ; respectively and k is the index for
    ; scanning across the ith row of the
    ; first matrix and the jth column of the
    ; second matrix.
    mov     ebp, esp                   ;use base pointer for indexing
    mov     edx, dword ptr [ebp+4]     ;offset Tmx in edx
    mov     ebx, dword ptr [ebp+8]     ;offset Bmx in ebx
    mov     eax, dword ptr [ebp=12]    ;offset Amx in eax
    ; setup esi and edi
    ; edi points to the column
    ; esi points to the row

      xor     esi, esi ; clear esi

NXT_ROW:
      call    matrix_row
```

Figure 20-8. Robot Arm Kinematics Example (Contd.)

```
        add     esi, 8
        cmp     esi, NUM_ROW*8
        jl      NXT_ROW
        ret     12 ;pop off matrix pointers

matrixmul_proc endp

trans_code ends

;*****************************************
;                                       ;
;                                       ;
;                                       ;
;           Main program                ;
;                                       ;
;                                       ;
;                                       ;
;*****************************************

main_code segment er

START:

        mov  esp,  stackstart trans_stack
      ; save all registers

        pushad

      ; ECX denotes the number of joints
      ; where no of matrices = NUM_JOINT + 1
      ; Find the first matrix( from the base
      ; of the system to the first joint)
      ; and call it Bmx
        xor  ecx, ecx            ; 1st matrix
        mov  ebx, offset Bmx     ;
        call trans_proc          ; is Bmx
        inc  ecx

NXT_MATRIX:
      ; From the 2nd matrix and on, it
      ; will be stored in Amx.
      ; The result from the first matrix mult.
      ; is stored in Tmx but will be accessed
      ; as Bmx in the next multiplication.
      ; As a matter of fact, the roles of Bmx
      ; and Tmx alternate in successive
      ; multiplications. This is achieved by
      ; reversing the order of the Bmx and Tmx
      ; pointers being passed onto the program
      ; stack. Thus, this is invisible to the
      ; matrix multiplication procedure.
      ; REVERSE serves as the indicator;
      ; REVERSE = 0 means that the result
      ;               is to placed in Tmx.
```

Figure 20-8. Robot Arm Kinematics Example (Contd.)

```
        mov     ebx, offset Amx  ;find Amx
        call    trans_proc
        inc     ecx
        xor     REVERSE, 1h
        jnz     Bmx_as_Tmx

      ; no reversing.  Bmx as the second input
      ; matrix while Tmx as the output matrix.
        push    offset Amx
        push    offset Bmx
        push    offset Tmx
        jmp     CONTINUE

      ; reversing. Tmx as the second input
      ; matrix while Bmx as the output matrix.
Bmx_as_Tmx:
        push    offset Amx
        push    offset Tmx  ;reversing the
        push    offset Bmx  ;pointers passed

CONTINUE:
        call    matrixmul_proc
        cmp     ecx, NUM_JOINT
        jle     NXT_MATRIX

      ; if REVERSE = 1 then the final answer
      ; will be in Bmx otherwise, in Tmx.

        popad

main_code  ends

end START, ds:trans_data, ss:trans_stack
```

Figure 20-8. Robot Arm Kinematics Example (Contd.)

Part IV
Compatibility

21

Executing 80286 and 386™ DX or SX CPU Programs

CHAPTER 21
EXECUTING 80286 AND 386™ DX OR SX CPU PROGRAMS

In general, programs written for protected mode on an 80286 processor run without modification on the i486™ processor. The features of the 80286 processor are an object-code compatible subset of those of the i486 processor. The Default bit in segment descriptors indicates whether the processor is to treat a code, data, or stack segment as an 80286 or 386™/ i486 CPU segment.

To software, the features of the 386 DX or SX processors are virtually identical to the i486 processor. For the most part, the differences are in the underlying hardware implementation.

The segment descriptors used by the 80286 processor are supported by the i486 processor if the Intel®-reserved word (highest word) of the descriptor is clear. On the i486 processor, this word includes the upper bits of the base address and the segment limit.

The segment descriptors for data segments, code segments, local descriptor tables (there are no descriptors for global descriptor tables), and task gates are the same for the 80286, 386, and i486 processors. Other 80286 CPU descriptors (TSS segment, call gate, interrupt gate, and trap gate) are supported by the i486 processor. The i486 processor also has descriptors for TSS segments, call gates, interrupt gates, and trap gates which support the 32-bit architecture of the i486 processor. Both kinds of descriptors can be used in the same system.

For those segment descriptors common to both the 80286 and i486 processors, clear bits in the reserved word cause the i486 processor to interpret these descriptors exactly as an 80286 processor does; for example:

Base Address—The upper eight bits of the 32-bit base address are clear, which limits base addresses to 24 bits.

Limit—The upper four bits of the limit field are clear, restricting the value of the limit field to 64K bytes.

Granularity bit—The Granularity bit is clear, indicating the value of the 16-bit limit is interpreted in units of 1 byte.

Big bit—In a data-segment descriptor, the B bit is clear, indicating the segment is no larger than 64 Kbytes.

Default bit—In an code-segment descriptor, the D bit is clear, indicating 16-bit addressing and operands are the default. In a stack-segment descriptor, the D bit is clear, indicating use of the SP register (instead of the ESP register) and a 64K byte maximum segment limit.

For formats of these descriptors and documentation of their use see the *iAPX 286 Programmer's Reference Manual*.

21.1 TWO WAYS TO RUN 80286 CPU TASKS

When porting 80286 programs to the i486 processor, there are two approaches to consider:

1. Porting an entire 80286 software system to the i486 processor, complete with the old operating system, loader, and system builder.

   In this case, all tasks will have 80286 TSSs. The i486 processor is being used as if it were a faster version of the 80286 processor.

2. Porting selected 80286 applications to run in an i486 CPU processor environment with an i486 CPU operating system, loader, and system builder.

   In this case, the TSSs used to represent 80286 tasks should be changed to i486 CPU TSSs. It is possible to mix 80286 and i486 CPU TSSs, but the benefits are small and the problems are great. All tasks in an i486 CPU software system should have i486 CPU TSSs. It is not necessary to change the 80286 object modules themselves; TSSs are usually constructed by the operating system, by the loader, or by the system builder. See Chapter 24 for more discussion of the interface between 16-bit and 32-bit code.

21.2 DIFFERENCES FROM 80286 CPU

The few differences between the 80286 and i486 processors affect operating systems more than application programs.

21.2.1 Wraparound of 80286 Processor 24-Bit Physical Address Space

With the 80286 processor, any base and offset combination which addresses beyond 16 megabytes wraps around to the first megabyte of the address space. With the i486 processor, because it has a greater physical address space, any such address maps to the 17th megabyte. In the unlikely event that any software depends on address wraparound, the same effect can be simulated on the i486 processor by using paging to map the first 64K bytes past the top of the 16-megabyte address space to the bottom 64K bytes of the segment.

21.2.2 Reserved Word of Segment Descriptor

Because the i486 processor uses the contents of the reserved word of 80286 segment descriptors, 80286 programs which place values in this word may not run correctly on the i486 processor.

21.2.3 New Segment Descriptor Type Codes

Operating-system code which manages space in descriptor tables often uses an invalid value in the access-rights field of descriptor-table entries to identify unused entries. Access rights values of 80H and 00H remain invalid for both the 80286 and i486 processors. Other values which were invalid on the 80286 processor may be valid on the i486 processor because uses for these bits are defined for the i486 processor.

21.2.4 Restricted Semantics of LOCK Prefix

The 80286 processor performs the bus lock function differently than the i486 processor. Programs which use forms of memory locking specific to the 80286 processor may not run properly when run on the i486 processor.

The LOCK prefix and its bus signal only should be used to prevent other bus masters from interrupting a data movement operation. The LOCK prefix only may be used with the following i486 instructions when they modify memory. An invalid-opcode exception results from using the LOCK prefix before any other instruction, or with these instructions when no write operation is made to memory (i.e., when the destination operand is in a register).

- Bit test and change: the BTS, BTR, and BTC instructions.
- Exchange: the XCHG, XADD, and CMPXCHG instructions (no LOCK prefix is needed for the XCHG instruction).
- One-operand arithmetic and logical: the INC, DEC, NOT, NEG instructions.
- Two-operand arithmetic and logical: the ADD, ADC, SUB, SBB, AND, OR, and XOR instructions.

A locked instruction is guaranteed to lock only the area of memory defined by the destination operand, but may lock a larger memory area. For example, typical 8086 and 80286 configurations lock the entire physical memory space.

On the 80286 processor, the LOCK prefix is sensitive to IOPL; if CPL is less privileged than the IOPL, a general protection exception is generated. On the 386 DX and i486 processors, no check against IOPL is performed.

21.2.5 Additional Exceptions

The 386 and i486 processors have new exceptions which can occur even in systems designed for the 80286 processor.

- Exception #6 – invalid opcode

  This exception can result from improper use of the LOCK instruction prefix.

- Exception #14 – page fault

  This exception may occur in an 80286 program if the operating system enables paging. Paging can be used in a system with 80286 tasks if all tasks use the same page directory. Because there is no place in an 80286 TSS to store the PDBR register, switching to an 80286 task does not change the value of the PDBR register. Tasks ported from the 80286 processor should be given i486 CPU TSSs so they can make full use of paging.

21.3 DIFFERENCES FROM 386™ CPU

Very few differences exist between the programming models of the 386 DX or SX and i486 processors. The i486 processor defines new bits in the EFLAGS, CR0, and CR3 registers, and in entries in the first- and second-level page tables. On the 386 processors, these bits were reserved, so the new architectural features should not be a compatibility issue.

21.3.1 New Flag

The AC flag (bit position 18), in conjunction with the AM bit in the CR0 register, controls alignment checking.

21.3.2 New Exception

The alignment-check exception (exception vector 17) reports unaligned memory references when alignment checking is being performed.

21.3.3 New Instructions

There are three new application instructions:

- the BSWAP instruction
- the XADD instruction
- the CMPXCHG instruction

There are three new system instructions, used for managing the cache and TLB:

- the INVD instruction
- the WBINVD instruction
- the INVLPG instruction

The form of the MOV instruction used to access the test registers has changed. New test registers have been defined for the cache, and the model of the TLB accessed through the test registers has changed.

21.3.4 New Control Register Bits

Five new bits have been defined in the CR0 register:

- the NE bit
- the WP bit
- the AM bit
- the NW bit
- the CD bit

Two new bits have been defined in the CR3 register:

- the PCD bit
- the PWT bit

21.3.5 New Page-Table Entry Bits

Two bits have been defined in page table entries for controlling caching of pages:

- the PCD bit
- the PWT bit

21.3.6 Changes in Segment Descriptor Loads

On the 386 processors, loading a segment descriptor would always cause a locked read and write to set the Accessed bit of the descriptor. On the i486 processor, the locked read and write occur only if the bit is not already set.

Real-Address Mode 22

CHAPTER 22
REAL-ADDRESS MODE

The real-address mode of the i486™ processor runs programs written for the 8086, 8088, 80186, or 80188 processors, or for the real-address mode of an 80286 or 386™ processor.

The architecture of the i486 processor in this mode is almost identical to that of the 8086, 8088, 80186, and 80188 processors. To a programmer, an i486 processor in real-address mode appears as a high-speed 8086 processor with extensions to the instruction set and registers. The principal features of this architecture are defined in Chapters 2 and 3.

This chapter discusses certain additional topics which complete the system programmer's view of the i486 processor in real-address mode:

- Address formation.
- Extensions to registers and instructions.
- Interrupt and exception handling.
- Entering and leaving real-address mode.
- Real-address mode exceptions.
- Differences from 8086 processor.
- Differences from 80286 processor in real-address mode.
- Differences from 386 processors in real-address mode.
- Processor detection code

22.1 ADDRESS TRANSLATION

In real-address mode, the i486 processor does not interpret 8086 selectors by referring to descriptors; instead, it forms linear addresses as an 8086 processor would. It shifts the selector left by four bits to form a 20-bit base address. The effective address is extended with four clear bits in the upper bit positions and added to the base address to create a linear address, as shown in Figure 22-1.

Because of the possibility of a carry, the resulting linear address may have as many as 21 significant bits. An 8086 program may generate linear addresses anywhere in the range 0 to 10FFEFH (1 megabyte plus approximately 64K bytes) of the linear address space. Because paging is not available in real-address mode, the linear address is used as the physical address.

Unlike the 8086 and 80286 processors, but like the 386 processors, the i486 processor can generate 32-bit effective addresses using an address override prefix; however in real-address mode, the value of a 32-bit address may not exceed 65,535 without causing

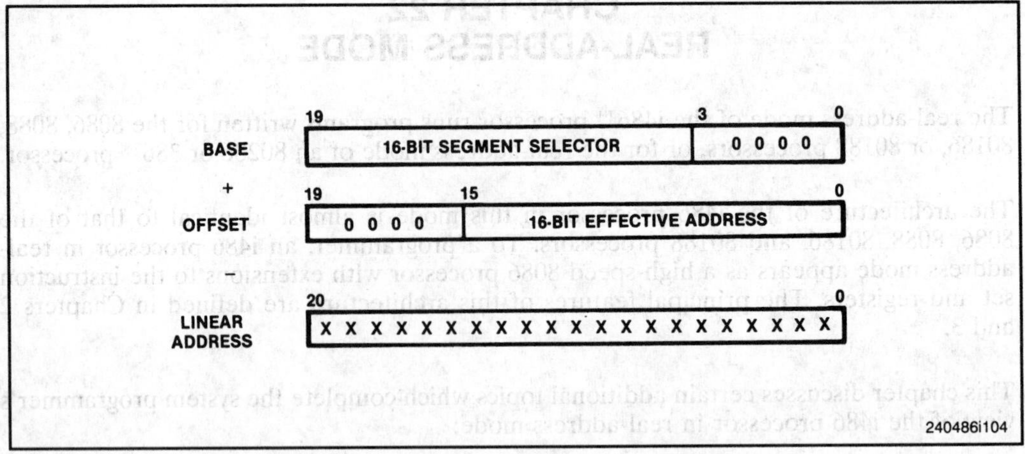

Figure 22-1. 8086 Address Translation

an exception. For full compatibility with 80286 real-address mode, pseudo-protection faults (interrupt 12 or 13 with no error code) occur if an effective address is generated outside the range 0 through 65,535.

22.2 REGISTERS AND INSTRUCTIONS

The register set available in real-address mode includes all the registers defined for the 8086 processor plus the new registers introduced with the 386 processor and 387™ coprocessor: FS, GS, debug registers, control registers, test registers, and floating-point unit registers. New instructions which explicitly operate on the segment registers FS and GS are available, and the new segment-override prefixes can be used to cause instructions to use the FS and GS registers for address calculations.

The instruction codes which generate invalid-opcode exceptions include instructions from protected mode which move or test i486 CPU segment selectors and segment descriptors, i.e., the VERR, VERW, LAR, LSL, LTR, STR, LLDT, and SLDT instructions. Programs executing in real-address mode are able to take advantage of the new application-oriented instructions added to the architecture with the introduction of the 80186, 80188, 80286, 386 DX, SX and i486 processors:

- New instructions introduced on the 80186, 80188, and 80286 processors.
  - PUSH immediate data
  - Push all and pop all (PUSHA and POPA)
  - Multiply immediate data
  - Shift and rotate by immediate count
  - String I/O
  - ENTER and LEAVE instructions
  - BOUND instruction

- New instructions introduced on the 386 DX processor.
  - LSS, LFS, LGS instructions
  - Long-displacement conditional jumps
  - Single-bit instructions
  - Bit scan instructions
  - Double-shift instructions
  - Byte set on condition instruction
  - Move with sign/zero extension
  - Generalized multiply instruction
  - MOV to and from control registers
  - MOV to and from test registers
  - MOV to and from debug registers
- New instructions introduced on the i486 processor.
  - BSWAP instruction
  - XADD instruction
  - CMPXCHG instruction
  - INVD instruction
  - WBINVD instruction
  - INVLPG instruction

22.3 INTERRUPT AND EXCEPTION HANDLING

Interrupts and exceptions in i486 CPU real-address mode work much as they do on an 8086 processor. Interrupts and exceptions call interrupt procedures through an interrupt table. The processor scales the interrupt or exception identifier by four to obtain an index into the interrupt table. The entries of the interrupt table are far pointers to the entry points of interrupt or exception handler procedures. When an interrupt occurs, the processor pushes the current values of the CS and IP registers onto the stack, disables interrupts, clears the TF flag, and transfers control to the location specified in the interrupt table. An IRET instruction at the end of the handler procedure reverses these steps before returning control to the interrupted procedure. Exceptions do not return error codes in real-address mode.

The primary difference in the interrupt handling of the i486 processor compared to the 8086 processor is the location and size of the interrupt table depend on the contents of the IDTR register. Ordinarily, this fact is not apparent to programmers, because, after reset initialization, the IDTR register contains a base address of 0 and a limit of 3FFH, which is compatible with the 8086 processor. However, the LIDT instruction can be used in real-address mode to change the base and limit values in the IDTR register. See Chapter 9 for details on the IDTR register, and the LIDT and SIDT instructions. If an interrupt occurs and its entry in the interrupt table is beyond the limit stored in the IDTR register, a double-fault exception is generated.

22.4 ENTERING AND LEAVING REAL-ADDRESS MODE

Real-address mode is in effect after reset initialization. Even if the system is going to run in protected mode, the start-up program runs in real-address mode while preparing to switch to protected mode.

22.4.1 Switching to Protected Mode

The only way to leave real-address mode is to switch to protected mode. The processor enters protected mode when a MOV to CR0 instruction sets the PE (protection enable) bit in the CR0 register. (For compatibility with the 80286 processor, the LMSW instruction also may be used to set the PE bit.)

See Chapter 10 "Initialization" for other aspects of switching to protected mode.

22.5 SWITCHING BACK TO REAL-ADDRESS MODE

The processor re-enters real-address mode if software clears the PE bit in the CR0 register with a MOV CR0 instruction (for compatibility with the 80286 processor, the LMSW instruction can set the PE bit, but cannot clear it). A procedure which re-enters real-address mode should proceed as follows:

1. If paging is enabled, perform the following sequence:
   - Transfer control to linear addresses which have an identity mapping; i.e., linear addresses equal physical addresses.
   - Clear the PG bit in the CR0 register.
   - Move a 0 into the CR3 register to flush the TLB.
2. Transfer control to a segment which has a limit of 64K (0FFFFH). This loads the CS register with the segment limit it needs to have in real mode.
3. Load segment registers SS, DS, ES, FS, and GS with a selector for a descriptor containing the following values, which are appropriate for real mode:
   - Limit = 64K (0FFFFH)
   - Byte granular (G =0)
   - Expand up (E = 0)
   - Writable (W = 1)
   - Present (P =1)
   - Base = any value

   Note that if the segment registers are not reloaded, execution continues using the descriptors loaded during protected mode.
4. Disable interrupts. A CLI instruction disables INTR interrupts. NMI interrupts can be disabled with external circuitry.
5. Clear the PE bit in the CR0 register.

6. Jump to the real mode program using a far JMP instruction. This flushes the instruction queue and puts appropriate values in the access rights of the CS register.
7. Use the LIDT instruction to load the base and limit of the real-mode interrupt vector table.
8. Enable interrupts.
9. Load the segment registers as needed by the real-mode code.

22.6 REAL-ADDRESS MODE EXCEPTIONS

The i486 processor reports some exceptions differently when executing in real-address mode than when executing in protected mode. Table 22-1 details the real-address-mode exceptions.

22.7 DIFFERENCES FROM 8086 CPU

In general, the i486 processor in real-address mode will correctly run ROM-based software designed for the 8086, 8088, 80186, and 80188 processors. Following is a list of the minor differences between program execution on the 8086 and i486 processors.

1. Instruction clock counts.

   The i486 processor takes fewer clocks for most instructions than the 8086 processor. The areas most likely to be affected are:

   - Delays required by I/O devices between I/O operations.
   - Assumed delays with 8086 processor operating in parallel with an 8087.

2. Divide-error exceptions point to the DIV instruction.

   Divide-error exceptions on the i486 processor always leave the saved CS:IP value pointing to the instruction which failed. On the 8086 processor, the CS:IP value points to the next instruction.

3. Undefined 8086 processor opcodes.

   Opcodes which were not defined for the 8086 processor generate an invalid-opcode exception or execute one of the new instructions introduced with the 80286, 386 DX or i486 processors.

4. Value written by PUSH SP.

   The i486 processor pushes a different value on the stack for a PUSH SP instruction than the 8086 processor. The i486 processor pushes the value of the SP register before it is decremented as part of the push operation; the 8086 processor pushes the value of the SP register after it is decremented. If the value pushed is important, replace PUSH SP instructions with the following three instructions:

```
PUSH    BP
MOV     BP, SP
XCHG    BP, [BP]
```

   This code functions as the 8086 processor PUSH SP instruction on the i486 processor.

Table 22-1. Exceptions and Interrupts

Description	Vector	Source of the Exception	Does the Return Address Point to the Instruction Which Caused the Exception?
Divide Error	0	DIV and IDIV instructions	yes
Debug	1	any	*[1]
Breakpoint	3	INT instruction	no
Overflow	4	INTO instruction	no
Bounds Check	5	BOUND instruction	yes
Invalid Opcode	6	reserved opcodes and improper use of LOCK prefix	yes
Device not available	7	ESC or WAIT instructions	yes
Double Fault	8	any	yes
Reserved	9		
Invalid Task State Segment	10	JMP, CALL, IRET instructions, interrupts and exceptions	yes
Segment not present	11	any instruction which changes segments	yes
Stack Exception	12	stack operation crosses address limit	yes
Protection	13	operand crosses address limit, instruction crosses address limit, or instruction exceeds 15 bytes	yes
Page Fault	14	any instruction that references memory	yes
Reserved	15		
Floating-Point Error	16	ESC or WAIT instructions	yes[2]
Software Interrupt	0 to 255	INT *n* instructions	no

1. Some debug exceptions point to the faulting instruction, others point to the following instruction. The exception handler can test the DR6 register to determine which has occurred.
2. Floating-point errors are reported on the first ESC or WAIT instruction after the ESC instruction which generated the error.

5. Shift or rotate by more than 31 bits.

   The i486 processor masks all shift and rotate counts to the lowest five bits. This MOD 32 operation limits the count to a maximum of 31 bits, which limits the amount of time that interrupt response may be delayed while the instruction is executing.

6. Redundant prefixes.

   The i486 processor sets a limit of 15 bytes on instruction length. The only way to violate this limit is by putting redundant prefixes before an instruction. A general-protection exception is generated if the limit on instruction length is violated. The 8086 processor has no instruction length limit.

7. Operand crossing offset 0 or 65,535.

   On the 8086 processor, an attempt to access a memory operand which crosses offset 65,535 (e.g., MOV a word to offset 65,535) or offset 0 (e.g., PUSH a word when SP = 1) causes the offset to wrap around modulo 65,536. The i486 processor generates an exception in these cases: a general-protection exception if the segment is a data segment (i.e. if the CS, DS, ES, FS, or GS register is being used to address the segment) or a stack exception if the segment is a stack segment (i.e., if the SS register is being used).

8. Sequential execution across offset 65,535.

   On the 8086 processor, if sequential execution of instructions proceeds past offset 65,535, the processor fetches the next instruction byte from offset 0 of the same segment. On the i486 processor, the processor generates a general-protection exception in such a case.

9. LOCK is restricted to certain instructions.

   The LOCK prefix and its output signal should only be used to prevent other bus masters from interrupting a data movement operation. The LOCK prefix only may be used with the following i486 CPU instructions when they modify memory. An invalid-opcode exception results from using LOCK before any other instruction, or with these instructions when no write operation is made to memory.

   - Bit test and change: the BTS, BTR, and BTC instructions.
   - Exchange: the XCHG, XADD, and CMPXCHG instructions (no LOCK prefix is needed for the XCHG instruction).
   - One-operand arithmetic and logical: the INC, DEC, NOT, NEG instructions.
   - Two-operand arithmetic and logical: the ADD, ADC, SUB, SBB, AND, OR, and XOR instructions.

10. Single-stepping external interrupt handlers.

    The priority of the i486 CPU single-step exception is different from the 8086 processor. The change prevents an external interrupt handler from being single-stepped if the interrupt occurs while a program is being single-stepped. The i486 CPU single-step exception has higher priority than any external interrupt. The i486 processor still may single-step through an interrupt handler called by the INT instructions or by an exception.

11. IDIV exceptions for quotients of 80H or 8000H.

    The i486 processor can generate the largest negative number as a quotient for the IDIV instruction. The 8086 processor generates a divide-error exception instead.

12. Flags in stack.

    The setting of the flags stored by the PUSHF instruction, by interrupts, and by exceptions is different from that stored by the 8086 processor in bit positions 12 through 15. On the 8086 processor these bits are set, but in the i486 CPU real-address mode, bit 15 is always clear, and bits 14 through 12 have the last value loaded into them.

13. NMI interrupting NMI handlers.

    After an NMI interrupt is recognized by the i486 processor, the NMI interrupt is masked until an IRET instruction is executed.

14. Floating-point errors call the floating-point error exception.

    Floating-point exceptions on the i486 processor call the floating-point error exception handler. If an 8086 processor uses another exception for the 8087 interrupt, both exception vectors should call the floating-point error exception handler. The i486 processor has signals which, with the addition of external logic, support user-defined error reporting for emulation of the interrupt mechanism used in many personal computers.

15. Numeric exception handlers should allow prefixes.

    On the i486 processor, the value of the CS and IP registers saved for floating-point exceptions points at any prefixes which come before the ESC instruction. On the 8086 processor, the saved CS:IP points to the ESC instruction.

16. Floating-Point Unit does not use interrupt controller.

    The floating-point error signal to the i486 processor does not pass through an interrupt controller (an INT signal from 8087 coprocessor does). Some instructions in a floating-point error exception handler may need to be deleted if they use the interrupt controller. The i486 processor has signals which, with the addition of external logic, support user-defined error reporting for emulation of the interrupt mechanism used in many personal computers.

17. Seven new interrupt vectors.

    The i486 processor adds seven exceptions which are generated on an 8086 processor only by program bugs. Exception handlers should be added which treat these exceptions as invalid operations. This additional software does not significantly affect the existing 8086 processor software, because these interrupts do not occur normally. These interrupt identifiers should not already have been used by the 8086 processor software, because they are reserved by Intel®. Table 22-2 describes the new i486 processor exceptions.

18. The denormal exception of the i486 FPU is handled differently than on the 8087 math coprocessor. See Section 16.2.4 for more details.

19. One megabyte wraparound.

    The address space of the i486 processor may not wraparound at 1 megabyte in real-address mode. An external pin A20M# forces wraparound if enabled. On members of the 8086 family, it possible to specify addresses greater than 1 megabyte. For example, with a selector value 0FFFFH and an offset of 0FFFFH, the effective address would be 10FFEFH (1 megabyte + 65519 bytes). The 8086 processor, which can form addresses up to 20 bits long, truncates the uppermost bit, which "wraps" this address to 0FFEFH. However, the i486 processor does not truncate this bit if A20M# is not enabled.

Table 22-2. New i486™ CPU Exceptions

Vector	Description
5	A BOUND instruction was executed with a register value outside the limit values.
6	A reserved opcode was encountered, or a LOCK prefix was used properly.
7	The EM bit in the CR0 register was set when an ESC instruction executed, or the TS bit was set when a WAIT instruction was executed.
8	A vector indexes to an entry in the IDT which is beyond the segment limit for the IDT. This can only occur if the default limit has been changed.
12	A stack operation crossed the address limit.
13	An operation (other than a stack operation) exceeds the base or bounds of a segment, instruction execution is crossing the address limit (0FFFFH), or an instruction exceeds 15 bytes.
17	Alignment-check. Cannot occur without setting previously reserved bits.

20. Response to bus hold.

    Unlike the 8086 and 80286 processors, but like the 386 processors, the i486 processor responds to requests for control of the bus from other potential bus masters, such as DMA controllers, between transfers of parts of an unaligned operand, such as two words which form a doubleword. Unlike the 386 processors, the i486 processor responds to bus hold during reset initialization.

21. Interrupt vector table limit.

    The LIDT instruction can be used to set a limit on the size of the interrupt vector table. Shutdown occurs if an interrupt or exception attempts to read a vector beyond the limit. (The 8086 processor does not have a shutdown mode.)

22. If a stack operation wraps around the address limit, shutdown occurs. (The 8086 processor does not have a shutdown mode.)

22.8 DIFFERENCES FROM 80286 CPU IN REAL-ADDRESS MODE

The few differences which exist between i486 CPU real-address mode and 80286 CPU real-address mode are not likely to affect any existing 80286 CPU programs except possibly the system initialization procedures.

22.8.1 Bus Lock

The 80286 processor implements the bus lock function differently than the i486 processor. Programs which use forms of memory locking specific to the 80286 processor may not run properly if transported to a specific application of the i486 processor.

The LOCK prefix and its bus signal only should be used to prevent other bus masters from interrupting a data movement operation. The LOCK prefix only may be used with the following i486 CPU instructions when they modify memory. An invalid-opcode exception results from using the LOCK prefix before any other instruction, or with these instructions when no write operation is made to memory (i.e., when the destination operand is in a register).

- Bit test and change: the BTS, BTR, and BTC instructions.
- Exchange: the XCHG, XADD, and CMPXCHG instructions (no LOCK prefix is needed for the XCHG instruction).
- One-operand arithmetic and logical: the INC, DEC, NOT, NEG instructions.
- Two-operand arithmetic and logical: the ADD, ADC, SUB, SBB, AND, OR, and XOR instructions.

A locked instruction is guaranteed to lock only the area of memory defined by the destination operand, but may lock a larger memory area. For example, typical 8086 and 80286 CPU configurations lock the entire physical memory space.

22.8.2 Location of First Instruction

The starting location is 0FFFFFFF0H (16 bytes from end of the 32-bit address space) on the i486 processor rather than 0FFFFF0H (16 bytes from end of the 24-bit address space) as on the 80286 processor. Many 80286 ROM initialization programs will work correctly in this new environment. Others can be made to work correctly with external hardware to interpret the signals on the address signals A_{31-20}.

22.8.3 Initial Values of General Registers

On the i486 processor, certain general registers may contain different values after reset initialization than on the 80286 processor. This should not cause compatibility problems, because the contents of 8086 registers after reset initialization are undefined. If self-test is requested during the reset sequence and errors are detected in the i486 processor, the EAX register will contain a non-zero value. The EDX register contains the component and revision identifier. See Chapter 10 for more information.

22.8.4 Bus Hold

Unlike the 8086 and 80286 processors, the 386 and i486 processors respond to requests for control of the bus from other potential bus masters, such as DMA controllers, between transfers of parts of an unaligned operand, such as two words which form a doubleword.

22.8.5 Math Coprocessor Differences

The i486 FPU denormal exception works differently than on the 80287 math coprocessor. See Section 16.2.4 for more details.

The MP bit of MSW should always be set. An ET bit has been added to MSW which should be set. Exception 9 cannot occur on i486 microprocessors.

22.9 DIFFERENCES FROM 386™ DX CPU IN REAL-ADDRESS MODE

The instructions and architectural features which are new with the i486 processor can be accessed in real-address mode. This should not affect most software, because the new opcodes previously generated the invalid-opcode exception. The new flag and register bits were previously reserved, so there should be no software which uses them improperly.

Caching can be enabled in real-address mode. For maximum performance, initialization software must enable caching.

22.10 PROCESSOR DETECTION CODE

The following code sequence (see Figure 22-2) can be used to distinguish between 8086, 80286 and 386 processors. This code is intended for application programs executing in real-address mode.

```
is_386(TM)      proc    near
;
; Returns the processor type in the AX register.
;

    pushf                       ; save FLAG register
    pop bx                      ; store FLAGs in BX
    and bx,0fffh                ; clear bits 12-15
    push bx                     ; store on stack
    popf                        ; pop word into the FLAG register
    pushf                       ; store FLAGs on stack
    pop ax                      ; recover FLAG word

    and ax,0f000h               ; if bits 12-15 are set, then the
    cmp ax,0f000h               ;    processor is an 8086
    jz is_8086                  ;

    or bx,0f000h                ; try to set FLAG bits 12-15
    push bx                     ; store on stack
    popf                        ; pop word into the FLAG register
    pushf                       ; store FLAGs on stack
    pop ax                      ; recover FLAG word

    and ax,0f000h               ; if bits 12-15 are cleared, then
    jz is_80286                 ;    the processor is an 80286

is_80386:                       ; else the processor is a 386 DX CPU
    mov ax,386h                 ; set the 386 DX CPU indicator
    jmp done
is_80286:
    mov ax,286h                 ; set the 80286 indicator
    jmp done
is_8086:
    mov ax,86h                  ; set the 8086 indicator

done:
    popf                        ; recover FLAG register
    ret

is_386    endp
```

Figure 22-2. Real-Address Detection Code

Virtual-8086 Mode 23

CHAPTER 23
VIRTUAL-8086 MODE

The i486™ processor supports execution of one or more 8086, 8088, 80186, or 80188 programs in an i486 protected-mode environment. An 8086 program runs in this environment as part of a virtual-8086 task. Virtual-8086 tasks take advantage of the hardware support of multitasking offered by the protected mode. Not only can there be multiple virtual-8086 tasks, each one running an 8086 program, but virtual-8086 tasks can run in multitasking with other i486 tasks.

The purpose of a virtual-8086 task is to form a "virtual machine" for running programs written for the 8086 processor. A complete virtual machine consists of i486 hardware and system software. The emulation of an 8086 processor is the result of software using hardware in the following ways:

- The hardware provides a virtual set of registers (through the TSS), a virtual memory space (the first megabyte of the linear address space of the task), and directly executes all instructions which deal with these registers and with this address space.
- The software controls the external interfaces of the virtual machine (I/O, interrupts, and exceptions) in a manner consistent with the larger environment in which it runs. In the case of I/O, software can choose either to emulate I/O instructions or to let the hardware execute them directly without software intervention.

Software which supports virtual 8086 machines is called a virtual-8086 monitor.

23.1 EXECUTING 8086 CPU CODE

The processor runs in virtual-8086 mode when the VM (virtual machine) bit in the EFLAGS register is set. The processor tests this flag under two general conditions:

1. When loading segment registers, to know whether to use 8086-style address translation.
2. When decoding instructions, to determine which instructions are sensitive to IOPL, and which instructions are not supported (as in real mode).

23.1.1 Registers and Instructions

The register set available in virtual-8086 mode includes all the registers defined for the 8086 processor plus the new registers introduced by the i486 processor: FS, GS, debug registers, control registers, and test registers. New instructions which explicitly operate on the segment registers FS and GS are available, and the new segment-override prefixes can be used to cause instructions to use the FS and GS registers for address calculations. Instructions can use 32-bit operands through the use of the operand size prefix.

Programs running as virtual-8086 tasks can take advantage of the new application-oriented instructions added to the architecture by the introduction of the 80186, 80188, 80286, 386™ DX, SX and i486 processors:

- New instructions introduced on the 80186, 80188, and 80286 processors.
  - PUSH immediate data
  - Push all and pop all (PUSHA and POPA)
  - Multiply immediate data
  - Shift and rotate by immediate count
  - String I/O
  - ENTER and LEAVE instructions
  - BOUND instruction
- New instructions introduced on the 386 DX and SX processors.
  - LSS, LFS, LGS instructions
  - Long-displacement conditional jumps
  - Single-bit instructions
  - Bit scan instructions
  - Double-shift instructions
  - Byte set on condition instruction
  - Move with sign/zero extension
  - Generalized multiply instruction
  - MOV to and from control registers
  - MOV to and from test registers
  - MOV to and from debug registers
- New instructions introduced on the i486 processor.
  - BSWAP instruction
  - XADD instruction
  - CMPXCHG instruction

23.1.2 Address Translation

In virtual-8086 mode, the i486 processor does not interpret 8086 selectors by referring to descriptors; instead, it forms linear addresses as an 8086 processor would. It shifts the selector left by four bits to form a 20-bit base address. The effective address is extended with four clear bits in the upper bit positions and added to the base address to create a linear address, as shown in Figure 23-1.

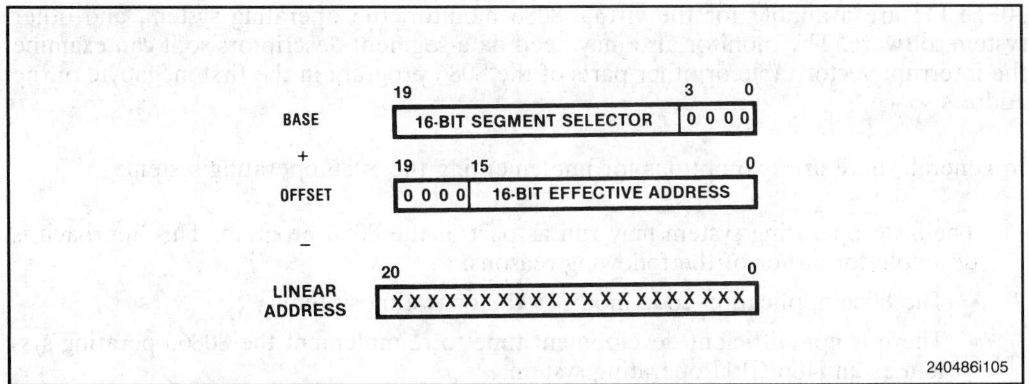

Figure 23-1. 8086 Address Translation

Because of the possibility of a carry, the resulting linear address may have as many as 21 significant bits. An 8086 program may generate linear addresses anywhere in the range 0 to 10FFEFH (1 megabyte plus approximately 64K bytes) of the task's linear address space.

Virtual-8086 tasks generate 32-bit linear addresses. While an 8086 program only can use the lowest 21 bits of a linear address, the linear address can be mapped using paging to any 32-bit physical address.

Unlike the 8086 and 80286 processors, but like the 386 processors, the i486 processor can generate 32-bit effective addresses using an address override prefix; however in virtual-8086 mode, the value of a 32-bit address may not exceed 65,535 without causing an exception. For full compatibility with 80286 real-address mode, pseudo-protection faults (interrupt 12 or 13 with no error code) occur if an effective address is generated outside the range 0 through 65,535.

23.2 STRUCTURE OF A VIRTUAL-8086 TASK

A virtual-8086 task consists of the 8086 program to be run and the i486 CPU "native mode" code which serves as the virtual-machine monitor. The task must be represented by an i486 CPU TSS (not an 80286 TSS). The processor enters virtual-8086 mode to run the 8086 program and returns to protected mode to run the monitor or other i486 CPU tasks.

To run in virtual-8086 mode, an existing 8086 processor program needs the following:

- A virtual-8086 monitor.
- Operating-system services.

The virtual-8086 monitor is i486 CPU protected-mode code which runs at privilege-level 0 (most privileged). The monitor mostly consists of initialization and exception-handling procedures. As with any other i486 CPU program, code-segment descriptors for the monitor must exist in the GDT or in the task's LDT. The linear addresses above

10FFEFH are available for the virtual-8086 monitor, the operating system, and other system software. The monitor also may need data-segment descriptors so it can examine the interrupt vector table or other parts of the 8086 program in the first megabyte of the address space.

In general, there are two options for implementing the 8086 operating system:

1. The 8086 operating system may run as part of the 8086 program. This approach is desirable for either of the following reasons:
   - The 8086 application code modifies the operating system.
   - There is not sufficient development time to reimplement the 8086 operating system as an i486 CPU operating system.
2. The 8086 operating system may be implemented or emulated in the virtual-8086 monitor. This approach is desirable for any of the following reasons:
   - Operating system functions can be more easily coordinated among several virtual-8086 tasks.
   - The functions of the 8086 operating system can be easily emulated by calls to the i486 CPU operating system.

Note that the approach chosen for implementing the 8086 processor operating system may have different virtual-8086 tasks using different 8086 operating systems.

23.2.1 Paging for Virtual-8086 Tasks

Paging is not necessary for a single virtual-8086 task, but paging is useful or necessary for any of the following reasons:

- Creating multiple virtual-8086 tasks. Each task must map the lower megabyte of linear addresses to different physical locations.
- Emulating the address wraparound which occurs at 1 megabyte. With members of the 8086 family, it is possible to specify addresses larger than 1 megabyte. For example, with a selector value of 0FFFFH and an offset of 0FFFFH, the effective address would be 10FFEFH (1 megabyte plus 65519 bytes). The 8086 processor, which can form addresses only up to 20 bits long, truncates the high-order bit, thereby "wrapping" this address to 0FFEFH. The i486 processor, however, does not truncate such an address. If any 8086 processor programs depend on address wraparound, the same effect can be achieved in a virtual-8086 task by mapping linear addresses between 100000H and 110000H and linear addresses between 0 and 10000H to the same physical addresses.
- Creating a virtual address space larger than the physical address space.
- Sharing 8086 operating system or ROM code which is common to several 8086 programs running in multitasking.
- Redirecting or trapping references to memory-mapped I/O devices.

23.2.2 Protection within a Virtual-8086 Task

Protection is not enforced between the segments of an 8086 program. To protect the system software running in a virtual-8086 task from the 8086 application program, software designers may follow either of these approaches:

- Reserve the first megabyte (plus 64K bytes) of each task's linear address space for the 8086 processor program. An 8086 processor task cannot generate addresses outside this range.
- Use the U/S bit of page-table entries to protect the virtual-machine monitor and other system software in each virtual-8086 task's space. When the processor is in virtual-8086 mode, the CPL is 3 (least privileged). Therefore, an 8086 processor program has only user privileges. If the pages of the virtual-machine monitor have supervisor privilege, they cannot be accessed by the 8086 program.

23.3 ENTERING AND LEAVING VIRTUAL-8086 Mode

Figure 23-2 summarizes the ways to enter and leave an 8086 program. Virtual-8086 mode is entered by setting the VM flag. There are two ways to do this:

1. A task switch to an i486 processor task loads the image of the EFLAGS register from the new TSS. The TSS of the new task must be an i486 CPU TSS, not an 80286 TSS, because the 80286 TSS does not load the high word of the EFLAGS register, which contains the VM flag. A set VM flag in the new contents of the EFLAGS register indicates that the new task is executing 8086 instructions; therefore, while loading the segment registers from the TSS, the i486 processor forms base addresses in the 8086 style.
2. An IRET instruction from a procedure of an i486 CPU task loads the EFLAGS register from the stack. A set VM flag indicates the procedure to which control is being returned to be an 8086 procedure. The CPL at the time the IRET instruction is executed must be 0, otherwise the processor does not change the state of the VM flag.

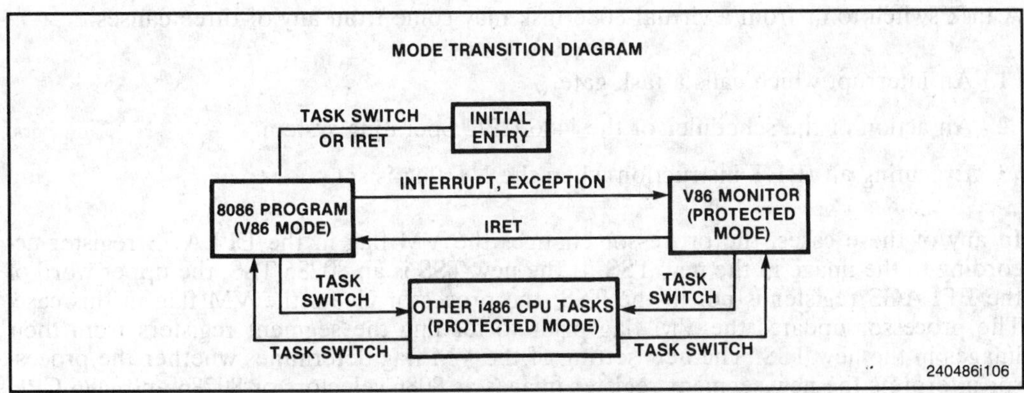

Figure 23-2. Entering and Leaving Virtual-8086 Mode

When a task switch is used to enter virtual-8086 mode, the segment registers are loaded from a TSS. But when an IRET instruction is used to set the VM flag, the segment registers keep the contents loaded during protected mode. Software should then reload these registers with segment selectors appropriate for virtual-8086 mode.

The processor leaves virtual-8086 mode when an interrupt or exception occurs. There are two cases:

1. The interrupt or exception causes a task switch. A task switch from a virtual-8086 task to any other task loads the EFLAGS register from the TSS of the new task. If the new TSS is an i486 TSS and the VM flag in the new contents of the EFLAGS register is clear or if the new TSS is an 80286 TSS, the processor clears the VM flag of the EFLAGS register, loads the segment registers from the new TSS using i486 CPU-style address formation, and begins executing the instructions of the new task in i486 CPU protected mode.

2. The interrupt or exception calls a privilege-level 0 procedure (most privileged). The processor stores the current contents of the EFLAGS register on the stack, then clears the VM flag. The interrupt or exception handler, therefore, runs as "native" i486 CPU protected-mode code. If an interrupt or exception calls a procedure in a conforming segment or in a segment at a privilege level other than 0 (most privileged), the processor generates a general-protection exception; the error code is the selector of the code segment to which a call was attempted.

System software does not change the state of the VM flag directly, but instead changes states in the image of the EFLAGS register stored on the stack or in the TSS. The virtual-8086 monitor sets the VM flag in the EFLAGS image on the stack or in the TSS when first creating a virtual-8086 task. Exception and interrupt handlers can examine the VM flag on the stack. If the interrupted procedure was running in virtual-8086 mode, the handler may need to call the virtual-8086 monitor.

23.3.1 Transitions Through Task Switches

A task switch to or from a virtual-8086 task may come from any of three causes:

1. An interrupt which calls a task gate.
2. An action of the scheduler of the i486 CPU operating system.
3. Executing an IRET instruction when the NT flag is set.

In any of these cases, the processor changes the VM flag in the EFLAGS register according to the image in the new TSS. If the new TSS is an 80286 TSS, the upper word of the EFLAGS register is not in the TSS; the processor clears the VM flag in this case. The processor updates the VM flag prior to loading the segment registers from their images in the new TSS. The new setting of the VM flag determines whether the processor interprets the new segment-register images as 8086 selectors or 80286 and i486 CPU selectors.

23.3.2 Transitions Through Trap Gates and Interrupt Gates

The i486 processor leaves virtual-8086 mode as the result of an exception or interrupt which calls a trap or interrupt gate. The exception or interrupt handler returns to the 8086 program by executing an IRET instruction.

Because it was designed to run on an 8086 processor, an 8086 program in a virtual-8086 task will have an 8086-style interrupt table, which starts at linear address 0. However, the i486 processor does not use this table directly. For all exceptions and interrupts which occur virtual-8086 mode, the processor calls handlers through the IDT. The IDT entry for an interrupt or exception in a virtual-8086 task must contain either:

- A task gate.
- An i486 CPU trap gate (descriptor type 14) or i486 CPU interrupt gate (descriptor type 15), which must point to a nonconforming, privilege-level 0 (most privileged), code segment.

Interrupts and exceptions which call i486 CPU trap or interrupt gates use privilege-level 0. The contents of the segment registers are stored on the stack for this privilege level. Figure 23-3 shows the format of this stack after an exception or interrupt which occurs while a virtual-8086 task is running an 8086 program.

After the processor saves the 8086 segment registers on the stack for privilege level 0, it clears the segment registers before running the handler procedure. This lets the interrupt handler safely save and restore the DS, ES, FS, and GS registers as though they

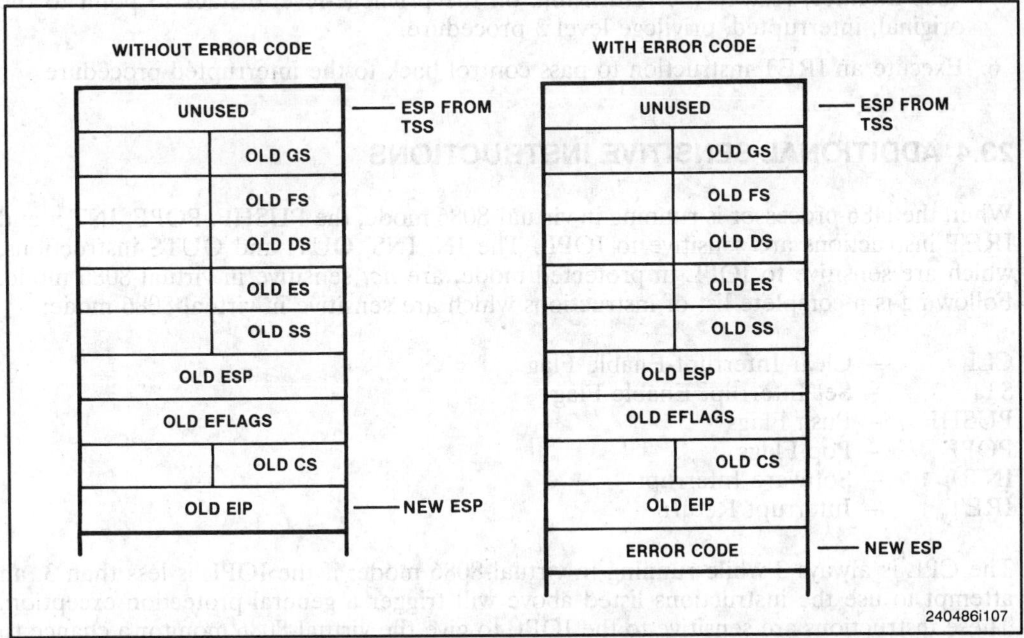

Figure 23-3. Privilege Level 0 Stack After Interrupt in Virtual-8086 Mode

were i486 CPU selectors. Interrupt handlers, which may be called in the context of either a regular task or a virtual-8086 task, can use the same code sequences for saving and restoring the registers for any task. Clearing these registers before execution of the IRET instruction does not cause a trap in the interrupt handler. Interrupt procedures which expect values in the segment registers or which return values in the segment registers must use the register images saved on the stack for privilege level 0. Interrupt handlers which need to know whether the interrupt occurred in virtual-8086 mode can examine the VM flag in the stored contents of the EFLAGS register.

An interrupt handler passes control to the virtual-8086 monitor if the VM flag is set in the EFLAGS image stored on the stack and the interrupt or exception is one which the monitor needs to handle. The virtual-8086 monitor may either:

- Handle the interrupt within the virtual-8086 monitor.
- Call the 8086 program's interrupt handler.

Sending an interrupt or exception back to the 8086 program involves the following steps:

1. Use the 8086 interrupt vector to locate the appropriate handler procedure.
2. Store the state of the 8086 program on the privilege-level 3 stack (least privileged).
3. Change the return link on the privilege-level 0 stack (most privileged) to point to the privilege-level 3 handler procedure.
4. Execute an IRET instruction to pass control to the handler.
5. When the IRET instruction from the privilege-level 3 handler again calls the virtual-8086 monitor, restore the return link on the privilege-level 0 stack to point to the original, interrupted, privilege-level 3 procedure.
6. Execute an IRET instruction to pass control back to the interrupted procedure.

23.4 ADDITIONAL SENSITIVE INSTRUCTIONS

When the i486 processor is running in virtual-8086 mode, the PUSHF, POPF, INT *n* and IRET instructions are sensitive to IOPL. The IN, INS, OUT, and OUTS instructions, which are sensitive to IOPL in protected mode, are *not* sensitive in virtual-8086 mode. Following is a complete list of instructions which are sensitive in virtual-8086 mode:

CLI — Clear Interrupt-Enable Flag
STI — Set Interrupt-Enable Flag
PUSHF — Push Flags
POPF — Pop Flags
INT *n* — Software Interrupt
IRET — Interrupt Return

The CPL is always 3 while running in virtual-8086 mode; if the IOPL is less than 3, an attempt to use the instructions listed above will trigger a general-protection exception. These instructions are sensitive to the IOPL to give the virtual-8086 monitor a chance to emulate the facilities they affect.

23.4.1 Emulating 8086 Operating System Calls

The INT *n* instruction is sensitive to IOPL so a virtual-8086 monitor can intercept calls to the 8086 operating system. Many 8086 operating systems are called by pushing parameters onto the stack, then executing an INT *n* instruction. If the IOPL is less than 3, INT *n* instructions are intercepted by the virtual-8086 monitor. The virtual-8086 monitor then can emulate the function of the 8086 operating system or send the interrupt back to the 8086 operating system.

23.4.2 Emulating the Interrupt-Enable Flag

When the i486 processor is running an 8086 program in a virtual-8086 task, the PUSHF, POPF, and IRET instructions are sensitive to the IOPL. This lets the virtual-8086 monitor protect the interrupt-enable flag (IF). Other instructions which affect the IF flag (such as the STI and CLI instructions) are sensitive to the IOPL in both 8086 and i486 CPU programs.

Many 8086 programs written for non-multitasking systems set and clear the IF flag to control interrupts. This may cause problems in a multitasking environment. If the IOPL is less than 3, all instructions which change or test the IF flag generate an exception. The virtual-8086 monitor then can control the IF flag in a manner compatible with the i486 CPU environment and transparent to 8086 programs.

23.5 VIRTUAL I/O

Many 8086 programs written for non-multitasking systems directly access I/O ports. This may cause problems in a multitasking environment. If more than one program accesses the same port, they may interfere with each other. Most multitasking systems require application programs to access I/O ports through the operating system. This results in simplified, centralized control.

The i486 processor provides I/O protection for creating I/O which is compatible with the i486 CPU environment and transparent to 8086 programs. Designers may take any of several possible approaches to protecting I/O ports:

- Protect the I/O address space and generate exceptions for all attempts to perform I/O directly.
- Let the 8086 processor program perform I/O directly.
- Generate exceptions on attempts to access specific I/O ports.
- Generate exceptions on attempts to access specific memory-mapped I/O ports.

The method of controlling access to I/O ports depends upon whether they are I/O-mapped or memory-mapped.

23.5.1 I/O-Mapped I/O

The I/O address space in virtual-8086 mode differs from protected mode only because the IOPL is not checked. Only the I/O permission bit map is checked when virtual-8086 tasks access the I/O address space.

The I/O permission bit map can be used to generate exceptions on attempts to access specific I/O addresses. The I/O permission bit map of each virtual-8086 task determines which I/O addresses generate exceptions for that task. Because each task may have a different I/O permission bit map, the addresses which generate exceptions for one task may be different from the addresses for another task. See Chapter 8 for more information about the I/O permission bit map.

23.5.2 Memory-Mapped I/O

In systems which use memory-mapped I/O, the paging facilities of the i486 processor can be used generate exceptions for attempts to access I/O ports. The virtual-8086 monitor may use paging to control memory-mapped I/O in these ways:

- Map part of the linear address space of each task which needs to perform I/O to the physical address space where I/O ports are placed. By putting the I/O ports at different addresses (in different pages), the paging mechanism can enforce isolation between tasks.
- Map part of the linear address space to pages which are not-present. This generates an exception whenever a task attempts to perform I/O to those pages. System software then can interpret the I/O operation being attempted.

Software emulation of the I/O space may require too much operating system intervention under some conditions. In these cases, it may be possible to generate an exception for only the first attempt to access I/O. The system software then may determine whether a program can be given exclusive control of I/O temporarily, the protection of the I/O space may be lifted, and the program allowed to run at full speed.

23.5.3 Special I/O Buffers

Buffers of intelligent controllers (for example, a bit-mapped frame buffer) also can be emulated using page mapping. The linear space for the buffer can be mapped to a different physical space for each virtual-8086 task. The virtual-8086 monitor then can control which virtual buffer to copy onto the real buffer in the physical address space.

23.6 DIFFERENCES FROM 8086 CPU

In general, virtual-8086 mode will run software written for the 8086, 8088, 80186, and 80188 processors. The following list shows the minor differences between the 8086 processor and the virtual-8086 mode of the i486 processor.

1. Instruction clock counts.

   The i486 processor takes fewer clocks for most instructions than the 8086 processor. The areas most likely to be affected are:

   - Delays required by I/O devices between I/O operations.
   - Assumed delays with 8086 processor operating in parallel with an 8087.

2. Divide exceptions point to the DIV instruction.

   Divide exceptions on the i486 processor always leave the saved CS:IP value pointing to the instruction which failed. On the 8086 processor, the CS:IP value points to the next instruction.

3. Undefined 8086 processor opcodes.

   Opcodes which were not defined for the 8086 processor generate an invalid-opcode or execute as one of the new instructions defined for the i486 processor.

4. Value written by PUSH SP.

   The i486 processor pushes a different value on the stack for PUSH SP than the 8086 processor. The i486 processor pushes the value in the SP register before it is decremented as part of the push operation; the 8086 processor pushes the value of the SP register after it is decremented. If the pushed value is important, replace PUSH SP instructions with the following three instructions:

```
PUSH    BP
MOV     BP, SP
XCHG    BP, [BP]
```

   This code functions as the 8086 PUSH SP instruction on the i486 processor.

5. Shift or rotate by more than 31 bits.

   The i486 processor masks all shift and rotate counts to the lowest five bits. This limits the count to a maximum of 31 bit positions, thereby limiting the time that interrupt response is delayed while the instruction executes.

6. Redundant prefixes.

   The i486 processor limits instructions to 15 bytes. The only way to violate this limit is with redundant prefixes before an instruction. A general-protection exception is generated if the limit on instruction length is violated. The 8086 processor has no instruction length limit.

7. Operand crossing offset 0 or 65,535.

   On the 8086 processor, an attempt to access a memory operand which crosses offset 65,535 (e.g., MOV a word to offset 65,535) or offset 0 (e.g., PUSH a word when the contents of the SP register are 1) causes the offset to wrap around modulo 65,536. The i486 processor generates an exception in these cases, a general-protection exception if the segment is a data segment (i.e., if the CS, DS, ES, FS, or GS register is being used to address the segment), or a stack exception if the segment is a stack segment (i.e., if the SS register is being used).

8. Sequential execution across offset 65,535.

   On the 8086 processor, if sequential execution of instructions proceeds past offset 65,535, the processor fetches the next instruction byte from offset 0 of the same segment. On the i486 processor, the processor generates a general-protection exception.

9. LOCK is restricted to certain instructions.

   The LOCK prefix and its output signal should only be used to prevent other bus masters from interrupting a data movement operation. The LOCK prefix only may be used with the following i486 CPU instructions when they modify memory. An invalid-opcode exception results from using LOCK before any other instruction, or with these instructions when no write operation is made to memory.

   - Bit test and change: the BTS, BTR, and BTC instructions.
   - Exchange: the XCHG, XADD, and CMPXCHG instructions (no LOCK prefix is needed for the XCHG instruction).
   - One-operand arithmetic and logical: the INC, DEC, NOT, NEG instructions.
   - Two-operand arithmetic and logical: the ADD, ADC, SUB, SBB, AND, OR, and XOR instructions.

10. Single-stepping external interrupt handlers.

    The priority of the i486 processor single-step exception is different from that of the 8086 processor. This change prevents an external interrupt handler from being single-stepped if the interrupt occurs while a program is being single-stepped. The i486 processor single-step exception has higher priority than any external interrupt. The i486 processor will still single-step through an interrupt handler called by the INT instruction or by an exception.

11. IDIV exceptions for quotients of 80H or 8000H.

    The i486 processor can generate the largest negative number as a quotient from the IDIV instruction. The 8086 processor generates a divide-error exception instead.

12. Flags in stack.

    The contents of the EFLAGS register stored by the PUSHF instruction, by interrupts, and by exceptions is different from that stored by the 8086 processor in bit positions 12 through 15. On the 8086 processor these bits are stored as though they were set, but in virtual-8086 mode bit 15 is always clear, and bits 14 through 12 have the last value loaded into them.

13. NMI interrupting NMI handlers.

    After an NMI interrupt is accepted by the i486 processor, the NMI interrupt is masked until an IRET instruction is executed.

14. Floating-point errors call the floating-point-error exception.

    Floating-point exceptions on the i486 processor call the floating-point error exception handler. If an 8086 processor uses another exception for the 8087 interrupt, both exception vectors should call the floating-point error exception handler. The i486 processor has signals which, with the addition of external logic, support user-defined error reporting for emulation of the interrupt mechanism used in many personal computers.

15. Numeric exception handlers should allow prefixes.

    On the i486 processor, the value of the CS and IP registers saved for floating-point exceptions points at any prefixes which come before the ESC instruction. On the 8086 processor, the saved CS:IP points to the ESC instruction.

16. Floating-Point Unit does not use interrupt controller.

    The floating-point error signal to the i486 processor does not pass through an interrupt controller (an INT signal from 8087 coprocessor does). Some instructions in a coprocessor-error exception handler may need to be deleted if they use the interrupt controller. The i486 processor has signals which, with the addition of external logic, support user-defined error reporting for emulation of the interrupt mechanism used in many personal computers.

17. Response to bus hold.

    Unlike the 8086 and 80286 processors, the i486 processor responds to requests for control of the bus from other potential bus masters, such as DMA controllers, between transfers of parts of an unaligned operand, such as two words which form a doubleword.

18. CPL is 3 in virtual-8086 mode.

    The 8086 processor does not support protection, so it has no CPL. Virtual-8086 mode uses a CPL of 3, which prevents the execution of privileged instructions. These are:

    - LIDT instruction
    - LGDT instruction
    - LMSW instruction
    - special forms of the MOV instruction for loading and storing the control registers
    - CLTS instruction
    - HLT instruction
    - INVD instruction
    - WBINVD instruction
    - INVLPG instruction

    These instructions may be executed while the processor is in real-address mode following reset initialization. They allow system data structures, such as descriptor tables, to be set up before entering protected mode. Virtual-8086 mode is entered from protected mode, so it has no need for these instructions.

19. Denormal exception handling is different. See Section 16.2.4.

23.7 DIFFERENCES FROM 80286 CPU IN REAL-ADDRESS MODE

The differences between virtual-8086 mode and 80286 real-address mode affect the interface between applications and the operating system. The application runs at privilege level 3 (user mode), so all attempts to use privilege-protected instructions and architectural features generate calls to the virtual-machine monitor. The monitor examines these calls and emulates them.

23.7.1 Privilege Level

Programs running in virtual-8086 mode have a privilege level of 3 (user mode), which prevents the execution of privileged instructions. These are:

- LIDT instruction
- LGDT instruction
- LMSW instruction
- special forms of the MOV instruction for loading and storing the control registers
- CLTS instruction
- HLT instruction
- INVD instruction
- WBINVD instruction
- INVLPG instruction

Virtual-8086 mode is entered from protected mode, so it has no need for these instructions. These instructions can be executed in real-address mode.

23.7.2 Bus Lock

The 80286 processor implements the bus lock function differently than the 386 DX and i486 processors. This fact may or may not be apparent to 8086 programs, depending on how the virtual-8086 monitor handles the LOCK prefix. Instructions with the LOCK prefix are sensitive to the IOPL; software designers can choose to emulate its function. If, however, 8086 programs are allowed to execute LOCK directly, programs which use forms of memory locking specific to the 8086 processor may not run properly when run on the i486 processor.

The LOCK prefix and its bus signal only should be used to prevent other bus masters from interrupting a data movement operation. The LOCK prefix only may be used with the following i486 CPU instructions when they modify memory. An invalid-opcode exception results from using the LOCK prefix before any other instruction, or with these instructions when no write operation is made to memory (i.e., when the destination operand is in a register).

- Bit test and change: the BTS, BTR, and BTC instructions.
- Exchange: the XCHG, XADD, and CMPXCHG instructions (no LOCK prefix is needed for the XCHG instruction).
- One-operand arithmetic and logical: the INC, DEC, NOT, NEG instructions.
- Two-operand arithmetic and logical: the ADD, ADC, SUB, SBB, AND, OR, and XOR instructions.

A locked instruction is guaranteed to lock only the area of memory defined by the destination operand, but may lock a larger memory area. For example, typical 8086 and 80286 configurations lock the entire physical memory space.

Unlike the 8086 and 80286 processors, the 386 and i486 processors respond to requests for control of the bus from other potential bus masters, such as DMA controllers, between transfers of parts of an unaligned operand, such as two words which form a doubleword.

23.8 DIFFERENCES FROM 386™ DX AND SX CPUs

Real-address mode and virtual-8086 mode are implemented in the same way on the i486 processor as on the 386 processors. For maximum performance, programs ported to the i486 processor should be run with the cache enabled.

24

Mixing 16-Bit and 32-Bit Code

CHAPTER 24
MIXING 16-BIT AND 32-BIT CODE

The i486™ processor running in protected mode, like the 386™ processors is a complete 32-bit architecture, but it supports programs written for the 16-bit architecture of earlier Intel® processors. There are three levels of this support:

1. Running 8086 and 80286 code with complete compatibility.
2. Mixing 16-bit modules with 32-bit modules.
3. Mixing 16-bit and 32-bit addresses and data within one module.

The first level is discussed in Chapter 21, Chapter 22, and Chapter 23. This chapter shows how 16-bit and 32-bit modules can cooperate with one another, and how one module can use both 16-bit and 32-bit operands and addressing.

The i486 processor functions most efficiently when it is possible to distinguish between pure 16-bit modules and pure 32-bit modules. A pure 16-bit module has these characteristics:

- All segments occupy 64K bytes or less.
- Data items are either 8 bits or 16 bits wide.
- Pointers to code and data have 16-bit offsets.
- Control is transferred only among 16-bit segments.

A pure 32-bit module has these characteristics:

- Segments may occupy more than 64K bytes (0 bytes to 4 gigabytes).
- Data items are either 8 bits or 32 bits wide.
- Pointers to code and data have 32-bit offsets.
- Control is transferred only among 32-bit segments.

A program written for 16-bit processor would be pure 16-bit code. A new program written for the protected mode of the i486 processor would be pure 32-bit code. As applications move from 16-bit processors to the 32-bit i486 processor, there will be cases where 16-bit and 32-bit code will need to be mixed. Reasons for mixing code are:

- Modules will be converted one-by-one from 16-bit environments to 32-bit environments.
- Older, 16-bit compilers and software-development tools will be used in the new 32-bit operating environment until new 32-bit tools are available.
- The source code of 16-bit modules is not available for modification.
- The specific data structures used by a given module are fixed at 16-bit word size.
- The native word size of the source language is 16 bits.

24.1 USING 16-BIT AND 32-BIT ENVIRONMENTS

The features of the architecture which permit the i486 processor to mix 16-bit and 32-bit address and operand size include:

- The D-bit (default bit) of code-segment descriptors, which determines the default choice of operand-size and address-size for the instructions of a code segment. (In real-address mode and virtual-8086 mode, which do not use descriptors, the default is 16 bits.) A code segment whose D-bit is set is a 32-bit segment; a code segment whose D-bit is clear is a 16-bit segment. The D-bit eliminates the need to put the operand size and address size in instructions when all instructions use operands and effective addresses of the same size.
- Instruction prefixes to override the default choice of operand size and address size (available in protected mode as well as in real-address mode and virtual-8086 mode).
- Separate 32-bit and 16-bit gates for intersegment control transfers (including call gates, interrupt gates, and trap gates). The operand size for the control transfer is determined by the type of gate, not by the D-bit or prefix of the transfer instruction.
- Registers which can be used both for 16-bit and 32-bit operands and effective-address calculations.
- The B bit (Big bit) of data-segment descriptors, which specifies the size of stack pointer (the 32-bit ESP register or the 16-bit SP register) used by the processor for implicit stack references.

24.2 MIXING 16-BIT AND 32-BIT OPERATIONS

The i486 processor has two instruction prefixes which allow mixing of 32-bit and 16-bit operations within one segment:

- The operand-size prefix (66H)
- The address-size prefix (67H)

These prefixes *reverse* the default size selected by the Default bit. For example, the processor can interpret the MOV mem, reg instruction in any of four ways:

- In a 32-bit segment:
  1. Moves 32 bits from a 32-bit register to memory using a 32-bit effective address.
  2. If preceded by an operand-size prefix, moves 16 bits from a 16-bit register to memory using a 32-bit effective address.
  3. If preceded by an address-size prefix, moves 32 bits from a 32-bit register to memory using a 16-bit effective address.
  4. If preceded by both an address-size prefix and an operand-size prefix, moves 16 bits from a 16-bit register to memory using a 16-bit effective address.
- In a 16-bit segment:
  1. Moves 16 bits from a 16-bit register to memory using a 16-bit effective address.
  2. If preceded by an operand-size prefix, moves 32 bits from a 32-bit register to memory using a 16-bit effective address.

3. If preceded by an address-size prefix, moves 16 bits from a 16-bit register to memory using a 32-bit effective address.
4. If preceded by both an address-size prefix and an operand-size prefix, moves 32 bits from a 32-bit register to memory using a 32-bit effective address.

These examples show that any instruction can generate any combination of operand size and address size regardless of whether the instruction is in a 16- or 32-bit segment. The choice of the 16- or 32-bit default for a code segment is based upon these criteria:

1. The need to address instructions or data in segments which are larger than 64K bytes.
2. The predominant size of operands.
3. The addressing modes desired.

The Default bit should be given a setting which allows the predominant size of operands to be accessed without operand-size prefixes.

24.3 SHARING DATA AMONG MIXED-SIZE CODE SEGMENTS

Because the choice of operand size and address size is specified in code segments and their descriptors, data segments can be shared freely among both 16-bit and 32-bit code segments. The only limitation is imposed by pointers with 16-bit offsets, which only can point to the first 64K bytes of a segment. When a data segment with more than 64K bytes is to be shared among 16- and 32-bit segments, the data which is to be accessed by the 16-bit segments must be located within the first 64K bytes.

A stack which spans less than 64K bytes can be shared by both 16- and 32-bit code segments. This class of stacks includes:

- Stacks in expand-up segments with the Granularity and Big bits clear.
- Stacks in expand-down segments with the Granularity and Big bits clear.
- Stacks in expand-up segments with the Granularity bit set and the Big bit clear, in which the stack is contained completely within the lower 64K bytes. (Offsets greater than 0FFFFH can be used for data, other than the stack, which is not shared.)

The B-bit of a stack segment cannot, in general, be used to change the size of stack used by a 16-bit code segment. The size of stack pointer used by the processor for *implicit* stack references is controlled by the B-bit of the data-segment descriptor for the stack. Implicit references are those caused by interrupts, exceptions, and instructions such as the PUSH, POP, CALL, and RET instructions. Although it seems like the B bit could be used to increase the stack segment for 16-bit programs beyond 64K bytes, this may not be done. The B-bit does not control *explicit* stack references, such as accesses to parameters or local variables. A 16-bit code segment can use a "big" stack only if the code is modified so that all explicit references to the stack are preceded by the address-size prefix, causing those references to use 32-bit addressing.

In big, expand-down segments (the Granularity, Big, and Expand-down bits set), all offsets are greater than 64K, therefore 16-bit code cannot use this kind of stack segment unless the code segment is modified to use 32-bit addressing. (See Chapter 6 for more information about the G, B, and E bits.)

24.4 TRANSFERRING CONTROL AMONG MIXED-SIZE CODE SEGMENTS

When transferring control among procedures in 16-bit and 32-bit code segments, programmers must be aware of three points:

- Addressing limitations imposed by pointers with 16-bit offsets.
- Matching of operand-size attribute in effect for the CALL/RET instruction pair and the Interrupt/IRET pair for managing the stack correctly.
- Translation of parameters, especially pointer parameters.

Clearly, 16-bit effective addresses cannot be used to address data or code located beyond 0FFFFH in a 32-bit segment, nor can large 32-bit parameters be squeezed into a 16-bit word; however, except for these obvious limits, most interface problems between 16-bit and 32-bit modules can be solved. Some solutions involve inserting interface code between modules.

24.4.1 Size of Code-Segment Pointer

For control-transfer instructions which use a pointer to identify the next instruction (i.e., those which do not use gates), the size of the offset portion of the pointer is determined by the operand-size attribute. The implications of the use of two different sizes of code-segment pointer are:

- A JMP, CALL, or RET instruction from a 32-bit segment to a 16-bit segment is always possible using a 32-bit operand size.
- A JMP, CALL, or RET instruction from a 16-bit segment using a 16-bit operand size cannot address a destination in a 32-bit segment if the address of the destination is greater than 0FFFFH.

An interface procedure can provide a mechanism for transfers from 16-bit segments to destinations in 32-bit segments beyond 64K. The requirements for this kind of interface procedure are discussed later in this chapter.

24.4.2 Stack Management for Control Transfers

Because stack management is different for 16-bit CALL and RET instructions than for 32-bit CALL and RET instructions, the operand size of the RET instruction must match the CALL instruction. (See Figure 24-1. A 16-bit CALL instruction pushes the contents of the 16-bit IP register and (for calls between privilege levels) the 16-bit SP register. The matching RET instruction also must use a 16-bit operand size to pop these 16-bit values from the stack into the 16-bit registers. A 32-bit CALL instruction pushes the

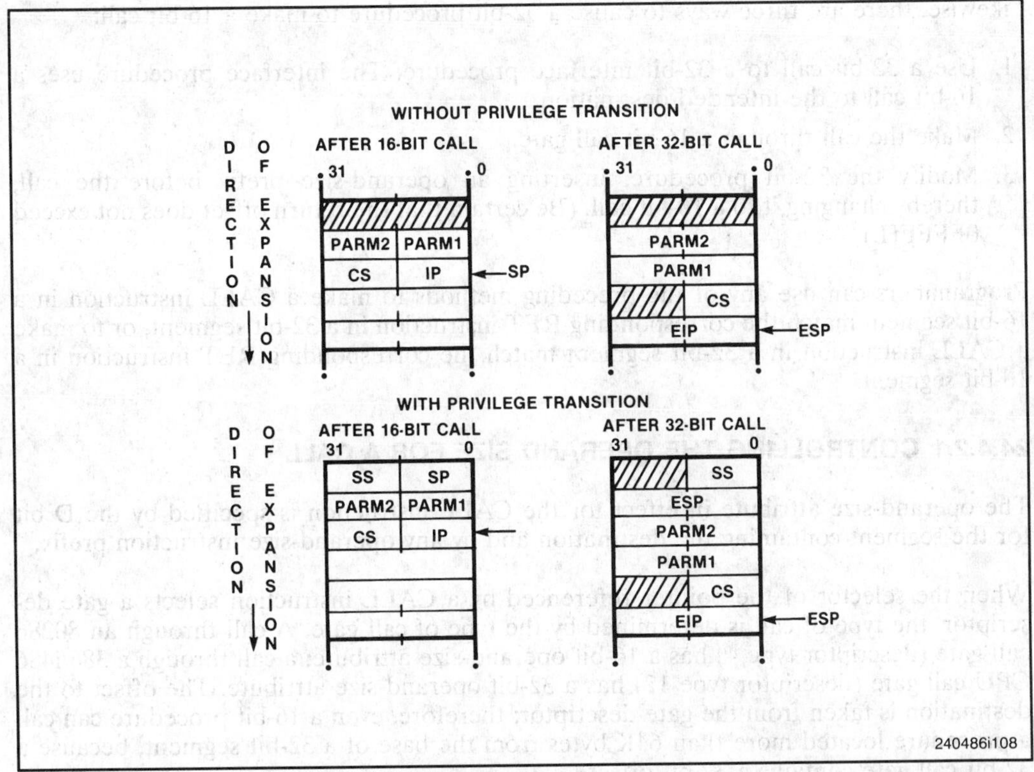

Figure 24-1. Stack After Far 16- and 32-Bit Calls

contents of the 32-bit EIP register and (for interlevel calls) the 32-bit ESP register. The matching RET instruction also must use a 32-bit operand size to pop these 32-bit values from the stack into the 32-bit registers. If the two parts of a CALL/RET instruction pair do not have matching operand sizes, the stack will not be managed correctly and the values of the instruction pointer and stack pointer will not be restored to correct values.

When the CALL instruction and its matching RET instruction are in segments which have D bits with the same values (i.e., both have 32-bit defaults or both have 16-bit defaults), the default settings may be used. When the CALL instruction and its matching RET instruction are in segments which have different D-bit values, an operand size prefix must be used.

There are three ways for a 16-bit procedure to make a 32-bit call:

1. Use a 16-bit call to a 32-bit interface procedure. The interface procedure uses a 32-bit call to the intended destination.
2. Make the call through a 32-bit call gate.
3. Modify the 16-bit procedure, inserting an operand-size prefix before the call, to change it to a 32-bit call.

Likewise, there are three ways to cause a 32-bit procedure to make a 16-bit call:

1. Use a 32-bit call to a 32-bit interface procedure. The interface procedure uses a 16-bit call to the intended destination.
2. Make the call through a 16-bit call gate.
3. Modify the 32-bit procedure, inserting an operand-size prefix before the call, thereby changing it to a 16-bit call. (Be certain that the return offset does not exceed 0FFFFH.)

Programmers can use any of the preceding methods to make a CALL instruction in a 16-bit segment match the corresponding RET instruction in a 32-bit segment, or to make a CALL instruction in a 32-bit segment match the corresponding RET instruction in a 16-bit segment.

24.4.2.1 CONTROLLING THE OPERAND SIZE FOR A CALL

The operand-size attribute in effect for the CALL instruction is specified by the D bit for the segment containing the destination and by any operand-size instruction prefix.

When the selector of the pointer referenced by a CALL instruction selects a gate descriptor, the type of call is determined by the type of call gate. A call through an 80286 call gate (descriptor type 4) has a 16-bit operand-size attribute; a call through a 386/i486 CPU call gate (descriptor type 12) has a 32-bit operand-size attribute. The offset to the destination is taken from the gate descriptor; therefore, even a 16-bit procedure can call a procedure located more than 64K bytes from the base of a 32-bit segment, because a 32-bit call gate contains a 32-bit offset.

An unmodified 16-bit code segment which has run successfully on an 8086 processor or in real-mode on an 80286 processor will have a D-bit which is clear and will not use operand-size override prefixes; therefore, it will use 16-bit versions of the CALL instruction. The only modification needed to make a 16-bit procedure produce a 32-bit call is to relink the call to a 386/i486 CPU call gate.

24.4.2.2 CHANGING SIZE OF A CALL

When adding 32-bit gates to 16-bit procedures, it is important to consider the number of parameters. The count field of the gate descriptor specifies the size of the parameter string to copy from the current stack to the stack of the more privileged procedure. The count field of a 16-bit gate specifies the number of *words* to be copied, whereas the count field of a 32-bit gate specifies the number of *doublewords* to be copied; therefore, the 16-bit procedure must use an even number of words as parameters.

24.4.3 Interrupt Control Transfers

With a control transfer caused by an exception or interrupt, a gate is used. The operand-size attribute for the interrupt is determined by the gate descriptor in the interrupt descriptor table (IDT).

A 386/i486 CPU interrupt or trap gate (descriptor type 14 or 15) to a 32-bit interrupt handler can be used to interrupt either 32-bit or 16-bit procedures. However, sometimes it is not practical to permit an interrupt or exception to call a 16-bit handler when 32-bit code is running, because a 16-bit interrupt procedure has a return offset of only 16 bits saved on its stack. If the 32-bit procedure is running at an address beyond 0FFFFH, the 16-bit interrupt procedure cannot provide the return address.

24.4.4 Parameter Translation

When segment offsets or pointers (which contain segment offsets) are passed as parameters between 16-bit and 32-bit procedures, some translation is required. If a 32-bit procedure passes a pointer to data located beyond 64K to a 16-bit procedure, the 16-bit procedure cannot use it. Except for this limitation, interface code can perform any format conversion between 32-bit and 16-bit pointers which may be needed.

Parameters passed by value between 32-bit and 16-bit code also may require translation between 32-bit and 16-bit formats. The form of the translation is application-dependent.

24.4.5 The Interface Procedure

Placing interface code between 32-bit and 16-bit procedures can be the solution to several interface problems:

- Allowing procedures in 16-bit segments to call procedures with offsets greater than 0FFFFH in 32-bit segments.
- Matching operand size between CALL and RET instructions.
- Translating parameters (data).

The interface code is simplified where these restrictions are followed.

- Interface code resides in a code segment whose D-bit is set, which indicates a default operand size of 32-bits.
- All procedures which may be called by 16-bit procedures have offsets which are not greater than 0FFFFH.
- All return addresses saved by 16-bit procedures also have offsets not greater than 0FFFFH.

The interface code becomes more complex if any of these restrictions are violated. For example, if a 16-bit procedure calls a 32-bit procedure with an entry point beyond 0FFFFH, the interface code will have to provide the offset to the entry point. The mapping between 16- and 32-bit addresses only is performed automatically when a call gate is used, because the descriptor for a call gate contains a 32-bit address. When a call gate is not used, the descriptor must provide the 32-bit address.

The interface code calls procedures in other segments. There may be two kinds of interface:

- Where 16-bit procedures call 32-bit procedures. The interface code is called by 16-bit CALL instructions and uses the operand-size prefix before RET instructions for performing a 16-bit RET instruction. Calls to 32-bit segments are 32-bit CALL instructions (by default, because the D-bit is set), and the 32-bit code returns with 32-bit RET instructions.
- Where 32-bit procedures call 16-bit procedures. The interface code is called by 32-bit CALL instructions, and returns with 32-bit RET instructions (by default, because the D-bit is set). CALL instructions to 16-bit procedures use the operand-size prefix; 16-bit procedures return with 16-bit RET instructions.

25 Compatibility with the 387™, 80287 and 8087 Math Coprocessors

CHAPTER 25
COMPATIBILITY WITH THE 387™, 80287 AND 8087 MATH COPROCESSORS

This chapter addresses the issues that must be faced when transporting numerical software to the i486™ processor from one of its predecessor systems. To software, the i486 processor looks very much like a 386™ CPU/387™ math coprocessor system. Software which runs on a 386 CPU/387 NPX system, whether it was originally created for the 386 CPU/387 or was transported from an 80286/80287 or 8086/8087 system, will run with at most minor modifications on the i486 processor. To transport code directly from an 80286/80287 or 8086/8087 system to the i486 processor, certain additional issues must be addressed. Separate sections of this chapter are devoted to the differences between the i486 processor and each of its predecessors.

25.1 DIFFERENCES FROM 386™ CPU/387™ NPX SYSTEMS

This section summarizes those differences between the 386 CPU/387 NPX system and the i486 processor which may affect numerical software.

1. *Control Register Bits:*

   The ET (Extention Type) bit of the CR0 control register is used in the 386 processor to indicate whether the math coprocessor in the system is an 80287 (ET=0) or a 387 DX (ET=1). This bit is not used by i486 processor hardware. On reset, the ET bit is initialized to 0.

   The NE (Numeric Exception) bit of the CR0 register is used in the i486 processor to determine whether unmasked floating-point exceptions are reported internally via interrupt vector 16 (NE=1) or through external interrupt (NE=0). On reset, the NE bit is initialized to 0, so software using the automatic internal error-reporting mechanism must set this bit to 1.

   As on the 80286 and 386 processors, the MP (Monitor coProcessor) bit of the CR0 control register determines whether WAIT instructions trap when the context of the FPU is different from that of the currently-executing task. If MP=1 and TS=1, then a WAIT instruction will cause a Device Not Available fault (interrupt vector 7). The MP bit is used on the 80286 and 386 microprocessors to support the use of a WAIT instruction to wait on a device other than a numeric coprocessor. The device reports its status through the BUSY# pin. Since the i486 processor does not have such a pin, the MP bit has no relevant use, and should be set to 1 for normal operation.

2. *Initialization and RESET:*

   Upon hardware RESET, the floating-point registers will remain unchanged unless the Built-In Self-Test (BIST) is requested. When the BIST is requested, hardware RESET has almost the same effect as the FINIT instruction; the only difference is that FINIT leaves the stack registers unchanged, while hardware RESET with BIST resets them to 0.

Upon hardware RESET or FINIT, the 387 math coprocessor signals an error condition. The i486 processor, like the 80287 coprocessor, does not.

On the i486 processor, the FINIT instruction clears the error pointers (data and instruction).

3. *Exceptions:*

   On the i486 processor, an undefined ESC opcode will cause an Illegal Opcode exception (interrupt vector 6). Undefined ESC opcodes, like legal ESC opcodes, cause a Device Not Available exception (interrupt vector 7) when either the TS or the EM bit of CR0 is set. The i486 processor does *not* check for floating-point error conditions on encountering an undefined ESC opcode.

   A misaligned data operand will cause an alignment exception (interrupt vector 17) in level 3 software, except for the stack portion of an FSAVE/FRSTOR operation.

   On the i486 processor, a WAIT instruction will sometimes be executed as NOP. This happens when the WAIT precedes an instruction which itself waits anywhere in the course of its execution. In such a case, the report of a numeric exception may come one instruction later on the i486 processor than on a 386 CPU/387 NPX system.

   On the i486 processor, when the first half of an operand to be written is inside a page or segment and the second half is outside, a memory fault can cause the first half to be stored without the second. In such cases, 386 CPU/387 NPX systems store nothing.

   On the i486 processor, when a segment fault occurs in the middle of an FLDENV operation, it can happen that part of the environment is loaded and part not. In such cases, the FPU control word is left with a value of 007F H.

   Interrupt 9 does not occur in the i486 processor. In cases where the 387 would cause interrupt 9, the i486 processor simply aborts the instruction. Some care is necessary, however. Memory faults (especially page faults), if they occur in FLDENV or FRSTOR while the operating system is performing a task switch, can cause the floating-point environment to be lost. Intel strongly recommends that the floating-point save area be the same page as the TSS.

4. *Transcendental Instructions:*

   On the i486 processor, transcendental instructions can be aborted at certain checkpoints during execution if an INTR is pending. Transcendental instructions should therefore be used only in an environment where INTRs are not expected to come as close as 200 clocks apart.

25.2 DIFFERENCES FROM 80286/80287 SYSTEMS

This section summarizes the differences between i486 processor and 386 CPU/387 math coprocessor systems on the one hand, and 80286/80287 and 8086/8087 systems on the other, and analyzes the impact of these differences on software that must be transported from an 80286/80287 system to the i486 processor. Any migration directly from the 8086/8087 must also take into account the additional issues addressed in Section 25.3.

25.2.1 Data Types and Exception Handling

Issue	Difference Description		Impact on Software	Reason for the Difference
	i486™ CPU/387™ NPX Behavior	80287/8087 Behavior		
NaN	The i486™ CPU/387™ NPX distinguishes between signaling NaNs and quiet NaNs. The i486 CPU/387 NPX only generates quiet NaNs. An invalid-operation exception is raised only upon encountering a signaling NaN (except for FCOM, FIST, and FBSTP which also raise IE for quiet NaNs).	The 80287/8087 only generates one kind of NaN (the equivalent of a quiet NaN) but raises an invalid-operation exception upon encountering any kind of NaN.	Uninitialized memory locations that contain QNaNs should be changed to SNaNs to cause the i486 CPU/387 NPX to fault when uninitialized memory locations are referenced.	IEEE Standard 754 compatibility.
Pseudozero, Pseudo-NaN, Pseudoinfinity, and Unnormal Formats	The i486 CPU/387 NPX neither generates not supports these formats; it raises an invalid-operation exception whenever it encounters them in an arithmetic operation.	The 80287/8087 defines and supports special handling for these formats.	None. The i486 CPU/387 DX does not generate these formats, and therefore will not encounter them unless a programmer deliberately enters them.	IEEE Standard 754 compatibility.
Tag Word Bits for Unsupported Data Formats	The encoding in the tag word for the unsupported data formats mentioned in Section 25.2.1 is "special data" (type 10).	The encoding for pseudo-zero and unnormal is "valid" (type 00); the others are "special data" (type 10).	The exception handler may need to be changed if programmers use such data types.	IEEE Standard 754 compatibility.
Invalid-Operation Exception	No invalid-operation exception is raised upon encountering a denormal in FSQRT, FDIV, or FPREM or upon conversion to BCD or to integer. The operation proceeds by first normalizing the value.	Upon encountering a denormal in FSQRT, FDIV, or FPREM or upon conversion to BCD or to integer, the invalid-operation exception is raised.	None. Software on the i486 CPU/387 NPX will continue to execute in cases where the 80287/8087 would trap.	Upgrade, to eliminate exception.

Issue	Difference Description		Impact on Software	Reason for the Difference
	i486™ CPU/387™ NPX Behavior	80287/8087 Behavior		
Denormal Exception	The denormal exception is raised in transcendental instructions and FXTRACT.	The denormal exception is not raised in transcendental instructions and FXTRACT.	The exception handler needs to be changed only if it gives special treatment to different opcodes.	Performance enhancement for normal case.
Overflow Exception	Overflow exception masked. If the rounding mode is set to chop (toward zero), the result is the most positive or more negative number.	Overflow exception masked. The 80287/8087 does not signal the overflow exception when the masked response is not infinity; i.e., it signals overflow only when the rounding control is not set to round to zero. If rounding is set to chop (toward zero), the result is positive or negative infinity.	Overflow exception masked. Under the most common rounding modes, no impact. If rounding is toward zero (chop), a program on the i486 CPU/387 NPX produces under overflow conditions a result that is different in the least significant bit of the significand, compared to the result on the 80287.	IEEE Standard 754 compatibility.
	Overflow exception not masked. The precision exception is flagged. When the result is stored in the stack, the significand is rounded according to the precision control (PC) bit of the control word or according to the opcode.	Overflow exception not masked. The precision exception is not flagged and the signficand is not rounded.	Overflow exception not masked. If the result is stored on the stack, a program on the i486 CPU/387 NPX produces a different result under overflow conditions than on the 80287/8087. The difference is apparent only to the exception handler.	

Issue	Difference Description		Impact on Software	Reason for the Difference
	i486™ CPU/387™ NPX Behavior	80287/8087 Behavior		
Underflow Exception Two related events contribute to underflow: 1. The creation *tiny* result. A tiny number, because it is so small, may cause some other exception later (such as overflow upon division). 2. Loss of accuracy during the denormalization of a tiny number. Which of these events triggers the underflow exception depends on whether the underflow exception is masked.	Conditions for underflow. When the underflow exception is masked, the underflow exception is signaled when both the result is tiny and denormalization results in a loss of accuracy. Response to underflow. When the underflow exception is unmasked and the instruction is supposed to store the result on the stack, the significand is rounded to the appropriate precision (according to the precision control (PC) bit of the control word, for those instructions controlled by PC, otherwise to extended precision).	Conditions for underflow. When the underflow exception is masked and rounding is toward zero, the underflow exception flag is raised on tininess, regardless of loss of accuracy. Response to underflow. When the underflow exception is not masked and the destination is the stack, the signficand is not rounded but rather is left as is.	Underflow exception masked. No impact. The underflow exception occurs less often when rounding is toward zero. Underflow exception not masked. A program on the i486 CPU/387 NPX produces a different result during underflow conditions than on the 80287/8087 if the result is stored on the stack. The difference is only in the least significant bit of the significand and is apparent only to the exception handler.	IEEE Standard 754 compatibility.
Exception Precedence	There is no difference in the precedence of the denormal exception, whether it be masked or not.	When the denormal exception is not masked, it takes precedence over all other exceptions.	None, but some unneeded normalization of denormal operands is prevented on the i486 CPU/387 NPX.	Operational improvement.

25.2.2 Tag, Status, and Control Words

Issue	Difference Description		Impact on Software	Reason for the Difference
	i486™ CPU/387™ NPX Behavior	80287/8087 Behavior		
Bits C3-C0 of Status Word	After FINIT, incomplete FPREM, and hardware reset, these bits are set to zero.	After FINIT, incomplete FPREM, and hardware reset, the 80287/8087 leaves these bits intact (they contain the prior value).	None.	Upgrade, to provide consistent state after reset.
Bit C2 of Status Word	Bit 10 (C2) serves as an incomplete bit for FPTAN.	This bit is undefined for FPTAN.	None. Programs don't check C2 after FPTAN.	Upgrade to allow fast checking of operand range.
Infinity Control	Only affine closure is supported. Bit 12 remains programmable but has no effect on operation.	Both affine and projective closures are supported. After RESET, the default value in the control word is projective.	Software that requires projective infinity arithmetic may give different results.	IEEE Standard 754 compatibility.
Status Word Bit 6 for Stack Fault	When an invalid-operation exception occurs due to stack overflow or underflow, not only is bit 0 (IE) of the status word set, but also bit 6 is set to indicate a stack fault and bit 9 (C1) specifies overflow or underflow. Bit 6 is called SF and serves to distinguish invalid exceptions caused by stack overflow/underflow from those caused by numeric operations.	When an invalid-operation exception occurs due to stack overflow or underflow, only bit 0 (IE) of the status word is set. Bit 6 is RESERVED.	None. Existing exception handlers need not change, but may be upgraded to take advantage of the additional information. Newly written handlers will be more effective.	Upgrade and performance improvement.

Issue	Difference Description		Impact on Software	Reason for the Difference
	i486™ CPU/387™ NPX Behavior	80287/8087 Behavior		
Tag Word	When loading the tag word with an FLDENV or FRSTOR instruction, the only interpretations of tag values are *empty* (value 11) and *nonempty* (values 00, 01, and 10). Subsequent operations on a nonempty register always examine the value in the register, not the value in its tag. The FSTENV and FSAVE instructions examine the nonempty registers and put the correct values in the tags before storing the tag word.	The corresponding tag is checked before each register access to determine the class of operand in the register; the tag is updated after every change to a register so that the tag always reflects the most recent status of the register. Programmers can load a tag with a value that disagrees with the contents of a register (for example, the register contains valid contents, but the tag says *special*; the 80287/8087, in this case, honors the tag and does not examine the register).	Software may not operate correctly if it uses FLDENV or FRSTOR to change tags to values (other than empty) that are different from actual register contents.	Performance improvement.

25.2.3 Instruction Set

Issue	Difference Description		Impact on Software	Reason for the Difference
	i486™ CPU/387™ NPX Behavior	80287/8087 Behavior		
FBSTP, FDIV, FIST(P), FPREM, FSQRT	Operation on denormal operand is supported. An underflow exception can occur.	Operation on denormal operand and raises invalid-operation exception. Underflow is not possible.	The exception handler for underflow may require change only if it gives different treatment to different opcodes. Possibly fewer invalid-operation exceptions will occur.	IEEE Standard 754 compatibility.

Issue	Difference Description		Impact on Software	Reason for the Difference
	i486™ CPU/387™ NPX Behavior	80287/8087 Behavior		
FSCALE	The range of the scaling operand is not restricted. If 0 < | ST(1) | < 1, the scaling factor is zero; therefore, ST(0) remains unchanged. If the rounded result is not exact or if there was a loss of accuracy (masked underflow), the precision exception is signaled.	The range of the scaling operand is restricted. If 0 < | ST(1) | < 1, the result is undefined and no exception is signaled.	Different result when 0 < | ST(1) | < 1.	Upgrade.
FPREM1	Performs partial remainder according to IEEE Standard 754 standard.	Does not exist.	None.	IEEE Standard 754 compatibility and upgrade.
FPREM	Bits C0, C3, C1 of the status word, correctly reflect the three low-order bits of the quotient.	The quotient bits are incorrect when performing a reduction of $64^N + M$ when N ≥ 1 and M = 1 or M = 2.	None. Software that works around the bug should not be affected.	Upgrade.
FUCOM, FUCOMP, FUCOMPP	Perform unordered compare according to IEEE Standard 754 standard.	Do not exist.	None.	IEEE Standard 754 compatibility.
FPTAN	Range of operand is much less restricted (| ST(0) | < 2^{63}); reduces operand internally using an internal π/4 constant that is more accurate.	Range of operand is restricted (| ST(0) | < π/4); operand must be reduced to range using FPREM.	None.	Upgrade.
	After a stack overflow when the invalid-operation exception is masked, both ST and ST(1) contain quiet NaNs.	After a stack overflow when the invalid-operation exception is masked, the original operand remains unchanged, but is pushed to ST(1).		IEEE Standard 754 compatibility.

Issue	Difference Description		Impact on Software	Reason for the Difference
	i486™ CPU/387™ NPX Behavior	80287/8087 Behavior		
FSIN, FCOS, FSINCOS	Perform three common trigonometric functions.	Do not exist.	None.	Upgrade.
FPATAN	Range of operands is unrestricted.	| ST(0) | must be smaller than | ST(1) |.	None.	Upgrade.
F2XM1	Wider range of operand $(-1 \leq ST(0) \leq +1)$.	The supported operand range is $0 \leq ST(0) \leq 0.5$.	None.	Upgrade.
FLD extended-real	Does not report denormal exception because the instruction is not arithmetic.	Reports denormal exception.	None.	Upgrade.
FXTRACT	If the operand is zero, the zero-divide exception is reported and ST(1) is $-\infty$. If the operand is $+\infty$, no exception is reported.	If the operand is zero, ST(1) is zero and no exception is reported. If the operand is $+\infty$, the invalid-operation exception is reported.	None. Software usually bypasses zero and ∞.	IEEE 754 recommendation to fully support the logb function.
FLD constant	Rounding control is in effect.	Rounding control is not in effect.	Results are the same as for the 80287/8087 when rounding control is set to round to zero, round to $-\infty$, and (in the case of FLDL2T) round to nearest. Results are different by one in the least significant bit of the significand in round to $+\infty$ and round to nearest (excluding FLDL2T). FLD1 and FLDZ are always the same.	IEEE 754 recommendations.

Issue	Difference Description		Impact on Software	Reason for the Difference
	i486™ CPU/387™ NPX Behavior	80287/8087 Behavior		
FLD single/double precision	Loading a denormal causes the number to be converted to extended precision (because it is put on the stack).	Loading a denormal causes the number to be converted to an unnormal.	If the next instruction is FXTRACT or FXAM, the i486 CPU/387 NPX will give a different result than the 80287/8087.	IEEE Standard 754 compatibility.
FLD single/double precision	When loading a signaling NaN, raises invalid exception.	Does not raise an exception when loading a signaling NaN.	The exception handler needs to be updated to handle this condition.	IEEE Standard 754 compatibility.
FSETPM	Treated as FNOP (no operation).	Informs the 80287 that the system is in protected mode.	None.	The i486/386 CPU handles all addressing and exception-pointer information, whether in protected mode or not.
FXAM	Encountering an empty register will not generate combinations of C3-C0 equal to 1101 or 1111.	May generate these combinations, among others.	None.	Upgrade, to provide repeatable results.
All Transcendental Instructions	May generate different results in round-up bit of status word.	Round-up bit of status word is undefined for these instructions.	None.	Upgrade, to signal rounding status.

25.3 DIFFERENCES FROM 8086/8087 SYSTEMS

The i486 processor operating in real-address mode will execute 8087 programs without major modification. However, because of differences in the handling of numeric exceptions between the i486 processor and the 8087 NPX, exception-handling routines *may* need to be changed. This section provides details showing how 8087 programs can be ported to the i486 processor.

1. The 8087 requires an interrupt controller (8259A) to interrupt the CPU when an unmasked exception occurs. Therefore, any interrupt-controller-oriented instructions in numeric exception handlers for the 8087 should be deleted.

2. The 8087 instructions FENI/FNENI and FDISI/FNDISI perform no useful function in the i486 processor. If the i486 processor encounters one of these opcodes in its instruction stream, the instruction will effectively be ignored – none of the i486 processor internal states will be updated. While 8087 code containing these instructions may be executed on the i486 processor, it is unlikely that the exception-handling routines containing these instructions will be completely portable.

3. In real mode and protected mode (not including virtual 8086 mode), interrupt vector 16 must point to the numeric exception handling routine. In virtual 8086 mode, the V86 monitor can be programmed to accommodate a different location of the interrupt vector for numeric exceptions.

4. The ESC instruction address saved in the i486 processor includes any leading prefixes before the ESC opcode. The corresponding address saved in the 8086/8087 does not include leading prefixes.

5. In protected mode (not including virtual 8086 mode), the format of the i486 processor saved instruction and address pointers is different than for the 8087. The instruction opcode is not saved in protected mode – exception handlers will have to retrieve the opcode from memory if needed.

6. Interrupt 7 will occur in the i486 processor when executing ESC instructions with either TS (task switched) or EM (emulation) of the MSW set (TS = 1 or EM = 1). If TS is set, then a WAIT instruction will also cause interrupt 7. An exception handler should be included in i486 processor code to handle these situations.

7. Interrupt 13 will occur if the starting address of a numeric operand falls outside a segment's size. An exception handler should be included to report these programming errors.

8. Except for the FPU control instructions, all of the i486 processor numeric instructions are automatically synchronized – the processor automatically waits until all operands have been transferred before executing the next ESC instruction. No explicit WAIT instructions are required to assure this synchronization. For the 8087 used with 8086 and 8088 processors, explicit WAITs are required before each numeric instruction to ensure synchronization. Although 8087 programs having explicit WAIT instructions will execute perfectly on the i486 processor without reassembly, these WAIT instructions are unnecessary.

9. Since the i486 processor does not require WAIT instructions before each numeric instruction, the ASM386/486 assembler does not automatically generate these WAIT instructions. The ASM86 assembler, however, automatically precedes every ESC instruction with a WAIT instruction. Although numeric routines generated using the ASM86 assembler will generally execute correctly on the i486 processor, reassembly using ASM386/486 may result in a more compact code image and faster execution.

   The control instructions for the i486 FPU can be coded using either a WAIT or No-WAIT form of mnemonic. The WAIT forms of these instructions cause ASM386/486 to precede the ESC instruction with a WAIT instruction, in the identical manner as does ASM86.

10. The address of a memory operand stored by FSAVE or FSTENV is undefined if the previous ESC instruction did not refer to memory.

11. Because the i486 processor automatically normalizes denormal numbers when possible, an 8087 program that uses the denormal exception solely to normalize denormal operands can run on an i486 processor by masking the denormal exception. The 8087 denormal exception handler would not be used by the i486 processor in this case. A numerics program runs faster when the i486 processor performs normalization of denormal operands.

Part V
Instruction Set

Instruction Set 26

CHAPTER 26
INSTRUCTION SET

This chapter presents instructions for the i486™ processor in alphabetical order. For each instruction, the forms are given for each operand combination, including object code produced, operands required, execution time, and a description. For each instruction, there is an operational description and a summary of exceptions generated.

26.1 OPERAND-SIZE AND ADDRESS-SIZE ATTRIBUTES

When executing an instruction, the i486 processor can address memory using either 16 or 32-bit addresses. Consequently, each instruction that uses memory addresses has associated with it an address-size attribute of either 16 or 32 bits. The use of 16-bit addresses implies both the use of 16-bit displacements in instructions and the generation of 16-bit address offsets (segment relative addresses) as the result of the effective address calculations. 32-bit addresses imply the use of 32-bit displacements and the generation of 32-bit address offsets. Similarly, an instruction that accesses words (16 bits) or doublewords (32 bits) has an operand-size attribute of either 16 or 32 bits.

The attributes are determined by a combination of defaults, instruction prefixes, and (for programs executing in protected mode) size-specification bits in segment descriptors.

26.1.1 Default Segment Attribute

For programs running in protected mode, the D bit in executable-segment descriptors specifies the default attribute for both address size and operand size. These default attributes apply to the execution of all instructions in the segment. A clear D bit sets the default address size and operand size to 16 bits; a set D bit, to 32 bits.

Programs that execute in real mode or virtual-8086 mode have 16-bit addresses and operands by default.

26.1.2 Operand-Size and Address-Size Instruction Prefixes

The internal encoding of an instruction can include two byte-long prefixes: the address-size prefix, 67H, and the operand-size prefix, 66H. (A later section, "Instruction Format," shows the position of the prefixes in an instruction's encoding.) These prefixes *override* the default segment attributes for the instruction that follows. Table 26-1 shows the effect of each possible combination of defaults and overrides.

Table 26-1. Effective Size Attributes

Segment Default D = ...	0	0	0	0	1	1	1	1
Operand-Size Prefix 66H	N	N	Y	Y	N	N	Y	Y
Address-Size Prefix 67H	N	Y	N	Y	N	Y	N	Y
Effective Operand Size	16	16	32	32	32	32	16	16
Effective Address Size	16	32	16	32	32	16	32	16

Y = Yes, this instruction prefix is present
N = No, this instruction prefix is not present

26.1.3 Address-Size Attribute for Stack

Instructions that use the stack implicitly (for example: POP EAX) also have a stack address-size attribute of either 16 or 32 bits. Instructions with a stack address-size attribute of 16 use the 16-bit SP stack pointer register; instructions with a stack address-size attribute of 32 bits use the 32-bit ESP register to form the address of the top of the stack.

The stack address-size attribute is controlled by the B bit of the data-segment descriptor in the SS register. A value of zero in the B bit selects a stack address-size attribute of 16; a value of one selects a stack address-size attribute of 32.

26.2 INSTRUCTION FORMAT

All instruction encodings are subsets of the general instruction format shown in Figure 26-1. Instructions consist of optional instruction prefixes, one or two primary opcode bytes, possibly an address specifier consisting of the ModR/M byte and the SIB (Scale Index Base) byte, a displacement, if required, and an immediate data field, if required.

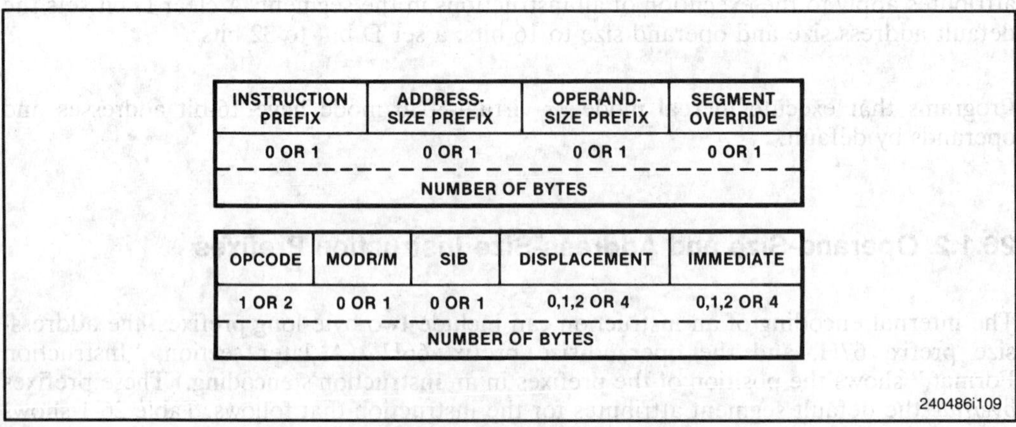

Figure 26-1. i486™ Processor Instruction Format

Smaller encoding fields can be defined within the primary opcode or opcodes. These fields define the direction of the operation, the size of the displacements, the register encoding, or sign extension; encoding fields vary depending on the class of operation.

Most instructions that can refer to an operand in memory have an addressing form byte following the primary opcode byte(s). This byte, called the ModR/M byte, specifies the address form to be used. Certain encodings of the ModR/M byte indicate a second addressing byte, the SIB (Scale Index Base) byte, which follows the ModR/M byte and is required to fully specify the addressing form.

Addressing forms can include a displacement immediately following either the ModR/M or SIB byte. If a displacement is present, it can be 8-, 16- or 32-bits.

If the instruction specifies an immediate operand, the immediate operand always follows any displacement bytes. The immediate operand, if specified, is always the last field of the instruction.

The following are the allowable instruction prefix codes:

F3H	REP prefix (used only with string instructions)
F3H	REPE/REPZ prefix (used only with string instructions)
F2H	REPNE/REPNZ prefix (used only with string instructions)
F0H	LOCK prefix

The following are the segment override prefixes:

2EH	CS segment override prefix
36H	SS segment override prefix
3EH	DS segment override prefix
26H	ES segment override prefix
64H	FS segment override prefix
65H	GS segment override prefix
66H	Operand-size override
67H	Address-size override

26.2.1 ModR/M and SIB Bytes

The ModR/M and SIB bytes follow the opcode byte(s) in many of the i486 processor instructions. They contain the following information:

- The indexing type or register number to be used in the instruction
- The register to be used, or more information to select the instruction
- The base, index, and scale information

The ModR/M byte contains three fields of information:

- The **mod** field, which occupies the two most significant bits of the byte, combines with the r/m field to form 32 possible values: eight registers and 24 indexing modes.

- The **reg** field, which occupies the next three bits following the mod field, specifies either a register number or three more bits of opcode information. The meaning of the reg field is determined by the first (opcode) byte of the instruction.

- The **r/m** field, which occupies the three least significant bits of the byte, can specify a register as the location of an operand, or can form part of the addressing-mode encoding in combination with the **mod** field as described above.

The based indexed and scaled indexed forms of 32-bit addressing require the SIB byte. The presence of the SIB byte is indicated by certain encodings of the ModR/M byte. The SIB byte then includes the following fields:

- The **ss** field, which occupies the two most significant bits of the byte, specifies the scale factor.

- The **index** field, which occupies the next three bits following the **ss** field and specifies the register number of the index register.

- The **base** field, which occupies the three least significant bits of the byte, specifies the register number of the base register.

Figure 26-2 shows the formats of the ModR/M and SIB bytes.

The values and the corresponding addressing forms of the ModR/M and SIB bytes are shown in Tables 26-2, 26-3, and 26-4. The 16-bit addressing forms specified by the ModR/M byte are in Table 26-2. The 32-bit addressing forms specified by the ModR/M byte are in Table 26-3. Table 26-4 shows the 32-bit addressing forms specified by the SIB byte.

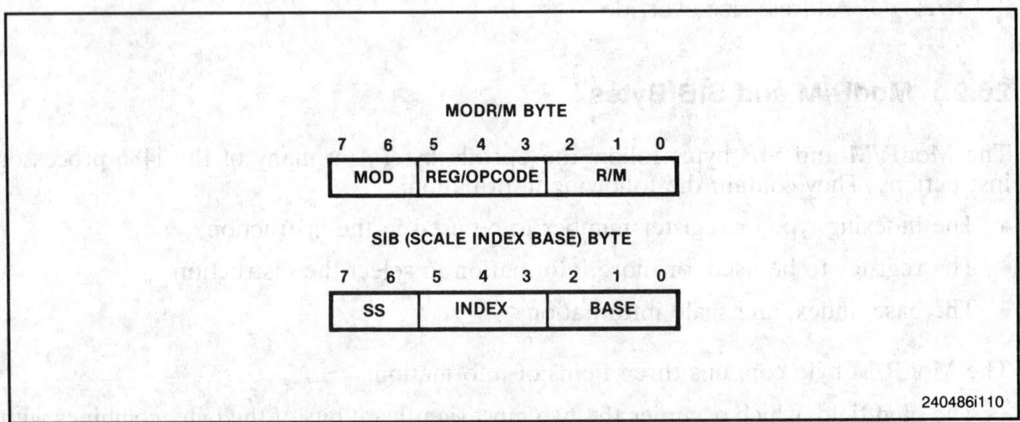

Figure 26-2. ModR/M and SIB Byte Formats

Table 26-2. 16-Bit Addressing Forms with the ModR/M Byte

r8(/r)			AL	CL	DL	BL	AH	CH	DH	BH
r16(/r)			AX	CX	DX	BX	SP	BP	SI	DI
r32(/r)			EAX	ECX	EDX	EBX	ESP	EBP	ESI	EDI
/digit (Opcode)			0	1	2	3	4	5	6	7
REG =			000	001	010	011	100	101	110	111
Effective Address	Mod	R/M	ModR/M Values in Hexadecimal							
[BX+SI]	00	000	00	08	10	18	20	28	30	38
[BX+DI]		001	01	09	11	19	21	29	31	39
[BP+SI]		010	02	0A	12	1A	22	2A	32	3A
[BP+DI]		011	03	0B	13	1B	23	2B	33	3B
[SI]		100	04	0C	14	1C	24	2C	34	3C
[DI]		101	05	0D	15	1D	25	2D	35	3D
disp16		110	06	0E	16	1E	26	2E	36	3E
[BX]		111	07	0F	17	1F	27	2F	37	3F
[BX+SI]+disp8	01	000	40	48	50	58	60	68	70	78
[BX+DI]+disp8		001	41	49	51	59	61	69	71	79
[BP+SI]+disp8		010	42	4A	52	5A	62	6A	72	7A
[BP+DI]+disp8		011	43	4B	53	5B	63	6B	73	7B
[SI]+disp8		100	44	4C	54	5C	64	6C	74	7C
[DI]+disp8		101	45	4D	55	5D	65	6D	75	7D
[BP]+disp8		110	46	4E	56	5E	66	6E	76	7E
[BX]+disp8		111	47	4F	57	5F	67	6F	77	7F
[BX+SI]+disp16	10	000	80	88	90	98	A0	A8	B0	B8
[BX+DI]+disp16		001	81	89	91	99	A1	A9	B1	B9
[BX+SI]+disp16		010	82	8A	92	9A	A2	AA	B2	BA
[BX+DI]+disp16		011	83	8B	93	9B	A3	AB	B3	BB
[SI]+disp16		100	84	8C	94	9C	A4	AC	B4	BC
[DI]+disp16		101	85	8D	95	9D	A5	AD	B5	BD
[BP]+disp16		110	86	8E	96	9E	A6	AE	B6	BE
[BX]+disp16		111	87	8F	97	9F	A7	AF	B7	BF
EAX/AX/AL	11	000	C0	C8	D0	D8	E0	E8	F0	F8
ECX/CX/CL		001	C1	C9	D1	D9	EQ	E9	F1	F9
EDX/DX/DL		010	C2	CA	D2	DA	E2	EA	F2	FA
EBX/BX/BL		011	C3	CB	D3	DB	E3	EB	F3	FB
ESP/SP/AH		100	C4	CC	D4	DC	E4	EC	F4	FC
EBP/BP/CH		101	C5	CD	D5	DD	E5	ED	F5	FD
ESI/SI/DH		110	C6	CE	D6	DE	E6	EE	F6	FE
EDI/DI/BH		111	C7	CF	D7	DF	E7	EF	F7	FF

NOTES: disp8 denotes an 8-bit displacement following the ModR/M byte, to be sign-extended and added to the index. **disp16** denotes a 16-bit displacement following the ModR/M byte, to be added to the index. Default segment register is SS for the effective addresses containing a BP index, DS for other effective addresses.

Table 26-3. 32-Bit Addressing Forms with the ModR/M Byte

r8(/r) r16(/r) r32(/r) /digit (Opcode) REG =			AL AX EAX 0 000	CL CX ECX 1 001	DL DX EDX 2 010	BL BX EBX 3 011	AH SP ESP 4 100	CH BP EBP 5 101	DH SI ESI 6 110	BH DI EDI 7 111
Effective Address	Mod	R/M	ModR/M Values in Hexadecimal							
[EAX]	00	000	00	08	10	18	20	28	30	38
[ECX]		001	01	09	11	19	21	29	31	39
[EDX]		010	02	0A	12	1A	22	2A	32	3A
[EBX]		011	03	0B	13	1B	23	2B	33	3B
[--][--]		100	04	0C	14	1C	24	2C	34	3C
disp32		101	05	0D	15	1D	25	2D	35	3D
[ESI]		110	06	0E	16	1E	26	2E	36	3E
[EDI]		111	07	0F	17	1F	27	2F	37	3F
disp8[EAX]	01	000	40	48	50	58	60	68	70	78
disp8[ECX]		001	41	49	51	59	61	69	71	79
disp8[EDX]		010	42	4A	52	5A	62	6A	72	7A
disp8[EPX];		011	43	4B	53	5B	63	6B	73	7B
disp8[--][--]		100	44	4C	54	5C	64	6C	74	7C
disp8[ebp]		101	45	4D	55	5D	65	6D	75	7D
disp8[ESI]		110	46	4E	56	5E	66	6E	76	7E
disp8[EDI]		111	47	4F	57	5F	67	6F	77	7F
disp32[EAX]	10	000	80	88	90	98	A0	A8	B0	B8
disp32[ECX]		001	81	89	91	99	A1	A9	B1	B9
disp32[EDX]		010	82	8A	92	9A	A2	AA	B2	BA
disp32[EBX]		011	83	8B	93	9B	A3	AB	B3	BB
disp32[--][--]		100	84	8C	94	9C	A4	AC	B4	BC
disp32[EBP]		101	85	8D	95	9D	A5	AD	B5	BD
disp32[ESI]		110	86	8E	96	9E	A6	AE	B6	BE
disp32[EDI]		111	87	8F	97	9F	A7	AF	B7	BF
EAX/AX/AL	11	000	C0	C8	D0	D8	E0	E8	F0	F8
ECX/CX/CL		001	C1	C9	D1	D9	E1	E9	F1	F9
EDX/DX/DL		010	C2	CA	D2	DA	E2	EA	F2	FA
EBX/BX/BL		011	C3	CB	D3	DB	E3	EB	F3	FB
ESP/SP/AH		100	C4	CC	D4	DC	E4	EC	F4	FC
EBP/BP/CH		101	C5	CD	D5	DD	E5	ED	F5	FD
ESI/SI/DH		110	C6	CE	D6	DE	E6	EE	F6	FE
EDI/DI/BH		111	C7	CF	D7	DF	E7	EF	F7	FF

NOTES: **[--][--]** means a SIB follows the ModR/M byte. **disp8** denotes an 8-bit displacement following the SIB byte, to be sign-extended and added to the index. **disp32** denotes a 32-bit displacement following the ModR/M byute, to be added to the index.

Table 26-4. 32-Bit Addressing Forms with the SIB Byte

r32 Base = Base =			EAX 0 000	ECX 1 001	EDX 2 010	EBX 3 011	ESP 4 100	[*] 5 101	ESI 6 110	EDI 7 111
Scaled Index	SS	Index	ModR/M Values in Hexadecimal							
[EAX]	00	000	00	01	02	03	04	05	06	07
[ECX]		001	08	09	0A	0B	0C	0D	0E	0F
[EDX]		010	10	11	12	13	14	15	16	17
[EBX]		011	18	19	1A	1B	1C	1D	1E	1F
none		100	20	21	22	23	24	25	26	27
[EBP]		101	28	29	2A	2B	2C	2D	2E	2F
[ESI]		110	30	31	32	33	34	35	36	37
[EDI]		111	38	39	3A	3B	3C	3D	3E	3F
[EAX*2]	01	000	40	41	42	43	44	45	46	47
[ECX*2]		001	48	49	4A	4B	4C	4D	4E	4F
[ECX*2]		010	50	51	52	53	54	55	56	57
[EBX*2]		011	58	59	5A	5B	5C	5D	5E	5F
none		100	60	61	62	63	64	65	66	67
[EBP*2]		101	68	69	6A	6B	6C	6D	6E	6F
[ESI*2]		110	70	71	72	73	74	75	76	77
[EDI*2]		111	78	79	7A	7B	7C	7D	7E	7F
[EAX*4]	10	000	80	81	82	83	84	85	86	87
[ECX*4]		001	88	89	8A	8B	8C	8D	8E	8F
[EDX*4]		010	90	91	92	93	94	95	96	97
[EBX*4]		011	98	89	9A	9B	9C	9D	9E	9F
none		100	A0	A1	A2	A3	A4	A5	A6	A7
[EBP*4]		101	A8	A9	AA	AB	AC	AD	AE	AF
[ESI*4]		110	B0	B1	B2	B3	B4	B5	B6	B7
[EDI*4]		111	B8	B9	BA	BB	BC	BD	BE	BF
[EAX*8]	11	000	C0	C1	C2	C3	C4	C5	C6	C7
[ECX*8]		001	C8	C9	CA	CB	CC	CD	CE	CF
[EDX*8]		010	D0	D1	D2	D3	D4	D5	D6	D7
[EBX*8]		011	D8	D9	DA	DB	DC	DD	DE	DF
none		100	E0	E1	E2	E3	E4	E5	E6	E7
[EBP*8]		101	E8	E9	EA	EB	EC	ED	EE	EF
[ESI*8]		110	F0	F1	F2	F3	F4	F5	F6	F7
[EDI*8]		111	F8	F9	FA	FB	FC	FD	FE	FF

NOTES: [*] means a disp32 with no base if MOD is 00, [ESP] otherwise. This provides the following addressing modes:

disp32[index]	(MOD = 00)
disp8[EBP][index]	(MOD = 01)
disp32[EBP][index]	(MOD = 10)

26.2.2 How to Read the Instruction Set Pages

The following is an example of the format used for each i486 processor instruction description in this chapter:

CMC—Complement Carry Flag

Opcode	Instruction	Clocks	Description
F5	CMC	2	Complement carry flag

The above table is followed by paragraphs labelled "Operation," "Description," "Flags Affected," "Protected Mode Exceptions," "Real Address Mode Exceptions," and, optionally, "Notes." The following sections explain the notational conventions and abbreviations used in these paragraphs of the instruction descriptions.

26.2.2.1 OPCODE COLUMN

The "Opcode" column gives the complete object code produced for each form of the instruction. When possible, the codes are given as hexadecimal bytes, in the same order in which they appear in memory. Definitions of entries other than hexadecimal bytes are as follows:

/digit: (digit is between 0 and 7) indicates that the ModR/M byte of the instruction uses only the r/m (register or memory) operand. The **reg** field contains the digit that provides an extension to the instruction's opcode.

/r: indicates that the ModR/M byte of the instruction contains both a register operand and an r/m operand.

cb, cw, cd, cp: a 1-byte (cb), 2-byte (cw), 4-byte (cd) or 6-byte (cp) value following the opcode that is used to specify a code offset and possibly a new value for the code segment register.

ib, iw, id: a 1-byte (ib), 2-byte (iw), or 4-byte (id) immediate operand to the instruction that follows the opcode, ModR/M bytes or scale-indexing bytes. The opcode determines if the operand is a signed value. All words and doublewords are given with the low-order byte first.

+rb, +rw, +rd: a register code, from 0 through 7, added to the hexadecimal byte given at the left of the plus sign to form a single opcode byte. The codes are –

rb		rw		rd	
AL	= 0	AX	= 0	EAX	= 0
CL	= 1	CX	= 1	ECX	= 1
DL	= 2	DX	= 2	EDX	= 2
BL	= 3	BX	= 3	EBX	= 3

rb		rw		rd	
AH	= 4	SP	= 4	ESP	= 4
CH	= 5	BP	= 5	EBP	= 5
DH	= 6	SI	= 6	ESI	= 6
BH	= 7	DI	= 7	EDI	= 7

+i: used in floating-point instructions when one of the operands is ST(i) from the FPU register stack. The number i (which can range from 0 to 7) is added to the hexadecimal byte given at the left of the plus sign to form a single opcode byte.

26.2.2.2 INSTRUCTION COLUMN

The "Instruction" column gives the syntax of the instruction statement as it would appear in an ASM386 program. The following is a list of the symbols used to represent operands in the instruction statements:

rel8: a relative address in the range from 128 bytes before the end of the instruction to 127 bytes after the end of the instruction.

rel16, rel32: a relative address within the same code segment as the instruction assembled. **rel16** applies to instructions with an operand-size attribute of 16 bits; **rel32** applies to instructions with an operand-size attribute of 32 bits.

ptr16:16, ptr16:32: a far pointer, typically in a code segment different from that of the instruction. The notation **16:16** indicates that the value of the pointer has two parts. The value to the left of the colon is a 16-bit selector or value destined for the code segment register. The value to the right corresponds to the offset within the destination segment. **ptr16:16** is used when the instruction's operand-size attribute is 16 bits; **ptr16:32** is used with the 32-bit attribute.

r8: one of the byte registers AL, CL, DL, BL, AH, CH, DH, or BH.

r16: one of the word registers AX, CX, DX, BX, SP, BP, SI, or DI.

r32: one of the doubleword registers EAX, ECX, EDX, EBX, ESP, EBP, ESI, or EDI.

imm8: an immediate byte value. **imm8** is a signed number between −128 and +127 inclusive. For instructions in which **imm8** is combined with a word or doubleword operand, the immediate value is sign-extended to form a word or doubleword. The upper byte of the word is filled with the topmost bit of the immediate value.

imm16: an immediate word value used for instructions whose operand-size attribute is 16 bits. This is a number between −32768 and +32767 inclusive.

imm32: an immediate doubleword value used for instructions whose operand-size attribute is 32-bits. It allows the use of a number between +2147483647 and −2147483648 inclusive.

r/m8: a one-byte operand that is either the contents of a byte register (AL, BL, CL, DL, AH, BH, CH, DH), or a byte from memory.

r/m16: a word register or memory operand used for instructions whose operand-size attribute is 16 bits. The word registers are: AX, BX, CX, DX, SP, BP, SI, DI. The contents of memory are found at the address provided by the effective address computation.

r/m32: a doubleword register or memory operand used for instructions whose operand-size attribute is 32-bits. The doubleword registers are: EAX, EBX, ECX, EDX, ESP, EBP, ESI, EDI. The contents of memory are found at the address provided by the effective address computation.

m8: a memory byte addressed by DS:SI or ES:DI (used only by string instructions).

m16: a memory word addressed by DS:SI or ES:DI (used only by string instructions).

m32: a memory doubleword addressed by DS:SI or ES:DI (used only by string instructions).

m16:16, m16:32: a memory operand containing a far pointer composed of two numbers. The number to the left of the colon corresponds to the pointer's segment selector. The number to the right corresponds to its offset.

m16&32, m16&16, m32&32: a memory operand consisting of data item pairs whose sizes are indicated on the left and the right side of the ampersand. All memory addressing modes are allowed. **m16&16** and **m32&32** operands are used by the BOUND instruction to provide an operand containing an upper and lower bounds for array indices. **m16&32** is used by LIDT and LGDT to provide a word with which to load the limit field, and a doubleword with which to load the base field of the corresponding Global and Interrupt Descriptor Table Registers.

moffs8, moffs16, moffs32: (memory offset) a simple memory variable of type BYTE, WORD, or DWORD used by some variants of the MOV instruction. The actual address is given by a simple offset relative to the segment base. No ModR/M byte is used in the instruction. The number shown with **moffs** indicates its size, which is determined by the address-size attribute of the instruction.

Sreg: a segment register. The segment register bit assignments are ES=0, CS=1, SS=2, DS=3, FS=4, and GS=5.

m32real, m64real, m80real: (respectively) single-, double-, and extended-real floating-point operands in memory.

m16int, m32int, m64int: (respectively) word-, short-, and long-integer floating-point operands in memory.

mNbyte: *N*-byte floating-point operand in memory.

ST or ST(0): Top element of the FPU register stack.

ST(i): i^{th} element from the top of the FPU register stack. (i=0..7)

26.2.2.3 CLOCKS COLUMN

The "Clocks" column gives the approximate number of clock cycles the instruction takes to execute. The clock count calculations makes the following assumptions:

- Data and instruction accesses hit in the cache.
- The target of a jump instruction is in the cache.
- No invalidate cycles contend with the instruction for use of the cache.
- Page translation hits in the TLB.
- Memory operands are aligned.
- Effective address calculations use one base register and no index register, and the base register is not the destination register of the preceding instruction.
- Displacement and immediate are not used together.
- No exceptions are detected during execution.
- There are no write-buffer delays.

For a discussion of the performance penalties incurred when these conditions do not hold, see Appendix E.

The following symbols are used in the clock count specifications:

- **n**, which represents a number of repetitions.
- **m**, which represents the number of components in the next instruction executed, where the entire displacement (if any) counts as one component, the entire immediate data (if any) counts as one component, and every other byte of the instruction and prefix(es) each counts as one component.
- **pm=**, a clock count that applies when the instruction executes in Protected Mode. **pm=** is not given when the clock counts are the same for Protected and Real Address Modes.

When an exception occurs during the execution of an instruction and the exception handler is in another task, the instruction execution time is increased by the number of clocks to effect a task switch. This parameter depends on several factors:

- The type of TSS used to represent the new task (i486 CPU TSS or 80286 TSS).
- Whether the current task is in V86 mode.
- Whether the new task is in V86 mode.
- Whether accesses hit in the cache.
- Whether a task gate on an interrupt/trap gate is used.

Table 26-5 summarizes the task switch times for exceptions, assuming cache hits and the use of task gates. For full details, see Appendix E.

26.2.2.4 DESCRIPTION COLUMN

The "Description" column following the "Clocks" column briefly explains the various forms of the instruction. The "Operation" and "Description" sections contain more details of the instruction's operation.

26.2.2.5 OPERATION

The "Operation" section contains an algorithmic description of the instruction which uses a notation similar to the Algol or Pascal language. The algorithms are composed of the following elements:

Comments are enclosed within the symbol pairs "(*" and "*)".

Compound statements are enclosed between the keywords of the "if" statement (IF, THEN, ELSE, FI) or of the "do" statement (DO, OD), or of the "case" statement (CASE ... OF, ESAC).

A register name implies the contents of the register. A register name enclosed in brackets implies the contents of the location whose address is contained in that register. For example, ES:[DI] indicates the contents of the location whose ES segment relative address is in register DI. [SI] indicates the contents of the address contained in register SI relative to SI's default segment (DS) or overridden segment.

Table 26-5. Task Switch Times for Exceptions

Old Task	New Task		
	to i486™ CPU TSS	to 80286 TSS	to VM TSS
VM/i486 CPU/80286 TSS	199	180	177

Brackets also used for memory operands, where they mean that the contents of the memory location is a segment-relative offset. For example, [SRC] indicates that the contents of the source operand is a segment-relative offset.

A ← B; indicates that the value of B is assigned to A.

The symbols =, <>, ≥, and ≤ are relational operators used to compare two values, meaning equal, not equal, greater or equal, less or equal, respectively. A relational expression such as A = B is TRUE if the value of A is equal to B; otherwise it is FALSE.

The following identifiers are used in the algorithmic descriptions:

- **OperandSize** represents the operand-size attribute of the instruction, which is either 16 or 32 bits. **AddressSize** represents the address-size attribute, which is either 16 or 32 bits. For example,

```
IF instruction = CMPSW
THEN OperandSize ← 16;
ELSE
    IF instruction = CMPSD
    THEN OperandSize ← 32;
    FI;
FI;
```

  indicates that the operand-size attribute depends on the form of the CMPS instruction used. Refer to the explanation of address-size and operand-size attributes at the beginning of this chapter for general guidelines on how these attributes are determined.
- **StackAddrSize** represents the stack address-size attribute associated with the instruction, which has a value of 16 or 32 bits, as explained earlier in the chapter.
- **SRC** represents the source operand. When there are two operands, SRC is the one on the right.
- **DEST** represents the destination operand. When there are two operands, DEST is the one on the left.
- **LeftSRC, RightSRC** distinguishes between two operands when both are source operands.
- **eSP** represents either the SP register or the ESP register depending on the setting of the B-bit for the current stack segment.

The following functions are used in the algorithmic descriptions:

- **Truncate to 16 bits(value)** reduces the size of the value to fit in 16 bits by discarding the uppermost bits as needed.
- **Addr(operand)** returns the effective address of the operand (the result of the effective address calculation prior to adding the segment base).
- **ZeroExtend(value)** returns a value zero-extended to the operand-size attribute of the instruction. For example, if OperandSize = 32, ZeroExtend of a byte value of −10 converts the byte from F6H to doubleword with hexadecimal value 000000F6H. If the value passed to ZeroExtend and the operand-size attribute are the same size, ZeroExtend returns the value unaltered.

- **SignExtend(value)** returns a value sign-extended to the operand-size attribute of the instruction. For example, if OperandSize = 32, SignExtend of a byte containing the value −10 converts the byte from F6H to a doubleword with hexadecimal value FFFFFFF6H. If the value passed to SignExtend and the operand-size attribute are the same size, SignExtend returns the value unaltered.

- **Push(value)** pushes a value onto the stack. The number of bytes pushed is determined by the operand-size attribute of the instruction. The action of Push is as follows:

```
IF StackAddrSize = 16
THEN
    IF OperandSize = 16
    THEN
        SP ← SP − 2;
        SS:[SP] ← value; (* 2 bytes assigned starting at
                            byte address in SP *)
    ELSE (* OperandSize = 32 *)
        SP ← SP − 4;
        SS:[SP] ← value; (* 4 bytes assigned starting at
                            byte address in SP *)
    FI;
ELSE (* StackAddrSize = 32 *)
    IF OperandSize = 16
    THEN
        ESP ← ESP − 2;
        SS:[ESP] ← value; (* 2 bytes assigned starting at
                             byte address in ESP*)
    ELSE (* OperandSize = 32 *)
        ESP ← ESP − 4;
        SS:[ESP] ← value; (* 4 bytes assigned starting at
                             byte address in ESP*)
    FI;
FI;
```

- **Pop(value)** removes the value from the top of the stack and returns it. The statement EAX ← Pop( ); assigns to EAX the 32-bit value that Pop took from the top of the stack. Pop will return either a word or a doubleword depending on the operand-size attribute. The action of Pop is as follows:

```
IF StackAddrSize = 16
THEN
    IF OperandSize = 16
    THEN
        ret val ← SS:[SP]; (* 2-byte value *)
        SP ← SP + 2;
    ELSE (* OperandSize = 32 *)
        ret val ← SS:[SP]; (* 4-byte value *)
        SP ← SP + 4;
    FI;
ELSE (* StackAddrSize = 32 *)
```

```
        IF OperandSize = 16
        THEN
                ret val ← SS:[ESP]; (* 2 bytes value *)
                ESP ← ESP + 2;
        ELSE (* OperandSize = 32 *)
                ret val ← SS:[ESP]; (* 4 bytes value *)
                ESP ← ESP + 4;
        FI;
FI;
RETURN(ret val); (*returns a word or doubleword*)
```

Pop ST is used on floating-point instruction pages to mean *pop the FPU register stack*.

- **Bit[BitBase, BitOffset]** returns the address of a bit within a bit string, which is a sequence of bits in memory or a register. Bits are numbered from low-order to high-order within registers and within memory bytes. In memory, the two bytes of a word are stored with the low-order byte at the lower address.

  If the base operand is a register, the offset can be in the range 0..31. This offset addresses a bit within the indicated register. An example, 'BIT[EAX, 21]' is illustrated in Figure 26-3.

  If BitBase is a memory address, BitOffset can range from −2 gigabits to 2 gigabits. The addressed bit is numbered (Offset MOD 8) within the byte at address (BitBase + (BitOffset DIV 8)), where DIV is signed division with rounding towards negative infinity, and MOD returns a positive number. This is illustrated in Figure 26-4.

- **I-O-Permission(I-O-Address, width)** returns TRUE or FALSE depending on the I/O permission bitmap and other factors. This function is defined as follows:

```
IF TSS type is 80286 THEN RETURN FALSE; FI;
Ptr ← [TSS + 66]; (* fetch bitmap pointer *)
BitStringAddr ← SHR (I-O-Address, 3) + Ptr;
MaskShift ← I-O-Address AND 7;
CASE width OF:
        BYTE: nBitMask ← 1;
        WORD: nBitMask ← 3;
        DWORD: nBitMask ← 15;
```

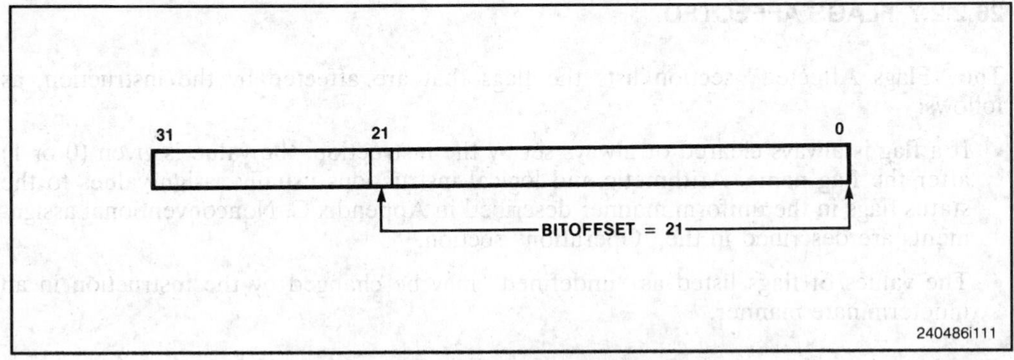

Figure 26-3. Bit Offset for BIT[EAX, 21]

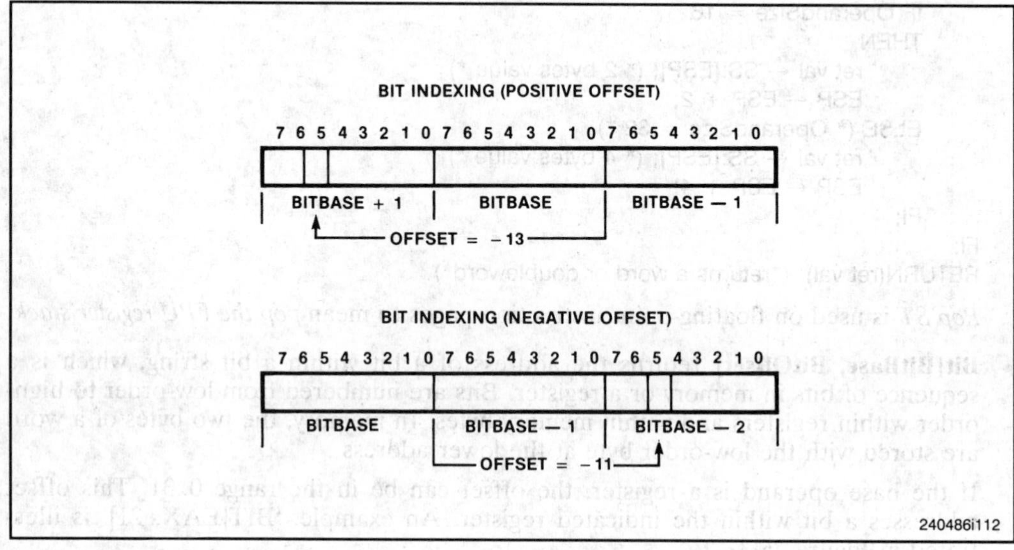

Figure 26-4. Memory Bit Indexing

```
ESAC;
mask ← SHL (nBitMask, MaskShift);
CheckString ← [BitStringAddr] AND mask;
IF CheckString = 0
THEN RETURN (TRUE);
ELSE RETURN (FALSE);
FI;
```

- **Switch-Tasks** is the task switching function described in Chapter 7.

26.2.2.6 DESCRIPTION

The "Description" section contains further explanation of the instruction's operation.

26.2.2.7 FLAGS AFFECTED

The "Flags Affected" section lists the flags that are affected by the instruction, as follows:

- If a flag is always cleared or always set by the instruction, the value is given (0 or 1) after the flag name. Arithmetic and logical instructions usually assign values to the status flags in the uniform manner described in Appendix C. Nonconventional assignments are described in the "Operation" section.
- The values of flags listed as "undefined" may be changed by the instruction in an indeterminate manner.

All flags not listed are unchanged by the instruction.

The floating-point instruction pages have a section called "FPU Flags Affected," which tells how each instruction can affect the four condition code bits of the FPU status word. These pages also have a section called "Numeric Exceptions," which lists the exception flags of the FPU status word that each instruction can set.

26.2.2.8 PROTECTED MODE EXCEPTIONS

This section lists the exceptions that can occur when the instruction is executed in protected mode. The exception names are a pound sign (#) followed by two letters and an optional error code in parentheses. For example, #GP(0) denotes a general protection exception with an error code of 0. Table 26-6 associates each two-letter name with the corresponding interrupt number.

Chapter 9 describes the exceptions and the i486 processor state upon entry to the exception.

Application programmers should consult the documentation provided with their operating systems to determine the actions taken when exceptions occur.

26.2.2.9 REAL ADDRESS MODE EXCEPTIONS

Because less error checking is performed by the i486 processor in Real Address Mode, this mode has fewer exception conditions. Refer to Chapter 22 for further information on these exceptions.

26.2.2.10 VIRTUAL-8086 MODE EXCEPTIONS

Virtual 8086 tasks provide the ability to simulate Virtual 8086 machines. Virtual 8086 Mode exceptions are similar to those for the 8086 processor, but there are some differences. Refer to Chapter 23 for details.

Table 26-6. Exceptions

Mnemonic	Interrupt	Description
#UD	6	Invalid opcode
#NM	7	Device not available
#DF	8	Doubel fault
#TS	10	Invalid TSS
#NP	11	Segment or gate not present
#SS	12	Stack fault
#GP	13	General protection fault
#PF	14	Page fault
#MF	16	Floating-point error
#AC	17	Alignment check

AAA—ASCII Adjust after Addition

Opcode	Instruction	Clocks	Description
37	AAA	3	ASCII adjust AL after addition

Operation

```
IF ((AL AND 0FH) > 9) OR (AF = 1)
THEN
   AL ← (AL + 6) AND 0FH;
   AH ← AH + 1;
   AF ← 1;
   CF ← 1;
ELSE
   CF ← 0;
   AF ← 0;
FI;
```

Description

Execute the AAA instruction only following an ADD instruction that leaves a byte result in the AL register. The lower nibbles of the operands of the ADD instruction should be in the range 0 through 9 (BCD digits). In this case, the AAA instruction adjusts the AL register to contain the correct decimal digit result. If the addition produced a decimal carry, the AH register is incremented, and the CF and AF flags are set. If there was no decimal carry, the CF and AF flags are cleared and the AH register is unchanged. In either case, the AL register is left with its top nibble set to 0. To convert the AL register to an ASCII result, follow the AAA instruction with OR AL, 30H.

Flags Affected

The AF and CF flags are set if there is a decimal carry, cleared if there is no decimal carry; the OF, SF, ZF, and PF flags are undefined

Protected Mode Exceptions

None

Real Address Mode Exceptions

None

Virtual 8086 Mode Exceptions

None

AAD—ASCII Adjust AX before Division

Opcode	Instruction	Clocks	Description
D5 0A	AAD	14	ASCII adjust AX before division

Operation

AL ← AH * 10 + AL;
AH ← 0;

Description

The AAD instruction is used to prepare two unpacked BCD digits (the least-significant digit in the AL register, the most-significant digit in the AH register) for a division operation that will yield an unpacked result. This is accomplished by setting the AL register to AL + (10 * AH), and then clearing the AH register. The AX register is then equal to the binary equivalent of the original unpacked two-digit number.

Flags Affected

The SF, ZF, and PF flags are set according to the result; the OF, AF, and CF flags are undefined

Protected Mode Exceptions

None

Real Address Mode Exceptions

None

Virtual 8086 Mode Exceptions

None

AAM — ASCII Adjust AX after Multiply

Opcode	Instruction	Clocks	Description
D4 0A	AAM	15	ASCII adjust AX after multiply

Operation

AH ← AL / 10;
AL ← AL MOD 10;

Description

Execute the AAM instruction only after executing a MUL instruction between two unpacked BCD digits that leaves the result in the AX register. Because the result is less than 100, it is contained entirely in the AL register. The AAM instruction unpacks the AL result by dividing AL by 10, leaving the quotient (most-significant digit) in the AH register and the remainder (least-significant digit) in the AL register.

Flags Affected

The SF, ZF, and PF flags are set according to the result; the OF, AF, and CF flags are undefined

Protected Mode Exceptions

None

Real Address Mode Exceptions

None

Virtual 8086 Mode Exceptions

None

AAS — ASCII Adjust AL after Subtraction

Opcode	Instruction	Clocks	Description
3F	AAS	3	ASCII adjust AL after subtraction

Operation

```
IF (AL AND 0FH) > 9 OR AF = 1
THEN
   AL ← AL − 6;
   AL ← AL AND 0FH;
   AH ← AH − 1;
   AF ← 1;
   CF ← 1;
ELSE
   CF ← 0;
   AF ← 0;
FI;
```

Description

Execute the AAS instruction only after a SUB instruction that leaves the byte result in the AL register. The lower nibbles of the operands of the SUB instruction must have been in the range 0 through 9 (BCD digits). In this case, the AAS instruction adjusts the AL register so it contains the correct decimal digit result. If the subtraction produced a decimal carry, the AH register is decremented, and the CF and AF flags are set. If no decimal carry occurred, the CF and AF flags are cleared, and the AH register is unchanged. In either case, the AL register is left with its top nibble set to 0. To convert the AL result to an ASCII result, follow the AAS instruction with OR AL, 30H.

Flags Affected

The AF and CF flags are set if there is a decimal carry, cleared if there is no decimal carry; the OF, SF, ZF, and PF flags are undefined

Protected Mode Exceptions

None

Real Address Mode Exceptions

None

Virtual 8086 Mode Exceptions

None

ADC—Add with Carry

Opcode	Instruction	Clocks	Description
14 *ib*	ADC AL,*imm8*	1	Add with carry immediate byte to AL
15 *iw*	ADC AX,*imm16*	1	Add with carry immediate word to AX
15 *id*	ADC EAX,*imm32*	1	Add with carry immediate dword to EAX
80 /2 *ib*	ADC *r/m8,imm8*	1/3	Add with carry immediate byte to *r/m* byte
81 /2 *iw*	ADC *r/m16,imm16*	1/3	Add with carry immediate word to *r/m* word
81 /2 *id*	ADC *r/m32,imm32*	1/3	Add with CF immediate dword to *r/m* dword
83 /2 *ib*	ADC *r/m16,imm8*	1/3	Add with CF sign-extended immediate byte to *r/m* word
83 /2 *ib*	ADC *r/m32,imm8*	1/3	Add with CF sign-extended immediate byte into *r/m* dword
10 /*r*	ADC *r/m8,r8*	1/3	Add with carry byte register to *r/m* byte
11 /*r*	ADC *r/m16,r16*	1/3	Add with carry word register to *r/m* word
11 /*r*	ADC *r/m32,r32*	1/3	Add with CF dword register to *r/m* dword
12 /*r*	ADC *r8,r/m8*	1/2	Add with carry *r/m* byte to byte register
13 /*r*	ADC *r16,r/m16*	1/2	Add with carry *r/m* word to word register
13 /*r*	ADC *r32,r/m32*	1/2	Add with CF *r/m* dword to dword register

Operation

DEST ← DEST + SRC + CF;

Description

The ADC instruction performs an integer addition of the two operands DEST and SRC and the carry flag, CF. The result of the addition is assigned to the first operand (DEST), and the flags are set accordingly. The ADC instruction is usually executed as part of a multi-byte or multi-word addition operation. When an immediate byte value is added to a word or doubleword operand, the immediate value is first sign-extended to the size of the word or doubleword operand.

Flags Affected

The OF, SF, ZF, AF, CF, and PF flags are set according to the result

Protected Mode Exceptions

#GP(0) if the result is in a nonwritable segment; #GP(0) for an illegal memory operand effective address in the CS, DS, ES, FS, or GS segments; #SS(0) for an illegal address in the SS segment; #PF(fault-code) for a page fault; #AC for unaligned memory reference if the current privilege level is 3.

Real Address Mode Exceptions

Interrupt 13 if any part of the operand would lie outside of the effective address space from 0 to 0FFFFH

Virtual 8086 Mode Exceptions

Same exceptions as in Real Address Mode; #PF(fault-code) for a page fault; #AC for unaligned memory reference if the current privilege level is 3

ADD—Add

Opcode	Instruction	Clocks	Description
04 *ib*	ADD AL,*imm8*	1	Add immediate byte to AL
05 *iw*	ADD AX,*imm16*	1	Add immediate word to AX
05 *id*	ADD EAX,*imm32*	1	Add immediate dword to EAX
80 /0 *ib*	ADD *r/m8,imm8*	1/3	Add immediate byte to *r/m* byte
81 /0 *iw*	ADD *r/m16,imm16*	1/3	Add immediate word to *r/m* word
81 /0 *id*	ADD *r/m32,imm32*	1/3	Add immediate dword to *r/m* dword
83 /0 *ib*	ADD *r/m16,imm8*	1/3	Add sign-extended immediate byte to *r/m* word
83 /0 *ib*	ADD *r/m32,imm8*	1/3	Add sign-extended immediate byte to *r/m* dword
00 /*r*	ADD *r/m8,r8*	1/3	Add byte register to *r/m* byte
01 /*r*	ADD *r/m16,r16*	1/3	Add word register to *r/m* word
01 /*r*	ADD *r/m32,r32*	1/3	Add dword register to *r/m* dword
02 /*r*	ADD *r8,r/m8*	1/2	Add *r/m* byte to byte register
03 /*r*	ADD *r16,r/m16*	1/2	Add *r/m* word to word register
03 /*r*	ADD *r32,r/m32*	1/2	Add *r/m* dword to dword register

Operation

DEST ← DEST + SRC;

Description

The ADD instruction performs an integer addition of the two operands (DEST and SRC). The result of the addition is assigned to the first operand (DEST), and the flags are set accordingly.

When an immediate byte is added to a word or doubleword operand, the immediate value is sign-extended to the size of the word or doubleword operand.

Flags Affected

The OF, SF, ZF, AF, CF, and PF flags are set according to the result

Protected Mode Exceptions

#GP(0) if the result is in a nonwritable segment; #GP(0) for an illegal memory operand effective address in the CS, DS, ES, FS, or GS segments; #SS(0) for an illegal address in the SS segment; #PF(fault-code) for a page fault; #AC for unaligned memory reference if the current privilege level is 3

Real Address Mode Exceptions

Interrupt 13 if any part of the operand would lie outside of the effective address space from 0 to 0FFFFH

Virtual 8086 Mode Exceptions

Same exceptions as in Real Address Mode; #PF(fault-code) for a page fault; #AC for unaligned memory reference if the current privilege level is 3

AND – Logical AND

Opcode	Instruction	Clocks	Description
24 *ib*	AND AL,*imm8*	1	AND immediate byte to AL
25 *iw*	AND AX,*imm16*	1	AND immediate word to AX
25 *id*	AND EAX,*imm32*	1	AND immediate dword to EAX
80 /4 *ib*	AND *r/m8,imm8*	1/3	AND immediate byte to *r/m* byte
81 /4 *iw*	AND *r/m16,imm16*	1/3	AND immediate word to *r/m* word
81 /4 *id*	AND *r/m32,imm32*	1/3	AND immediate dword to *r/m* dword
83 /4 *ib*	AND *r/m16,imm8*	1/3	AND sign-extended immediate byte with *r/m* word
83 /4 *ib*	AND *r/m32,imm8*	1/3	AND sign-extended immediate byte with *r/m*dword
20 /*r*	AND *r/m8,r8*	1/3	AND byte register to *r/m* byte
21 /*r*	AND *r/m16,r16*	1/3	AND word register to *r/m* word
21 /*r*	AND *r/m32,r32*	1/3	AND dword register to *r/m* dword
22 /*r*	AND *r8,r/m8*	1/2	AND *r/m* byte to byte register
23 /*r*	AND *r16,r/m16*	1/2	AND *r/m* word to word register
23 /*r*	AND *r32,r/m32*	1/2	AND *r/m* dword to dword register

Operation

DEST ← DEST AND SRC;
CF ← 0;
OF ← 0;

Description

Each bit of the result of the AND instruction is a 1 if both corresponding bits of the operands are 1; otherwise, it becomes a 0.

Flags Affected

The CF and OF flags are cleared; the PF, SF, and ZF flags are set according to the result

Protected Mode Exceptions

#GP(0) if the result is in a nonwritable segment; #GP(0) for an illegal memory operand effective address in the CS, DS, ES, FS, or GS segments; #SS(0) for an illegal address in the SS segment; #PF(fault-code) for a page fault; #AC for unaligned memory reference if the current privilege level is 3

Real Address Mode Exceptions

Interrupt 13 if any part of the operand would lie outside of the effective address space from 0 to 0FFFFH

Virtual 8086 Mode Exceptions

Same exceptions as in Real Address Mode; #PF(fault-code) for a page fault; #AC for unaligned memory reference if the current privilege level is 3

ARPL—Adjust RPL Field of Selector

Opcode	Instruction	Clocks	Description
63 /r	ARPL *r/m16,r16*	9/9	Adjust RPL of *r/m16* to not less than RPL of *r16*

Operation

```
IF RPL bits(0,1) of DEST < RPL bits(0,1) of SRC
THEN
   ZF ← 1;
   RPL bits(0,1) of DEST ← RPL bits(0,1) of SRC;
ELSE
   ZF ← 0;
FI;
```

Description

The ARPL instruction has two operands. The first operand is a 16-bit memory variable or word register that contains the value of a selector. The second operand is a word register. If the RPL field ("requested privilege level"—bottom two bits) of the first operand is less than the RPL field of the second operand, the ZF flag is set and the RPL field of the first operand is increased to match the second operand. Otherwise, the ZF flag is cleared and no change is made to the first operand.

The ARPL instruction appears in operating system software, not in application programs. It is used to guarantee that a selector parameter to a subroutine does not request more privilege than the caller is allowed. The second operand of the ARPL instruction is normally a register that contains the CS selector value of the caller.

Flags Affected

The ZF flag is set if the RPL field of the first operand is less than that of the second operand

Protected Mode Exceptions

#GP(0) if the result is in a nonwritable segment; #GP(0) for an illegal memory operand effective address in the CS, DS, ES, FS, or GS segments; #SS(0) for an illegal address in the SS segment; #PF(fault-code) for a page fault; #AC for unaligned memory reference if the current privilege level is 3

Real Address Mode Exceptions

Interrupt 6; the ARPL instruction is not recognized in Real Address Mode

Virtual 8086 Mode Exceptions

Same exceptions as in Real Address Mode; #PF(fault-code) for a page fault; #AC for unaligned memory reference if the current privilege level is 3

BOUND—Check Array Index Against Bounds

Opcode	Instruction	Clocks	Description
62 /r	BOUND *r16,m16&16*	7	Check if *r16* is within bounds (passes test)
62 /r	BOUND *r32,m32&32*	7	Check if *r32* is within bounds (passes test)

Operation

```
IF (LeftSRC < [RightSRC] OR LeftSRC > [RightSRC + OperandSize/8])
   (* Under lower bound or over upper bound *)
THEN Interrupt 5;
FI;
```

Description

The BOUND instruction ensures that a signed array index is within the limits specified by a block of memory consisting of an upper and a lower bound. Each bound uses one word when the operand-size attribute is 16 bits and a doubleword when the operand-size attribute is 32 bits. The first operand (a register) must be greater than or equal to the first bound in memory (lower bound), and less than or equal to the second bound in memory (upper bound) plus the number of bytes occupied for the operand size. If the register is not within bounds, an Interrupt 5 occurs; the return EIP points to the BOUND instruction.

The bounds limit data structure is usually placed just before the array itself, making the limits addressable via a constant offset from the beginning of the array.

Flags Affected

None

Protected Mode Exceptions

Interrupt 5 if the bounds test fails, as described above; #GP(0) for an illegal memory operand effective address in the CS, DS, ES, FS, or GS segments; #SS(0) for an illegal address in the SS segment; #PF(fault-code) for a page fault; #AC for unaligned memory reference if the current privilege level is 3

The second operand must be a memory operand, not a register. If the BOUND instruction is executed with a ModR/M byte representing a register as the second operand, #UD occurs.

Real Address Mode Exceptions

Interrupt 5 if the bounds test fails; Interrupt 13 if any part of the operand would lie outside of the effective address space from 0 to 0FFFFH; Interrupt 6 if the second operand is a register

Virtual 8086 Mode Exceptions

Same exceptions as in Real Address Mode; #PF(fault-code) for a page fault; #AC for unaligned memory reference if the current privilege level is 3

BSF—Bit Scan Forward

Opcode	Instruction	Clocks	Description
0F BC	BSF *r16,r/m16*	6-42/7-43	Bit scan forward on *r/m* word
0F BC	BSF *r32,r/m32*	6-42/7-43	Bit scan forward on *r/m* dword

Notes

n is the number of leading zero bits.

Operation

```
IF r/m = 0
THEN
   ZF ← 1;
   register ← UNDEFINED;
ELSE
   temp ← 0;
   ZF ← 0;
   WHILE BIT[r/m, temp = 0]
   DO
      temp ← temp + 1;
      register ← temp;
   OD;
FI;
```

Description

The BSF instruction scans the bits in the second word or doubleword operand starting with bit 0. The ZF flag is set if all the bits are 0; otherwise, the ZF flag is cleared and the destination register is loaded with the bit index of the first set bit.

Flags Affected

The ZF flag is set if all bits are 0; otherwise, the ZF flag is cleared

Protected Mode Exceptions

#GP(0) for an illegal memory operand effective address in the CS, DS, ES, FS, or GS segments; #SS(0) for an illegal address in the SS segment; #PF(fault-code) for a page fault; #AC for unaligned memory reference if the current privilege level is 3

Real Address Mode Exceptions

Interrupt 13 if any part of the operand would lie outside of the effective address space from 0 to 0FFFFH

Virtual 8086 Mode Exceptions

Same exceptions as in Real Address Mode; #PF(fault-code) for a page fault; #AC for unaligned memory reference if the current privilege level is 3

BSR—Bit Scan Reverse

Opcode	Instruction	Clocks	Description
0F BD	BSR *r16,r/m16*	6-103/7-104	Bit scan reverse on *r/m* word
0F BD	BSR *r32,r/m32*	6-103/7-104	Bit scan reverse on *r/m* dword

Operation

```
IF r/m = 0
THEN
   ZF ← 1;
   register ← UNDEFINED;
ELSE
   temp ← OperandSize − 1;
   ZF ← 0;
   WHILE BIT[r/m, temp] = 0
   DO
      temp ← temp − 1;
      register ← temp;
   OD;
FI;
```

Description

The BSR instruction scans the bits in the second word or doubleword operand from the most significant bit to the least significant bit. The ZF flag is set if all the bits are 0; otherwise, the ZF flag is cleared and the destination register is loaded with the bit index of the first set bit found when scanning in the reverse direction.

Flags Affected

The ZF flag is set if all bits are 0; otherwise, the ZF flag is cleared

Protected Mode Exceptions

#GP(0) if the result is in a nonwritable segment; #GP(0) for an illegal memory operand effective address in the CS, DS, ES, FS, or GS segments; #SS(0) for an illegal address in the SS segment; #PF(fault-code) for a page fault; #AC for unaligned memory reference if the current privilege level is 3

Real Address Mode Exceptions

Interrupt 13 if any part of the operand would lie outside of the effective address space from 0 to 0FFFFH

Virtual 8086 Mode Exceptions

Same exceptions as in Real Address Mode; #PF(fault-code) for a page fault; #AC for unaligned memory reference if the current privilege level is 3

BSWAP — Byte Swap

Opcode	Instruction	Clocks	Description
0F C8/r	BSWAP *r32*	1	Swap bytes to convert little/big endian data in a 32-bit register to big/little endian form.

Operation

TEMP ← r32
r32(7..0) ← TEMP(31..24)
r32(15..8) ← TEMP(23..16)
r32(23..16) ← TEMP(15..8)
r32(31..24) ← TEMP(7..0)

Description

The BSWAP instruction reverses the byte order of a 32-bit register, converting a value in little/big endian form to big/little endian form. When BSWAP is used with 16-bit operand size, the result left in the destination register is undefined.

Flags Affected

None

Protected Mode Exceptions

None

Real Address Mode Exceptions

None

Virtual 8086 Mode Exceptions

None

Notes

BSWAP is not supported on 386 processors. See Section 3.11 to use BSWAP compatible with 386 processors.

BT—Bit Test

Opcode	Instruction	Clocks	Description
0F A3	BT *r/m16,r16*	3/8	Save bit in carry flag
0F A3	BT *r/m32,r32*	3/8	Save bit in carry flag
0F BA /	BT *r/m16,imm8*	3/3	Save bit in carry flag
0F BA /4 *ib*	BT *r/m32,imm8*	3/3	Save bit in carry flag

Operation

CF ← BIT[LeftSRC, RightSRC];

Description

The BT instruction saves the value of the bit indicated by the base (first operand) and the bit offset (second operand) into the CF flag.

Flags Affected

The CF flag contains the value of the selected bit

Protected Mode Exceptions

#GP(0) for an illegal memory operand effective address in the CS, DS, ES, FS, or GS segments; #SS(0) for an illegal address in the SS segment; #PF(fault-code) for a page fault; #AC for unaligned memory reference if the current privilege level is 3

Real Address Mode Exceptions

Interrupt 13 if any part of the operand would lie outside of the effective address space from 0 to 0FFFFH

Virtual 8086 Mode Exceptions

Same exceptions as in Real Address Mode; #PF(fault-code) for a page fault; #AC for unaligned memory reference if the current privilege level is 3

Notes

The index of the selected bit can be given by the immediate constant in the instruction or by a value in a general register. Only an 8-bit immediate value is used in the instruction. This operand is taken modulo 32, so the range of immediate bit offsets is 0..31. This allows any bit within a register to be selected. For memory bit strings, this immediate field gives only the bit offset within a word or doubleword. Immediate bit offsets larger than 31 are supported by using the immediate bit offset field in combination with the

displacement field of the memory operand. The low-order 3 to 5 bits of the immediate bit offset are stored in the immediate bit offset field, and the high-order 27 to 29 bits are shifted and combined with the byte displacement in the addressing mode.

When accessing a bit in memory, the processor may access four bytes starting from the memory address given by:

Effective Address + (4 * (BitOffset DIV 32))

for a 32-bit operand size, or two bytes starting from the memory address given by:

Effective Address + (2 * (BitOffset DIV 16))

for a 16-bit operand size. It may do so even when only a single byte needs to be accessed in order to reach the given bit. You must therefore avoid referencing areas of memory close to address space holes. In particular, avoid references to memory-mapped I/O registers. Instead, use the MOV instructions to load from or store to these addresses, and use the register form of these instructions to manipulate the data.

BTC — Bit Test and Complement

Opcode	Instruction	Clocks	Description
0F BB	BTC *r/m16,r16*	6/13	Save bit in carry flag and complement
0F BB	BTC *r/m32,r32*	6/13	Save bit in carry flag and complement
0F BA /7 *ib*	BTC *r/m16,imm8*	6/8	Save bit in carry flag and complement
0F BA /7 *ib*	BTC *r/m32,imm8*	6/8	Save bit in carry flag and complement

Operation

CF ← BIT[LeftSRC, RightSRC];
BIT[LeftSRC, RightSRC] ← NOT BIT[LeftSRC, RightSRC];

Description

The BTC instruction saves the value of the bit indicated by the base (first operand) and the bit offset (second operand) into the CF flag and then complements the bit.

Flags Affected

The CF flag contains the complement of the selected bit

Protected Mode Exceptions

#GP(0) if the result is in a nonwritable segment; #GP(0) for an illegal memory operand effective address in the CS, DS, ES, FS, or GS segments; #SS(0) for an illegal address in the SS segment; #PF(fault-code) for a page fault; #AC for unaligned memory reference if the current privilege level is 3

Real Address Mode Exceptions

Interrupt 13 if any part of the operand would lie outside of the effective address space from 0 to 0FFFFH

Virtual 8086 Mode Exceptions

Same exceptions as in Real Address Mode; #PF(fault-code) for a page fault; #AC for unaligned memory reference if the current privilege level is 3

Notes

The index of the selected bit can be given by the immediate constant in the instruction or by a value in a general register. Only an 8-bit immediate value is used in the instruction. This operand is taken modulo 32, so the range of immediate bit offsets is 0..31. This allows any bit within a register to be selected. For memory bit strings, this immediate field gives only the bit offset within a word or doubleword. Immediate bit offsets larger than 31 are supported by using the immediate bit offset field in combination with the

displacement field of the memory operand. The low-order 3 to 5 bits of the immediate bit offset are stored in the immediate bit offset field, and the high-order 27 to 29 bits are shifted and combined with the byte displacement in the addressing mode.

When accessing a bit in memory, the processor may access four bytes starting from the memory address given by:

Effective Address + (4 * (BitOffset DIV 32))

for a 32-bit operand size, or two bytes starting from the memory address given by:

Effective Address + (2 * (BitOffset DIV 16))

for a 16-bit operand size. It may do so even when only a single byte needs to be accessed in order to reach the given bit. You must therefore avoid referencing areas of memory close to address space holes. In particular, avoid references to memory-mapped I/O registers. Instead, use the MOV instructions to load from or store to these addresses, and use the register form of these instructions to manipulate the data.

BTR — Bit Test and Reset

Opcode	Instruction	Clocks	Description
0F B3	BTR *r/m16,r16*	6/13	Save bit in carry flag and reset
0F B3	BTR *r/m32,r32*	6/13	Save bit in carry flag and reset
0F BA /6 *ib*	BTR *r/m16,imm8*	6/8	Save bit in carry flag and reset
0F BA /6 *ib*	BTR *r/m32,imm8*	6/8	Save bit in carry flag and reset

Operation

```
CF ← BIT[LeftSRC, RightSRC];
BIT[LeftSRC, RightSRC] ← 0;
```

Description

The BTR instruction saves the value of the bit indicated by the base (first operand) and the bit offset (second operand) into the CF flag and then stores 0 in the bit.

Flags Affected

The CF flag contains the value of the selected bit

Protected Mode Exceptions

#GP(0) if the result is in a nonwritable segment; #GP(0) for an illegal memory operand effective address in the CS, DS, ES, FS, or GS segments; #SS(0) for an illegal address in the SS segment; #PF(fault-code) for a page fault; #AC for unaligned memory reference if the current privilege level is 3

Real Address Mode Exceptions

Interrupt 13 if any part of the operand would lie outside of the effective address space from 0 to 0FFFFH

Virtual 8086 Mode Exceptions

Same exceptions as in Real Address Mode; #PF(fault-code) for a page fault; #AC for unaligned memory reference if the current privilege level is 3

Notes

The index of the selected bit can be given by the immediate constant in the instruction or by a value in a general register. Only an 8-bit immediate value is used in the instruction. This operand is taken modulo 32, so the range of immediate bit offsets is 0..31. This allows any bit within a register to be selected. For memory bit strings, this immediate field gives only the bit offset within a word or doubleword. Immediate bit offsets larger than 31 (or 15) are supported by using the immediate bit offset field in combination with the displacement field of the memory operand. The low-order 3 to 5 bits of the immediate bit offset are stored in the immediate bit offset field, and the high-order 27 to 29 bits are shifted and combined with the byte displacement in the addressing mode.

When accessing a bit in memory, the processor may access four bytes starting from the memory address given by:

Effective Address + 4 * (BitOffset DIV 32)

for a 32-bit operand size, or two bytes starting from the memory address given by:

Effective Address + 2 * (BitOffset DIV 16)

for a 16-bit operand size. It may do so even when only a single byte needs to be accessed in order to reach the given bit. You must therefore avoid referencing areas of memory close to address space holes. In particular, avoid references to memory-mapped I/O registers. Instead, use the MOV instructions to load from or store to these addresses, and use the register form of these instructions to manipulate the data.

BTS — Bit Test and Set

Opcode	Instruction	Clocks	Description
0F AB	BTS *r/m16,r16*	6/13	Save bit in carry flag and set
0F AB	BTS *r/m32,r32*	6/13	Save bit in carry flag and set
0F BA /5 *ib*	BTS *r/m16,imm8*	6/8	Save bit in carry flag and set
0F BA /5 *ib*	BTS *r/m32,imm8*	6/8	Save bit in carry flag and set

Operation

```
CF ← BIT[LeftSRC, RightSRC];
BIT[LeftSRC, RightSRC] ← 1;
```

Description

The BTS instruction saves the value of the bit indicated by the base (first operand) and the bit offset (second operand) into the CF flag and then stores 1 in the bit.

Flags Affected

The CF flag contains the value of the selected bit

Protected Mode Exceptions

#GP(0) if the result is in a nonwritable segment; #GP(0) for an illegal memory operand effective address in the CS, DS, ES, FS, or GS segments; #SS(0) for an illegal address in the SS segment; #PF(fault-code) for a page fault; #AC for unaligned memory reference if the current privilege level is 3

Real Address Mode Exceptions

Interrupt 13 if any part of the operand would lie outside of the effective address space from 0 to 0FFFFH

Virtual 8086 Mode Exceptions

Same exceptions as in Real Address Mode; #PF(fault-code) for a page fault; #AC for unaligned memory reference if the current privilege level is 3

Notes

The index of the selected bit can be given by the immediate constant in the instruction or by a value in a general register. Only an 8-bit immediate value is used in the instruction. This operand is taken modulo 32, so the range of immediate bit offsets is 0..31. This allows any bit within a register to be selected. For memory bit strings, this immediate field gives only the bit offset within a word or doubleword. Immediate bit offsets larger than 31 are supported by using the immediate bit offset field in combination with the

displacement field of the memory operand. The low-order 3 to 5 bits of the immediate bit offset are stored in the immediate bit offset field, and the high order 27 to 29 bits are shifted and combined with the byte displacement in the addressing mode.

When accessing a bit in memory, the processor may access four bytes starting from the memory address given by:

Effective Address + (4 * (BitOffset DIV 32))

for a 32-bit operand size, or two bytes starting from the memory address given by:

Effective Address + (2 * (BitOffset DIV 16))

for a 16-bit operand size. It may do this even when only a single byte needs to be accessed in order to get at the given bit. You must therefore be careful to avoid referencing areas of memory close to address space holes. In particular, avoid references to memory-mapped I/O registers. Instead, use the MOV instructions to load from or store to these addresses, and use the register form of these instructions to manipulate the data.

CALL—Call Procedure

Opcode	Instruction	Clocks	Description
E8 *cw*	CALL *rel16*	3	Call near, displacement relative to next instruction
FF /2	CALL *r/m16*	5/5	Call near, register indirect/memory indirect
9A *cd*	CALL *ptr16:16*	18,*pm*=20	Call intersegment, to full pointer given
9A *cd*	CALL *ptr16:16*	*pm*=35	Call gate, same privilege
9A *cd*	CALL *ptr16:16*	*pm*=69	Call gate, more privilege, no parameters
9A *cd*	CALL *ptr16:16*	*pm*=77+4*x*	Call gate, more privilege, *x* parameters
9A *cd*	CALL *ptr16:16*	*pm*=37+ts	Call to task
FF /3	CALL *m16:16*	17,*pm*=20	Call intersegment, address at *r/m* dword
FF /3	CALL *m16:16*	*pm*=35	Call gate, same privilege
FF /3	CALL *m16:16*	*pm*=69	Call gate, more privilege, no parameters
FF /3	CALL *m16:16*	*pm*=77+4*x*	Call gate, more privilege, *x* parameters
FF /3	CALL *m16:16*	*pm*=37+ts	Call to task
E8 *cd*	CALL *rel32*	3	Call near, displacement relative to next instruction
FF /2	CALL *r/m32*	5/5	Call near, indirect
9A *cp*	CALL *ptr16:32*	18,*pm*=20	Call intersegment, to full pointer given
9A *cp*	CALL *ptr16:32*	*pm*=35	Call gate, same privilege
9A *cp*	CALL *ptr16:32*	*pm*=69	Call gate, more privilege, no parameters
9A *cp*	CALL *ptr32:32*	*pm*=77+4*x*	Call gate, more privilege, *x* parameters
9A *cp*	CALL *ptr16:32*	*pm*=37+ts	Call to task
FF /3	CALL *m16:32*	17,*pm*=20	Call intersegment, address at *r/m* dword
FF /3	CALL *m16:32*	*pm*=35	Call gate, same privilege
FF /3	CALL *m16:32*	*pm*=69	Call gate, more privilege, no parameters
FF /3	CALL *m16:32*	*pm*=77+4*x*	Call gate, more privilege, *x* parameters
FF /3	CALL *m16:32*	*pm*=37+ts	Call to task

NOTE: Values of **ts** are given by the following table:

Old Task	New Task		
	to i486™ CPU TSS	**to 80286 TSS**	**to VM TSS**
VM/i486 CPU/80286 TSS	199	180	177

Operation

```
IF rel16 or rel32 type of call
THEN (* near relative call *)
   IF OperandSize = 16
   THEN
      Push(IP);
      EIP ← (EIP + rel16) AND 0000FFFFH;
   ELSE (* OperandSize = 32 *)
      Push(EIP);
      EIP ← EIP + rel32;
   FI;
FI;

IF r/m16 or r/m32 type of call
THEN (* near absolute call *)
   IF OperandSize = 16
   THEN
      Push(IP);
```

```
    EIP ← [r/m16] AND 0000FFFFH;
  ELSE (* OperandSize = 32 *)
    Push(EIP);
    EIP ← [r/m32];
  FI;
FI;

IF (PE = 0 OR (PE = 1 AND VM = 1))
(* real mode or virtual 8086 mode *)
  AND instruction = far CALL
  (* i.e., operand type is m16:16, m16:32, ptr16:16, ptr16:32 *)
THEN
  IF OperandSize = 16
  THEN
    Push(CS);
    Push(IP); (* address of next instruction; 16 bits *)
  ELSE
    Push(CS); (* padded with 16 high-order bits *)
    Push(EIP); (* address of next instruction; 32 bits *)
  FI;
  IF operand type is m16:16 or m16:32
  THEN (* indirect far call *)
    IF OperandSize = 16
    THEN
      CS:IP ← [m16:16];
      EIP ← EIP AND 0000FFFFH; (* clear upper 16 bits *)
    ELSE (* OperandSize = 32 *)
      CS:EIP ← [m16:32];
    FI;
  FI;
  IF operand type is ptr16:16 or ptr16:32
  THEN (* direct far call *)
    IF OperandSize = 16
    THEN
      CS:IP ← ptr16:16;
      EIP ← EIP AND 0000FFFFH; (* clear upper 16 bits *)
    ELSE (* OperandSize = 32 *)
      CS:EIP ← ptr16:32;
    FI;
  FI;
FI;

IF (PE = 1 AND VM = 0) (* Protected mode, not V86 mode *)
  AND instruction = far CALL
THEN
  If indirect, then check access of EA doubleword;
    #GP(0) if limit violation;
  New CS selector must not be null else #GP(0);
  Check that new CS selector index is within its
```

```
      descriptor table limits; else #GP(new CS selector);
    Examine AR byte of selected descriptor for various legal values;
      depending on value:
      go to CONFORMING-CODE-SEGMENT;
      go to NONCONFORMING-CODE-SEGMENT;
      go to CALL-GATE;
      go to TASK-GATE;
      go to TASK-STATE-SEGMENT;
    ELSE #GP(code segment selector);
FI;

CONFORMING-CODE-SEGMENT:
    DPL must be ≤ CPL ELSE #GP(code segment selector);
    Segment must be present ELSE #NP(code segment selector);
    Stack must be big enough for return address ELSE #SS(0);
    Instruction pointer must be in code segment limit ELSE #GP(0);
    Load code segment descriptor into CS register;
    Load CS with new code segment selector;
    Load EIP with zero-extend(new offset);
    IF OperandSize=16 THEN EIP ← EIP AND 0000FFFFH; FI;

NONCONFORMING-CODE-SEGMENT:
    RPL must be ≤ CPL ELSE #GP(code segment selector)
    DPL must be = CPL ELSE #GP(code segment selector)
    Segment must be present ELSE #NP(code segment selector)
    Stack must be big enough for return address ELSE #SS(0)
    Instruction pointer must be in code segment limit ELSE #GP(0)
    Load code segment descriptor into CS register
    Load CS with new code segment selector
    Set RPL of CS to CPL
    Load EIP with zero-extend(new offset);
    IF OperandSize=16 THEN EIP ← EIP AND 0000FFFFH; FI;

CALL-GATE:
    Call gate DPL must be ≥ CPL ELSE #GP(call gate selector)
    Call gate DPL must be ≥ RPL ELSE #GP(call gate selector)
    Call gate must be present ELSE #NP(call gate selector)
    Examine code segment selector in call gate descriptor:
      Selector must not be null ELSE #GP(0)
      Selector must be within its descriptor table
        limits ELSE #GP(code segment selector)
      AR byte of selected descriptor must indicate code
        segment ELSE #GP(code segment selector)
      DPL of selected descriptor must be ≤ CPL ELSE
        #GP(code segment selector)
      IF non-conforming code segment AND DPL < CPL
      THEN go to MORE-PRIVILEGE
      ELSE go to SAME-PRIVILEGE
      FI;
```

```
MORE-PRIVILEGE:
  Get new SS selector for new privilege level from TSS
    Check selector and descriptor for new SS:
      Selector must not be null ELSE #TS(0)
      Selector index must be within its descriptor
        table limits ELSE #TS(SS selector)
      Selector's RPL must equal DPL of code segment
        ELSE #TS(SS selector)
      Stack segment DPL must equal DPL of code
        segment ELSE #TS(SS selector)
      Descriptor must indicate writable data segment
        ELSE #TS(SS selector)
      Segment present ELSE #SS(SS selector)
    IF OperandSize=32
    THEN
      New stack must have room for parameters plus 16 bytes
        ELSE #SS(SS selector)
      EIP must be in code segment limit ELSE #GP(0)
      Load new SS:eSP value from TSS
      Load new CS:EIP value from gate
    ELSE
      New stack must have room for parameters plus 8 bytes

        ELSE #SS(SS selector)
      IP must be in code segment limit ELSE #GP(0)
      Load new SS:eSP value from TSS
      Load new CS:IP value from gate
    FI;
    Load CS descriptor
    Load SS descriptor
    Push long pointer of old stack onto new stack
    Get word count from call gate, mask to 5 bits
    Copy parameters from old stack onto new stack
    Push return address onto new stack
    Set CPL to stack segment DPL
    Set RPL of CS to CPL

SAME-PRIVILEGE:
  IF OperandSize=32
  THEN
    Stack must have room for 6-byte return address (padded to 8 bytes)
      ELSE #SS(0)
    EIP must be within code segment limit ELSE #GP(0)
    Load CS:EIP from gate
  ELSE
    Stack must have room for 4-byte return address ELSE #SS(0)
    IP must be within code segment limit ELSE #GP(0)
    Load CS:IP from gate
  FI;
```

```
    Push return address onto stack
    Load code segment descriptor into CS register
    Set RPL of CS to CPL

TASK-GATE:
    Task gate DPL must be ≥ CPL ELSE #TS(gate selector)
    Task gate DPL must be ≥ RPL ELSE #TS(gate selector)
    Task Gate must be present ELSE #NP(gate selector)
    Examine selector to TSS, given in Task Gate descriptor:
        Must specify global in the local/global bit ELSE #TS(TSS selector)
        Index must be within GDT limits ELSE #TS(TSS selector)
        TSS descriptor AR byte must specify nonbusy TSS
            ELSE #TS(TSS selector)
        Task State Segment must be present ELSE #NP(TSS selector)
    SWITCH-TASKS (with nesting) to TSS
    IP must be in code segment limit ELSE #TS(0)

TASK-STATE-SEGMENT:
    TSS DPL must be ≥ CPL else #TS(TSS selector)
    TSS DPL must be ≥ RPL ELSE #TS(TSS selector)
    TSS descriptor AR byte must specify available TSS
        ELSE #TS(TSS selector)
    Task State Segment must be present ELSE #NP(TSS selector)
    SWITCH-TASKS (with nesting) to TSS
    IP must be in code segment limit ELSE #TS(0)
```

Description

The CALL instruction causes the procedure named in the operand to be executed. When the procedure is complete (a return instruction is executed within the procedure), execution continues at the instruction that follows the CALL instruction.

The action of the different forms of the instruction are described below.

Near calls are those with destinations of type *r/m16*, *r/m32*, *rel16*, *rel32*; changing or saving the segment register value is not necessary. The CALL *rel16* and CALL *rel32* forms add a signed offset to the address of the instruction following the CALL instruction to determine the destination. The *rel16* form is used when the instruction's operand-size attribute is 16 bits; *rel32* is used when the operand-size attribute is 32 bits. The result is stored in the 32-bit EIP register. With *rel16*, the upper 16 bits of the EIP register are cleared, resulting in an offset whose value does not exceed 16 bits. CALL *r/m16* and CALL *r/m32* specify a register or memory location from which the absolute segment offset is fetched. The offset fetched from *r/m* is 32 bits for an operand-size attribute of 32 (*r/m32*), or 16 bits for an operand-size of 16 (*r/m16*). The offset of the instruction following the CALL instruction is pushed onto the stack. It will be popped by a near RET instruction within the procedure. The CS register is not changed by this form of CALL.

The far calls, CALL *ptr16:16* and CALL *ptr16:32*, use a four-byte or six-byte operand as a long pointer to the procedure called. The CALL *m16:16* and *m16:32* forms fetch the long pointer from the memory location specified (indirection). In Real Address Mode or Virtual 8086 Mode, the long pointer provides 16 bits for the CS register and 16 or 32 bits for the EIP register (depending on the operand-size attribute). These forms of the instruction push both the CS and IP or EIP registers as a return address.

In Protected Mode, both long pointer forms consult the AR byte in the descriptor indexed by the selector part of the long pointer. Depending on the value of the AR byte, the call will perform one of the following types of control transfers:

- A far call to the same protection level
- An inter-protection level far call
- A task switch

For more information on Protected Mode control transfers, refer to Chapter 6 and Chapter 7.

Flags Affected

All flags are affected if a task switch occurs; no flags are affected if a task switch does not occur

Protected Mode Exceptions

For far calls: #GP, #NP, #SS, and #TS, as indicated in the "Operation" section

For near direct calls: #GP(0) if procedure location is beyond the code segment limits; #SS(0) if pushing the return address exceeds the bounds of the stack segment; #PF (fault-code) for a page fault; #AC for unaligned memory reference if the current privilege level is 3

For a near indirect call: #GP(0) for an illegal memory operand effective address in the CS, DS, ES, FS, or GS segments; #SS(0) for an illegal address in the SS segment; #GP(0) if the indirect offset obtained is beyond the code segment limits; #PF(fault-code) for a page fault; #AC for unaligned memory reference if the current privilege level is 3

Real Address Mode Exceptions

Interrupt 13 if any part of the operand would lie outside of the effective address space from 0 to 0FFFFH

Virtual 8086 Mode Exceptions

Same exceptions as in Real Address Mode; #PF(fault-code) for a page fault; #AC for unaligned memory reference if the current privilege level is 3

Notes

Any far call from a 32-bit code segment to a 16-bit code segment should be made from the first 64K bytes of the 32-bit code segment, because the operand-size attribute of the instruction is set to 16, allowing only a 16-bit return address offset to be saved.

CBW/CWDE—Convert Byte to Word/Convert Word to Doubleword

Opcode	Instruction	Clocks	Description
98	CBW	3	AX ← sign-extend of AL
98	CWDE	3	EAX ← sign-extend of AX

Operation

```
IF OperandSize = 16 (* instruction = CBW *)
THEN AX ← SignExtend(AL);
ELSE (* OperandSize = 32, instruction = CWDE *)
  EAX ← SignExtend(AX);
FI;
```

Description

The CBW instruction converts the signed byte in the AL register to a signed word in the AX register by extending the most significant bit of the AL register (the sign bit) into all of the bits of the AH register. The CWDE instruction converts the signed word in the AX register to a doubleword in the EAX register by extending the most significant bit of the AX register into the two most significant bytes of the EAX register. Note that the CWDE instruction is different from the CWD instruction. The CWD instruction uses the DX:AX register pair rather than the EAX register as a destination.

Flags Affected

None

Protected Mode Exceptions

None

Real Address Mode Exceptions

None

Virtual 8086 Mode Exceptions

None

CLC – Clear Carry Flag

Opcode	Instruction	Clocks	Description
F8	CLC	2	Clear carry flag

Operation

CF ← 0;

Description

The CLC instruction clears the CF flag. It does not affect other flags or registers.

Flags Affected

The CF flag is cleared

Protected Mode Exceptions

None

Real Address Mode Exceptions

None

Virtual 8086 Mode Exceptions

None

CLD – Clear Direction Flag

Opcode	Instruction	Clocks	Description
FC	CLD	2	Clear direction flag; SI and DI will increment during string instructions

Operation

DF ← 0;

Description

The CLD instruction clears the direction flag. No other flags or registers are affected. After a CLD instruction is executed, string operations will increment the index registers (SI and/or DI) that they use.

Flags Affected

The DF flag is cleared

Protected Mode Exceptions

None

Real Address Mode Exceptions

None

Virtual 8086 Mode Exceptions

None

CLI — Clear Interrupt Flag

Opcode	Instruction	Clocks	Description
FA	CLI	5	Clear interrupt flag; interrupts disabled

Operation

IF ← 0;

Description

The CLI instruction clears the IF flag if the current privilege level is at least as privileged as IOPL. No other flags are affected. External interrupts are not recognized at the end of the CLI instruction or from that point on until the IF flag is set.

Flags Affected

The IF flag is cleared

Protected Mode Exceptions

#GP(0) if the current privilege level is greater (has less privilege) than the I/O privilege level in the flags register. The I/O privilege level specifies the least privileged level at which I/O can be performed.

Real Address Mode Exceptions

None

Virtual 8086 Mode Exceptions

#GP(0) as for Protected Mode

CLTS — Clear Task-Switched Flag in CR0

Opcode	Instruction	Clocks	Description
OF 06	CLTS	7	Clear task-switched flag

Operation

TS Flag in CR0 ← 0;

Description

The CLTS instruction clears the task-switched (TS) flag in the CR0 register. This flag is set by the processor every time a task switch occurs. The TS flag is used to manage processor extensions as follows:

- Every execution of an ESC instruction is trapped if the TS flag is set.
- Execution of a WAIT instruction is trapped if the MP flag and the TS flag are both set.

Thus, if a task switch was made after an ESC instruction was begun, the floating-point unit's context may need to be saved before a new ESC instruction can be issued. The fault handler saves the context and clears the TS flag.

The CLTS instruction appears in operating system software, not in application programs. It is a privileged instruction that can only be executed at privilege level 0.

Flags Affected

The TS flag is cleared (the TS flag is in the CR0 register, not the flags register)

Protected Mode Exceptions

#GP(0) if the CLTS instruction is executed with a current privilege level other than 0

Real Address Mode Exceptions

None (valid in Real Address Mode to allow initialization for Protected Mode)

Virtual 8086 Mode Exceptions

None

CMC—Complement Carry Flag

Opcode	Instruction	Clocks	Description
F5	CMC	2	Complement carry flag

Operation

CF ← NOT CF;

Description

The CMC instruction reverses the setting of the CF flag. No other flags are affected.

Flags Affected

The CF flag contains the complement of its original value

Protected Mode Exceptions

None

Real Address Mode Exceptions

None

Virtual 8086 Mode Exceptions

None

CMP – Compare Two Operands

Opcode	Instruction	Clocks	Description
3C *ib*	CMP AL,*imm8*	1	Compare immediate byte to AL
3D *iw*	CMP AX,*imm16*	1	Compare immediate word to AX
3D *id*	CMP EAX,*imm32*	1	Compare immediate dword to EAX
80 /7 *ib*	CMP *r/m8,imm8*	1/2	Compare immediate byte to *r/m* byte
81 /7 *iw*	CMP *r/m16,imm16*	1/2	Compare immediate word to *r/m* word
81 /7 *id*	CMP *r/m32,imm32*	1/2	Compare immediate dword to *r/m* dword
83 /7 *ib*	CMP *r/m16,imm8*	1/2	Compare sign extended immediate byte to *r/m* word
83 /7 *ib*	CMP *r/m32,imm8*	1/2	Compare sign extended immediate byte to *r/m* dword
38 /r	CMP *r/m8,r8*	1/2	Compare byte register to *r/m* byte
39 /r	CMP *r/m16,r16*	1/2	Compare word register to *r/m* word
39 /r	CMP *r/m32,r32*	1/2	Compare dword register to *r/m* dword
3A /r	CMP *r8,r/m8*	1/2	Compare *r/m* byte to byte register
3B /r	CMP *r16,r/m16*	1/2	Compare *r/m* word to word register
3B /r	CMP *r32,r/m32*	1/2	Compare *r/m* dword to dword register

Operation

LeftSRC - SignExtend(RightSRC);
(* CMP does not store a result; its purpose is to set the flags *)

Description

The CMP instruction subtracts the second operand from the first but, unlike the SUB instruction, does not store the result; only the flags are changed. The CMP instruction is typically used in conjunction with conditional jumps and the SETcc instruction. (Refer to Appendix D for the list of signed and unsigned flag tests provided.) If an operand greater than one byte is compared to an immediate byte, the byte value is first sign-extended.

Flags Affected

The OF, SF, ZF, AF, PF, and CF flags are set according to the result

Protected Mode Exceptions

#GP(0) for an illegal memory operand effective address in the CS, DS, ES, FS, or GS segments; #SS(0) for an illegal address in the SS segment; #PF(fault-code) for a page fault; #AC for unaligned memory reference if the current privilege level is 3

Real Address Mode Exceptions

Interrupt 13 if any part of the operand would lie outside of the effective address space from 0 to 0FFFFH

Virtual 8086 Mode Exceptions

Same exceptions as in Real Address Mode; #PF(fault-code) for a page fault; #AC for unaligned memory reference if the current privilege level is 3

CMPS/CMPSB/CMPSW/CMPSD—Compare String Operands

Opcode	Instruction	Clocks	Description
A6	CMPS *m8,m8*	8	Compare bytes ES:[(E)DI] (second operand) with [(E)SI] (first operand)
A7	CMPS *m16,m16*	8	Compare words ES:[(E)DI] (second operand) with [(E)SI] (first operand)
A7	CMPS *m32,m32*	8	Compare dwords ES:[(E)DI] (second operand) with [(E)SI] (first operand)
A6	CMPSB	8	Compare bytes ES:[(E)DI] with DS:[SI]
A7	CMPSW	8	Compare words ES:[(E)DI] with DS:[SI]
A7	CMPSD	8	Compare dwords ES:[(E)DI] with DS:[SI]

Operation

```
IF (instruction = CMPSD) OR
  (instruction has operands of type DWORD)
THEN OperandSize ← 32;
ELSE OperandSize ← 16;
FI;
IF AddressSize = 16
THEN
  use SI for source-index and DI for destination-index
ELSE (* AddressSize = 32 *)
  use ESI for source-index and EDI for destination-index;
FI;
IF byte type of instruction
THEN
  [source-index] - [destination-index]; (* byte comparison *)
  IF DF = 0 THEN IncDec ← 1 ELSE IncDec ← −1; FI;
ELSE
  IF OperandSize = 16
  THEN
    [source-index] - [destination-index]; (* word comparison *)
    IF DF = 0 THEN IncDec ← 2 ELSE IncDec ← −2; FI;
  ELSE (* OperandSize = 32 *)
    [source-index] - [destination-index]; (* dword comparison *)
    IF DF = 0 THEN IncDec ← 4 ELSE IncDec ← −4; FI;
  FI;
FI;
source-index = source-index + IncDec;
destination-index = destination-index + IncDec;
```

Description

The CMPS instruction compares the byte, word, or doubleword pointed to by the source-index register with the byte, word, or doubleword pointed to by the destination-index register.

If the address-size attribute of this instruction is 16 bits, the SI and DI registers will be used for source- and destination-index registers; otherwise the ESI and EDI registers will be used. Load the correct index values into the SI and DI (or ESI and EDI) registers before executing the CMPS instruction.

The comparison is done by subtracting the operand indexed by the destination-index register from the operand indexed by the source-index register.

Note that the direction of subtraction for the CMPS instruction is [SI] − [DI] or [ESI] − [EDI]. The left operand (SI or ESI) is the source and the right operand (DI or EDI) is the destination. This is the reverse of the usual Intel convention in which the left operand is the destination and the right operand is the source.

The result of the subtraction is not stored; only the flags reflect the change. The types of the operands determine whether bytes, words, or doublewords are compared. For the first operand (SI or ESI), the DS register is used, unless a segment override byte is present. The second operand (DI or EDI) must be addressable from the ES register; no segment override is possible.

After the comparison is made, both the source-index register and destination-index register are automatically advanced. If the DF flag is 0 (a CLD instruction was executed), the registers increment; if the DF flag is 1 (an STD instruction was executed), the registers decrement. The registers increment or decrement by 1 if a byte is compared, by 2 if a word is compared, or by 4 if a doubleword is compared.

The CMPSB, CMPSW and CMPSD instructions are synonyms for the byte, word, and doubleword CMPS instructions, respectively.

The CMPS instruction can be preceded by the REPE or REPNE prefix for block comparison of CX or ECX bytes, words, or doublewords. Refer to the description of the REP instruction for more information on this operation.

Flags Affected

The OF, SF, ZF, AF, PF, and CF flags are set according to the result

Protected Mode Exceptions

#GP(0) for an illegal memory operand effective address in the CS, DS, ES, FS, or GS segments; #SS(0) for an illegal address in the SS segment; #PF(fault-code) for a page fault; #AC for unaligned memory reference if the current privilege level is 3

Real Address Mode Exceptions

Interrupt 13 if any part of the operand would lie outside of the effective address space from 0 to 0FFFFH

Virtual 8086 Mode Exceptions

Same exceptions as in Real Address Mode; #PF(fault-code) for a page fault; #AC for unaligned memory reference if the current privilege level is 3

CMPXCHG — Compare and Exchange

Opcode	Instruction	Clocks	Description
0F A6/*r*	CMPXCHG *r/m8,r8*	6/7 if comparison is successful; 6/10 if comparison fails	Compare AL with r/m byte. If equal, set ZF and load byte reg into r/m byte. Else, clear ZF and load r/m byte into AL.
0F A7/*r*	CMPXCHG *r/m16,r16*	6/7 if comparison is successful; 6/10 if comparison fails	Compare AX with r/m word. If equal, set ZF and load word reg into r/m word. Else, clear ZF and load r/m word into AX.
0F A7/*r*	CMPXCHG *r/m32,r32*	6/7 if comparison is successful; 6/10 if comparison fails	Compare EAX with r/m dword. If equal, set ZF and load dword reg into r/m dword. Else, clear ZF and load r/m dword into EAX.

Operation

```
IF accumulator = DEST
        ZF ← 1
        DEST ← SRC
ELSE
        ZF ← 0
        accumulator ← DEST
```

Description

The CMPXCHG instruction compares the accumulator (AL, AX, or EAX register) with DEST. If they are equal, SRC is loaded into DEST. Otherwise, DEST is loaded into the accumulator.

Flags Affected

The CF, PF, AF, SF, and OF flags are affected as if a CMP instruction had been executed with DEST and the accumulator as operands. The ZF flag is set if the destination operand and the accumulator are equal; otherwise it is cleared.

Protected Mode Exceptions

#GP(0) if the result is in a nonwritable segment; #GP(0) for an illegal memory operand effective address in the CS, DS, ES, FS, or GS segments; #SS(0) for an illegal address in the SS segment; #PF (fault code) for a page fault; #AC for unaligned memory reference if the current privilege level is 3.

Real Address Mode Exceptions

Interrupt 13 if any part of the operand would lie outside the effective address space from 0 to 0FFFFH.

Virtual 8086 Mode Exceptions

Same exceptions as in real-address mode; #PF (fault code) for a page fault; #AC for unaligned memory reference if the current privilege level is 3.

Notes

This instruction can be used with a LOCK prefix. In order to simplify interface to the processor's bus, the destination operand receives a write cycle without regard to the result of the comparison. DEST is written back if the comparison fails, and SRC is written into the destination otherwise. (The processor never produces a locked read without also producing a locked write.) This instruction is not supported on 386 processors. See Section 3.11 to use CMPXCHG compatible with 386 processors.

CWD/CDQ—Convert Word to Doubleword/Convert Doubleword to Quadword

Opcode	Instruction	Clocks	Description
99	CWD	3	DX:AX ← sign-extend of AX
99	CDQ	3	EDX:EAX ← sign-extend of EAX

Operation

```
IF OperandSize = 16 (* CWD instruction *)
THEN
   IF AX < 0 THEN DX ← 0FFFFH; ELSE DX ← 0; FI;
ELSE (* OperandSize = 32, CDQ instruction *)
   IF EAX < 0 THEN EDX ← 0FFFFFFFFH; ELSE EDX ← 0; FI;
FI;
```

Description

The CWD instruction converts the signed word in the AX register to a signed doubleword in the DX:AX register pair by extending the most significant bit of the AX register into all the bits of the DX register. The CDQ instruction converts the signed doubleword in the EAX register to a signed 64-bit integer in the register pair EDX:EAX by extending the most significant bit of the EAX register (the sign bit) into all the bits of the EDX register. Note that the CWD instruction is different from the CWDE instruction. The CWDE instruction uses the EAX register as a destination, instead of the DX:AX register pair.

Flags Affected

None

Protected Mode Exceptions

None

Real Address Mode Exceptions

None

Virtual 8086 Mode Exceptions

None

DAA – Decimal Adjust AL after Addition

Opcode	Instruction	Clocks	Description
27	DAA	2	Decimal adjust AL after addition

Operation

```
IF ((AL AND 0FH) > 9) OR (AF = 1)
THEN
   AL ← AL + 6;
   AF ← 1;
ELSE
   AF ← 0;
FI;
IF (AL > 9FH) OR (CF = 1)
THEN
   AL ← AL + 60H;
   CF ← 1;
ELSE CF ← 0;
FI;
```

Description

Execute the DAA instruction only after executing an ADD instruction that leaves a two-BCD-digit byte result in the AL register. The ADD operands should consist of two packed BCD digits. The DAA instruction adjusts the AL register to contain the correct two-digit packed decimal result.

Flags Affected

The AF and CF flags are set if there is a decimal carry, cleared if there is no decimal carry; the SF, ZF, PF, and CF flags are set according to the result.

Protected Mode Exceptions

None

Real Address Mode Exceptions

None

Virtual 8086 Mode Exceptions

None

DAS—Decimal Adjust AL after Subtraction

Opcode	Instruction	Clocks	Description
2F	DAS	2	Decimal adjust AL after subtraction

Operation

```
IF (AL AND 0FH) > 9 OR AF = 1
THEN
   AL ← AL − 6;
   AF ← 1;
ELSE
   AF ← 0;
FI;
IF (AL > 9FH) OR (CF = 1)
THEN
   AL ← AL − 60H;
   CF ← 1;
ELSE CF ← 0;
FI;
```

Description

Execute the DAS instruction only after a subtraction instruction that leaves a two-BCD-digit byte result in the AL register. The operands should consist of two packed BCD digits. The DAS instruction adjusts the AL register to contain the correct packed two-digit decimal result.

Flags Affected

The AF and CF flags are set if there is a decimal carry, cleared if there is no decimal carry; the SF, ZF, and PF flags are set according to the result.

Protected Mode Exceptions

None

Real Address Mode Exceptions

None

Virtual 8086 Mode Exceptions

None

DEC — Decrement by 1

Opcode	Instruction	Clocks	Description
FE /1	DEC r/m8	1/3	Decrement r/m byte by 1
FF /1	DEC r/m16	1/3	Decrement r/m word by 1
	DEC r/m32	1/3	Decrement r/m dword by 1
48+rw	DEC r16	1	Decrement word register by 1
48+rw	DEC r32	1	Decrement dword register by 1

Operation

DEST ← DEST − 1;

Description

The DEC instruction subtracts 1 from the operand. The DEC instruction does not change the CF flag. To affect the CF flag, use the SUB instruction with an immediate operand of 1.

Flags Affected

The OF, SF, ZF, AF, and PF flags are set according to the result.

Protected Mode Exceptions

#GP(0) if the result is a nonwritable segment; #GP(0) for an illegal memory operand effective address in the CS, DS, ES, FS, or GS segments; #SS(0) for an illegal address in the SS segment; #PF(fault-code) for a page fault; #AC for unaligned memory reference if the current privilege level is 3

Real Address Mode Exceptions

Interrupt 13 if any part of the operand would lie outside of the effective address space from 0 to 0FFFFH

Virtual 8086 Mode Exceptions

Same exceptions as in Real Address Mode; #PF(fault-code) for a page fault; #AC for unaligned memory reference if the current privilege level is 3

DIV — Unsigned Divide

Opcode	Instruction	Clocks	Description
F6 /6	DIV AL,*r/m8*	16/16	Unsigned divide AX by *r/m* byte (AL = Quo, AH = Rem)
F7 /6	DIV AX,*r/m16*	24/24	Unsigned divide DX:AX by *r/m* word (AX = Quo, DX = Rem)
F7 /6	DIV EAX,*r/m32*	40/40	Unsigned divide EDX:EAX by *r/m* dword (EAX = Quo, EDX = Rem)

Operation

```
temp ← dividend / divisor;
IF temp does not fit in quotient
THEN Interrupt 0;
ELSE
  quotient ← temp;
  remainder ← dividend MOD (r/m);
FI;
```

Note: Divisions are unsigned. The divisor is given by the *r/m* operand. The dividend, quotient, and remainder use implicit registers. Refer to the table under "Description."

Description

The DIV instruction performs an unsigned division. The dividend is implicit; only the divisor is given as an operand. The remainder is always less than the divisor. The type of the divisor determines which registers to use as follows:

Size	Divisor	Quotient	Remainder	Dividend
byte	AX	*r/m8*	AL	AH
word	DX:AX	*r/m16*	AX	DX
dword	EDX:EAX	*r/m32*	EAX	EDX

Flags Affected

The OF, SF, ZF, AF, PF, CF flags are undefined.

Protected Mode Exceptions

Interrupt 0 if the quotient is too large to fit in the designated register (AL, AX, or EAX), or if the divisor is 0; #GP(0) for an illegal memory operand effective address in the CS, DS, ES, FS, or GS segments; #SS(0) for an illegal address in the SS segment; #PF(fault-code) for a page fault; #AC for unaligned memory reference if the current privilege level is 3

Real Address Mode Exceptions

Interrupt 0 if the quotient is too big to fit in the designated register (AL, AX, or EAX), or if the divisor is 0; Interrupt 13 if any part of the operand would lie outside of the effective address space from 0 to 0FFFFH

Virtual 8086 Mode Exceptions

Same exceptions as in Real Address Mode; #PF(fault-code) for a page fault; #AC for unaligned memory reference if the current privilege level is 3

ENTER—Make Stack Frame for Procedure Parameters

Opcode	Instruction	Clocks	Description
C8 *iw* 00	ENTER *imm16*,0	14	Make procedure stack frame
C8 *iw* 01	ENTER *imm16*,1	17	Make stack frame for procedure parameters
C8 *iw* ib	ENTER *imm16,imm8*	17+3*n*	Make stack frame for procedure parameters

Operation

```
level ← level MOD 32
IF OperandSize = 16 THEN Push(BP) ELSE Push (EBP) FI;
   (* Save stack pointer *)
frame-ptr ← eSP
IF level > 0
THEN (* level is rightmost parameter *)
   FOR i ← 1 TO level − 1
   DO
      IF OperandSize = 16
      THEN
         BP ← BP − 2;
         Push[BP]
      ELSE (* OperandSize = 32 *)
         EBP ← EBP − 4;
         Push[EBP];
      FI;
   OD;
   Push(frame-ptr)
FI;
IF OperandSize = 16 THEN BP ← frame-ptr ELSE EBP ← frame-ptr; FI;
IF StackAddrSize = 16
THEN SP ← SP − First operand;
ELSE ESP ← ESP − ZeroExtend(First operand);
FI;
```

Description

The ENTER instruction creates the stack frame required by most block-structured high-level languages. The first operand specifies the number of bytes of dynamic storage allocated on the stack for the routine being entered. The second operand gives the lexical nesting level (0 to 31) of the routine within the high-level language source code. It determines the number of stack frame pointers copied into the new stack frame from the preceding frame. The BP register (or EBP, if the operand-size attribute is 32 bits) is the current stack frame pointer.

If the operand-size attribute is 16 bits, the processor uses the BP register as the frame pointer and the SP register as the stack pointer. If the operand-size attribute is 32 bits, the processor uses the EBP register for the frame pointer and the ESP register for the stack pointer.

If the second operand is 0, the ENTER instruction pushes the frame pointer (BP or EBP register) onto the stack; the ENTER instruction then subtracts the first operand from the stack pointer and sets the frame pointer to the current stack-pointer value.

For example, a procedure with 12 bytes of local variables would have an ENTER 12,0 instruction at its entry point and a LEAVE instruction before every RET instruction. The 12 local bytes would be addressed as negative offsets from the frame pointer.

Flags Affected

None

Protected Mode Exceptions

#SS(0) if the SP or ESP value would exceed the stack limit at any point during instruction execution; #PF(fault-code) for a page fault

Real Address Mode Exceptions

None

Virtual 8086 Mode Exceptions

None

F2XM1 — Computer $2^x - 1$

Opcode	Instruction	Clocks	Concurrent Execution	Description
D9 F0	F2XM1	242 (140-279)	2	Replace ST with ($2^{ST} - 1$)

Operation

ST ← ($2^{ST} - 1$);

Description

F2XM1 replaces the contents of ST with ($2^{ST} - 1$). ST must lie in the range $-1 < ST < 1$.

FPU Flags Affected

C1 as described in Table 15-1; C0, C2, C3 undefined

Numeric Exceptions

P, U, D, I, IS

Protected Mode Exceptions

#NM if either EM or TS in CR0 is set

Real Address Mode Exceptions

Interrupt 7 if either EM or TS in CR0 is set

Virtual 8086 Mode Exceptions

#NM if either EM or TS in CR0 is set

Notes

If the operand is outside the acceptable range, the result of F2XM1 is undefined.

The F2XM1 instruction is designed to produce a very accurate result even when the operand is close to zero. Larger errors are incurred for operands with magnitudes very close to 1.

Values other than 2 can be exponentiated using the formula

$$x^y = 2^{(y \times \log_2 x)}$$

The instructions FLDL2T and FLDL2E load the constants $\log_2 10$ and $\log_2 e$, respectively. FYL2X can be used to calculate $y \times \log_2 x$ for arbitrary positive x.

FABS — Absolute Value

Opcode	Instruction	Clocks	Description
D9 E1	FABS	3	Replace ST with its absolute value.

Operation

sign bit of ST ← 0

Description

The absolute value instruction clears the sign bit of ST. This operation leaves a positive value unchanged, or replaces a negative value with a positive value of equal magnitude.

FPU Flags Affected

C1 as described in Table 15-1; C0, C2, C3 undefined

Numeric Exceptions

IS

Protected Mode Exceptions

#NM if either EM or TS in CR0 is set

Real Address Mode Exceptions

Interrupt 7 if either EM or TS in CR0 is set

Virtual 8086 Mode Exceptions

#NM if either EM or TS in CR0 is set

Notes

The invalid-operation exception is raised only on stack underflow, even if the operand is signalling NaN or is in an unsupported format.

FADD/FADDP/FIADD — Add

Opcode	Instruction	Clocks	Concurrent Execution	Description
D8 /0	FADD *m32 real*	10 (8-20)	7 (5-17)	Add *m32real* to ST.
DC /0	FADD *m64real*	10 (8-20)	7 (5-17)	Add *m64real* to ST.
D8 C0+i	FADD ST, ST(i)	10 (8-20)	7 (5-17)	Add ST(i) to ST.
DC C0+i	FADD ST(i), ST	10 (8-20)	7 (5-17)	Add ST to ST(i).
DE C0+i	FADDP ST(i), ST	10 (8-20)	7 (5-17)	Add ST to ST(i) and pop ST.
DE C1	FADD	10 (8-20)	7 (5-17)	Add ST to ST(1) and pop ST.
DA /0	FIADD *m32int*	22.5 (19-32)	7 (5-17)	Add *m32int* to ST.
DE /0	FIADD *m16int*	24 (20-35)	7 (5-17)	Add *m16int* to ST]

Operation

```
DEST ← DEST +SRC;
If instruction = FADDP THEN pop ST FI;
```

Description

The addition instructions add the source and destination operands and return the sum to the destination. The operand at the stack top can be doubled by coding:

FADD ST, ST(0)

FPU Flags Affected

C1 as described in Table 15-1; C0, C2, C3 undefined

Numeric Exceptions

P, U, O, D, I, IS

Protected Mode Exceptions

#GP(0) for an illegal memory operand effective address in the CS, DS, ES, FS, or GS segments; #SS(0) for an illegal address in the SS segment; #PF (fault-code) for a page fault; #NM if either EM or TS in CR0 is set; #AC for unaligned memory reference if the current privilege level is 3

Real Address Mode Exceptions

Interrupt 13 if any part of the operand would lie outside the effective address space from 0 to 0FFFFH; Interrupt 7 if either EM or TS in CR0 is set

Virtual 8086 Mode Exceptions

Same exceptions as in Real Address Mode; #PF (fault code) for a page fault; #AC for unaligned memory reference if the current privilege level is 3

Notes

If the source operand is in memory, it is automatically converted to the extended-real format.

FBLD—Load Binary Coded Decimal

Opcode	Instruction	Clocks	Concurrent Execution	Description
D8 /4	FBLD *m80 dec*	75 (70-103)	7.7 (2-8)	Push *m80dec* onto the FPU stack.

Operation

Decrement FPU stack-top pointer;
ST(0) ← SRC;

Description

FBLD converts the BCD source operand into extended-real format, and pushes it onto the FPU stack. See Figure 15-10 for BCD data layout.

FPU Flags Affected

C1 as described in Table 15-1; C0, C2, C3 undefined

Numeric Exceptions

IS

Protected Mode Exceptions

#GP(0) for an illegal memory operand effective address in the CS, DS, ES, FS, or GS segments; #SS(0) for an illegal address in the SS segment; #PF (fault-code) for a page fault; #NM if either EM or TS in CR0 is set; #AC for unaligned memory reference if the current privilege level is 3

Real Address Mode Exceptions

Interrupt 13 if any part of the operand would like outside the effective address space from 0 to 0FFFFH; Interrupt 7 if either EM or TS in CR0 is set

Virtual 8086 Mode Exceptions

Same exceptions as in Real Address Mode; #PF (fault code) for a page fault; #AC for unaligned memory reference if the current privilege level is 3

Notes

The source is loaded without rounding error. The sign of the source is preserved, including the case where the value is negative zero.

The packed decimal digits are assumed to be in the range 0-9. The instruction does not check for invalid digits (A-FH), and the result of attempting to load an invalid encoding is undefined.

ST(7) must be empty to avoid causing an invalid-operation exception.

FBSTP — Store Binary Coded Decimal and Pop

Opcode	Instruction	Clocks	Description
DF /6	FBSTP m80dec	175 (172-176)	Store ST in m80dec and pop ST.

Operation

DEST ← ST(0);
pop ST FI;

Description

FBSTP converts the value in ST into a packed decimal integer, stores the result at the destination in memory, and pops ST. Non-integral values are first rounded according to the RC field of the control word. See Figure 15-10 for BCD data layout.

FPU Flags Affected

C1 as described in Table 15-1; C0, C2, C3 undefined

Numeric Exceptions

P, I, IS

Protected Mode Exceptions

#GP(0) if the destination is in a nonwritable segment; #GP(0) for an illegal memory operand effective address in the CS, DS, ES, FS, or GS segments; #SS(0) for an illegal address in the SS segment; #PF (fault-code) for a page fault; #NM if either EM or TS in CR0 is set; #AC for unaligned memory reference if the current privilege level is 3

Real Address Mode Exceptions

Interrupt 13 if any part of the operand would like outside the effective address space from 0 to 0FFFFH; Interrupt 7 if either EM or TS in CR0 is set

Virtual 8086 Mode Exceptions

Same exceptions as in Real Address Mode; #PF (fault code) for a page fault; #AC for unaligned memory reference if the current privilege level is 3

FCHS—Change Sign

Opcode	Instruction	Clocks	Description
D9 E0	FCHS	6	Replace ST with a value of opposite sign.

Operation

sign bit of ST ← NOT (sign bit of ST)

Description

The change sign instruction inverts the sign bit of ST. This operation replaces a positive value with a negative value of equal magnitude, or vice-versa.

FPU Flags Affected

C1 as described in Table 15-1; C0, C2, C3 undefined

Numeric Exceptions

IS

Protected Mode Exceptions

#NM if either EM or TS in CR0 is set

Real Address Mode Exceptions

Interrupt 7 if either EM or TS in CR0 is set

Virtual 8086 Mode Exceptions

#NM if either EM or TS in CR0 is set

Notes

The invalid-operation exception is raised only on stack underflow, even if the operand is a signalling NaN or is in an unsupported format.

FCLEX/FNCLEX — Clear Exceptions

Opcode	Instruction	Clocks	Description
9B DB E2	FCLEX	7 + at least 3 for FWAIT	Clear floating-point exception flags after checking for floating-point error conditions.
DB E2	FNCLEX	7	Clear floating-point exception flags without checking for floating-point error conditions.

Operation

SW[0..7] ← 0;
SW[15] ← 0;

Description

FCLEX clears the exception flags, the exception status flag, and the busy flag of the FPU status word.

FPU Flags Affected

C0, C1, C2, C3 undefined

Numeric Exceptions

None

Protected Mode Exceptions

#NM if either EM or TS in CR0 is set

Real Address Mode Exceptions

Interrupt 7 if either EM or TS in CR0 is set

Virtual 8086 Mode Exceptions

#NM if either EM or TS in CR0 is set

Notes

FCLEX checks for unmasked floating-point error conditions before clearing the exception flags; FNCLEX does not.

FCOM/FCOMP/FCOMPP—Compare Real

Opcode	Instruction	Clocks	Description
D8 /2	FCOM *m32real*	4	Compare ST with *m32real*.
DC /2	FCOM *m64real*	4	Compare ST with *m64real*.
D8 D0+i	FCOM ST(i)	4	Compare ST with ST(i).
D8 D1	FCOM	4	Compare ST with ST(1).
D8 /3	FCOMP *m32real*	4	Compare ST with *m32real* and pop ST.
DC /3	FCOMP *m64real*	4	Compare ST with m64real and pop ST.
D8 D8+i	FCOMP ST(i)	4	Compare ST with ST(i) and pop ST.
D8 D9	FCOMP	4	Compare ST with ST(1) and pop ST.
DE D9	FCOMPP	5	Compare ST with ST(1) and pop ST twice.

Operation

```
CASE (relation of operands) OF
    Not comparable:   C3, C2, C0 ← 111;
    ST > SRC:         C3, C2, C0 ← 000;
    ST < SRC:         C3, C2, C0 ← 001;
    ST = SRC:         C3, C2, C0 ← 100;
IF instruction = FCOMP THEN pop ST; FI;
IF instruction = FCOMPP THEN pop ST; pop ST; FI;
```

FPU Flags	EFlags
C_0	CF
C_1	(none)
C_2	PF
C_3	ZF

Description

The compare real instructions compare the stack top to the source, which can be a register or a single- or double-real memory operand. If no operand is encoded, ST is compared to ST(1). Following the instruction, the condition codes reflect the relation between ST and the source operand.

FPU Flags Affected

C1 as described in Table 15-1; C0, C2, C3 as specified above

Numeric Exceptions

D, I, IS

Protected Mode Exceptions

#GP(0) for an illegal memory operand effective address in the CS, DS, ES, FS, or GS segments; #SS(0) for an illegal address in the SS segment; #PF (fault-code) for a page fault; #NM if either EM or TS in CR0 is set; #AC for unaligned memory reference if the current privilege level is 3

Real Address Mode Exceptions

Interrupt 13 if any part of the operand would lie outside the effective address space from 0 to 0FFFFH; Interrupt 7 if either EM or TS in CR0 is set

Virtual 8086 Mode Exceptions

Same exceptions as in Real Address Mode; #PF (fault code) for a page fault; #AC for unaligned memory reference if the current privilege level is 3

Notes

If either operand is a NaN or is in an undefined format, or if a stack fault occurs, the invalid-operation exception is raised, and the condition bits are set to "unordered."

The sign of zero is ignored, so that $-0.0 = - +0.0$.

FCOS — Cosine

Opcode	Instruction	Clocks	Concurrent Execution	Description
D9 FF	FCOS	241 (193-279)	2	Replace ST with its cosine

Operation

```
IF operand is in range
THEN
    C2 ← 0;
    ST ← cos(ST);
ELSE
    C2 ← 1;
FI;
```

Description

The cosine instruction replaces the contents of ST with cos(ST). ST, expressed in radians, must lie in the range $|\theta| < 2^{63}$.

FPU Flags Affected

C1, C2 as described in Table 15-1; C0, C3 undefined

Numeric Exceptions

P, U, D, I, IS

Protected Mode Exceptions

#NM if either EM or TS in CR0 is set

Real Address Mode Exceptions

Interrupt 7 if either EM or TS in CR0 is set

Virtual 8086 Mode Exceptions

#NM if either EM or TS in CR0 is set

Notes

If the operand is outside the acceptable range, the C2 flag is set, and ST remains unchanged. It is the programmer's responsibility to reduce the operand to an absolute value smaller than 2^{63} by subtracting an appropriate integer multiple of 2π. See Section 17.5 for a discussion of the proper value touse for π in performing such reductions.

The i486 CPU checks for interrupts while performing this instruction. It will be aborted to service an interrupt.

FDECSTP—Decrement Stack-Top Pointer

Opcode	Instruction	Clocks	Description
D9 F6	FDECSTP	3	Decrement top-of-stack pointer for FPU register stack.

Operation

```
IF TOP=0
THEN TOP ← 7;
ELSE TOP ← TOP−1;
FI;
```

Description

FDECSTP subtracts one (without carry) from the three-bit TOP field of the FPU status word.

FPU Flags Affected

C1 as described in Table 15-1; C0, C2, C3 undefined

Numeric Exceptions

None

Protected Mode Exceptions

#NM if either EM or TS in CR0 is set

Real Address Mode Exceptions

Interrupt 7 if either EM or TS in CR0 is set

Virtual 8086 Mode Exceptions

#NM if either EM or TS in CR0 is set

Notes

The effect of FDECSTP is to rotate the stack. If does not alter register tags or contents, nor does it transfer data.

FDIV/FDIVP/FIDIV—Divide

Opcode	Instruction	Clocks	Concurrent Execution	Description
D8 /6	FDIV *m32real*	73	70	Divide ST by *m32real.*
DC /6	FDIV *m64real*	73	70	Divide ST by *m64real.*
D8 F0+i	FDIV ST, ST(i)	73	70	Divide ST by ST(i)
DC F8+i	FDIV ST(i), ST	73	70	Replace ST(i) with ST ÷ ST(i)
DE F8+i	FDIVP ST(i), ST	73	70	Replace ST(i) with ST ÷ ST(i); pop ST.
DE F9	FDIV	73	70	Replace ST(1) with ST ÷ ST(1); pop ST.
DA /6	FIDIV *m32int*	73	70	Divide ST by *m32int.*
DE /6	FIDIV *m16int*	73	70	Divide ST by *m16int.*

Operation

DEST ← ST ÷ Other Operand;
IF instruction = FDIVP THEN pop ST FI;

Description

The division instructions divide the stack top by the other operand and return the quotient to the destination.

FPU Flags Affected

C1 as described in Table 15-1; C0, C2, C3 undefined

Numeric Exceptions

P, U, O, Z, D, I, IS

Protected Mode Exceptions

#GP(0) for an illegal memory operand effective address in the CS, DS, ES, FS, or GS segments; #SS(0) for an illegal address in the SS segment; #PF(fault-code) for a page fault; #NM if either EM or TS in CR0 is set; #AC for unaligned memory reference if the current privilege level is 3

Real Address Mode Exceptions

Interrupt 13 if any part of the operand would lie outside the effective address space from 0 to 0FFFFH; Interrupt 7 if either EM or TS in CR0 is set

Virtual 8086 Mode Exceptions

Same exceptions as in Real Address Mode; #PF(fault code) for a page fault; #AC for unaligned memory reference if the current privilege level is 3

Notes

If the source operand is in memory, it is automatically converted to the extended-real format.

The performance of the division instructions depends on the PC (Precision Control) field of the FPU control word. If PC specifies a precision of 53 bits, the division instructions will execute in 62 clocks. If the specified precision is 24 bits, the division instructions will take only 35 clocks.

FDIVR/FDIVPR/FIDIVR — Reverse Divide

Opcode	Instruction	Clocks	Concurrent Execution	Description
D8 /7	FDIVR *m32real*	73	70	Replaces ST with *m32real* ÷ ST.
DC /7	FDIVR *m64real*	73	70	Replace ST with *m64real* ÷ ST.
D8 F8+i	FDIVR ST, ST(i)	73	70	Replace ST by ST(i) ÷ ST.
DC F0+i	FDIVR ST(i), ST	73	70	Divide ST(i) by ST.
DE F0+i	FDIVRP ST(i), ST	73	70	Divide ST(i) by ST and pop ST.
DE F1	FDIVR	73	70	Divide ST(1) by ST and pop ST.
DA /7	FIDIVR *m32int*	73	70	Replace ST with *m32int* ÷ ST.
DE /7	FIDIVR *m16int*	73	70	Replace ST with *m16int* ÷ ST.

Operation

DEST ← Other Operand ÷ ST;
IF instruction = FDIVRP THEN pop ST FI;

Description

The division instructions divide the other operand by the stack top and return the quotient to the destination.

FPU Flags Affected

C1 as described in Table 15-1; C0, C2, C3 undefined

Numeric Exceptions

P, U, O, Z, D, I, IS

Protected Mode Exceptions

#GP(0) for an illegal memory operand effective address in the CS, DS, ES, FS, or GS segments; #SS(0) for an illegal address in the SS segment; #PF(fault-code) for a page fault; #NM if either EM or TS in CR0 is set; #AC for unaligned memory reference if the current privilege level is 3

Real Address Mode Exceptions

Interrupt 13 if any part of the operand would lie outside the effective address space from 0 to 0FFFFH; Interrupt 7 if either EM or TS in CR0 is set

Virtual 8086 Mode Exceptions

Same exceptions as in Real Address Mode; #PF(fault code) for a page fault; #AC for unaligned memory reference if the current privilege level is 3

Notes

If the source operand is in memory, it is automatically converted to the extended-real format.

The performance of the reverse division instructions depends on the PC (Precision Control) field of the FPU control word. If PC specifies a precision of 53 bits, the reverse division instructions will execute in 62 clocks. If the specified precision is 24 bits, the reverse division instructions will take only 35 clocks.

FFREE — Free Floating-Point Register

Opcode	Instruction	Clocks	Description
DD C0+i	FFREE ST(i)	3	Tag ST(i) as *empty*.

Operation

TAG(i) ← 11B;

Description

FFREE tags the destination register as *empty*.

FPU Flags Affected

C0, C1, C2, C3 undefined

Numeric Exceptions

None

Protected Mode Exceptions

#NM if either EM or TS in CR0 is set

Real Address Mode Exceptions

Interrupt 7 if either EM or TS in CR0 is set

Virtual 8086 Mode Exceptions

#NM if either EM or TS in CR0 is set

Notes

FFREE does not affect the contents of the destination register. The floating-point stack-top pointer (TOP) is also unaffected.

FICOM/FICOMP – Compare Integer

Opcode	Instruction	Clocks	Concurrent Execution	Description
DE /2	FICOM *m16real*	18 (16-20)	1	Compare ST with *m16int*.
DA /2	FICOM *m32real*	16.5 (15-17)	1	Compare ST with *m32int*.
DE /3	FICOMP *m16int*	18 (16-20)	1	Compare ST with *m16int* and pop ST.
DA /3	FICOMP *m32int*	16.5 (15-17)	1	Compare ST with *m32int* and pop ST.

Operation

```
CASE (relation of operands) OF
    Not comparable:   C3, C2, C0 ← 111;
    ST > SRC:         C3, C2, C0 ← 000;
    ST < SRC:         C3, C2, C0 ← 001;
    ST = SRC:         C3, C2, C0 ← 100;
IF instruction = FICOMP THEN pop ST; FI;
```

FPU Flags	EFlags
C_0	CF
C_1	(none)
C_2	PF
C_3	ZF

Description

The compare integer instructions compare the stack top to the source. Following the instruction, the condition codes reflect the relation between ST and the source operand.

FPU Flags Affected

C1 as described in Table 15-1; C0, C2, C3 as specified above

Numeric Exceptions

D, I, IS

Protected Mode Exceptions

#GP(0) for an illegal memory operand effective address in the CS, DS, ES, FS, or GS segments; #SS(0) for an illegal address in the SS segment; #PF(fault-code) for a page fault; #NM if either EM or TS in CR0 is set; #AC for unaligned memory reference if the current privilege level is 3

Real Address Mode Exceptions

Interupt 13 if any part of the operand would lie outside the effective address space from 0 to 0FFFFH; Interrupt 7 if either EM or TS in CR0 is set

Virtual 8086 Mode Exceptions

Same exceptions as in Real Address Mode; #PF(fault code) for a page fault; #AC for unaligned memory reference if the current privilege level is 3

Notes

The memory operand is converted to extended-real format before the comparison is performed.

If either operand is a NaN or is in an undefined format, or if a stack fault occurs, the invalid-operation exception is raised, and the condition bits are set to "unordered."

FILD – Load Integer

Opcode	Instruction	Clocks	Concurrent Execution	Description
DF /0	FILD *m16int*	14.5 (13-16)	4	Push *m16int* onto the FPU stack.
DB /0	FILD *m32int*	11.5 (9-12)	4 (2-4)	Push *m32int* onto the FPU stack.
DF /5	FILD *m64int*	16.8 (10-18)	7.8 (2-8)	Push *m64int* onto the FPU stack.

Operation

Decrement FPU stack-top pointer;
ST(0) ← SRC;

Description

FILD converts the source signed integer operand into extended-real format, and pushes it onto the FPU stack.

FPU Flags Affected

C1 as described in Table 15-1; C0, C2, C3 undefined

Numeric Exceptions

IS

Protected Mode Exceptions

#GP(0) for an illegal memory operand effectivfe address in the CS, DS, ES, FS, or GS segments; #SS(0) for an illegal address in the SS segment; #PF(fault-code) fora page fault; #NM if either EM or TS in CR0 is set; #AC for unaligned memory reference if the current privilege level is 3

Real Address Mode Exceptions

Interrupt 13 if any part of the operand would lie outside the effective address space from 0 to 0FFFFH; Interrupt 7 if either EM or TS in CR0 is set

Virtual 8086 Mode Exceptions

Same exceptions as in Real Address Mode; #PF(fault code) for a page fault; #AC for unaligned memory reference if the current privilege level is 3

Notes

The source is loaded without rounding error.

ST(7) must be empty to avoid causing an invalid-operation exception.

FINCSTP — Increment Stack-Top Pointer

Opcode	Instruction	Clocks	Description
D9 F7	FINCSTP	3	Increment top-of-stack pointer for FPU register stack.

Operation

```
IF TOP = 7
THEN TOP ← 0;
ELSE TOP ← TOP + 1;
FI;
```

Description

FINCSTP adds one (without carry) to the three-bit TOP field of the FPU status word.

FPU Flags Affected

C1 as described in Table 15-1; C0, C2, C3 undefined

Numeric Exceptions

None

Protected Mode Exceptions

#NM if either EM or TS in CR0 is set

Real Address Mode Exceptions

Interrupt 7 if either EM or TS in CR0 is set

Virtual 8086 Mode Exceptions

#NM is either EM or TS in CR0 is set

Notes

The effect of FINCSTP is to rotate the stack. It does not alter register tags or contents, nor does it transfer data. It is not equivalent to popping the stack, because it does not set the tag of the old stack-top to *empty*.

FINIT/FNINIT—Initialize Floating-Point Unit

Opcode	Instruction	Clocks	Description
DB E3	FINIT	17+at least 3 for FWAIT	Initialize FPU after checking for unmasked floating-point error condition.
DB/E3	FNINIT	17	Initialize FPU without checking for unmasked floating-point error condition.

Operation

```
CW ← 037FH;                     (* Control word *)
SW ← 0;                         (* Status word *)
TW ← FFFFH;                     (* Tag word *)
FEA ← 0; FDS ← 0;               (* Data pointer *)
FIP ← 0; FOP ← 0; FCS ← 0;      (* Instruction pointer *)
```

Description

The initialization instructions set the FPU into a known state, unaffected by any previous activity.

The FPU control word is set to 037FH (round to nearest, all exceptions masked, 64-bit prevision). The status word is cleared (no exception flags set, stack register R0=stack-top). The stack registers are all tagged as *empty*. The error pointers (both instruction and data) are cleared.

FPU Flags Affected

C0, C1, C2, C3 cleared

Numeric Exceptions

None

Protected Mode Exceptions

#NM if either EM or TS in CR0 is set

Real Address Mode Exceptions

Interrupt 7 if either EM or TS in CR0 is set

Virtual 8086 Mode Exceptions

#NM if either EM or TS in CR0 is set

Notes

FINIT checks for unmasked floating-point error conditions before performing the initialization; FNINIT does not.

FINIT and FNINIT leave the FPU in the same state as that which results from a hardware RESET signal with Built-In Self-Test.

On the i486 processor, unlike the 387 math coprocessor, FINIT and FNINIT clear the error pointers.

FIST/FISTP — Store Integer

Opcode	Instruction	Clocks	Description
DF /2	FIST *m16int*	33.4 (29-34)	Store ST in *m16int.*
DB /2	FIST *m32int*	32.4 (28-34)	Store ST in *m32int.*
DF /3	FISTP *m16int*	33.4 (29-34)	Store ST in *m16int* and pop ST.
DB /3	FISTP *m32int*	33.4 (29-34)	Store ST in *m32int* and pop ST.
DF /7	FISTP *m64int*	33.4 (29-34)	Store ST in *m64int* and pop ST.

Operation

DEST ← ST(0);
IF instruction = FISTP THEN pop ST FI;

Description

FIST converts the value in ST into a signed integer according to the RC field of the control word and transfers the result to the destination. ST remains unchanged. FIST accepts word and short integer destinations; FISTP accepts these and long integers as well.

FPU Flags Affected

C1 as described in Table 15-1; C0, C2, C3 undefined

Numeric Exceptions

P, I, IS

Protected Mode Exceptions

#GP(0) if the destination is in a nonwritable segment; #GP(0) for an illegal memory operand effective address in the CS, DS, ES, FS, or GS segments; #SS(0) for an illegal address in the SS segment; #PF(fault-code) for a page fault; #NM if either EM or TS in CR0 is set; #AC for unaligned memory reference if the current privilege level is 3

Real Address Mode Exceptions

Interupt 13 if any part of the operand would lie outside the effective address space from 0 to 0FFFFH; Interrupt 7 if either EM or TS in CR0 is set

Virtual 8086 Mode Exceptions

Same exceptions as in Real Address Mode; #PF(fault code) for a page fault; #AC for unaligned memory reference if the current privilege level is 3

Notes

Negative zero is stored with the same encoding (00..00) as positive zero.

If the value is too large to represent as an integer, an I exception is raised. The masked response is to write the most negative integer to memory.

FLD — Local Real

Opcode	Instruction	Clocks	Description
D9 /0	FLD *m32real*	3	Push *m32real* onto the FPU stack.
DD /0	FLD *m64real*	3	Push *m64real* onto the FPU stack.
DB /5	FLD *m80real*	6	Push *m80real* onto the FPU stack.
D9 C0+i	FLD ST(i)	4	Push ST(i) onto the FPU stack.

Operation

Decrement FPU stack-top pointer;
ST(0) ← SRC;

Description

FLD pushes the source operand onto the FPU stack. If the source is a register, the register number used is that before the stack-top pointer is decremented. In particular, coding

FLD ST(0)

duplicates the stack top.

FPU Flags Affected

C1 as described in Table 15-1; C0, C2, C3 undefined

Numeric Exceptions

D, I, IS

Protected Mode Exceptions

#GP(0) for an illegal memory operand effective address in the CS, DS, ES, FS, or GS segments; #SS(0) for an illegal address in the SS segment; #PF(fault-code) for a page fault; #NM if either EM or TS in CR0 is set; #AC for unaligned memory reference if the current privilege level is 3

Real Address Mode Exceptions

Interrupt 13 if any part of the operand would lie outside the effective address space from 0 to 0FFFFH; Interrupt 7 if either EM or TS in CR0 is set

Virtual 8086 Mode Exceptions

Same exceptions as in Real Address Mode; #PF(fault code) for a page fault; #AC for unaligned memory reference if the current privilege level is 3

Notes

If the source operand is in single- or double-real format, it is automatically converted to the extended-real format. Loading an extended-real operand does not require conversion, so the I and D exceptions will not occur in this case.

ST(7) must be empty to avoid causing an invalid-operation exception.

FLD1/FLDL2T/FLDL2E/ FLDPI/FLDLG2/FLDLN2/FLDZ—Load Constant

Opcode	Instruction	Clocks	Concurrent Execution	Description
D9 E8	FLD1	4	–	Push +1.0 onto the FPU Stack.
D9 E9	FLDL2T	8	2	Push $\log_2 10$ onto the FPU Stack.
D9 EA	FLDL2E	8	2	Push $\log_2 e$ onto the FPU Stack.
D9 EB	FLDPI	8	2	Push π onto the FPU Stack.
D9 EC	FLDLG2	8	2	Push $\log_{10} 2$ onto the FPU Stack.
D9 ED	FLDLN2	8	2	Push $\log_e 2$ onto the FPU Stack.
D9 EE	FLDZ	4	–	Push +0.0 onto the FPU Stack.

Operation

Decrement FPU stack-top pointer;
ST(0) ← CONSTANT;

Description

Each of the constant instructions pushes a commonly-used (in extended-real format) onto the FPU stack.

FPU Flags Affected

C1 as described in Table 15-1; C0, C2, C3 undefined

Numeric Exceptions

IS

Protected Mode Exceptions

#NM if either EM or TS in CR0 is set

Real Address Mode Exceptions

Interrupt 7 if either EM or TS in CR0 is set

Virtual 8086 Mode Exceptions

#NM if either EM or TS in CR0 is set

Notes

ST(7) must be empty to avoid an invalid exception.

An internal 66-bit constant is used and rounded to external-real format (as specified by the RC bit of the control words). The precision exception is not raised.

FLDCW—Load Control Word

Opcode	Instruction	Clocks	Description
D9 /5	FNLDCW m2byte	4	Load FPU control word from *m2byte.*

Operation

CW ← SRC;

Description

FLDCW replaces the current value of the FPU control word with the value contained in the specified memory word.

FPU Flags Affected

C0, C1, C2, C3 undefined

Numeric Exceptions

None, except for unmasking an existing exception

Protected Mode Exceptions

#GP(0) for an illegal memory operand effective address in the CS, DS, ES, FS, or GS segments; #SS(0) for an illegal address in the SS segment; #PF(fault-code) for a page fault; #NM if either EM or TS in CR0 is set; #AC for unaligned memory reference if the current privilege level is 3

Real Address Mode Exceptions

Interrupt 13 if any part of the operand would lie outside the effective address space from 0 to 0FFFFH; Interrupt 7 if either EM or TS in CR0 is set

Virtual 8086 Mode Exceptions

Same exceptions as in Real Address Mode; #PF(fault code) for a page fault; #AC for unaligned memory reference if the current privilege level is 3

Notes

FLDCW is typically used to establish or change the FPU's mode of operation.

In an exception bit in the status word is set, loading a new control word that unmasks that exception will result in a floating-point error condition. When changing modes, the recommended procedure is to clear any pending exceptions before loading the new control word.

FLDENV—Load FPU Environment

Opcode	Instruction	Clocks	Description
D9 /4	FLDENV *m14/ 28byte*	44 real or virtual/34 protected	Load FPU environment from *m14byte* or *m28byte*.

Operation

FPU environment ← SRC;

Description

FLDENV reloads the FPU environment from the memory area defined by the source operand. This data should have been written by previous FSTENV or FNSTENV instruction.

The FPU environment consists of the FPU control word, status word, tag word, and error pointers (both data and instruction). The environment layout in memory depends on both the operand size and the current operating mode of the processor. The USE attribute of the current code segment determines the operand size: the 14-byte operand applies to a USE16 segment, and the 28-byte operand applies to a USE32 segment. Figures 15-5 ;through 15-8 show the environment layouts for both operand sizes in both real mode and protected mode. (In virtual-8086 mode, the real mode layout is used.) FLDENV should be executed in the same operating mode as the corresponding FSTENV or FNSTENV.

FPU Flags Affected

C0, C1, C2, C3 as loaded

Numeric Exceptions

None, except for loading an unmasked exception

Protected Mode Exceptions

#GP(0) for an illegal memory operand effective address in the CS, DS, ES, FS, or GS segments; #SS(0) for an illegal address in the SS segment; #PF(fault-code) for a page fault; #NM if either EM or TS in CR0 is set; #AC for unaligned memory reference if the current privilege level is 3

Real Address Mode Exceptions

Interrupt 13 if any part of the operand would lie outside the effective address space from 0 to 0FFFFH; Interrupt 7 if either EM or TS in CR0 is set

Virtual 8086 Mode Exceptions

Same exceptions as in Real Address Mode; #PF(fault code) for a page fault; #AC for unaligned memory reference if the current privilege level is 3

Notes

If the environment image contains an unmasked exception, loading it will result in a floating-point error condition.

FMUL/FMULP/FIMUL—Multiply

Opcode	Instruction	Clocks	Concurrent Execution	Description
D8 /1	FMUL *m32real*	11	8	Multiply ST by *m32real.*
DC /1	FMUL *m64real*	14	11	Multiply ST by *m64real.*
D8 C8+i	FMUL ST, ST(i)	16	13	Multiply ST by ST(i)
DC C8+i	FMUL ST(i), ST	16	13	Multiply ST(i) by ST.
DE C8+i	FMULP ST(i), ST	16	13	Multiply ST(i) by ST and pop ST.
DE C9	FMUL	16	13	Multiply ST(1) by ST and pop ST.
DA /1	FIMUL *m32int*	23.5 (22-24)	8	Multiply ST by *m32int.*
DE /1	FIMUL *m16int*	25 (23-27)	8	Multiply ST by *m16int.*

Operation

DEST ← DEST x SRC;
IF instruction = FMULP THEN pop ST FI;

Description

The multiplication instructions multiply the destination operand by the source operand and return the product to the destination.

FPU Flags Affected

C1 as described in Table 15-1; C0, C2, C3 undefined

Numeric Exceptions

P, U, O, D, I, I

Protected Mode Exceptions

#GP(0) for an illegal memory operand effective address in the CS, DS, ES, FS, or GS segments; #SS(0) for an illegal address in the SS segment; #PF(fault-code) for a page fault; #NM if either EM or TS in CR0 is set; #AC for unaligned memory reference if the current privilege level is 3

Real Address Mode Exceptions

Interrupt 13 if any part of the operand would lie outside the effective address space from 0 to 0FFFFH; Interrupt 7 if either EM or TS in CR0 is set

Virtual 8086 Mode Exceptions

Same exceptions as in Real Address Mode; #PF(fault code) for a page fault; #AC for unaligned memory reference if the current privilege level is 3

Notes

If the source operand is in memory, it is automatically converted to the extended-real format.

FNOP — No Operation

Opcode	Instruction	Clocks	Description
D9 D0	FNOP	3	No operation is performed.

Description

FNOP performs no operation. It affects nothing except instruction pointers.

FPU Flags Affected

C0, C1, C2, C3 undefined

Numeric Exceptions

None

Protected Mode Exceptions

#NM if either EM or TS in CR0 is set

Real Address Mode Exceptions

Interrupt 7 if either EM or TS in CR0 is set

Virtual 8086 Mode Exceptions

#NM if either EM or TS in CR0 is set

FPATAN — Partial Arctangent

Opcode	Instruction	Clocks	Concurrent Execution	Description
D9 F3	FPATAN	289 (218-303)	5 (2-17)	Replace ST(1) with arctan(ST(1) ÷ ST) and pop ST.

Operation

ST(1) ← arctan(ST(1) ÷ ST);
pop ST;

Description

The partial arctangent instruction computes the arctangent of ST(1) ÷ ST, and returns the computed value, expressed in radians, to ST(1). It then pops ST. The result has the same sign as the operand from ST(1), and a magnitude less than π.

FPU Flags Affected

C1 as described in Table 15-1; C0, C2, C3 undefined

Numeric Exceptions

P, U, D, I, IS

Protected Mode Exceptions

#NM if either EM or TS in CR0 is set

Real Address Mode Exceptions

Interrupt 7 if either EM or TS in CR0 is set

Virtual 8086 Mode Exceptions

#NM if either EM or TS in CR0 is set

Notes

There is no restriction on the range of arguments that FPATAN can accept.

The fact that FPATAN takes two arguments and computes the arctangent of their ratio simplifies the calculation of other trigonometric functions. For instance, arcsin(x) (which is the arctangent of $x \div \sqrt{(1-x^2)}$) can be computed using the following sequence of operations: Push x onto the FPU stack; compute $\sqrt{(1-x^2)}$ and push the resulting value onto the stack; execute FPATAN.

The i486 CPU checks for interrupts while performing this instruction. It will abort this instruction to serve an interrupt.

FPREM — Partial Remainder

Opcode	Instruction	Clocks	Concurrent Execution	Description
D9 F8	FPREM	84 (70-138)	2 (2-8)	Replace ST with the remainder obtained on dividing ST by ST(1).

Operation

```
EXPDIF ← exponent(ST) – exponent(ST(1));
IF EXPDIF < 64
THEN
    Q ← integer obtained by chopping ST ÷ ST(1) toward zero;
    ST ← ST – (ST(1) x Q);
    C2 ← 0;
    C0, C1, C3 ← three least-significant bits of Q; (* Q2, Q1, Q0 *)
ELSE
    C2 ← 1;
    N ← a number between 32 and 63;
    QQ ← integer obtained by chopping (ST ÷ ST(1)) ÷ 2^(EXPDIF-N)
        toward zero;
    ST ← ST – (ST(1) x QQ x 2^(EXPDIF-N);
FI;
```

Description

The partial remainder instruction computes the remainder obtained on dividing ST by ST(1), and leaves the result in ST. The sign of the remainder is the same as the sign of the original dividend in ST. The magnitude of the remainder is less than that of the modulus.

FPU Flags Affected

C0, C1, C2, C3 as described in Table 15-1

Numeric Exceptions

U, D, I, IS

Protected Mode Exceptions

#NM if either EM or TS in CR0 is set

Real Address Mode Exceptions

Interrupt 7 if either EM or TS in CR0 is set

Virtual 8086 Mode Exceptions

#NM if either EM or TS in CR0 is set

Notes

FPREM produces an exact result; the precision (inexact) exception does not occur and the rounding control has no effect.

The FPREM instruction is not the remainder operation specified in IEEE Std 754. To get that remainder, the FPREM1 instruction should be used. FPREM is supported for compatibility with the 8087 and 80287 math coprocessors.

FPREM works by iterative subtraction, and can reduce the exponent of ST by no more than 63 in one execution. If FPREM succeeds in producing a remainder that is less than the modulus, the function is complete and the C2 flag is cleared. Otherwise, C2 is set, and the result in ST is called the *partial* remainder. The exponent of the partial remainder is less than the exponent of the original dividend by at least 32. Software can re-execute the instruction (using the partial remainder in ST as the dividend) until C2 is cleared. A higher-priority interrupting routine that needs the FPU can force a context switch between the instructions in the remainder loop.

An important use of FPREM is to reduce the arguments of periodic functions. When reduction is complete, FPREM provides the three least-significant bits of the quotient in flags C3, C1, and C0. This is important in argument reduction for the tangent function (using a modulus of $\pi/4$), because it locates the original angle in the correct one of eight sectors of the unit circle.

FPREM1 — Partial Remainder

Opcode	Instruction	Clocks	Concurrent Execution	Description
D9 F5	FPREM1	94.5 (72-167)	5.5 (2-18)	Replace ST with the remainder obtained on dividing ST by ST(1).

Operation

```
EXPDIF ← exponent(ST) − exponent(ST(1));
IF EXPDIF < 64
THEN
    Q ← integer obtained by chopping ST ÷ ST(1) toward zero;
    ST ← ST − (ST(1) x Q);
    C2 ← 0;
    C0, C1, C3 ← three least-significant bits of Q; (* Q2, Q1, Q0 *)
ELSE
    C2 ← 1;
    N ← a number between 32 and 63;
    QQ ← integer nearest to (ST ÷ ST(1)) ÷ 2^(EXPDIF-N);
    ST ← ST − (ST(1) x QQ x 2^(EXPDIF-N);
FI;
```

Description

The partial remainder instruction computes the remainder obtained on dividing ST by ST(1), and leaves the result in ST. The magnitude of the remainder is less than half the magnitude of the modulus.

FPU Flags Affected

C0, C1, C2, C3 as described in Table 15-1

Numeric Exceptions

U, D, I, IS

Protected Mode Exceptions

#NM if either EM or TS in CR0 is set

Real Address Mode Exceptions

Interrupt 7 if either EM or TS in CR0 is set

Virtual 8086 Mode Exceptions

#NM if either EM or TS in CR0 is set

Notes

FPREM1 produces an exact result; the precision (inexact) exception does not occur and the rounding control has no effect.

The FPREM1 instruction is the remainder operation specified in IEEE Std 754. It differs from FPREM in the way it rounds the quotient of ST and ST(1).

FPREM1 works by iterative subtraction, and can reduce the exponent of ST by no more than 63 in one execution. If FPREM1 succeeds in producing a remainder that is less than one half the modulus, the function is complete and the C2 flag is cleared. Otherwise, C2 is set, and the result in ST is called the *partial* remainder. The exponent of the partial remainder is less than the exponent of the original dividend by at least 32. Software can re-execute the instruction (using the partial remainder in ST as the dividend) until C2 is cleared. A higher-priority interrupting routine that needs the FPU can force a context switch between the instructions in the remainder loop.

An important use of FPREM1 is to reduce the arguments of periodic functions. When reduction is complete, FPREM1 provides the three least-significant bits of the quotient in flags C3, C1, and C0. This is important in argument reduction for the tangent function (using a modulus of $\pi/4$), because it locates the original angle in the correct one of eight sectors of the unit circle.

FPTAN — Partial Tangent

Opcode	Instruction	Clocks	Concurrent Execution	Description
D9 F2	FPTAN	244 (200-273)	70	Replace ST with its tangent and push 1 onto the FPU stack.

Operation

```
IF operand is in range
THEN
    C2 ← 0;
    ST ← tan(ST);
    Decrement stack-top pointer;
    ST ← 1.0;
ELSE
    C2 ← 1;
FI;
```

Description

The partial tangent instruction replaces the contents of ST with tan(ST), and then pushes 1.0 onto the FPU stack. ST, expressed in radians, must lie in the range $| \theta | < 2^{63}$.

FPU Flags Affected

C1, C2 as described in Table 15-1; C0, C3 undefined

Numeric Exceptions

P, U, D, I, IS

Protected Mode Exceptions

#NM if either EM or TS in CR0 is set

Real Address Mode Exceptions

Interrupt 7 if either EM or TS in CR0 is set

Virtual 8086 Mode Exceptions

#NM if either EM or TS in CR0 is set

Notes

If the operand is outside the acceptable range, the C2 flag is set, and ST remains unchanged. It is the programmer's responsibility to reduce the operand to an absolute value smaller than 2^{63} by subtracting an appropriate integer multiple of 2π. See Section 17.5 for a discussion of the proper value to use for π in performing such reductions.

The fact that FPTAN pushes 1.0 onto the FPU stack after computing tan(ST) maintains compatibility with the 8087 and 80287 math coprocessors, and simplifies the calculation of other trigonometric functions. For instance, the cotangent (which is the reciprocal of the tangent) can be computed by executing FDIVR after FPTAN.

ST(7) must be empty to avoid an invalid-operation exception.

The i486 CPU periodically checks for interrupts while performing this instruction. It will be aborted to service an interrupt.

FRNDINT — Round to Integer

Opcode	Instruction	Clocks	Concurrent Execution	Description
D9 FC	FRNDINT	29.1 (21-30)	7.4 (2-8)	Round ST to an integer.

Operation

ST ← rounded ST;

Description

The round to integer instruction rounds the value in ST to an integer according to the RC field of the FPU control word.

FPU Flags Affected

C1 as described in Table 15-1; C0, C2, C3 undefined

Numeric Exceptions

P, D, I, IS

Protected Mode Exceptions

#NM if either EM or TS in CR0 is set

Real Address Mode Exceptions

Interrupt 7 if either EM or TS in CR0 is set

Virtual 8086 Mode Exceptions

#NM if either EM or TS in CR0 is set

FRSTOR—Restore FPU State

Opcode	Instruction	Clocks	Description
DB /4	FRSTOR *m94/108byte*	131 real or virtual/120 protected	Load FPU state from *m94byte* or *m108byte*.

Operation

FPU state ← SRC;

Description

FRSTOR reloads the FPU state (environment and register stack) from the memory area defined by the source operand. This data should have been written by a previous FSAVE or FNSAVE instruction.

The FPU environment consists of the FPU control word, status word, tag word, and error pointers (both data and instruction). The environment layout in memory depends on both the operand size and the current operating mode of the processor. The USE attribute of the current code segment determines the operand size: the 14-byte operand applies to a USE16 segment, and the 28-byte operand applies to a USE32 segment. Figures 15-5 through 15-8 show the environment layouts for both operand sizes in both real mode and protected mode. (In virtual-8086 mode, the real mode layout is used.) The stack registers, beginning with ST and ending with ST(7), are in the 80 bytes that immediately follow the environment image. FRSTOR should be executed in the same operating mode as the corresponding FSAVE or FNSAVE.

FPU Flags Affected

C0, C1, C2, C3 as loaded

Numeric Exceptions

None, except for loading an unmasked exception

Protected Mode Exceptions

#GP(0) for an illegal memory operand effective address in the CS, DS, ES, FS, or GS segments; #SS(0) for an illegal address in the SS segment; #PF(fault-code) for a page fault; #NM if either EM or TS in CR0 is set; #AC for unaligned memory reference if the current privilege level is 3

Real Address Mode Exceptions

Interrupt 13 if any part of the operand would lie outside the effective address space from 0 to 0FFFFH; Interrupt 7 if either EM or TS in CR0 is set

Virtual 8086 Mode Exceptions

Same exceptions as in Real Address Mode; #PF(fault code) for a page fault; #AC for unaligned memory reference if the current privilege level is 3

Notes

If the state image contains an unmasked exception, loading it will result in a floating-point error condition.

FSAVE/FNSAVE—Store FPU State

Opcode	Instruction	Clocks	Description
9B DD /6	FSAVE *m94/108byte*	154 real or virtual/143 protected; + at least 3 for FWAIT	Store FPU state to *m94byte* or *m108byte* after checking for unmasked floating-point error condition. Then re-initialize the FPU.
DD /6	FNSAVE *m94/108byte*	154 real or virtual/143 protected	Store FPU environment to *m94byte* or *m108byte* without checking for unmasked floating-point error condition. Then re-initialize the FPU.

Operation

DEST ← FPU state;
initialize FPU; (* Equivalent to FNINIT *)

Description

The save instructions write the current FPU state (environment and register stack) to the specified destination, and then re-initialize the FPU. The environment consists of the FPU control word, status word, tag word, and error pointers (both data and instruction).

The state layout in memory depends on both the operand size and the current operating mode of the processor. The USE attribute of the current code segment determines the operand size: the 94-byte operand applies to USE16 segment, and the 108-byte operand applies to a USE32 segment. Figures 15-5 through 15-8 show the environment layouts for both operand sizes in both real mode and protected mode. (In virtual-8086 mode, the real mode layout is used.) The stack registers, beginning with ST and ending with ST(7), are stored in the 80 bytes that immediately follow the environment image.

FPU Flags Affected

C0, C1, C2, C3 cleared

Numeric Exceptions

None

Protected Mode Exceptions

#GP(0) if the destination is in a nonwritable segment; #GP(0) for an illegal memory operand effective address in the CS, DS, ES, FS, or GS segments; #SS(0) for an illegal address in the SS segment; #PF(fault-code) for a page fault; #NM if either EM or TS in CR0 is set; #AC for unaligned memory reference if the current privilege level is 3

Real Address Mode Exceptions

Interrupt 13 if any part of the operand would lie outside the effective address space from 0 to 0FFFFH; Interrupt 7 if either EM or TS in CR0 is set

Virtual 8086 Mode Exceptions

Same exceptions as in Real Address Mode; #PF(fault code) for a page fault; #AC for unaligned memory reference if the current privilege level is 3

Notes

FSAVE and FNSAVE do not store the FPU state until all FPU activity is complete. Thus, the saved image reflects the state of the FPU after any previously decoded instruction has been executed.

If a program is to read from the memory image of the state following a save instruction, it must issue an FWAIT instruction to ensure that the storage is complete.

The save instructions are typically used when an operating system needs to perform a context switch, or an exception handler needs to use the FPU, or an application program wants to pass a "clean" FPU to a subroutine.

FSCALE — Scale

Opcode	Instruction	Clocks	Concurrent Execution	Description
D9 FD	FSCALE	31 (30-32)	2	Scale ST by ST(1).

Operation

ST ← ST × $2^{ST(1)}$;

Description

The scale instruction interprets the value in ST(1) as an integer, and adds this integer to the exponent of ST. Thus, FSCALE provides rapid multiplication or division by integral powers of 2.

FPU Flags Affected

C1 as described in Table 15-1; C0, C2, C3 undefined

Numeric Exceptions

P, U, O, D, I, IS

Protected Mode Exceptions

#NM if either EM or TS in CR0 is set

Real Address Mode Exceptions

Interrupt 7 if either EM or TS in CR0 is set

Virtual 8086 Mode Exceptions

#NM if either EM or TS in CR0 is set

Notes

FSCALE can be used as an inverse to FXTRACT. Since FSCALE does not pop the exponent part, however, FSCALE must be followed by FSTP ST(1) in order to completely undo the effect of a preceding FXTRACT.

There is no limit on the range of the scale factor in ST(1). If the value is not integral, FSCALE uses the nearest integer smaller in magnitude; i.e., it chops the value toward 0. If the resulting integer is zero, the value in ST is not changed.

FSIN — Sine

Opcode	Instruction	Clocks	Concurrent Execution	Description
D9 FE	FSIN	241 (193-279)	2	Replace ST with its sine.

Operation

```
IF operand is in range
THEN
    C2 ← 0;
    ST ← sin(ST);
ELSE
    C2 ← 1;
FI:
```

Description

The sine instruction replaces the contents of ST with sin(ST). ST, expressed in radians, must lie in the range $| \theta | < 2^{63}$.

FPU Flags Affected

C1, C2 as described in Table 15-1; C0, C3 undefined

Numeric Exceptions

P, U, D, I, IS

Protected Mode Exceptions

#NM if either EM or TS in CR0 is set

Real Address Mode Exceptions

Interrupt 7 if either EM or TS in CR0 is set

Virtual 8086 Mode Exceptions

#NM if either EM or TS in CR0 is set

Notes

If the operand is outside the acceptable range, the C2 flag is set, and ST remains unchanged. It is the programmer's responsibility to reduce the operand to an absolute value smaller than 2^{63} by subtracting an appropriate integer multiple of 2π. See Section 17.5 for a discussion of the proper value to use for π in performing such reductions.

The i486 CPU periodically checks for interrupts while performing this instruction. It will be aborted to service an interrupt.

FSINCOS — Sine and Cosine

Opcode	Instruction	Clocks	Concurrent Execution	Description
D9 FB	FSINCOS	291 (243-329)	2	Compute the sine and cosine of ST; replace ST with the sine, and then push the cosine onto the FPU stack.

Operation

```
IF operand is in range
THEN
    C2 ← 0;
    TEMP ← cos(ST);
    ST ← sin(ST);
    Decrement FPU stack-top pointer;
    ST ← TEMP;
ELSE
    C2 ← 1;
FI:
```

Description

FSINCOS computes both sin(ST) and cos(ST), replaces ST with the sine and then pushes the cosine onto the FPU stack. ST, expressed in radians, must lie in the range $|\theta| < 2^{63}$.

FPU Flags Affected

C1, C2 as described in Table 15-1; C0, C3 undefined

Numeric Exceptions

P, U, D, I, IS

Protected Mode Exceptions

#NM if either EM or TS in CR0 is set

Real Address Mode Exceptions

Interrupt 7 if either EM or TS in CR0 is set

Virtual 8086 Mode Exceptions

#NM if either EM or TS in CR0 is set

Notes

If the operand is outside the acceptable range, the C2 flag is set, and ST remains unchanged. It is the programmer's responsibility to reduce the operand to an absolute value smaller than 2^{63} by subtracting an appropriate integer multiple of 2π. See Section 17.5 for a discussion of the proper value to use for π in performing such reductions.

It is faster to execute FSINCOS than to execute both FSIN and FCOS.

The i486 CPU periodically checks for interrupts while performing this instruction. It will be aborted to service an interrupt.

FSQRT — Square Root

Opcode	Instruction	Clocks	Concurrent Execution	Description
D9 FA	FSQRT	85.5 (83-87)	70	Replace ST with its square root.

Operation

ST ← square root of ST;

Description

The square root instruction replaces the value in ST with its square root.

FPU Flags Affected

C1 as described in Table 15-1; C0, C2, C3 undefined

Numeric Exceptions

P, D, I, IS

Protected Mode Exceptions

#NM if either EM or TS in CR0 is set

Real Address Mode Exceptions

Interrupt 7 if either EM or TS in CR0 is set

Virtual 8086 Mode Exceptions

#NM if either EM or TS in CR0 is set

Notes

The square root of −0 is −0.

FST/FSTP — Store Real

Opcode	Instruction	Clocks	Description
D9 /2	FST *m32real*	7	Copy ST to *m32real*.
DD /2	FST *m64real*	8	Copy ST to *m64real*.
DD D0+i	FST ST(i)	3	Copy ST to ST(i).
D9 /3	FSTP *m32real*	7	Copy ST to *m32real* and pop ST.
DD /3	FSTP *m64real*	8	Copy ST to *m64real* and pop ST.
DB /7	FSTP *m80real*	6	Copy ST to *m80real* and pop ST.
DD D8+i	FSTP ST(i)	3	Copy ST to ST(i) and pop ST.

Operation

```
DEST ← ST(0);
IF instruction = FSTP THEN pop ST FI;
```

Description

FST copies the current value in the ST register to the destination, which can be another register or a single- or double-real memory operand. FSTP copies and then pops ST; it accepts extended-real memory operands as well as the types accepted by FST.

If the source is a register, the register number used is that before the stack is popped.

FPU Flags Affected

C1 as described in Table 15-1; C0, C2, C3 undefined

Numeric Exceptions

Register or extended-real destinations: IS
Single- or double-real destinations: P, U, O, D, I, IS

Protected Mode Exceptions

#GP(0) if the destination is in a nonwritable segment; #GP(0) for an illegal memory operand effective address in the CS, DS, ES, FS, or GS segments; #SS(0) for an illegal address in the SS segment; #PF(fault-code) for a page fault; #NM if either EM or TS in CR0 is set; #AC for unaligned memory reference if the current privilege level is 3

Real Address Mode Exceptions

Interrupt 13 if any part of the operand would lie outside the effective address space from 0 to 0FFFFH; Interrupt 7 if either EM or TS in CR0 is set

Virtual 8086 Mode Exceptions

Same exceptions as in Real Address Mode; #PF(fault code) for a page fault; #AC for unaligned memory reference if the current privilege level is 3

Notes

If the destination is single- or double-real, the significand is rounded to the width of the destination according to the RC field of the control word, and the exponent is converted to the width and bias of the destination format. The over/underflow condition is checked for as well.

If ST contains zero, $\pm \infty$, or a NaN, then the significand is not rounded, but chopped (on the right) to fit the destination. Nor is the exponent converted; it too is chopped on the right. These operations preserve the value's identity as ∞ or NaN (exponent all ones).

The invalid-operation exception is not raised when the destination is a nonempty stack element.

FSTCW/FNSTCW—Store Control Word

Opcode	Instruction	Clocks	Description
9B D9 /7	FSTCW *m2byte*	3 + at least 3 for FWAIT	Store FPU control word to *m2byte* after checking for unmasked floating-point error condition.
D9 /7	FNSTCW *m2byte*	3	Store FPU control word to *m2byte* without checking for unmasked floating-point error condition.

Operation

DEST ← CW;

Description

FSTCW and FNSTCW write the current value of the FPU control word to the specified destination.

FPU Flags Affected

C0, C1, C2, C3 undefined

Numeric Exceptions

None

Protected Mode Exceptions

#GP(0) if the destination is in a nonwritable segment; #GP(0) for an illegal memory operand effective address in the CS, DS, ES, FS, or GS segments; #SS(0) for an illegal address in the SS segment; #PF(fault-code) for a page fault; #NM if either EM or TS in CR0 is set; #AC for unaligned memory reference if the current privilege level is 3

Real Address Mode Exceptions

Interrupt 13 if any part of the operand would lie outside the effective address space from 0 to 0FFFFH; Interrupt 7 if either EM or TS in CR0 is set

Virtual 8086 Mode Exceptions

Same exceptions as in Real Address Mode; #PF(fault code) for a page fault; #AC for unaligned memory reference if the current privilege level is 3

Notes

FSTCW checks for unmasked floating-point error conditions before storing the control word; FNSTCW does not.

FSTENV/FNSTENV — Store FPU Environment

Opcode	Instruction	Clocks	Description
9B D9 /6	FSTENV *m14/28byte*	67 real or virtual/56 protected; + at least 3 for FWAIT	Store FPU environment to *m14byte* or *m28byte* after checking for unmasked floating-point error condition. Then mask all floating-point exceptions.
D9 /6	FNSTENV *m14/28byte*	67 real or virtual/56 protected;	Store FPU environment to *m14byte* or *m28byte* without checking for unmasked floating-point error condition. Then mask all floating-point exceptions.

Operation

DEST ← FPU environment;
CW[0..5] ← 111111B;

Description

The store environment instructions write the current FPU environment to the specified destination, and then mask all floating-point exceptions. The FPU environment consists of the FPU control word, status word, tag word, and error pointer (both data and instruction).

The environment layout in memory depends on both the operand size and the current operating mode of the processor. The USE attribute of the current code segment determines the operand size: the 14-byte operand applies to a USE16 segment, and the 28-byte operand applies to a USE32 segment. Figures 15-5 through 15-8 show the environment layouts for both operand sizes in both real mode and protected mode. (In virtual-8086 mode, the real mode layout is used.)

FPU Flags Affected

C0, C1, C2, C3 undefined

Numeric Exceptions

None

Protected Mode Exceptions

#GP(0) if the destination is in a nonwritable segment; #GP(0) for an illegal memory operand effective address in the CS, DS, ES, FS, or GS segments; #SS(0) for an illegal address in the SS segment; #PF(fault-code) for a page fault; #NM if either EM or TS in CR0 is set; #AC for unaligned memory reference if the current privilege level is 3

Real Address Mode Exceptions

Interrupt 13 if any part of the operand would lie outside the effective address space from 0 to 0FFFFH; Interrupt 7 if either EM or TS in CR0 is set

Virtual 8086 Mode Exceptions

Same exceptions as in Real Address Mode; #PF(fault code) for a page fault; #AC for unaligned memory reference if the current privilege level is 3

Notes

FSTENV and FNSTENV do not store the environment until all FPU activity is complete. Thus, the saved environment reflects the state of the FPU after any previously decoded instruction has been executed.

The store environment instructions are often used by exception handlers because they provide access to the FPU error pointers. The environment is typically saved onto the memory stack. After saving the environment, FSTENV and FNSTENV sets all the exception masks in the FPU control word. This prevents floating-point errors from interrupting the exception handler.

FSTENV checks for unmasked floating-point error conditions before storing the FPU environment; FNSTENV does not.

FSTSW/FNSTSW — Store Status Word

Opcode	Instruction	Clocks	Description
9B DF /7	FSTSW *m2byte*	3 + at least 3 for FWAIT	Store FPU status word to *mbyte* after checking for unmasked floating-point error condition.
9B DF E0	FSTSW	3 + at least 3 for FWAIT	Store FPU status word to AX register after checking for unmasked floating-point error condition.
DF /7	FNSTSW *m2byte*	3	Store FPU status word to *m2byte* without checking for unmasked floating-point error condition.
DF E0	FNSTSW AX	3	Store FPU status word to AX register without checking for unmasked floating-point error condition.

Operation

DEST ← SW;

Description

FSTSW and FNSTSW write the current value of the FPU status word to the specified destination, which can be either a two-byte location in memory or the AX register.

FPU Flags Affected

C0, C1, C2, C3 undefined

Numeric Exceptions

None

Protected Mode Exceptions

#GP(0) if the destination is in a nonwritable segment; #GP(0) for an illegal memory operand effective address in the CS, DS, ES, FS, or GS segments; #SS(0) for an illegal address in the SS segment; #PF(fault-code) for a page fault; #NM if either EM or TS in CR0 is set; #AC for unaligned memory reference if the current privilege level is 3

Real Address Mode Exceptions

Interrupt 13 if any part of the operand would lie outside the effective address space from 0 to 0FFFFH; Interrupt 7 if either EM or TS in CR0 is set

Virtual 8086 Mode Exceptions

Same exceptions as in Real Address Mode; #PF(fault code) for a page fault; #AC for unaligned memory reference if the current privilege level is 3

Notes

FSTSW checks for unmasked floating-point error conditions before storing the status word; FNSTSW does not.

FSTSW and FNSTSW are used primarily in conditional branching (after a comparison, FPREM, FPREM1, or FXAM instruction). They can also be used to invoke exception handlers (by polling the exception bits) in environments that do not use interrupts.

When FNSTSW AX is executed, the AX register is updated before the i486 processor executes any further instructions. The status stored is that from the completion of the prior ESC instruction.

FSUB/FSUBP/FISUB — Subtract

Opcode	Instruction	Clocks	Concurrent Execution	Description
D8 /4	FSUB *m32real*	10 (8-20)	7 (5-17)	Subtract *m32real* from ST.
DC /4	FSUB *m64real*	10 (8-20)	7 (5-17)	Subtract *m64real* from ST.
D8 E0+i	FSUB ST, ST(i)	10 (8-20)	7 (5-17)	Subtract ST(i) from ST.
DC E8+i	FSUB ST(i), ST	10 (8-20)	7 (5-17)	Replace ST(i) with ST − ST(i).
DE E8+i	FSUBP ST(i), ST	10 (8-20)	7 (5-17)	Replace ST(i) with ST − ST(i); pop ST.
DE E9	FSUB	10 (8-20)	7 (5-17)	Replace ST(1) with ST − ST(1); pop ST.
DA /4	FISUB *m32int*	22.5 (19-32)	7 (5-17)	Subtract *m32int* from ST.
DE /4	FISUB*m16int*	24 (20-35)	7 (5-17)	Subtract *m16int* from ST.

Operation

DEST ← ST − Other Operand;
IF instruction = FSUBP THEN pop ST FI;

Description

The subtraction instructions subtract the other operand from the stack top and return the difference to the destination.

FPU Flags Affected

C1 as described in Table 15-1; C0, C2, C3 undefined

Numeric Exceptions

P, U, O, D, I, IS

Protected Mode Exceptions

#GP(0) for an illegal memory operand effective address in the CS, DS, ES, FS, or GS segments; #SS(0) for an illegal address in the SS segment; #PF(fault-code) for a page fault; #NM if either EM or TS in CR0 is set; #AC for unaligned memory reference if the current privilege level is 3

Real Address Mode Exceptions

Interrupt 13 if any part of the operand would lie outside the effective address space from 0 to 0FFFFH; Interrupt 7 if either EM or TS in CR0 is set

Virtual 8086 Mode Exceptions

Same exceptions as in Real Address Mode; #PF(fault code) for a page fault; #AC for unaligned memory reference if the current privilege level is 3

Notes

If the source operand is in memory, it is automatically converted to the extended-real format.

FSUBR/FSUBPR/FISUBR — Reverse Subtract

Opcode	Instruction	Clocks	Concurrent Execution	Description
D8 /5	FSUBR *m32real*	10 (8-20)	7 (5-17)	Replace ST with *m32real* − ST.
DC /5	FSUBR *m64real*	10 (8-20)	7 (5-17)	Replace ST with *m64real* − ST.
D8 E8+i	FSUBR ST, ST(i)	10 (8-20)	7 (5-17)	Replace ST with ST(i) − ST.
DC E0+i	FSUBR ST(i), ST	10 (8-20)	7 (5-17)	Subtract ST from ST(i).
DE E0+i	FSUBRP ST(i), ST	10 (8-20)	7 (5-17)	Subtract ST from ST(i) and pop ST.
DE E1	FSUBR	10 (8-20)	7 (5-17)	Subtract ST from ST(1) and pop ST.
DA /5	FISUBR *m32int*	22.5 (19-32)	7 (5-17)	Replace ST with *m32int* − ST.
DE /5	FISUBR *m16int*	24 (20-35)	7 (5-17)	Replace ST with *m16int* − ST.

Operation

DEST ← Other Operand − ST;
IF instruction = FSUBRP THEN pop ST FI;

Description

The reverse subtraction instructions subtract the stack top from the other operand and return the difference to the destination.

FPU Flags Affected

C1 as described in Table 15-1; C0, C2, C3 undefined

Numeric Exceptions

P, U, O, D, I, IS

Protected Mode Exceptions

#GP(0) for an illegal memory operand effective address in the CS, DS, ES, FS, or GS segments; #SS(0) for an illegal address in the SS segment; #PF(fault-code) for a page fault; #NM if either EM or TS in CR0 is set; #AC for unaligned memory reference if the current privilege level is 3

Real Address Mode Exceptions

Interrupt 13 if any part of the operand would lie outside the effective address space from 0 to 0FFFFH; Interrupt 7 if either EM or TS in CR0 is set

Virtual 8086 Mode Exceptions

Same exceptions as in Real Address Mode; #PF(fault code) for a page fault; #AC for unaligned memory reference if the current privilege level is 3

Notes

If the source operand is in memory, it is automatically converted to the extended-real format.

FTST—TEST

Opcode	Instruction	Clocks	Concurrent Execution	Description
D9 E4	FTST	4	1	Compare ST with 0.0.

Operation

CASE (relation of operands) OF
    Not comparable: C3, C2, C0 ← 111;
    ST > SRC: C3, C2, C0 ← 000;
    ST < SRC: C3, C2, C0 ← 001;
    ST = SRC: C3, C2, C0 ← 100;

FPU Flags	EFlags
C_0	CF
C_1	(none)
C_2	PF
C_3	ZF

Description

The test instruction compares the stack top to 0.0. Following the instruction, the condition codes reflect the result of the comparison.

FPU Flags Affected

C1 as described in Table 15-1; C0, C2, C3 as specified above

Numeric Exceptions

D, I, IS

Protected Mode Exceptions

#NM if either EM or TS in CR0 is set

Real Address Mode Exceptions

Interrupt 7 if either EM or TS in CR0 is set

Virtual 8086 Mode Exceptions

#NM if either EM or TS in CR0 is set

Notes

If ST contains a NaN or an object of undefined format, or if a stack fault occurs, the invalid-operation exception is raised, and the condition bits are set to "unordered."

The sign of zero is ignored, so that $-0.0 = - +0.0$.

FUCOM/FUCOMP/FUCOMPP—Unordered Compare Real

Opcode	Instruction	Clocks	Concurrent Execution	Description
DD E0+i	FUCOM ST(i)	4	1	Compare ST with ST(i).
DD E1	FUCOM	4	1	Compare ST with ST(1).
DD E8+i	FUCOMP ST(i)	4	1	Compare ST with ST(i) and pop ST.
DD E9	FUCOMP	4	1	Compare ST with ST(1) and pop ST.
DA E9	FUCOMPP	5	1	Compare ST with ST(1) and pop ST twice.

Operation

```
CASE (relation of operands) OF
    Not comparable:   C3, C2, C0 ← 111;
    ST > SRC:         C3, C2, C0 ← 000;
    ST < SRC:         C3, C2, C0 ← 001;
    ST = SRC:         C3, C2, C0 ← 100;
IF instruction = FUCOMP THEN pop ST; FI;
IF instruction = FUCOMPP THEN pop ST; pop ST; FI;
```

FPU Flags	EFlags
C_0	CF
C_1	(none)
C_2	PF
C_3	ZF

Description

The unordered compare real instructions compare the stack top to the source, which must be a register. If no operand is encoded, ST is compared to ST(1). Following the instruction, the condition codes reflect the relation between ST and the source operand.

FPU Flags Affected

C1 as described in Table 15-1; C0, C2, C3 as specified above

Numeric Exceptions

D, I, IS

Protected Mode Exceptions

#NM if either EM or TS in CR0 is set

Real Address Mode Exceptions

Interrupt 7 if either EM or TS in CR0 is set

Virtual 8086 Mode Exceptions

#NM if either EM or TS in CR0 is set

Notes

If either operand is an SNaN or is in an undefined format, or if a stack fault occurs, the invalid-operation exception is raised, and the condition bits are set to "unordered."

If either operand is a QNaN, the condition bits are set to "unordered." Unlike the ordinary compare instructions (FCOM, etc.), the unordered compare instructions do not raise the invalid-operation exception on account of a QNaN operand.

The sign of zero is ignored, so that $-0.0 = - +0.0$.

FWAIT — Wait

Opcode	Instruction	Clocks	Description
9B	FWAIT	(1-3)	Alias for WAIT.

Description

FWAIT causes the processor to check for pending unmasked numeric exceptions before proceding.

FPU Flags Affected

C0, C1, C2, C3 undefined

Numeric Exceptions

None

Protected Mode Exceptions

#NM if both MP and TS in CR0 are set

Real Address Mode Exceptions

Interrupt 7 if both MP and TS in CR0 are set

Virtual 8086 Mode Exceptions

#NM if both MP and TS in CR0 are set

Notes

As its opcode shows, FWAIT is not actually an ESC instruction, but an alternate mnemonic for WAIT.

Coding FWAIT after an ESC instruction ensures that any unmasked floating-point exceptions the instruction may cause are handled before the processor has a chance to modify the instruction's results.

Information about when to use FWAIT is given in Chapter 18, in the section on "Concurrent Processing."

FXAM — Examine

Opcode	Instruction	Clocks	Description
D9 E5	FXAM	8	Report the type of object in the ST register.

Operation

C1 ← sign bit of ST; (* 0 for positive, 1 for negative *)

```
CASE (type of object in ST) OF
    Unsupported:    C3, C2, C0 ← 000;
    NaN:            C3, C2, C0 ← 001;
    Normal:         C3, C2, C0 ← 010;
    Infinity:       C3, C2, C0 ← 011;
    Zero:           C3, C2, C0 ← 100;
    Empty:          C3, C2, C0 ← 101;
    Denormal:       C3, C2, C0 ← 110;
```

FPU Flags	EFlags
C_0	CF
C_1	(none)
C_2	PF
C_3	ZF

Description

The examine instruction reports the type of object contained in the ST register by setting the FPU Flags.

FPU Flags Affected

C0, C1, C2, C3 as shown above.

Numeric Exceptions

None

Protected Mode Exceptions

#NM if either EM or TS in CR0 is set

Real Address Mode Exceptions

Interrupt 7 if either EM or TS in CR0 is set

Virtual 8086 Mode Exceptions

#NM if either EM or TS in CR0 is set

FXCH — Exchange Register Contents

Opcode	Instruction	Clocks	Description
D9 C8+i	FXCH ST(i)	4	Exchange thecontents of ST and ST(i).
D9 C9	FXCH	4	Exchange the contents of ST and ST(1).

Operation

TEMP ← ST;
ST ← DEST;
DEST ← TEMP;

Description

FXCH swaps the contents of the destination and stack-top registers. If the destination is not coded explicitly, ST(1) is used.

FPU Flags Affected

C1 as described in Table 15-1; C0, C2, C3 undefined

Numeric Exceptions

IS

Protected Mode Exceptions

#NM if either EM or TS in CR0 is set

Real Address Mode Exceptions

Interrupt 7 if either EM or TS in CR0 is set

Virtual 8086 Mode Exceptions

#NM if either EM or TS in CR0 is set

Notes

Many numeric instructions operate only on the stack top; FXCH provides a simple means for using these instructions on lower stack elements. For example, the following sequence takes the square root of the third register form the top (assuming that ST is nonempty):

```
FXCH ST(3)
FSQRT
FXCH ST(3)
```

FXTRACT—Extract Exponent and Significand

Opcode	Instruction	Clocks	Concurrent Execution	Description
D9 F4	FXTRACT	19 (16-20)	4 (2-4)	Separate ST into its exponent and significand; replace ST with the exponent and then push the significand onto the FPU stack.

Operation

TEMP ← significand of ST;
ST ← exponent of ST;
Decrement FPU stack-top pointer;
ST ← TEMP;

Description

FXTRACT splits the value in ST into its exponent and significand. The exponent replaces the original operand on the stack and the significand is pushed onto the stack. Following execution of FXTRACT, ST (the new stack top) contains the value of the original significand expressed as a real number: its sign is the same as the operand's, its exponent is 0 true (16,383 or 3FFFH biased), and its significand is identical to the original operand's. ST(1) contains the value of the original operand's true (unbiased) exponent expressed as a real number.

To illustrate the operation of FXTRACT, assume that ST contains a number whose true exponent is +4 (i.e., its exponent field contains 4003H). After executing FXTRACT, ST(1) will contain the real number +4.0; its sign will be positive, its exponent field will contain 4001H (+2 true) and its significand field will contain $1_{\Delta}00...00B$. In other words, the value in ST(1) will be $1.0 \times 2^2 = 4$. If ST contains an operand whose true exponent is −7 (i.e., its exponent field contains 3FF8H), then FXTRACT will return an "exponent" of −7.0; after the instruction executes, ST(1)'s sign and exponent fields will contain C001H (negative sign, true exponent of 2), and its significand will be $1_{\Delta}1100...00B$. In other words, the value in ST(1) will be $-1.75 \times 2^2 = -7.0$. In both cases, following FXTRACT, ST's sign and significand fields will be the same as the original operand's, and its exponent field will contain 3FFFH (0 true).

FPU Flags Affected

C1 as described in Table 15-1; C0, C2, C3 undefined

Numeric Exceptions

Z, D, I, IS

Protected Mode Exceptions

#NM if either EM or TS in CR0 is set

Real Address Mode Exceptions

Interrupt 7 if either EM or TS in CR0 is set

Virtual 8086 Mode Exceptions

#NM if either EM or TS in CR0 is set

Notes

FXTRACT (extract exponent and significand) performs a superset of the IEEE-recommended **logb**(x) function.

If the original operand is zero, FXTRACT leaves $-\infty$ in ST(1) (the exponent) while ST is assigned the value zero with a sign equal to that of the original operand. The zero-divide exception is raised in this case, as well.

ST(7) must be empty to avoid the invalid-operation exception.

FXTRACT is useful for power and range scaling operations. Both FXTRACT and the base 2 exponential instruction F2XM1 are needed to perform a general power operation. Converting numbers in extended-real format to decimal representations (e.g., for printing or displaying) requires not only FBSTP but also FXTRACT to allow scaling that does not overflow the range of the extended format. FXTRACT can also be useful for debugging, because it allows the exponent and significand parts of a real number to be examined separately.

FYL2X—Compute y × $\log_2 x$

Opcode	Instruction	Clocks	Concurrent Execution	Description
D9 F1	FYL2X	311 (196-329)	13	Replace ST(1) with ST(1) × $\log_2$ST andpop ST.

Operation

ST(1) ← ST(1) × $\log_2$ST;
pop ST;

Description

FYL2X computes the base-2 logarithm of ST, multiplies the logarithm by ST(1), and returns the resulting value to ST(1). It then pops ST. The operand in ST cannot be negative.

FPU Flags Affected

C1 as described in Table 15-1; C0, C2, C3 undefined

Numeric Exceptions

P, U, O, Z, D, I, IS

Protected Mode Exceptions

#NM if either EM or TS in CR0 is set

Real Address Mode Exceptions

Interrupt 7 if either EM or TS in CR0 is set

Virtual 8086 Mode Exceptions

#NM if either EM or TS in CR0 is set

Notes

If the operand in ST is negative, the invalid-operation exception is raised.

The FYL2X instruction is designed with a built-in multiplication to optimize the calculation of logarithms with arbitrary positive base:

$$\log_b x = (\log_2 b)^{-1} \times \log_2 x$$

The instructions FLDL2T and FLDL2E load the constants $\log_2 10$ and $\log_2 e$, respectively.

The i486 CPU periodically checks interrupts while executing this instruction. It will be aborted to service an interrupt.

FYL2XP1 — Compute y × $\log_2(x + 1)$

Opcode	Instruction	Clocks	Concurrent Execution	Description
D9 F9	FYL2XP1	313 (171-326)	13	Replace ST(1) with ST(1) × $\log_2$(ST + 1.0) and pop ST.

Operation

ST(1) ← ST(1) × $\log_2$(ST + 1.0);
pop ST;

Description

FYL2XP1 computes the base-2 logarithm of (ST + 1.0), multiplies the logarithm by ST(1), and returns the resulting value to ST(1). It then pops ST. The operand in ST must be in the range

$-(1-(\sqrt{2}\ /\ 2)) \leq ST \leq \sqrt{2}\ -1$

FPU Flags Affected

C1 as described in Table 15-1; C0, C2, C3 undefined

Numeric Exceptions

P, U, D, I, IS

Protected Mode Exceptions

#NM if either EM or TS in CR0 is set

Real Address Mode Exceptions

Interrupt 7 if either EM or TS in CR0 is set

Virtual 8086 Mode Exceptions

#NM if either EM or TS in CR0 is set

Notes

If the operand in ST is outside the acceptable range, the result of FYL2XP1 is undefined.

The FYL2XP1 instruction provides improved accuracy over FYL2X when computing the logarithms of numbers very close to 1. When ε is small, more significant digits can be retained by providing ε as an argument to FYL2XP1 than by providing 1 + ε as an argument to FYL2X.

The i486 CPU periodically checks for interrupts while executing this instruction. It will be aborted to service an interrupt.

HLT — Halt

Opcode	Instruction	Clocks	Description
F4	HLT	4	Halt

Operation

Enter Halt state;

Description

The HLT instruction stops instruction execution and places the processor in a HALT state. An enabled interrupt, NMI, or a reset will resume execution. If an interrupt (including NMI) is used to resume execution after a HLT instruction, the saved CS:IP (or CS:EIP) value points to the instruction following the HLT instruction.

Flags Affected

None

Protected Mode Exceptions

The HLT instruction is a privileged instruction; #GP(0) if the current privilege level is not 0

Real Address Mode Exceptions

None

Virtual 8086 Mode Exceptions

#GP(0); the HLT instruction is a privileged instruction

IDIV—Signed Divide

Opcode	Instruction	Clocks	Description
F6 /7	IDIV *r/m8*	19/20	Signed divide AX by *r/m* byte (AL=Quo, AH=Rem)
F7 /7	IDIV AX,*r/m16*	27/28	Signed divide DX:AX by EA word (AX=Quo, DX=Rem)
F7 /7	IDIV EAX,*r/m32*	43/44	Signed divide EDX:EAX by DWORD byte (EAX=Quo, EDX=Rem)

Operation

```
temp ← dividend / divisor;
IF temp does not fit in quotient
THEN Interrupt 0;
ELSE
   quotient ← temp;
   remainder ← dividend MOD (r/m);
FI;
```

Notes: Divisions are signed. The divisor is given by the *r/m* operand. The dividend, quotient, and remainder use implicit registers. Refer to the table under "Description."

Description

The IDIV instruction performs a signed division. The dividend, quotient, and remainder are implicitly allocated to fixed registers. Only the divisor is given as an explicit *r/m* operand. The type of the divisor determines which registers to use as follows:

Size	Divisor	Quotient	Remainder	Dividend
byte	*r/m8*	AL	AH	AX
word	*r/m16*	AX	DX	DX:AX
dword	*r/m32*	EAX	EDX	EDX:EAX

If the resulting quotient is too large to fit in the destination, or if the division is 0, an Interrupt 0 is generated. Nonintegral quotients are truncated toward 0. The remainder has the same sign as the dividend and the absolute value of the remainder is always less than the absolute value of the divisor.

Flags Affected

The OF, SF, ZF, AF, PF, CF flags are undefined.

Protected Mode Exceptions

Interrupt 0 if the quotient is too large to fit in the designated register (AL or AX), or if the divisor is 0; #GP (0) for an illegal memory operand effective address in the CS, DS, ES, FS, or GS segments; #SS(0) for an illegal address in the SS segment; #PF(fault-code) for a page fault; #AC for unaligned memory reference if the current privilege level is 3

Real Address Mode Exceptions

Interrupt 0 if the quotient is too large to fit in the designated register (AL or AX), or if the divisor is 0; Interrupt 13 if any part of the operand would lie outside of the effective address space from 0 to 0FFFFH

Virtual 8086 Mode Exceptions

Same exceptions as in Real Address Mode; #PF(fault-code) for a page fault; #AC for unaligned memory reference if the current privilege level is 3

IMUL – Signed Multiply

Opcode	Instruction	Clocks	Description
F6 /5	IMUL *r/m8*	13-18/13-18	AX← AL * *r/m* byte
F7 /5	IMUL *r/m16*	13-26/13-26	DX:AX ← AX * *r/m* word
F7 /5	IMUL *r/m32*	12-42/13-42	EDX:EAX ← EAX * *r/m* dword
0F AF /r	IMUL *r16,r/m16*	13-26/13-26	word register ← word register * *r/m* word
0F AF /r	IMUL *r32,r/m32*	13-42/13-42	dword register ← dword register * *r/m* dword
6B /r ib	IMUL *r16,r/m16,imm8*	13-26/13-26	word register ← *r/m16* * sign-extended immediate byte
6B /r ib	IMUL *r32,r/m32,imm8*	13-42/13-42	dword register ← *r/m32* * sign-extended immediate byte
6B /r ib	IMUL *r16,imm8*	13-26	word register ← word register * sign-extended immediate byte
6B /r ib	IMUL *r32,imm8*	13-42	dword register ← dword register * sign-extended immediate byte
69 /r iw	IMUL *r16,r/ m16,imm16*	13-26/13-26	word register ← *r/m16* * immediate word
69 /r id	IMUL *r32,r/ m32,imm32*	13-42/13-42	dword register ← *r/m32* * immediate dword
69 /r iw	IMUL *r16,imm16*	13-26/13-26	word register ← *r/m16* * immediate word
69 /r id	IMUL *r32,imm32*	13-42/13-42	dword register ← *r/m32* * immediate dword

NOTES: The i486 processor uses an early-out multiply algorithm. The actual number of clocks depends on the position of the most significant bit in the optimizing multiplier. The optimization occurs for positive and negative values. Because of the early-out algorithm, clock counts given are minimum to maximum. To calculate the actual clocks, use the following formula:

Actual clock = if m <> 0 then max(ceiling($\log_2$ | m | 3) + 6 clocks
Actual clock = if m = 0 then 9 clocks
(where m is the multiplier)

Add three clocks if the multiplier is a memory operand.

Operation

result ← multiplicand * multiplier;

Description

The IMUL instruction performs signed multiplication. Some forms of the instruction use implicit register operands. The operand combinations for all forms of the instruction are shown in the "Description" column above.

The IMUL instruction clears the OF and CF flags under the following conditions:

Instruction Form	Condition for Clearing CF and OF
r/m8	AL = sign-extend of AL to 16 bits
r/m16	AX = sign-extend of AX to 32 bits
r/m32	EDX:EAX = sign-extend of EAX to 32 bits
r16,r/m16	Result exactly fits within *r16*
r/32,r/m32	Result exactly fits within *r32*
r16,r/m16,imm16	Result exactly fits within *r16*
r32,r/m32,imm32	Result exactly fits within *r32*

Flags Affected

The OF and CF flags as described in the table in the "Description" section above; the SF, ZF, AF, and PF flags are undefined

Protected Mode Exceptions

#GP(0) for an illegal memory operand effective address in the CS, DS, ES, FS, or GS segments; #SS(0) for an illegal address in the SS segment; #PF(fault-code) for a page fault; #AC for unaligned memory reference if the current privilege level is 3

Real Address Mode Exceptions

Interrupt 13 if any part of the operand would lie outside of the effective address space from 0 to 0FFFFH

Virtual 8086 Mode Exceptions

Same exeptions as in Real Address Mode; #PF(fault-code) for a page fault; #AC for unaligned memory reference if the current privilege level is 3

Notes

When using the accumulator forms (IMUL *r/m8*, IMUL *r/m16*, or IMUL *r/m32*), the result of the multiplication is available even if the overflow flag is set because the result is twice the size of the multiplicand and multiplier. This is large enough to handle any possible result.

IN — Input from Port

Opcode	Instruction	Clocks	Description
E4 *ib*	IN AL,*imm8*	14,pm=8*/ 28**,vm=27	Input byte from immediate port into AL
E5 *ib*	IN AX,*imm8*	14,pm=8*/ 28**,vm=27	Input word from immediate port into AX
E5 *ib*	IN EAX,*imm8*	14,pm=8*/ 28**,vm=27	Input dword from immediate port into EAX
EC	IN AL,DX	14,pm=8*/ 28**,vm=27	Input byte from port DX into AL
ED	IN AX,DX	14,pm=8*/ 28**,vm=27	Input word from port DX into AX
ED	IN EAX,DX	14,pm=8*/ 28**,vm=27	Input dword from port DX into EAX

NOTES: *If CPL ≤;le IOPL
**If CPL ≥ IOPL

Operation

```
IF (PE = 1) AND ((VM = 1) OR (CPL > IOPL))
THEN (* Virtual 8086 mode, or protected mode with CPL > IOPL *)
   IF NOT I-O-Permission (SRC, width(SRC))
   THEN #GP(0);
   FI;
FI;
DEST ← [SRC]; (* Reads from I/O address space *)
```

Description

The IN instruction transfers a data byte or data word from the port numbered by the second operand into the register (AL, AX, or EAX) specified by the first operand. Access any port from 0 to 65535 by placing the port number in the DX register and using an IN instruction with the DX register as the second parameter. These I/O instructions can be shortened by using an 8-bit port I/O in the instruction. The upper eight bits of the port address will be 0 when 8-bit port I/O is used.

Flags Affected

None

Protected Mode Exceptions

#GP(0) if the current privilege level is larger (has less privilege) than the I/O privilege level and any of the corresponding I/O permission bits in TSS equals 1

Real Address Mode Exceptions

None

Virtual 8086 Mode Exceptions

#GP(0) fault if any of the corresponding I/O permission bits in TSS equals 1

INC — Increment by 1

Opcode	Instruction	Clocks	Description
FE /0	INC *r/m8*	1/3	Increment *r/m* byte by 1
FF /0	INC *r/m16*	1/3	Increment *r/m* word by 1
FF /6	INC *r/m32*	1/3	Increment *r/m* dword by 1
40+ *rw*	INC *r16*	1	Increment word register by 1
40+ *rd*	INC *r32*	1	Increment dword register by 1

Operation

DEST ← DEST + 1;

Description

The INC instruction adds 1 to the operand. It does not change the CF flag. To affect the CF flag, use the ADD instruction with a second operand of 1.

Flags Affected

The OF, SF, ZF, AF, and PF flags are set according to the result

Protected Mode Exceptions

#GP(0) if the operand is in a nonwritable segment; #GP(0) for an illegal memory operand effective address in the CS, DS, ES, FS, or GS segments; #SS(0) for an illegal address in the SS segment; #PF(fault-code) for a page fault; #AC for unaligned memory reference if the current privilege level is 3

Real Address Mode Exceptions

Interrupt 13 if any part of the operand would lie outside of the effective address space from 0 to 0FFFFH

Virtual 8086 Mode Exceptions

Same exceptions as in Real Address Mode; #PF(fault-code) for a page fault; #AC for unaligned memory reference if the current privilege level is 3

INS/INSB/INSW/INSD—Input from Port to String

Opcode	Instruction	Clocks	Description
6C	INS *r/m8*,DX	17,pm=10*/ 32**,VM=30	Input byte from port DX into ES:(E)DI
6D	INS *r/m16*,DX	17,pm=10*/ 32**,VM=30	Input word from port DX into ES:(E)DI
6D	INS *r/m32*,DX	17,pm=10*/ 32**,VM=30	Input dword from port DX into ES:(E)DI
6C	INSB	17,pm=10*/ 32**,VM=30	Input byte from port DX into ES:(E)DI
6D	INSW	17,pm=10*/ 32**,VM=30	Input word from port DX into ES:(E)DI
6D	INSD	17,pm=10*/ 32**,VM=30	Input dword from port DX into ES:(E)DI

NOTES: *If CPL ≤ IOPL
**If CPL > IOPL

Operation

```
IF AddressSize = 16
THEN use DI for dest-index;
ELSE (* AddressSize = 32 *)
  use EDI for dest-index;
FI;
IF (PE = 1) AND ((VM = 1) OR (CPL > IOPL))
THEN (* Virtual 8086 mode, or protected mode with CPL > IOPL *)
  IF NOT I-O-Permission (SRC, width(SRC))
  THEN #GP(0);
  FI;
FI;
IF byte type of instruction
THEN
  ES:[dest-index] ← [DX]; (* Reads byte at DX from I/O address space *)
  IF DF = 0 THEN IncDec ← 1 ELSE IncDec ← −1; FI;
FI;
IF OperandSize = 16
THEN
  ES:[dest-index] ← [DX]; (* Reads word at DX from I/O address space *)
  IF DF = 0 THEN IncDec ← 2 ELSE IncDec ← −2; FI;
FI;
IF OperandSize = 32
THEN
  ES:[dest-index] ← [DX]; (* Reads dword at DX from I/O address space *)
  IF DF = 0 THEN IncDec ← 4 ELSE IncDec ← −4; FI;
FI;
dest-index ← dest-index + IncDec;
```

Description

The INS instruction transfers data from the input port numbered by the DX register to the memory byte or word at ES:dest-index. The memory operand must be addressable from the ES register; no segment override is possible. The destination register is the DI register if the address-size attribute of the instruction is 16 bits, or the EDI register if the address-size attribute is 32 bits.

The INS instruction does not allow the specification of the port number as an immediate value. The port must be addressed through the DX register value. Load the correct value into the DX register before executing the INS instruction.

The destination address is determined by the contents of the destination index register. Load the correct index into the destination index register before executing the INS instruction.

After the transfer is made, the DI or EDI register advances automatically. If the DF flag is 0 (a CLD instruction was executed), the DI or EDI register increments; if the DF flag is 1 (an STD instruction was executed), the DI or EDI register decrements. The DI register increments or decrements by 1 if a byte is input, by 2 if a word is input, or by 4 if a doubleword is input.

The INSB, INSW and INSD instructions are synonyms of the byte, word, and doubleword INS instructions. The INS instruction can be preceded by the REP prefix for block input of CX bytes or words. Refer to the REP instruction for details of this operation.

Flags Affected

None

Protected Mode Exceptions

#GP(0) if the current privilege level is numerically greater than the I/O privilege level and any of the corresponding I/O permission bits in TSS equals 1; #GP(0) if the destination is in a nonwritable segment; #GP(0) for an illegal memory operand effective address in the CS, DS, ES, FS, or GS segments; #SS(0) for an illegal address in the SS segment; #PF(fault-code) for a page fault; #AC for unaligned memory reference if the current privilege level is 3

Real Address Mode Exceptions

Interrupt 13 if any part of the operand would lie outside of the effective address space from 0 to 0FFFFH

Virtual 8086 Mode Exceptions

#GP(0) fault if any of the corresponding I/O permission bits in TSS equals 1; #PF(fault-code) for a page fault; #AC for unaligned memory reference if the current privilege level is 3

INT/INTO — Call to Interrupt Procedure

Opcode	Instruction	Clocks	Description
CC	INT 3	26	Interrupt 3 — trap to debugger
CC	INT 3	44	Interrupt 3 — Protected Mode, same privilege
CC	INT 3	71	Interrupt 3 — Protected Mode, more privilege
CC	INT 3	82	Interrupt 3 — from V86 mode to PL 0
CC	INT 3	37 + TS	Interrupt 3 — Protected Mode, via task gate
CD *ib*	INT *imm8*	30	Interrupt numbered by immediate byte
CD *ib*	INT *imm8*	44	Interrupt — Protected Mode, same privilege
CD *ib*	INT *imm8*	71	Interrupt — Protected Mode, more privilege
CD *ib*	INT *imm8*	86	Interrupt — from V86 mode to PL 0
CD *ib*	INT *imm8*	37 + TS	Interrupt — Protected Mode, via task gate
CE	INTO	Pass: 28, Fail: 3	Interrupt 4 — if overflow flag is 1
CE	INTO	46	Interrupt 4 — Protected Mode, same privilege
CE	INTO	73	Interrupt 4 — Protected Mode, more privilege
CE	INTO	84	Interrupt 4 — from V86 mode to PL 0
CE	INTO	39 + TS	Interrupt 4 — Protected Mode, via task gate

NOTE: Approximate values of **ts** are given by the following table:

Old Task	New Task		
	to i486™ CPU TSS	to 80286 TSS	to VM TSS
VM/i486 CPU/80286 TSS	199	180	177

Operation

NOTE: The following operational description applies not only to the above instructions but also to external interrupts and exceptions.

```
IF PE = 0
THEN GOTO REAL-ADDRESS-MODE;
pELSE GOTO PROTECTED-MODE;
FI;

REAL-ADDRESS-MODE:
   Push (FLAGS);
   IF ← 0; (* Clear interrupt flag *)
   TF ← 0; (* Clear trap flag *)
   Push(CS);
   Push(IP);
   (* No error codes are pushed *)
   CS ← IDT[Interrupt number * 4].selector;
   IP ← IDT[Interrupt number * 4].offset;

PROTECTED-MODE:
   Interrupt vector must be within IDT table limits,
      else #GP(vector number * 8+2+EXT);
   Descriptor AR byte must indicate interrupt gate, trap gate, or task gate,
      else #GP(vector number * 8+2+EXT);
   IF software interrupt (* i.e. caused by INT n, INT 3, or INTO *)
```

```
THEN
   IF gate descriptor DPL < CPL
   THEN #GP(vector number * 8+2+EXT);
   FI;
FI;
Gate must be present, else #NP(vector number * 8+2+EXT);
IF trap gate OR interrupt gate
THEN GOTO TRAP-GATE-OR-INTERRUPT-GATE;
ELSE GOTO TASK-GATE;
FI;

TRAP-GATE-OR-INTERRUPT-GATE:
  Examine CS selector and descriptor given in the gate descriptor;
  Selector must be non-null, else #GP (EXT);
  Selector must be within its descriptor table limits
    ELSE #GP(selector+EXT);
  Descriptor AR byte must indicate code segment
    ELSE #GP(selector + EXT);
  Segment must be present, else #NP(selector+EXT);

  IF code segment is non-conforming AND DPL < CPL
  THEN GOTO INTERRUPT-TO-INNER-PRIVILEGE;
  ELSE
    IF code segment is conforming OR code segment DPL = CPL
    THEN GOTO INTERRUPT-TO-SAME-PRIVILEGE-LEVEL;
    ELSE #GP(CS selector + EXT);
    FI;
  FI;

INTERRUPT-TO-INNER-PRIVILEGE:
  Check selector and descriptor for new stack in current TSS;
    Selector must be non-null, else #TS(EXT);
    Selector index must be within its descriptor table limits
      ELSE #TS(SS selector+EXT);
    Selector's RPL must equal DPL of code segment, else #TS(SS
      selector+EXT);
    Stack segment DPL must equal DPL of code segment, else #TS(SS
      selector+EXT);
    Descriptor must indicate writable data segment, else #TS(SS
      selector+EXT);
    Segment must be present, else #SS(SS selector+EXT);
  IF 32-bit gate
  THEN New stack must have room for 20 bytes else #SS(0)
  ELSE New stack must have room for 10 bytes else #SS(0)
  FI;
  Instruction pointer must be within CS segment boundaries else #GP(0);
  Load new SS and eSP value from TSS;
  IF 32-bit gate
  THEN CS:EIP ← selector:offset from gate;
```

```
   ELSE CS:IP ← selector:offset from gate;
   FI;
   Load CS descriptor into invisible portion of CS register;
   Load SS descriptor into invisible portion of SS register;
   IF 32-bit gate
   THEN
      Push (long pointer to old stack) (* 3 words padded to 4 *);
      Push (EFLAGS);
      Push (long pointer to return location) (* 3 words padded to 4*);
   ELSE
      Push (long pointer to old stack) (* 2 words *);
      Push (FLAGS);
      Push (long pointer to return location) (* 2 words *);
   FI;
   Set CPL to new code segment DPL;
   Set RPL of CS to CPL;
   IF interrupt gate THEN IF ← 0 (* interrupt flag to 0 (disabled) *); FI;
   TF ← 0;
   NT ← 0;

INTERRUPT-FROM-V86-MODE:
   TempEFlags ← EFLAGS;
   VM ← 0;
   TF ← 0;
   IF service through Interrupt Gate THEN IF ← 0;
   TempSS ← SS;
   TempESP ← ESP;
   SS ← TSS.SS0; (* Change to level 0 stack segment *)
   ESP ← TSS.ESP0; (* Change to level 0 stack pointer *)
   Push(GS); (* padded to two words *)
   Push(FS); (* padded to two words *)
   Push(DS); (* padded to two words *)
   Push(ES); (* padded to two words *)
   GS ;ID 0;
   FS ← 0;
   DS ← 0;
   ES ← 0;
   Push(TempSS); (* padded to two words *)
   Push(TempESP);
   Push(TempEFlags);
   Push(CS); (* padded to two words *)
   Push(EIP);
   CS:EIP ← selector:offset from interrupt gate;
   (* Starts execution of new routine in Protected Mode *)

INTERRUPT-TO-SAME-PRIVILEGE-LEVEL:
   IF 32-bit gate
   THEN Current stack limits must allow pushing 10 bytes, else #SS(0);
   ELSE Current stack limits must allow pushing 6 bytes, else #SS(0);
```

```
FI;
IF interrupt was caused by exception with error code
THEN Stack limits must allow push of two more bytes;
ELSE #SS(0);
FI;
Instruction pointer must be in CS limit, else #GP(0);
IF 32-bit gate
THEN
   Push (EFLAGS);
   Push (long pointer to return location); (* 3 words padded to 4 *)
   CS:EIP ← selector:offset from gate;
ELSE (* 16-bit gate *)
   Push (FLAGS);
   Push (long pointer to return location); (* 2 words *)
   CS:IP ← selector:offset from gate;
FI;
Load CS descriptor into invisible portion of CS register;
Set the RPL field of CS to CPL;
Push (error code); (* if any *)
IF interrupt gate THEN IF ← 0; FI;
TF ← 0;
NT ← 0;


TASK-GATE:
  Examine selector to TSS, given in task gate descriptor;
     Must specify global in the local/global bit, else #TS(TSS selector);
     Index must be within GDT limits, else #TS(TSS selector);
     AR byte must specify available TSS (bottom bits 00001),
        else #TS(TSS selector;
     TSS must be present, else #NP(TSS selector);
  SWITCH-TASKS with nesting to TSS;
  IF interrupt was caused by fault with error code
  THEN
     Stack limits must allow push of two more bytes, else #SS(0);
     Push error code onto stack;
  FI;
  Instruction pointer must be in CS limit, else #GP(0);
```

Description

The INT *n* instruction generates via software a call to an interrupt handler. The immediate operand, from 0 to 255, gives the index number into the Interrupt Descriptor Table (IDT) of the interrupt routine to be called. In Protected Mode, the IDT consists of an array of eight-byte descriptors; the descriptor for the interrupt invoked must indicate an interrupt, trap, or task gate. In Real Address Mode, the IDT is an array of four byte-long pointers. In Protected and Real Address Modes, the base linear address of the IDT is defined by the contents of the IDTR.

The INTO conditional software instruction is identical to the INT *n* interrupt instruction except that the interrupt number is implicitly 4, and the interrupt is made only if the i486 processor overflow flag is set.

The first 32 interrupts are reserved by Intel for system use. Some of these interrupts are use for internally generated exceptions.

The INT *n* instruction generally behaves like a far call except that the flags register is pushed onto the stack before the return address. Interrupt procedures return via the IRET instruction, which pops the flags and return address from the stack.

In Real Address Mode, the INT *n* instruction pushes the flags, the CS register, and the return IP onto the stack, in that order, then jumps to the long pointer indexed by the interrupt number.

Flags Affected

None

Protected Mode Exceptions

#GP, #NP, #SS, and #TS as indicated under "Operation" above

Real Address Mode Exceptions

None; if the SP or ESP register is 1, 3, or 5 before executing the INT or INTO instruction, the i486 processor will shut down due to insufficient stack space

Virtual 8086 Mode Exceptions

#GP(0) fault if IOPL is less than 3, for the INT *n* instruction only, to permit emulation; Interrupt 3 (0CCH) generates a breakpoint exception; the INTO instruction generates an overflow exception if the OF flag is set

INVD — Invalidate Cache

Opcode	Instruction	Clocks	Description
0F 08	INVD	4	Invalidate Entire Cache

Operation

FLUSH INTERNAL CACHE
SIGNAL EXTERNAL CACHE TO FLUSH

Description

The internal cache is flushed, and a special-function bus cycle is issued which indicates that external caches should also be flushed. Data held in write-back external caches is discarded.

Flags Affected

None

Protected Mode Exceptions

None

Real Address Mode Exceptions

None

Virtual 8086 Mode Exceptions

None

Notes

This instruction is implementation-dependent; its function may be implemented differently on future Intel processors.

It is the responsibility of hardware to respond to the external cache flush indication.

This instruction is not supported on 386 processors. See Section 3.11 for information on using this instruction compatible with 386 processors. See WBINVD description to write back dirty data to memory.

See Section 12.2 on disabling the cache.

INVLPG — Invalidate TLB Entry

Opcode	Instruction	Clocks	Description
0F 01/7	INVLPG m	12 for hit	Invalidate TLB Entry

Operation

INVALIDATE TLB ENTRY

Description

The INVLPG instruction is used to invalidate a single entry in the TLB, the cache used for page table entries. If the TLB contains a valid entry which maps the address of the memory operand, that TLB entry is marked invalid.

Flags Affected

None

Protected Mode Exceptions

An invalid-opcode exception is generated when used with a register operand.

Real Address Mode Exceptions

None

Virtual 8086 Mode Exceptions

An invalid-opcode exception is generated when used with a register operand.

Notes

This instruction is implementation-dependent; its function may be implemented differently on future Intel processors.

This instruction is not supported on 386 processors. See Section 3.11 for information on using this instruction compatible with 386 processors.

See Section 12.2 on disabling the cache.

IRET/IRETD—Interrupt Return

Opcode	Instruction	Clocks	Description
CF	IRET	15	Interrupt return (far return and pop flags)
CF	IRET	36	Interrupt return to lesser privilege
CF	IRET	TS+32	Interrupt return, different task (NT = 1)
CF	IRETD	15	Interrupt return (far return and pop flags)
CF	IRETD	36	Interrupt return to lesser privilege
CF	IRETD	15	Interrupt return to V86 mode
CF	IRETD	TS+32	Interrupt return, different task (NT = 1)

NOTE: Values of **ts** are given by the following table:

Old Task	New Task		
	to i486™ CPU TSS	to 80286 TSS	to VM TSS
VM/i486 CPU/80286 TSS	199	180	177

Operation

```
IF PE = 0
THEN (* Real-address mode *)
  IF OperandSize = 32 (* Instruction = IRETD *)
  THEN EIP ← Pop();
  ELSE (* Instruction = IRET *)
    IP ← Pop();
  FI;
  CS ← Pop();
  IF OperandSize = 32 (* Instruction = IRETD *)
  THEN EFLAGS ← Pop();
  ELSE (* Instruction = IRET *)
    FLAGS ← Pop();
  FI;
ELSE (* Protected mode *)
  IF VM = 1
  THEN #GP(0);
  ELSE
    IF NT = 1
    THEN GOTO TASK-RETURN;
    ELSE
      IF VM = 1 in flags image on stack
      THEN GO TO STACK-RETURN-TO-V86;
      ELSE GOTO STACK-RETURN;
      FI;
    FI;
  FI;
FI;STACK-RETURN-TO-V86: (* Interrupted procedure was in V86 mode *)
  IF top 36 bytes of stack not within limits
```

```
  THEN #SS(0);
  FI;
  IF instruction pointer not within code segment limit   THEN #GP(0);
  FI;

  EFLAGS ← SS:[ESP + 8]; (* Sets VM in interrupted routine *)
  EIP ← Pop();
  CS ← Pop(); (* CS behaves as in 8086, due to VM = 1 *)
  throwaway ← Pop(); (* pop away EFLAGS already read *)
  TempESP ← Pop();
  TempSS ← Pop();
  ES ← Pop(); (* pop 2 words; throw away high-order word *)
  DS ← Pop(); (* pop 2 words; throw away high-order word *)
  FS ← Pop(); (* pop 2 words; throw away high-order word *)
  GS ← Pop(); (* pop 2 words; throw away high-order word *)
    SS:ESP ← TempSS:TempESP;

  (* Resume execution in Virtual 8086 mode *)

TASK-RETURN:
  Examine Back Link Selector in TSS addressed by the current task
    register:
    Must specify global in the local/global bit, else #TS(new TSS selector);
    Index must be within GDT limits, else #TS(new TSS selector);
    AR byte must specify TSS, else #TS(new TSS selector);
    New TSS must be busy, else #TS(new TSS selector);
    TSS must be present, else #NP(new TSS selector);
  SWITCH-TASKS without nesting to TSS specified by back link selector;
  Mark the task just abandoned as NOT BUSY;
  Instruction pointer must be within code segment limit ELSE #GP(0);

STACK-RETURN:
  IF OperandSize=32
  THEN Third word on stack must be within stack limits, else #SS(0);
  ELSE Second word on stack must be within stack limits, else #SS(0);
  FI;
  Return CS selector RPL must be ≥ CPL, else #GP(Return selector);
  IF return selector RPL = CPL
  THEN GOTO RETURN-SAME-LEVEL;
  ELSE GOTO RETURN-OUTER-LEVEL;
  FI;

RETURN-SAME-LEVEL:
  IF OperandSize=32
  THEN
    Top 12 bytes on stack must be within limits, else #SS(0);
    Return CS selector (at eSP+4) must be non-null, else #GP(0);
  ELSE
    Top 6 bytes on stack must be within limits, else #SS(0);
```

```
    Return CS selector (at eSP+2) must be non-null, else #GP(0);
  FI;
  Selector index must be within its descriptor table limits, else #GP
    (Return selector);
  AR byte must indicate code segment, else #GP(Return selector);
  IF non-conforming
  THEN code segment DPL must = CPL;
  ELSE #GP(Return selector);
  FI;
  IF conforming
  THEN code segment DPL must be ≤ CPL, else #GP(Return selector);
  Segment must be present, else #NP(Return selector);
  Instruction pointer must be within code segment boundaries, else #GP(0);
  FI;
  IF OperandSize=32
  THEN
    Load CS:EIP from stack;
    Load CS-register with new code segment descriptor;
    Load EFLAGS with third doubleword from stack;
    Increment eSP by 12;
  ELSE
    Load CS-register with new code segment descriptor;
    Load FLAGS with third word on stack;
    Increment eSP by 6;
  FI;

RETURN-OUTER-LEVEL:
  IF OperandSize=32
  THEN Top 20 bytes on stack must be within limits, else #SS(0);
  ELSE Top 10 bytes on stack must be within limits, else #SS(0);
  FI;
  Examine return CS selector and associated descriptor:
    Selector must be non-null, else #GP(0);
    Selector index must be within its descriptor table limits;
      ELSE #GP(Return selector);
    AR byte must indicate code segment, else #GP(Return selector);
    IF non-conforming
    THEN code segment DPL must = CS selector RPL;
    ELSE #GP(Return selector);
    FI;
    IF conforming
    THEN code segment DPL must be > CPL;
    ELSE #GP(Return selector);
    FI;
    Segment must be present, else #NP(Return selector);

  Examine return SS selector and associated descriptor:
    Selector must be non-null, else #GP(0);
    Selector index must be within its descriptor table limits
```

```
        ELSE #GP(SS selector);
     Selector RPL must equal the RPL of the return CS selector
        ELSE #GP(SS selector);
     AR byte must indicate a writable data segment, else #GP(SS selector);
     Stack segment DPL must equal the RPL of the return CS selector
        ELSE #GP(SS selector);
     SS must be present, else #NP(SS selector);

  Instruction pointer must be within code segment limit ELSE #GP(0);
  IF OperandSize=32
  THEN
     Load CS:EIP from stack;
     Load EFLAGS with values at (eSP+8);
  ELSE
     Load CS:IP from stack;
     Load FLAGS with values at (eSP+4);
  FI;
  Load SS:eSP from stack;
  Set CPL to the RPL of the return CS selector;
  Load the CS register with the CS descriptor;
  Load the SS register with the SS descriptor;
  FOR each of ES, FS, GS, and DS
  DO;
     IF the current value of the register is not valid for the outer level;
     THEN zero the register and clear the valid flag;
     FI;
     To be valid, the register setting must satisfy the following properties:
        Selector index must be within descriptor table limits;
        AR byte must indicate data or readable code segment;
        IF segment is data or non-conforming code,
        THEN DPL must be > CPL, or DPL must be < RPL;
  OD;
```

Description

In Real Address Mode, the IRET instruction pops the instruction pointer, the CS register, and the flags register from the stack and resumes the interrupted routine.

In Protected Mode, the action of the IRET instruction depends on the setting of the nested task flag (NT) bit in the flag register. When the new flag image is popped from the stack, the IOPL bits in the flag register are changed only when CPL equals 0.

If the NT flag is cleared, the IRET instruction returns from an interrupt procedure without a task switch. The code returned to must be equally or less privileged than the interrupt routine (as indicated by the RPL bits of the CS selector popped from the stack). If the destination code is less privileged, the IRET instruction also pops the stack pointer and SS from the stack.

If the NT flag is set, the IRET instruction reverses the operation of a CALL or INT that caused a task switch. The updated state of the task executing the IRET instruction is saved in its task state segment. If the task is reentered later, the code that follows the IRET instruction is executed.

Flags Affected

All flags are affected; the flags register is popped from stack

Protected Mode Exceptions

#GP, #NP, or #SS, as indicated under "Operation" above

Real Address Mode Exceptions

Interrupt 13 if any part of the operand being popped lies beyond address 0FFFFH

Virtual 8086 Mode Exceptions

#GP(0) fault if the I/O privilege level is less than 3, to permit emulation

Jcc—Jump if Condition is Met

Opcode	Instruction	Clocks	Description
77 *cb*	JA *rel8*	3,1	Jump short if above (CF=0 and ZF=0)
73 *cb*	JAE *rel8*	3,1	Jump short if above or equal (CF=0)
72 *cb*	JB *rel8*	3,1	Jump short if below (CF=1)
76 *cb*	JBE *rel8*	3,1	Jump short if below or equal (CF=1 or ZF=1)
72 *cb*	JC *rel8*	3,1	Jump short if carry (CF=1)
E3 *cb*	JCXZ *rel8*	8,5	Jump short if CX register is 0
E3 *cb*	JECXZ *rel8*	8,5	Jump short if ECX register is 0
74 *cb*	JE *rel8*	3,1	Jump short if equal (ZF=1)
74 *cb*	JZ *rel8*	3,1	Jump short if 0 (ZF=1)
7F *cb*	JG *rel8*	3,1	Jump short if greater (ZF=0 and SF=OF)
7D *cb*	JGE *rel8*	3,1	Jump short if greater or equal (SF=OF)
7C *cb*	JL *rel8*	3,1	Jump short if less (SF< >OF)
7E *cb*	JLE *rel8*	3,1	Jump short if less or equal (ZF=1 or SF< >OF)
76 *cb*	JNA *rel8*	3,1	Jump short if not above (CF=1 or ZF=1)
72 *cb*	JNAE *rel8*	3,1	Jump short if not above or equal (CF=1)
73 *cb*	JNB *rel8*	3,1	Jump short if not below (CF=0)
77 *cb*	JNBE *rel8*	3,1	Jump short if not below or equal (CF=0 and ZF=0)
73 *cb*	JNC *rel8*	3,1	Jump short if not carry (CF=0)
75 *cb*	JNE *rel8*	3,1	Jump short if not equal (ZF=0)
7E *cb*	JNG *rel8*	3,1	Jump short if not greater (ZF=1 or SF< >OF)
7C *cb*	JNGE *rel8*	3,1	Jump short if not greater or equal (SF< >OF)
7D *cb*	JNL *rel8*	3,1	Jump short if not less (SF=OF)
7F *cb*	JNLE *rel8*	3,1	Jump short if not less or equal (ZF=0 and SF=OF)
71 *cb*	JNO *rel8*	3,1	Jump short if not overflow (OF=0)
7B *cb*	JNP *rel8*	3,1	Jump short if not parity (PF=0)
79 *cb*	JNS *rel8*	3,1	Jump short if not sign (SF=0)
75 *cb*	JNZ *rel8*	3,1	Jump short if not zero (ZF=0)
70 *cb*	JO *rel8*	3,1	Jump short if overflow (OF=1)
7A *cb*	JP *rel8*	3,1	Jump short if parity (PF=1)
7A *cb*	JPE *rel8*	3,1	Jump short if parity even (PF=1)
7B *cb*	JPO *rel8*	3,1	Jump short if parity odd (PF=0)
78 *cb*	JS *rel8*	3,1	Jump short if sign (SF=1)
74 *cb*	JZ *rel8*	3,1	Jump short if zero (ZF = 1)
0F 87 *cw/cd*	JA *rel16/32*	3,1	Jump near if above (CF=0 and ZF=0)
0F 83 *cw/cd*	JAE *rel16/32*	3,1	Jump near if above or equal (CF=0)
0F 82 *cw/cd*	JB *rel16/32*	3,1	Jump near if below (CF=1)
0F 86 *cw/cd*	JBE *rel16/32*	3,1	Jump near if below or equal (CF=1 or ZF=1)
0F 82 *cw/cd*	JC *rel16/32*	3,1	Jump near if carry (CF=1)
0F 84 *cw/cd*	JE *rel16/32*	3,1	Jump near if equal (ZF=1)
0F 84 *cw/cd*	JZ *rel16/32*	3,1	Jump near if 0 (ZF=1)
0F 8F *cw/cd*	JG *rel16/32*	3,1	Jump near if greater (ZF=0 and SF=OF)
0F 8D *cw/cd*	JGE *rel16/32*	3,1	Jump near if greater or equal (SF=OF)
0F 8C *cw/cd*	JL *rel16/32*	3,1	Jump near if less (SF< >OF)

Opcode	Instruction	Clocks	Description
0F 8E *cw/cd*	JLE *rel16/32*	3,1	Jump near if less or equal (ZF = 1 or SF < > OF)
0F 86 *cw/cd*	JNA *rel16/32*	3,1	Jump near if not above (CF = 1 or ZF = 1)
0F 82 *cw/cd*	JNAE *rel16/32*	3,1	Jump near if not above or equal (CF = 1)
0F 83 *cw/cd*	JNB *rel16/32*	3,1	Jump near if not below (CF = 0)
0F 87 *cw/cd*	JNBE *rel16/32*	3,1	Jump near if not below or equal (CF = 0 and ZF = 0)
0F 83 *cw/cd*	JNC *rel16/32*	3,1	Jump near if not carry (CF = 0)
0F 85 *cw/cd*	JNE *rel16/32*	3,1	Jump near if not equal (ZF = 0)
0F 8E *cw/cd*	JNG *rel16/32*	3,1	Jump near if not greater (ZF = 1 or SF < > OF)
0F 8C *cw/cd*	JNGE *rel16/32*	3,1	Jump near if not greater or equal (SF < > OF)
0F 8D *cw/cd*	JNL *rel16/32*	3,1	Jump near if not less (SF = OF)
0F 8F *cw/cd*	JNLE *rel16/32*	3,1	Jump near if not less or equal (ZF = 0 and SF = OF)
0F 81 *cw/cd*	JNO *rel16/32*	3,1	Jump near if not overflow (OF = 0)
0F 8B *cw/cd*	JNP *rel16/32*	3,1	Jump near if not parity (PF = 0)
0F 89 *cw/cd*	JNS *rel16/32*	3,1	Jump near if not sign (SF = 0)
0F 85 *cw/cd*	JNZ *rel16/32*	3,1	Jump near if not zero (ZF = 0)
0F 80 *cw/cd*	JO *rel16/32*	3,1	Jump near if overflow (OF = 1)
0F 8A *cw/cd*	JP *rel16/32*	3,1	Jump near if parity (PF = 1)
0F 8A *cw/cd*	JPE *rel16/32*	3,1	Jump near if parity even (PF = 1)
0F 8B *cw/cd*	JPO *rel16/32*	3,1	Jump near if parity odd (PF = 0)
0F 88 *cw/cd*	JS *rel16/32*	3,1	Jump near if sign (SF = 1)
0F 84 *cw/cd*	JZ *rel16/32*	3,1	Jump near if 0 (ZF = 1)

NOTES: The first clock count is for the true condition (branch taken); the second clock count is for the false condition (branch not taken). *rel16/32* indicates that these instructions map to two; one with a 16-bit relative displacement, the other with a 32-bit relative displacement, depending on the operand-size attribute of the instruction.

Operation

```
IF condition
THEN
   EIP ← EIP + SignExtend(rel8/16/32);
   IF OperandSize = 16
   THEN EIP ← EIP AND 0000FFFFH;
   FI;
FI;
```

Description

Conditional jumps (except the JCXZ instruction) test the flags which have been set by a previous instruction. The conditions for each mnemonic are given in parentheses after each description above. The terms “less” and “greater” are used for comparisons of signed integers; “above” and “below” are used for unsigned integers.

If the given condition is true, a jump is made to the location provided as the operand. Instruction coding is most efficient when the target for the conditional jump is in the current code segment and within −128 to +127 bytes of the next instruction’s first byte.

The jump can also target −32768 thru +32767 (segment size attribute 16) or -2^{31} thru $+2^{31}-1$ (segment size attribute 32) relative to the next instruction's first byte. When the target for the conditional jump is in a different segment, use the opposite case of the jump instruction (i.e., the JE and JNE instructions), and then access the target with an unconditional far jump to the other segment. For example, you cannot code–

```
JZ FARLABEL;
```

You must instead code–

```
        JNZ BEYOND;
        JMP FARLABEL;
BEYOND:
```

Because there can be several ways to interpret a particular state of the flags, ASM386 provides more than one mnemonic for most of the conditional jump opcodes. For example, if you compared two characters in AX and want to jump if they are equal, use the JE instruction; or, if you ANDed the AX register with a bit field mask and only want to jump if the result is 0, use the JZ instruction, a synonym for the JE instruction.

The JCXZ instruction differs from other conditional jumps because it tests the contents of the CX or ECX register for 0, not the flags. The JCXZ instruction is useful at the beginning of a conditional loop that terminates with a conditional loop instruction (such as LOOPNE TARGET LABEL. The JCXZ instruction prevents entering the loop with the CX or ECX register equal to zero, which would cause the loop to execute 64K or 32G times instead of zero times.

Flags Affected

None

Protected Mode Exceptions

#GP(0) if the offset jumped to is beyond the limits of the code segment

Real Address Mode Exceptions

None

Virtual 8086 Mode Exceptions

None

Notes

The JCXZ instruction takies longer to execute than a two-instruction sequence which compares the count register to zero and jumps if the count is zero.

All branches are converted into 16-byte code fetches regardless of jump address or cacheability.

JMP—Jump

Opcode	Instruction	Clocks	Description
EB *cb*	JMP *rel8*	3	Jump short
E9 *cw*	JMP *rel16*	3	Jump near, displacement relative to next instruction
FF /4	JMP *r/m16*	5/5	Jump near indirect
EA *cd*	JMP *ptr16:16*	17*pm*=19	Jump intersegment, 4-byte immediate address
EA *cd*	JMP *ptr16:16*	32	Jump to call gate, same privilege
EA *cd*	JMP *ptr16:16*	42+TS	Jump via task state segment
EA *cd*	JMP *ptr16:16*	43+TS	Jump via task gate
FF /5	JMP *m16:16*	13,*pm*=18	Jump *r/m16:16* indirect and intersegment
FF /5	JMP *m16:16*	31	Jump to call gate, same privilege
FF /5	JMP *m16:16*	41+TS	Jump via task state segment
FF /5	JMP *m16:16*	42+TS	Jump via task gate
E9 *cd*	JMP *rel32*	3	Jump near, displacement relative to next instruction
FF /4	JMP *r/m32*	5/5	Jump near, indirect
EA *cp*	JMP *ptr16:32*	13,*pm*=18	Jump intersegment, 6-byte immediate address
EA *cp*	JMP *ptr16:32*	31	Jump to call gate, same privilege
EA *cp*	JMP *ptr16:32*	42+TS	Jump via task state segment
EA *cp*	JMP *ptr16:32*	43+TS	Jump via task gate
FF /5	JMP *m16:32*	13,*pm*=18	Jump intersegment, address at *r/m* dword
FF /5	JMP *m16:32*	31	Jump to call gate, same privilege
FF /5	JMP *m16:32*	41+TS	Jump via task state segment
FF /5	JMP *m16:32*	42+TS	Jump via task gate

NOTE: Values of **ts** are given by the following table:

Old Task	New Task		
	to i486™ CPU TSS	to 80286 TSS	to VM TSS
VM/i486 CPU/80286 TSS	199	180	177

Operation

```
IF instruction = relative JMP
   (* i.e. operand is rel8, rel16, or rel32 *)
THEN
   EIP ← EIP + rel8/16/32;
   IF OperandSize = 16
   THEN EIP ← EIP AND 0000FFFFH;
   FI;
FI;

IF instruction = near indirect JMP
   (* i.e. operand is r/m16 or r/m32 *)
THEN
   IF OperandSize = 16
   THEN
      EIP ← [r/m16 AND 0000FFFFH;
```

```
   ELSE (* OperandSize = 32 *)
      EIP ← [r/m32;
   FI;
FI;

IF (PE = 0 OR (PE = 1 AND VM = 1)) (* real mode or V86 mode *)
   AND instruction = far JMP
   (* i.e., operand type is m16:16, m16:32, ptr16:16, ptr16:32 *)
THEN GOTO REAL-OR-V86-MODE;
   IF operand type = m16:16 or m16:32
   THEN (* indirect *)
      IF OperandSize = 16
      THEN
         CS:IP ← [m16:16;
         EIP ← EIP AND 0000FFFFH; (* clear upper 16 bits *)
      ELSE (* OperandSize = 32 *)
         CS:EIP ← [m16:32;
      FI;
   FI;
   IF operand type = ptr16:16 or ptr16:32
   THEN
      IF OperandSize = 16
      THEN
         CS:IP ← ptr16:16;
         EIP ← EIP AND 0000FFFFH; (* clear upper 16 bits *)
      ELSE (* OperandSize = 32 *)
         CS:EIP ← ptr16:32;
      FI;
   FI;
FI;

IF (PE = 1 AND VM = 0) (* Protected mode, not V86 mode *)
   AND instruction = far JMP
THEN
   IF operand type = m16:16 or m16:32
   THEN (* indirect *)
      check access of EA dword;
      #GP(0) or #SS(0) IF limit violation;
   FI;
   Destination selector is not null ELSE #GP(0)
   Destination selector index is within its descriptor table limits ELSE #GP(selector)
   Depending on AR byte of destination descriptor:
      GOTO CONFORMING-CODE-SEGMENT;
      GOTO NONCONFORMING-CODE-SEGMENT;
      GOTO CALL-GATE;
      GOTO TASK-GATE;
      GOTO TASK-STATE-SEGMENT;
   ELSE #GP(selector); (* illegal AR byte in descriptor *)
FI;
```

```
CONFORMING-CODE-SEGMENT:
  Descriptor DPL must be ≤ CPL ELSE #GP(selector);
  Segment must be present ELSE #NP(selector);
  Instruction pointer must be within code-segment limit ELSE #GP(0);
  IF OperandSize = 32
  THEN Load CS:EIP from destination pointer;
  ELSE Load CS:IP from destination pointer;
  FI;
  Load CS register with new segment descriptor;

NONCONFORMING-CODE-SEGMENT:
  RPL of destination selector must be ≤ CPL ELSE #GP(selector);
  Descriptor DPL must be = CPL ELSE #GP(selector);
  Segment must be present ELSE # NP(selector);
  Instruction pointer must be within code-segment limit ELSE #GP(0);
  IF OperandSize = 32
  THEN Load CS:EIP from destination pointer;
  ELSE Load CS:IP from destination pointer;
  FI;
  Load CS register with new segment descriptor;
  Set RPL field of CS register to CPL;

CALL-GATE:
  Descriptor DPL must be ≥ CPL ELSE #GP(gate selector);
  Descriptor DPL must be ≥ gate selector RPL ELSE #GP(gate selector);
  Gate must be present ELSE #NP(gate selector);
  Examine selector to code segment given in call gate descriptor:
    Selector must not be null ELSE #GP(0);
    Selector must be within its descriptor table limits ELSE
    #GP(CS selector);
    Descriptor AR byte must indicate code segment
      ELSE #GP(CS selector);
    IF non-conforming
    THEN code-segment descriptor, DPL must = CPL
    ELSE #GP(CS selector);
    FI;
    IF conforming
    THEN code-segment descriptor DPL must be ≤ CPL;
    ELSE #GP(CS selector);
    Code segment must be present ELSE #NP(CS selector);
    Instruction pointer must be within code-segment limit ELSE #GP(0);
    IF OperandSize = 32
    THEN Load CS:EIP from call gate;
    ELSE Load CS:IP from call gate;
    FI;
  Load CS register with new code-segment descriptor;
  Set RPL of CS to CPL

TASK-GATE:
  Gate descriptor DPL must be ≥ CPL ELSE #GP(gate selector);
```

```
Gate descriptor DPL must be ≥ gate selector RPL ELSE #GP(gate selector);
Task Gate must be present ELSE #NP(gate selector);
Examine selector to TSS, given in Task Gate descriptor:
   Must specify global in the local/global bit ELSE #GP(TSS selector);
   Index must be within GDT limits ELSE #GP(TSS selector);
   Descriptor AR byte must specify available TSS (bottom bits 00001);
      ELSE #GP(TSS selector);
   Task State Segment must be present ELSE #NP(TSS selector);
SWITCH-TASKS (without nesting) to TSS;
Instruction pointer must be within code-segment limit ELSE #GP(0);

TASK-STATE-SEGMENT:
TSS DPL must be ≥ CPL ELSE #GP(TSS selector);
TSS DPL must be ≥ TSS selector RPL ELSE #GP(TSS selector);
Descriptor AR byte must specify available TSS (bottom bits 00001)
   ELSE #GP(TSS selector);
Task State Segment must be present ELSE #NP(TSS selector);
SWITCH-TASKS (without nesting) to TSS;
Instruction pointer must be within code-segment limit ELSE #GP(0);
```

Description

The JMP instruction transfers control to a different point in the instruction stream without recording return information.

The action of the various forms of the instruction are shown below.

Jumps with destinations of type *r/m16*, *r/m32*, *rel16*, and *rel32*are near jumps and do not involve changing the segment register value.

The JMP *rel16* and JMP *rel32* forms of the instruction add an offset to the address of the instruction following the JMP to determine the destination. The *rel16* form is used when the instruction's operand-size attribute is 16 bits (segment size attribute 16 only); *rel32* is used when the operand-size attribute is 32 bits (segment size attribute 32 only). The result is stored in the 32-bit EIP register. With *rel16*, the upper 16 bits of the EIP register are cleared, which results in an offset whose value does not exceed 16 bits.

The JMP *r/m16* and JMP *r/m32* forms specify a register or memory location from which the absolute offset from the procedure is fetched. The offset fetched from *r/m* is 32 bits for an operand-size attribute of 32 bits (*r/m32*), or 16 bits for an operand-size attribute of 16 bits (*r/m16*).

The JMP *ptr16:16* and *ptr16:32* forms of the instruction use a four-byte or six-byte operand as a long pointer to the destination. The JMP *m16:16* and *m16:32* forms fetch the long pointer from the memory location specified (indirection). In Real Address Mode or Virtual 8086 Mode, the long pointer provides 16 bits for the CS register and 16 or 32 bits for the EIP register (depending on the operand-size attribute). In Protected Mode, both long pointer forms consult the Access Rights (AR) byte in the descriptor indexed by the selector part of the long pointer. Depending on the value of the AR byte, the jump will perform one of the following types of control transfers:

- A jump to a code segment at the same privilege level
- A task switch

For more information on protected mode control transfers, refer to Chapter 6 and Chapter 7.

Flags Affected

All if a task switch takes place; none if no task switch occurs

Protected Mode Exceptions

Far jumps: #GP, #NP, #SS, and #TS, as indicated in the list above.

Near direct jumps: #GP(0) if procedure location is beyond the code segment limits; #AC for unaligned memory reference if the current privilege level is 3

Near indirect jumps: #GP(0) for an illegal memory operand effective address in the CS, DS, ES, FS, or GS segments: #SS(0) for an illegal address in the SS segment; #GP if the indirect offset obtained is beyond the code segment limits; #PF(fault-code) for a page fault; #AC for unaligned memory reference if the current privilege level is 3

Real Address Mode Exceptions

Interrupt 13 if any part of the operand would be outside of the effective address space from 0 to 0FFFFH

Virtual 8086 Mode Exceptions

Same exceptions as under Real Address Mode; #PF(fault-code) for a page fault; #AC for unaligned memory reference if the current privilege level is 3

Notes

All branches are converted into 16-byte code fetches regardless of jump address or cacheability.

LAHF — Load Flags into AH Register

Opcode	Instruction	Clocks	Description
9F	LAHF	3	Load: AH = flags SF ZF xx AF xx PF xx CF

Operation

AH ← SF:ZF:xx:AF:xx:PF:xx:CF;

Description

The LAHF instruction transfers the low byte of the flags word to the AH register. The bits, from MSB to LSB, are sign, zero, indeterminate, auxiliary, carry, indeterminate, parity, indeterminate, and carry.

Flags Affected

None

Protected Mode Exceptions

None

Real Address Mode Exceptions

None

Virtual 8086 Mode Exceptions

None

LAR — Load Access Rights Byte

Opcode	Instruction	Clocks	Description
0F 02 /r	LAR *r16,r/m16*	11/11	*r16* ← *r/m16* masked by FF00
0F 02 /r	LAR *r32,r/m32*	11/11	*r32* ← *r/m32* masked by 00FxFF00

Description

The LAR instruction stores a marked form of the second doubleword of the descriptor for the source selector if the selector is visible at the current privilege level (modified by the selector's RPL) and is a valid descriptor type within the descriptor limits. The destination register is loaded with the high-order doubleword of the descriptor masked by 00FxFF00, and the ZF flag is set. The x indicates that the four bits corresponding to the upper four bits of the limit are undefined in the value loaded by the LAR instruction. If the selector is invisible or of the wrong type, the ZF flag is cleared.

If the 32-bit operand size is specified, the entire 32-bit value is loaded into the 32-bit destination register. If the 16-bit operand size is specified, the lower 16-bits of this value are stored in the 16-bit destination register.

All code and data segment descriptors are valid for the LAR instruction.

The valid special segment and gate descriptor types for the LAR instruction are given in the following table:

Type	Name	Valid/Invalid
0	Invalid	Invalid
1	Available 80286 TSS	Valid
2	LDT	Valid
3	Busy 80286 TSS	Valid
4	80286 call gate	Valid
5	80286/i486™ task gate	Valid
6	80286 trap gate	Valid
7	80286 interrupt gate	Valid
8	Invalid	Invalid
9	Available i486 TSS	Valid
A	Invalid	Invalid
B	Busy i486 TSS	Valid
C	i486 call gate	Valid
D	Invalid	Invalid
E	i486 trap gate	Valid
F	i486 interrupt gate	Valid

Flags Affected

The ZF flag is set unless the selector is invisible or of the wrong type, in which case the ZF flag is cleared.

Protected Mode Exceptions

#GP(0) for an illegal memory operand effective address in the CS, DS, ES, FS, or GS segments; #SS(0) for an illegal address in the SS segment; #PF(fault-code) for a page fault; #AC for unaligned memory reference if the current privilege level is 3

Real Address Mode Exceptions

Interrupt 6; the LAR instruction is unrecognized in Real Address Mode

Virtual 8086 Mode Exceptions

Same exceptions as in Real Address Mode

LEA — Load Effective Address

Opcode	Instruction	Clocks	Description
8D /r	LEA *r16,m*	1	Store effective address for *m* in register *r16*
8D /r	LEA *r32,m*	1	Store effective address for *m* in register *r32*
8D /r	LEA *r16,m*	1	Store effective address for *m* in register *r16*
8D /r	LEA *r32,m*	1	Store effective address for *m* in register *r32*

Operation

```
IF OperandSize = 16 AND AddressSize = 16
THEN r16 ← Addr(m);
ELSE
  IF OperandSize = 16 AND AddressSize = 32
  THEN
    r16 ← Truncate_to_16bits(Addr(m));        (* 32-bit address *
  ELSE
    IF OperandSize = 32 AND AddressSize = 16
    THEN
      r32 ← Truncate_to_16bits(Addr(m));
    ELSE
      IF OperandSize = 32 AND AddressSize = 32
      THEN    r32 ← Addr(m);
      FI;
    FI;
  FI;
FI;
```

Description

The LEA instruction calculates the effective address (offset part) and stores it in the specified register. The operand-size attribute of the instruction (represented by OperandSize in the algorithm under "Operation" above) is determined by the chosen register. The address-size attribute (represented by AddressSize) is determined by the USE attribute of the segment containing the second operand. The address-size and operand-size attributes affect the action performed by the LEA instruction, as follows:

Operand Size	Address Size	Action Performed
16	16	16-bit effective address is calculated and stored in requested 16-bit register destination.
16	32	32-bit effective address is calculated. The lower 16 bits of the address are stored in the requested 16-bit register destination.
32	16	16-bit effective address is calculated. The 16-bit address is zero-extended and stored in the requested 32-bit register destination.
32	32	32-bit effective address is calculated and stored in the requested 32-bit register destination.

Flags Affected

None

Protected Mode Exceptions

#UD if the second operand is a register

Real Address Mode Exceptions

Interrupt 6 if the second operand is a register

Virtual 8086 Mode Exceptions

Same exceptions as in Real Address Mode

LEAVE — High Level Procedure Exit

Opcode	Instruction	Clocks	Description
C9	LEAVE	5	Set SP to BP, then pop BP
C9	LEAVE	5	Set ESP to EBP, then pop EBP

Operation

```
IF StackAddrSize = 16
THEN
   SP ← BP;
ELSE (* StackAddrSize = 32 *)
   ESP ← EBP;
FI;
IF OperandSize = 16
THEN
   BP ← Pop();
ELSE (* OperandSize = 32 *)
   EBP ← Pop();
FI;
```

Description

The LEAVE instruction reverses the actions of the ENTER instruction. By copying the frame pointer to the stack pointer, the LEAVE instruction releases the stack space used by a procedure for its local variables. The old frame pointer is popped into the BP or EBP register, restoring the caller's frame. A subsequent RET *nn* instruction removes any arguments pushed onto the stack of the exiting procedure.

Flags Affected

None

Protected Mode Exceptions

#SS(0) if the BP register does not point to a location within the limits of the current stack segment

Real Address Mode Exceptions

Interrupt 13 if any part of the operand would lie outside of the effective address space from 0 to 0FFFFH

Virtual 8086 Mode Exceptions

Same exceptions as in Real Address Mode

LGDT/LIDT—Load Global/Interrupt Descriptor Table Register

Opcode	Instruction	Clocks	Description
0F 01 /2	LGDT *m16&32*	11	Load *m* into GDTR
0F 01 /3	LIDT *m16&32*	11	Load *m* into IDTR

Operation

```
IF instruction = LIDT
THEN
   IF OperandSize = 16
   THEN IDTR.Limit:Base ← m16:24 (* 24 bits of base loaded *)
   ELSE IDTR.Limit:Base ← m16:32
   FI;
ELSE (* instruction = LGDT *)
   IF OperandSize = 16
   THEN GDTR.Limit:Base ← m16:24 (* 24 bits of base loaded *)
   ELSE GDTR.Limit:Base ← m16:32;
   FI;
FI;
```

Description

The LGDT and LIDT instructions load a linear base address and limit value from a six-byte data operand in memory into the GDTR or IDTR, respectively. If a 16-bit operand is used with the LGDT or LIDT instruction, the register is loaded with a 16-bit limit and a 24-bit base, and the high-order eight bits of the six-byte data operand are not used. If a 32-bit operand is used, a 16-bit limit and a 32-bit base is loaded; the high-order eight bits of the six-byte operand are used as high-order base address bits.

The SGDT and SIDT instructions always store into all 48 bits of the six-byte data operand. With the 80286 processor, the upper eight bits are undefined after the SGDT or SIDT instruction is executed. With the 386 DX or i486 processors, the upper eight bits are written with the high-order eight address bits, for both a 16-bit operand and a 32-bit operand. If the LGDT or LIDT instruction is used with a 16-bit operand to load the register stored by the SGDT or SIDT instruction, the upper eight bits are stored as zeros.

The LGDT and LIDT instructions appear in operating system software; they are not used in application programs. They are the only instructions that directly load a linear address (i.e., not a segment relative address) in Protected Mode.

Flags Affected

None

Protected Mode Exceptions

#GP(0) if the current privilege level is not 0; #UD if the source operand is a register; #GP(0) for an illegal memory operand effective address in the CS, DS, ES, FS, or GS segments; #SS(0) for an illegal address in the SS segment; #PF(fault-code) for a page fault

Real Address Mode Exceptions

Interrupt 13 if any part of the operand would lie outside of the effective address space from 0 to 0FFFFH; Interrupt 6 if the source operand is a register

Note: These instructions are valid in Real Address Mode to allow power-up initialization for Protected Mode

Virtual 8086 Mode Exceptions

Same exceptions as in Real Address Mode; #PF(fault-code) for a page fault

LGS/LSS/LDS/LES/LFS — Load Full Pointer

Opcode	Instruction	Clocks	Description
C5 /r	LDS *r16,m16:16*	6/12	Load DS:*r16* with pointer from memory
C5 /r	LDS *r32,m16:32*	6/12	Load DS:*r32* with pointer from memory
0F B2 /r	LSS *r16,m16:16*	6/12	Load SS:*r16* with pointer from memory
0F B2 /r	LSS *r32,m16:32*	6/12	Load SS:*r32* with pointer from memory
C4 /r	LES *r16,m16:16*	6/12	Load ES:*r16* with pointer from memory
C4 /r	LES *r32,m16:32*	6/12	Load ES:*r32* with pointer from memory
0F B4 /r	LFS *r16,m16:16*	6/12	Load FS:*r16* with pointer from memory
0F B4 /r	LFS *r32,m16:32*	6/12	Load FS:*r32* with pointer from memory
0F B5 /r	LGS *r16,m16:16*	6/12	Load GS:*r16* with pointer from memory
0F B5 /r	LGS *r32,m16:32*	6/12	Load GS:*r32* with pointer from memory

Operation

```
CASE instruction OF
  LSS: Sreg is SS; (* Load SS register *)
  LDS: Sreg is DS; (* Load DS register *)
  LES: Sreg is ES; (* Load ES register *)
  LFS: Sreg is FS; (* Load FS register *)
  LGS: Sreg is DS; (* Load GS register *)
ESAC;
IF (OperandSize = 16)
THEN
  r16 ← [Effective Address]; (* 16-bit transfer *)
  Sreg ← [Effective Address + 2]; (* 16-bit transfer *)
  (* In Protected Mode, load the descriptor into the segment register *)
ELSE (* OperandSize = 32 *)
  r32 ← [Effective Address]; (* 32-bit transfer *)
  Sreg ← [Effective Address + 4]; (* 16-bit transfer *)
  (* In Protected Mode, load the descriptor into the segment register *)
FI;
```

Description

The LGS, LSS, LDS, LES, and LFS instructions read a full pointer from memory and store it in the selected segment register:register pair. The full pointer loads 16 bits into the segment register SS, DS, ES, FS, or GS. The other register loads 32 bits if the operand-size attribute is 32 bits, or loads 16 bits if the operand-size attribute is 16 bits. The other 16- or 32-bit register to be loaded is determined by the *r16* or *r32* register operand specified.

When an assignment is made to one of the segment registers, the descriptor is also loaded into the segment register. The data for the register is obtained from the descriptor table entry for the selector given.

A null selector (values 0000-0003) can be loaded into DS, ES, FS, or GS registers without causing a protection exception. (Any subsequent reference to a segment whose corresponding segment register is loaded with a null selector to address memory causes a #GP(0) exception. No memory reference to the segment occurs.)

The following is a listing of the Protected Mode checks and actions taken in the loading of a segment register:

```
IF SS is loaded:
   IF selector is null THEN #GP(0); FI;
   Selector index must be within its descriptor table limits ELSE
      #GP(selector);
   Selector's RPL must equal CPL ELSE #GP(selector);
   AR byte must indicate a writable data segment ELSE #GP(selector);
   DPL in the AR byte must equal CPL ELSE #GP(selector);
   Segment must be marked present ELSE #SS(selector);
   Load SS with selector;
   Load SS with descriptor;

IF DS, ES, FS, or GS is loaded with non-null selector:
   Selector index must be within its descriptor table limits ELSE
      #GP(selector);
   AR byte must indicate data or readable code segment ELSE
      #GP(selector);
   IF data or nonconforming code
   THEN both the RPL and the CPL must be less than or equal to DPL in
      AR byte;
   ELSE #GP(selector);
   Segment must be marked present ELSE #NP(selector);
Load segment register with selector and RPL bits;
Load segment register with descriptor;

IF DS, ES, FS or GS is loaded with a null selector:
   Load segment register with selector;
   Clear descriptor valid bit;
```

Flags Affected

None

Protected Mode Exceptions

#GP(0) for an illegal memory operand effective address in the CS, DS, ES, FS, or GS segments; #SS(0) for an illegal address in the SS segment; the second operand must be a memory operand, not a register; #GP(0) if a null selector is loaded into SS; #PF(fault-code) for a page fault; #AC for unaligned memory reference if the current privilege level is 3

Real Address Mode Exceptions

The second operand must be a memory operand, not a register; Interrupt 13 if any part of the operand would lie outside of the effective address space from 0 to 0FFFFH

Virtual 8086 Mode Exceptions

Same exceptions as in Real Address Mode; #PF(fault-code) for a page fault; #AC for unaligned memory reference if the current privilege level is 3

LLDT—Load Local Descriptor Table Register

Opcode	Instruction	Clocks	Description
0F 00 /2	LLDT *r/m16*	11/11	Load selector *r/m16* into LDTR

Operation

LDTR ← SRC;

Description

The LLDT instruction loads the Local Descriptor Table register (LDTR). The word operand (memory or register) to the LLDT instruction should contain a selector to the Global Descriptor Table (GDT). The GDT entry should be a Local Descriptor Table. If so, then the LDTR is loaded from the entry. The descriptor registers DS, ES, SS, FS, GS, and CS are not affected. The LDT field in the task state segment does not change.

The selector operand can be 0; if so, the LDTR is marked invalid. All descriptor references (except by the LAR, VERR, VERW or LSL instructions) cause a #GP fault.

The LLDT instruction is used in operating system software; it is not used in application programs.

Flags Affected

None

Protected Mode Exceptions

#GP(0) if the current privilege level is not 0; #GP(selector) if the selector operand does not point into the Global Descriptor Table, or if the entry in the GDT is not a Local Descriptor Table; #NP(selector) if the LDT descriptor is not present; #GP(0) for an illegal memory operand effective address in the CS, DS, ES, FS, or GS segments; #SS(0) for an illegal address in the SS segment; #PF(fault-code) for a page fault

Real Address Mode Exceptions

Interrupt 6; the LLDT instruction is not recognized in Real Address Mode

Virtual 8086 Mode Exceptions

Same exceptions as in Real Address Mode (because the instruction is not recognized, it will not execute or perform a memory reference)

Note

The operand-size attribute has no effect on this instruction.

LMSW – Load Machine Status Word

Opcode	Instruction	Clocks	Description
0F 01 /6	LMSW *r/m16*	13/13	Load *r/m16* in machine status word

Operation

MSW ← *r/m16*; (* 16 bits is stored in the machine status word *)

Description

The LMSW instruction loads the machine status word (part of the CR0 register) from the source operand. This instruction can be used to switch to Protected Mode; if so, it must be followed by an intrasegment jump to flush the instruction queue. The LMSW instruction will not switch back to Real Address Mode.

The LMSW instruction is used only in operating system software. It is not used in application programs.

Flags Affected

None

Protected Mode Exceptions

#GP(0) if the current privilege level is not 0; #GP(0) for an illegal memory operand effective address in the CS, DS, ES, FS, or GS segments; #SS(0) for an illegal address in the SS segment; #PF(fault-code) for a page fault

Real Address Mode Exceptions

Interrupt 13 if any part of the operand would lie outside of the effective address space from 0 to 0FFFFH

Virtual 8086 Mode Exceptions

Same exceptions as in Real Address Mode; #PF(fault-code) for a page fault

Notes

The operand-size attribute has no effect on this instruction. This instruction is provided for compatibility with the 80286 processor; programs for the i486 processor should use the MOV CR0, ... instruction instead. The LMSW instruction does not affect the PG or ET bits, and it cannot be used to clear the PE bit.

LOCK—Assert LOCK# Signal Prefix

Opcode	Instruction	Clocks	Description
F0	LOCK	1	Assert LOCK# signal for the next instruction

Description

The LOCK prefix causes the LOCK# signal of the i486 processor to be asserted during execution of the instruction that follows it. In a multiprocessor environment, this signal can be used to ensure that the i486 processor has exclusive use of any shared memory while LOCK# is asserted. The read-modify-write sequence typically used to implement test-and-set on the i486 processor is the BTS instruction.

The LOCK prefix functions only with the following instructions:

BTS, BTR, BTC	mem, reg/imm
XCHG	reg, mem
XCHG	mem, reg
ADD, OR, ADC, SBB, AND, SUB, XOR	mem, reg/imm
NOT, NEG, INC, DEC	mem

An undefined opcode trap will be generated if a LOCK prefix is used with any instruction not listed above.

The XCHG instruction always asserts LOCK# regardless of the presence or absence of the LOCK prefix.

The integrity of the LOCK prefix is not affected by the alignment of the memory field. Memory locking is observed for arbitrarily misaligned fields.

Flags Affected

None

Protected Mode Exceptions

#UD if the LOCK prefix is used with an instruction not listed in the "Description" section above; other exceptions can be generated by the subsequent (locked) instruction

Real Address Mode Exceptions

Interrupt 6 if the LOCK prefix is used with an instruction not listed in the "Description" section above; exceptions can still be generated by the subsequent (locked) instruction

Virtual 8086 Mode Exceptions

#UD if the LOCK prefix is used with an instruction not listed in the "Description" section above; exceptions can still be generated by the subsequent (locked) instruction

LODS/LODSB/LODSW/LODSD — Load String Operand

Opcode	Instruction	Clocks	Description
AC	LODS *m8*	5	Load byte [(E)SI] into AL
AD	LODS *m16*	5	Load word [(E)SI] into AX
AD	LODS *m32*	5	Load dword [(E)SI] into EAX
AC	LODSB	5	Load byte DS:[(E)SI] into AL
AD	LODSW	5	Load word DS:[(E)SI] into AX
AD	LODSD	5	Load dword DS:[(E)SI] into EAX

Operation

```
AddressSize = 16
THEN use SI for source-index
ELSE (* AddressSize = 32 *)
  use ESI for source-index;
FI;
IF byte type of instruction
THEN
  AL ← [source-index]; (* byte load *)
  IF DF = 0 THEN IncDec ← 1 ELSE IncDec ← −1; FI;
ELSE
  IF OperandSize = 16
  THEN
    AX ← [source-index]; (* word load *)
    IF DF = 0 THEN IncDec ← 2 ELSE IncDec ← −2; FI;
  ELSE (* OperandSize = 32 *)
    EAX ← [source-index]; (* dword load *)
    IF DF = 0 THEN IncDec ← 4 ELSE IncDec ← −4; FI;
  FI;
FI;
source-index ← source-index + IncDec
```

Description

The LODS instruction loads the AL, AX, or EAX register with the memory byte, word, or doubleword at the location pointed to by the source-index register. After the transfer is made, the source-index register is automatically advanced. If the DF flag is 0 (the CLD instruction was executed), the source index increments; if the DF flag is 1 (the STD instruction was executed), it decrements. The increment or decrement is 1 if a byte is loaded, 2 if a word is loaded, or 4 if a doubleword is loaded.

If the address-size attribute for this instruction is 16 bits, the SI register is used for the source-index register; otherwise the address-size attribute is 32 bits, and the ESI register is used. The address of the source data is determined solely by the contents of the ESI or SI register. Load the correct index value into the SI register before executing the LODS instruction. The LODSB, LODSW, and LODSD instructions are synonyms for the byte, word, and doubleword LODS instructions.

The LODS instruction can be preceded by the REP prefix; however, the LODS instruction is used more typically within a LOOP construct, because further processing of the data moved into the EAX, AX, or AL register is usually necessary.

Flags Affected

None

Protected Mode Exceptions

#GP(0) for an illegal memory operand effective address in the CS, DS, ES, FS, or GS segments; #SS(0) for an illegal address in the SS segment; #PF(fault-code) for a page fault; #AC for unaligned memory reference if the current privilege level is 3

Real Address Mode Exceptions

Interrupt 13 if any part of the operand would lie outside of the effective address space from 0 to 0FFFFH

Virtual 8086 Mode Exceptions

Same exceptions as in Real Address Mode; #PF(fault-code) for a page fault; #AC for unaligned memory reference if the current privilege level is 3

LOOP/LOOPcond – Loop Control with CX Counter

Opcode	Instruction	Clocks	Description
E2 *cb*	LOOP *rel8*	2,6	DEC count; jump short if count < > 0
E1 *cb*	LOOPE *rel8*	9,6	DEC count; jump short if count < > 0 and ZF = 1
E1 *cb*	LOOPZ *rel8*	9,6	DEC count; jump short if count < > 0 and ZF = 1
E0 *cb*	LOOPNE *rel8*	9,6	DEC count; jump short if count < > 0 and ZF = 0
E0 *cb*	LOOPNZ *rel8*	9,6	DEC count; jump short if count < > 0 and ZF = 0

Operation

```
IF AddressSize = 16 THEN CountReg is CX ELSE CountReg is ECX; FI;
CountReg ← CountReg − 1;

IF instruction < > LOOP
THEN
   IF (instruction = LOOPE) OR (instruction = LOOPZ)
   THEN BranchCond ← (ZF = 1) AND (CountReg < > 0);
   FI;
   IF (instruction = LOOPNE) OR (instruction = LOOPNZ)
   THEN BranchCond ← (ZF = 0) AND (CountReg < > 0);
   FI;
FI;

IF BranchCond
THEN
   IF OperandSize = 16
   THEN
      IP ← IP + SignExtend(rel8);
   ELSE (* OperandSize = 32 *)
      EIP ← EIP + SignExtend(rel8);
   FI;
FI;
```

Description

The LOOP instruction decrements the count register without changing any of the flags. Conditions are then checked for the form of the LOOP instruction being used. If the conditions are met, a short jump is made to the label given by the operand to the LOOP instruction. If the address-size attribute is 16 bits, the CX register is used as the count register; otherwise the ECX register is used. The operand of the LOOP instruction must be in the range from 128 (decimal) bytes before the instruction to 127 bytes ahead of the instruction.

The LOOP instructions provide iteration control and combine loop index management with conditional branching. Use the LOOP instruction by loading an unsigned iteration count into the count register, then code the LOOP instruction at the end of a series of instructions to be iterated. The destination of the LOOP instruction is a label that points to the beginning of the iteration.

Flags Affected

None

Protected Mode Exceptions

#GP(0) if the offset jumped to is beyond the limits of the current code segment

Real Address Mode Exceptions

None

Virtual 8086 Mode Exceptions

None

Notes

The unconditional LOOP instruction takes longer to execute than a two-instruction sequence which decrements the count register and jumps if the count does not equal zero.

All branches are converted into 16-byte code fetches regardless of jump address or cacheability.

LSL—Load Segment Limit

Opcode	Instruction	Clocks	Description
0F 03 /r	LSL *r16,r/m16*	10/10	Load: *r16* ← segment limit, selector *r/m16* (byte granular)
0F 03 /r	LSL *r32,r/m32*	10/10	Load: *r32* ← segment limit, selector *r/m32* (byte granular)
0F 03 /r	LSL *r16,r/m16*	10/10	Load: *r16* ← segment limit, selector *r/m16* (page granular)
0F 03 /r	LSL *r32,r/m32*	10/10	Load: *r32* ← segment limit, selector *r/m32* (page granular)

Description

The LSL instruction loads a register with an unscrambled segment limit, and sets the ZF flag, provided that the source selector is visible at the current privilege level and RPL, within the descriptor table, and that the descriptor is a type accepted by the LSL instruction. Otherwise, the ZF flag is cleared, and the destination register is unchanged. The segment limit is loaded as a byte granular value. If the descriptor has a page granular segment limit, the LSL instruction will translate it to a byte limit before loading it in the destination register (shift left 12 the 20-bit "raw" limit from descriptor, then OR with 00000FFFH).

The 32-bit forms of the LSL instruction store the 32-bit byte granular limit in the 16-bit destination register.

Code and data segment descriptors are valid for the LSL instruction.

The valid special segment and gate descriptor types for the LSL instruction are given in the following table:

Type	Name	Valid/Invalid
0	Invalid	Invalid
1	Available 80286 TSS	Valid
2	LDT	Valid
3	Busy 80286 TSS	Valid
4	80286 call gate	Invalid
5	80286/i486 task gate	Invalid
6	80286 trap gate	Invalid
7	80286 interrupt gate	Invalid
8	Invalid	Valid
9	Available i486 TSS	Valid
A	Invalid	Invalid
B	Busy i486 TSS	Valid
C	i486 call gate	Invalid
D	Invalid	Invalid
E	i486 trap gate	Invalid
F	i486 interrupt gate	Invalid

Flags Affected

The ZF flag is set unless the selector is invisible or of the wrong type, in which case the ZF flag is cleared

Protected Mode Exceptions

#GP(0) for an illegal memory operand effective address in the CS, DS, ES, FS, or GS segments; #SS(0) for an illegal address in the SS segment; #PF(fault-code) for a page fault; #AC for unaligned memory reference if the current privilege level is 3

Real Address Mode Exceptions

Interrupt 6; the LSL instruction is not recognized in Real Address Mode

Virtual 8086 Mode Exceptions

Same exceptions as in Real Address Mode; #AC for unaligned memory reference if the current privilege level is 3

LTR — Load Task Register

Opcode	Instruction	Clocks	Description
0F 00 /3	LTR *r/m16*	20/20	Load EA word into task register

Description

The LTR instruction loads the task register from the source register or memory location specified by the operand. The loaded TSS is marked busy. A task switch does not occur.

The LTR instruction is used only in operating system software; it is not used in application programs.

Flags Affected

None

Protected Mode Exceptions

#GP(0) for an illegal memory operand effective address in the CS, DS, ES, FS, or GS segments; #SS(0) for an illegal address in the SS segment; #GP(0) if the current privilege level is not 0; #GP(selector) if the object named by the source selector is not a TSS or is already busy; #NP(selector) if the TSS is marked "not present"; #PF(fault-code) for a page fault

Real Address Mode Exceptions

Interrupt 6; the LTR instruction is not recognized in Real Address Mode

Virtual 8086 Mode Exceptions

Same exceptions as in Real Address Mode

Notes

The operand-size attribute has no effect on this instruction.

MOV—Move Data

Opcode	Instruction	Clocks	Description
88 /r	MOV *r/m8,r8*	1	Move byte register to *r/m* byte
89 /r	MOV *r/m16,r16*	1	Move word register to *r/m* word
89 /r	MOV *r/m32,r32*	1	Move dword register to *r/m* dword
8A /r	MOV *r8,r/m8*	1	Move *r/m* byte to byte register
8B /r	MOV *r16,r/m16*	1	Move *r/m* word to word register
8B /r	MOV *r32,r/m32*	1	Move *r/m* dword to dword register
8C /r	MOV *r/m16,Sreg*	3/3	Move segment register to *r/m* word
8E /r	MOV *Sreg,r/m16*	3/9	Move *r/m* word to segment register
A0	MOV AL,*moffs8*	1	Move byte at (*seg:offset*) to AL
A1	MOV AX,*moffs16*	1	Move word at (*seg:offset*) to AX
A1	MOV EAX,*moffs32*	1	Move dword at (*seg:offset*) to EAX
A2	MOV *moffs8*,AL	1	Move AL to (*seg:offset*)
A3	MOV *moffs16*,AX	1	Move AX to (*seg:offset*)
A3	MOV *moffs32*,EAX	1	Move EAX to (*seg:offset*)
B0+ *rb*	MOV *reg8,imm8*	1	Move immediate byte to register
B8+ *rw*	MOV *reg16,imm16*	1	Move immediate word to register
B8+ *rd*	MOV *reg32,imm32*	1	Move immediate dword to register
C6	MOV *r/m8,imm8*	1	Move immediate byte to *r/m* byte
C7	MOV *r/m16,imm16*	1	Move immediate word to *r/m* word
C7	MOV *r/m32,imm32*	1	Move immediate dword to *r/m* dword

NOTES: *moffs8*, *moffs16*, and *moffs32* all consist of a simple offset relative to the segment base. The *8*, *16*, and *32* refer to the size of the data. The address-size attribute of the instruction determines the size of the offset, either 16 or 32 bits.

Operation

DEST ← SRC;

Description

The MOV instruction copies the second operand to the first operand.

If the destination operand is a segment register (DS, ES, SS, etc.), then data from a descriptor is also loaded into the register. The data for the register is obtained from the descriptor table entry for the selector given. A null selector (values 0000-0003) can be loaded into the DS and ES registers without causing an exception; however, use of the DS or ES register causes a #GP(0) exception, and no memory reference occurs.

A MOV into SS instruction inhibits all interrupts until after the execution of the next instruction (which is presumably a MOV into ESP instruction).

Loading a segment register under Protected Mode results in special checks and actions, as described in the following listing:

```
IF SS is loaded;
THEN
   IF selector is null THEN #GP(0);
FI;
   Selector index must be within its descriptor table limits else #GP(selector);
   Selector's RPL must equal CPL else #GP(selector);
```

```
AR byte must indicate a writable data segment else #GP(selector);
  DPL in the AR byte must equal CPL else #GP(selector);
  Segment must be marked present else #SS(selector);
  Load SS with selector;
  Load SS with descriptor.
FI;
IF DS, ES, FS or GS is loaded with non-null selector;
THEN
  Selector index must be within its descriptor table limits
    else #GP(selector);
  AR byte must indicate data or readable code segment else #GP(selector);
  IF data or nonconforming code segment
  THEN both the RPL and the CPL must be less than or equal to DPL in AR byte;
  ELSE #GP(selector);
  FI;
  Segment must be marked present else #NP(selector);
  Load segment register with selector;
  Load segment register with descriptor;
FI;
IF DS, ES, FS or GS is loaded with a null selector;
THEN
  Load segment register with selector;
  Clear descriptor valid bit;
FI;
```

Flags Affected

None

Protected Mode Exceptions

#GP, #SS, and #NP if a segment register is being loaded; otherwise, #GP(0) if the destination is in a nonwritable segment; #GP(0) for an illegal memory operand effective address in the CS, DS, ES, FS, or GS segments; #SS(0) for an illegal address in the SS segment; #PF(fault-code) for a page fault; #AC for unaligned memory reference if the current privilege level is 3

Real Address Mode Exceptions

Interrupt 13 if any part of the operand would lie outside of the effective address space from 0 to 0FFFFH

Virtual 8086 Mode Exceptions

Same exceptions as in Real Address Mode; #PF(fault-code) for a page fault; #AC for unaligned memory reference if the current privilege level is 3

MOV—Move to/from Special Registers

Opcode	Instruction	Clocks	Description
0F 22 /r	MOV CR0,*r32*	16	Move (register) to (control register)
0F 20 /r	MOV *r32*,CR0/CR2/CR3	4	Move (control register) to (register)
0F 22 /r	MOV CR2/CR3,*r32*	4	Move (register) to (control register)
0F21 /r	MOV *r32*,DR0 – 3	10	Move (debug register) to (register)
0F 21 /r	MOV *r32*,DR6/DR7	10	Move (debug register) to (register)
0F 23 /r	MOV DR0 – 3,*r32*	11	Move (register) to (debug register)
0F 23 /r	MOV DR6/DR7,*r32*	11	Move (register) to (debug register)
0F 24 /r	MOV *r32*,TR4/TR5/TR6/TR7	4	Move (test register) to (register)
0F 26 /r	MOV TR4/TR5/TR6/TR7,*r32*	4	Move (register) to (test register)
oF 24 /r	MOV *r32*, TR3	3	Move (test register3) to (register)
0F 26 /r	MOV TR3,*r32*	6	Move (registers) to (test register3)

Operation

DEST ← SRC;

Description

The above forms of the MOV instruction store or load the following special registers in or from a general purpose register:

- Control registers CR0, CR2, and CR3
- Debug Registers DR0, DR1, DR2, DR3, DR6, and DR7
- Test Registers TR3, TR4, TR5, TR6 and TR7

Thirty-two bit operands are always used with these instructions, regardless of the operand-size attribute.

Flags Affected

The OF, SF, ZF, AF, PF, and CF flags are undefined

Protected Mode Exceptions

#GP(0) if the current privilege level is not 0

Real Address Mode Exceptions

None

Virtual 8086 Mode Exceptions

#GP(0) if instruction execution is attempted

Notes

The instructions must be executed at privilege level 0 or in real-address mode; otherwise, a protection exception will be raised.

The *reg* field within the ModR/M byte specifies which of the special registers in each category is involved. The two bits in the *mod* field are always 11. The *r/m* field specifies the general register involved.

Always set undefined or reserved bits to the value previously read.

MOVS/MOVSB/MOVSW/MOVSD — Move Data from String to String

Opcode	Instruction	Clocks	Description
A4	MOVS *m8,m8*	7	Move byte [(E)SI] to ES:[(E)DI]
A5	MOVS *m16,m16*	7	Move word [(E)SI] to ES:[(E)DI]
A5	MOVS *m32,m32*	7	Move dword [(E)SI] to ES:[(E)DI]
A4	MOVSB	7	Move byte DS:[(E)SI] to ES:[(E)DI]
A5	MOVSW	7	Move word DS:[(E)SI] to ES:[(E)DI]
A5	MOVSD	7	Move dword DS:[(E)SI] to ES:[(E)DI]

Operation

```
IF (instruction = MOVSD) OR (instruction has doubleword operands)
THEN OperandSize ← 32;
ELSE OperandSize ← 16;
IF AddressSize = 16
THEN use SI for source-index and DI for destination-index;
ELSE (* AddressSize = 32 *)
  use ESI for source-index and EDI for destination-index;
FI;
IF byte type of instruction
THEN
  [destination-index] ← [source-index]; (* byte assignment *)
  IF DF = 0 THEN IncDec ← 1 ELSE IncDec ← −1; FI;
ELSE
  IF OperandSize = 16
  THEN
    [destination-index] ← [source-index]; (* word assignment *)
    IF DF = 0 THEN IncDec ← 2 ELSE IncDec ← −2; FI;
  ELSE (* OperandSize = 32 *)
    [destination-index] ← [source-index]; (* doubleword assignment *)
    IF DF = 0 THEN IncDec ← 4 ELSE IncDec ← −4; FI;
  FI;
FI;
source-index ← source-index + IncDec;
destination-index ← destination-index + IncDec;
```

Description

The MOVS instruction copies the byte or word at [(E)SI] to the byte or word at ES:[(E)DI]. The destination operand must be addressable from the ES register; no segment override is possible for the destination. A segment override can be used for the source operand; the default is the DS register.

The addresses of the source and destination are determined solely by the contents of the (E)SI and (E)DI registers. Load the correct index values into the (E)SI and (E)DI registers before executing the MOVS instruction. The MOVSB, MOVSW, and MOVSD instructions are synonyms for the byte, word, and doubleword MOVS instructions.

After the data is moved, both the (E)SI and (E)DI registers are advanced automatically. If the DF flag is 0 (the CLD instruction was executed), the registers are incremented; if the DF flag is 1 (the STD instruction was executed), the registers are decremented. The registers are incremented or decremented by 1 if a byte was moved, 2 if a word was moved, or 4 if a doubleword was moved.

The MOVS instruction can be preceded by the REP prefix for block movement of CX bytes or words. Refer to the REP instruction for details of this operation.

Flags Affected

None

Protected Mode Exceptions

#GP(0) if the result is in a nonwritable segment; #GP(0) for an illegal memory operand effective address in the CS, DS, ES, FS, or GS segments; #SS(0) for an illegal address in the SS segment; #PF(fault-code) for a page fault; #AC for unaligned memory reference if the current privilege level is 3

Real Address Mode Exceptions

Interrupt 13 if any part of the operand would lie outside of the effective address space from 0 to 0FFFFH

Virtual 8086 Mode Exceptions

Same exceptions as in Real Address Mode; #PF(fault-code) for a page fault; #AC for unaligned memory reference if the current privilege level is 3

MOVSX—Move with Sign-Extend

Opcode	Instruction	Clocks	Description
0F BE /r	MOVSX *r16,r/m8*	3/3	Move byte to word with sign-extend
0F BE /r	MOVSX *r32,r/m8*	3/3	Move byte to dword, sign-extend
0F BF /r	MOVSX *r32,r/m16*	3/3	Move word to dword, sign-extend

Operation

DEST ← SignExtend(SRC);

Description

The MOVSX instruction reads the contents of the effective address or register as a byte or a word, sign-extends the value to the operand-size attribute of the instruction (16 or 32 bits), and stores the result in the destination register.

Flags Affected

None

Protected Mode Exceptions

#GP(0) for an illegal memory operand effective address in the CS, DS, ES, FS or GS segments; #SS(0) for an illegal address in the SS segment; #PF(fault-code) for a page fault; #AC for unaligned memory reference if the current privilege level is 3

Real Address Mode Exceptions

Interrupt 13 if any part of the operand would lie outside of the effective address space from 0 to 0FFFFH

Virtual 8086 Mode Exceptions

Same exceptions as in Real Address Mode; #PF(fault-code) for a page fault; #AC for unaligned memory reference if the current privilege level is 3

MOVZX—Move with Zero-Extend

Opcode	Instruction	Clocks	Description
0F B6 /r	MOVZX *r16,r/m8*	3/3	Move byte to word with zero-extend
0F B6 /r	MOVZX *r32,r/m8*	3/3	Move byte to dword, zero-extend
0F B7 /r	MOVZX *r32,r/m16*	3/3	Move word to dword, zero-extend

Operation

DEST ← ZeroExtend(SRC);

Description

The MOVZX instruction reads the contents of the effective address or register as a byte or a word, zero extends the value to the operand-size attribute of the instruction (16 or 32 bits), and stores the result in the destination register.

Flags Affected

None

Protected Mode Exceptions

#GP(0) for an illegal memory operand effective address in the CS, DS, ES, FS, or GS segments; #SS(0) for an illegal address in the SS segment; #PF(fault-code) for a page fault; #AC for unaligned memory reference if the current privilege level is 3

Real Address Mode Exceptions

Interrupt 13 if any part of the operand would lie outside of the effective address space from 0 to 0FFFFH

Virtual 8086 Mode Exceptions

Same exceptions as in Real Address Mode; #PF(fault-code) for a page fault; #AC for unaligned memory reference if the current privilege level is 3

MUL — Unsigned Multiplication of AL or AX

Opcode	Instruction	Clocks	Description
F6 /4	MUL AL,*r/m8*	13/18,13/18	Unsigned multiply (AX ← AL * *r/m* byte)
F7 /4	MUL AX,*r/m16*	13/26,13/26	Unsigned multiply (DX:AX ← AX * *r/m* word)
F7 /4	MUL EAX,*r/m32*	13/42,13/42	Unsigned multiply (EDX:EAX ← EAX * *r/m* dword)

NOTES: The i486 processor uses an early-out multiply algorithm. The actual number of clocks depends on the position of the most significant bit in the optimizing multiplier, shown underlined above. The optimization occurs for positive and negative multiplier values. Because of the early-out algorithm, clock counts given are minimum to maximum. To calculate the actual clocks, use the following formula:

Actual clock = if **m** < > 0 then max(ceiling($\log_2$ | **m** |), 3) + 6 clocks;
Actual clock = if **m** = 0 then 9 clocks

where **m** is the multiplier.

Operation

```
IF byte-size operation
THEN AX ← AL * r/m8
ELSE (* word or doubleword operation *)
  IF OperandSize = 16
  THEN DX:AX ← AX * r/m16
  ELSE (* OperandSize = 32 *)
    EDX:EAX ← EAX * r/m32
  FI;
FI;
```

Description

The MUL instruction performs unsigned multiplication. Its actions depend on the size of its operand, as follows:

- A byte operand is multiplied by the AL value; the result is left in the AX register. The CF and OF flags are cleared if the AH value is 0; otherwise, they are set.
- A word operand is multiplied by the AX value; the result is left in the DX:AX register pair. The DX register contains the high-order 16 bits of the product. The CF and OF flags are cleared if the DX value is 0; otherwise, they are set.
- A doubleword operand is multiplied by the EAX value and the result is left in the EDX:EAX register. The EDX register contains the high-order 32 bits of the product. The CF and OF flags are cleared if the EDX value is 0; otherwise, they are set.

Flags Affected

The OF and CF flags are cleared if the upper half of the result is 0; otherwise they are set; the SF, ZF, AF, PF, and CF flags are undefined

Protected Mode Exceptions

#GP(0) for an illegal memory operand effective address in the CS, DS, ES, FS, or GS segments; #SS(0) for an illegal address in the SS segment; #PF(fault-code) for a page fault; #AC for unaligned memory reference if the current privilege level is 3

Real Address Mode Exceptions

Interrupt 13 if any part of the operand would lie outside of the effective address space from 0 to 0FFFFH

Virtual 8086 Mode Exceptions

Same exceptions as in Real Address Mode; #PF(fault-code) for a page fault; #AC for unaligned memory reference if the current privilege level is 3

NEG — Two's Complement Negation

Opcode	Instruction	Clocks	Description
F6 /3	NEG *r/m8*	1/3	Two's complement negate *r/m* byte
F7 3	NEG *r/m16*	1/3	Two's complement negate *r/m* word
F7 /3	NEG *r/m32*	1/3	Two's complement negate *r/m* dword

Operation

IF *r/m* = 0 THEN CF ← 0 ELSE CF ← 1; FI;
r/m ← − *r/m*

Description

The NEG instruction replaces the value of a register or memory operand with its two's complement. The operand is subtracted from zero, and the result is placed in the operand.

The CF flag is set, unless the operand is zero, in which case the CF flag is cleared.

Flags Affected

The CF flag is set unless the operand is zero, in which case the CF flag is cleared; the OF, SF, ZF, and PF flags are set according to the result

Protected Mode Exceptions

#GP(0) if the result is in a nonwritable segment; #GP(0) for an illegal memory operand effective address in the CS, DS, ES, FS, or GS segments; #SS(0) for an illegal address in the SS segment; #PF(fault-code) for a page fault; #AC for unaligned memory reference if the current privilege level is 3

Real Address Mode Exceptions

Interrupt 13 if any part of the operand would lie outside of the effective address space from 0 to 0FFFFH

Virtual 8086 Mode Exceptions

Same exceptions as in real-address mode; #PF(fault-code) for a page fault; #AC for unaligned memory reference if the current privilege level is 3

NOP — No Operation

Opcode	Instruction	Clocks	Description
90	NOP	1	No operation

Description

The NOP instruction performs no operation. The NOP instruction is a one-byte instruction that takes up space but affects none of the machine context except the (E)IP register.

The NOP instruction is an alias mnemonic for the XCHG (E)AX, (E)AX instruction.

Flags Affected

None

Protected Mode Exceptions

None

Real Address Mode Exceptions

None

Virtual 8086 Mode Exceptions

None

NOT—One's Complement Negation

Opcode	Instruction	Clocks	Description
F6 /2	NOT *r/m8*	1/3	Reverse each bit of *r/m* byte
F7 /2	NOT *r/m16*	1/3	Reverse each bit of *r/m* word
F7 /2	NOT *r/m32*	1/3	Reverse each bit of *r/m* dword

Operation

r/m ← NOT *r/m*;

Description

The NOT instruction inverts the operand; every 1 becomes a 0, and vice versa.

Flags Affected

None

Protected Mode Exceptions

#GP(0) if the result is in a nonwritable segment; #GP(0) for an illegal memory operand effective address in the CS, DS, ES, FS, or GS segments; #SS(0) for an illegal address in the SS segment; #PF(fault-code) for a page fault; #AC for unaligned memory reference if the current privilege level is 3

Real Address Mode Exceptions

Interrupt 13 if any part of the operand would lie outside of the effective address space from 0 to 0FFFFH

Virtual 8086 Mode Exceptions

Same exceptions as in real-address mode; #PF(fault-code) for a page fault; #AC for unaligned memory reference if the current privilege level is 3

OR—Logical Inclusive OR

Opcode	Instruction	Clocks	Description
0C *ib*	OR AL,*imm8*	1	OR immediate byte to AL
0D *iw*	OR AX,*imm16*	1	OR immediate word to AX
0D *id*	OR EAX,*imm32*	1	OR immediate dword to EAX
80 /1 *ib*	OR *r/m8,imm8*	1/3	OR immediate byte to *r/m* byte
81 /1 *iw*	OR *r/m16,imm16*	1/3	OR immediate word to *r/m* word
81 /1 *id*	OR *r/m32,imm32*	1/3	OR immediate dword to *r/m* dword
83 /1 *ib*	OR *r/m16,imm8*	1/3	OR sign-extended immediate byte with *r/m* word
83 /1 *ib*	OR *r/m32,imm8*	1/3	OR sign-extended immediate byte with *r/m* dword
08 /*r*	OR *r/m8,r8*	1/3	OR byte register to *r/m* byte
09 /*r*	OR *r/m16,r16*	1/3	OR word register to *r/m* word
09 /*r*	OR *r/m32,r32*	1/3	OR dword register to *r/m* dword
0A /*r*	OR *r8,r/m8*	1/2	OR byte register to *r/m* byte
0B /*r*	OR *r16,r/m16*	1/2	OR word register to *r/m* word
0B /*r*	OR *r32,r/m32*	1/2	OR dword register to *r/m* dword

Operation

DEST ← DEST OR SRC;
CF ← 0;
OF ← 0

Description

The OR instruction computes the inclusive OR of its two operands and places the result in the first operand. Each bit of the result is 0 if both corresponding bits of the operands are 0; otherwise, each bit is 1.

Flags Affected

The OF and CF flags are cleared; the SF, ZF, and PF flags are set according to the result; the AF flag is undefined

Protected Mode Exceptions

#GP(0) if the result is in a nonwritable segment; #GP(0) for an illegal memory operand effective address in the CS, DS, ES, FS, or GS segments; #SS(0) for an illegal address in the SS segment; #PF(fault-code) for a page fault; #AC for unaligned memory reference if the current privilege level is 3

Real Address Mode Exceptions

Interrupt 13 if any part of the operand would lie outside of the effective address space from 0 to 0FFFFH

Virtual 8086 Mode Exceptions

Same exceptions as in real-address mode; #PF(fault-code) for a page fault; #AC for unaligned memory reference if the current privilege level is 3

OUT – Output to Port

Opcode	Instruction	Clocks	Description
E6 *ib*	OUT *imm8*,AL	16,*pm*=11*/ 31**,VM=29	Output byte AL to immediate port number
E7 *ib*	OUT *imm8*,AX	16,*pm*=11*/ 31**,VM=29	Output word AL to immediate port number
E7 *ib*	OUT *imm8*,EAX	16,*pm*=11*/ 31**,VM=29	Output dword AL to immediate port number
EE	OUT DX,AL	16,*pm*=10*/ 30**,VM=29	Output byte AL to port number in DX
EF	OUT DX,AX	16,*pm*=10*/ 30**,VM=29	Output word AL to port number in DX
EF	OUT DX,EAX	16,*pm*=10*/ 30**,VM=29	Output dword AL to port number in DX

NOTES: *If CPL ≤ IOPL
**If CPL > IOPL

Operation

```
IF (PE = 1) AND ((VM = 1) OR (CPL > IOPL))
THEN (* Virtual 8086 mode, or protected mode with CPL > IOPL *)
  IF NOT I-O-Permission (DEST, width(DEST))
  THEN #GP(0);
  FI;
FI;
[DEST] ← SRC; (* I/O address space used *)
```

Description

The OUT instruction transfers a data byte or data word from the register (AL, AX, or EAX) given as the second operand to the output port numbered by the first operand. Output to any port from 0 to 65535 is performed by placing the port number in the DX register and then using an OUT instruction with the DX register as the first operand. If the instruction contains an eight-bit port ID, that value is zero-extended to 16 bits.

Flags Affected

None

Protected Mode Exceptions

#GP(0) if the current privilege level is higher (has less privilege) than the I/O privilege level and any of the corresponding I/O permission bits in the TSS equals 1

Real Address Mode Exceptions

None

Virtual 8086 Mode Exceptions

#GP(0) fault if any of the corresponding I/O permission bits in the TSS equals 1

OUTS/OUTSB/OUTSW/OUTSD – Output String to Port

Opcode	Instruction	Clocks	Description
6E	OUTS DX,*r/m8*	17,*pm*=10*/ 32**,VM=30	Output byte [(E)SI] to port in DX
6F	OUTS DX,*r/m16*	17,*pm*=10*/ 32**,VM=30	Output word [(E)SI] to port in DX
6F	OUTS DX,*r/m32*	17,*pm*=10*/ 32**,VM=30	Output dword [(E)SI] to port in DX
6E	OUTSB	17,*pm*=10*/ 32**,VM=30	Output byte DS:[(E)SI] to port in DX
6F	OUTSW	17,*pm*=10*/ 32**,VM=30	Output word DS:[(E)SI] to port in DX
6F	OUTSD	17,*pm*=10*/ 32**,VM=30	Output dword DS:[(E)SI] to port in DX

NOTES: *If CPL ≤ IOPL
**If CPL > IOPL

Operation

```
IF AddressSize = 16
THEN use SI for source-index;
ELSE (* AddressSize = 32 *)
   use ESI for source-index;
FI;


IF (PE = 1) AND ((VM = 1) OR (CPL > IOPL))
THEN (* Virtual 8086 mode, or protected mode with CPL > IOPL *)
   IF NOT I-O-Permission (DEST, width(DEST))
   THEN #GP(0);
   FI;
FI;
IF byte type of instruction
THEN
   [DX] ← [source-index]; (* Write byte at DX I/O address *)
   IF DF = 0 THEN IncDec ← 1 ELSE IncDec ← −1; FI;
FI;
IF OperandSize = 16
THEN
   [DX] ← [source-index]; (* Write word at DX I/O address *)
   IF DF = 0 THEN IncDec ← 2 ELSE IncDec ← −2; FI;
FI;
IF OperandSize = 32
THEN
   [DX] ← [source-index]; (* Write dword at DX I/O address *)
   IF DF = 0 THEN IncDec ← 4 ELSE IncDec ← −4; FI;
   FI;
FI;
source-index ← source-index + IncDec;
```

Description

The OUTS instruction transfers data from the memory byte, word, or doubleword at the source-index register to the output port addressed by the DX register. If the address-size attribute for this instruction is 16 bits, the SI register is used for the source-index register; otherwise, the address-size attribute is 32 bits, and the ESI register is used for the source-index register.

The OUTS instruction does not allow specification of the port number as an immediate value. The port must be addressed through the DX register value. Load the correct value into the DX register before executing the OUTS instruction.

The address of the source data is determined by the contents of source-index register. Load the correct index value into the SI or ESI register before executing the OUTS instruction.

After the transfer, source-index register is advanced automatically. If the DF flag is 0 (the CLD instruction was executed), the source-index register is incremented; if the DF flag is 1 (the STD instruction was executed), it is decremented. The amount of the increment or decrement is 1 if a byte is output, 2 if a word is output, or 4 if a doubleword is output.

The OUTSB, OUTSW, and OUTSD instructions are synonyms for the byte, word, and doubleword OUTS instructions. The OUTS instruction can be preceded by the REP prefix for block output of CX bytes or words. Refer to the REP instruction for details on this operation.

Flags Affected

None

Protected Mode Exceptions

#GP(0) if the current privilege level is greater than the I/O privilege level and any of the corresponding I/O permission bits in TSS equals 1; #GP(0) for an illegal memory operand effective address in the CS, DS, or ES segments; #SS(0) for an illegal address in the SS segment; #PF(fault-code) for a page fault; #AC for unaligned memory reference if the current privilege level is 3

Real Address Mode Exceptions

Interrupt 13 if any part of the operand would lie outside of the effective address space from 0 to 0FFFFH

Virtual 8086 Mode Exceptions

#GP(0) fault if any of the corresponding I/O permission bits in TSS equals 1; #PF(fault-code) for a page fault; #AC for unaligned memory reference if the current privilege level is 3

POP — Pop a Word from the Stack

Opcode	Instruction	Clocks	Description
8F /0	POP *m16*	6	Pop top of stack into memory word
8F /0	POP *m32*	6	Pop top of stack into memory dword
58+ *rw*	POP *r16*	4	Pop top of stack into word register
58+ *rd*	POP *r32*	4	Pop top of stack into dword register
1F	POP DS	3	Pop top of stack into DS
07	POP ES	3	Pop top of stack into ES
17	POP SS	3	Pop top of stack into SS
0F A1	POP FS	3	Pop top of stack into FS
0F A9	POP GS	3	Pop top of stack into GS

Operation

```
IF StackAddrSize = 16
THEN
  IF OperandSize = 16
  THEN
    DEST ← (SS:SP); (* copy a word *)
    SP ← SP + 2;
  ELSE (* OperandSize = 32 *)
    DEST ← (SS:SP); (* copy a dword *)
    SP ← SP + 4;
  FI;

ELSE (* StackAddrSize = 32 * )
  IF OperandSize = 16
  THEN
    DEST ← (SS:ESP); (* copy a word *)
    ESP ← ESP + 2;
  ELSE (* OperandSize = 32 *)
    DEST ← (SS:ESP); (* copy a dword *)
    ESP ← ESP + 4;
  FI;
FI;
```

Description

The POP instruction replaces the previous contents of the memory, the register, or the segment register operand with the word on the top of the i486 processor stack, addressed by SS:SP (address-size attribute of 16 bits) or SS:ESP (address-size attribute of 32 bits). The stack pointer SP is incremented by 2 for an operand-size of 16 bits or by 4 for an operand-size of 32 bits. It then points to the new top of stack.

The POP CS instruction is not an i486 processor instruction. Popping from the stack into the CS register is accomplished with a RET instruction.

If the destination operand is a segment register (DS, ES, FS, GS, or SS), the value popped must be a selector. In protected mode, loading the selector initiates automatic loading of the descriptor information associated with that selector into the hidden part of the segment register; loading also initiates validation of both the selector and the descriptor information.

A null value (0000-0003) may be popped into the DS, ES, FS, or GS register without causing a protection exception. An attempt to reference a segment whose corresponding segment register is loaded with a null value causes a #GP(0) exception. No memory reference occurs. The saved value of the segment register is null.

A POP SS instruction inhibits all interrupts, including NMI, until after execution of the next instruction. This allows sequential execution of POP SS and POP eSP instructions without danger of having an invalid stack during an interrupt. However, use of the LSS instruction is the preferred method of loading the SS and eSP registers.

Loading a segment register while in protected mode results in special checks and actions, as described in the following listing:

```
IF SS is loaded:
   IF selector is null THEN #GP(0);
   Selector index must be within its descriptor table limits ELSE
      #GP(selector);
   Selector's RPL must equal CPL ELSE #GP(selector);
   AR byte must indicate a writable data segment ELSE #GP(selector);
   DPL in the AR byte must equal CPL ELSE #GP(selector);
   Segment must be marked present ELSE #SS(selector);
   Load SS register with selector;
   Load SS register with descriptor;

IF DS, ES, FS or GS is loaded with non-null selector:
   AR byte must indicate data or readable code segment ELSE
      #GP(selector);
   IF data or nonconforming code
   THEN both the RPL and the CPL must be less than or equal to DPL in
      AR byte
   ELSE #GP(selector);
   FI;
   Segment must be marked present ELSE #NP(selector);
   Load segment register with selector;
   Load segment register with descriptor;

IF DS, ES, FS, or GS is loaded with a null selector:
   Load segment register with selector
   Clear valid bit in invisible portion of register
```

Flags Affected

None

Protected Mode Exceptions

#GP, #SS, and #NP if a segment register is being loaded; #SS(0) if the current top of stack is not within the stack segment; #GP(0) if the result is in a nonwritable segment; #GP(0) for an illegal memory operand effective address in the CS, DS, ES, FS, or GS segments; #SS(0) for an illegal address in the SS segment; #PF(fault-code) for a page fault; #AC for unaligned memory reference if the current privilege level is 3

Real Address Mode Exceptions

Interrupt 13 if any part of the operand would lie outside of the effective address space from 0 to 0FFFFH

Virtual 8086 Mode Exceptions

Same exceptions as in real-address mode; #PF(fault-code) for a page fault; #AC for unaligned memory reference if the current privilege level is 3

Notes

Back-to-back PUSH/POP instruction sequences are allowed without incurring an additional clock.

POPA/POPAD — Pop all General Registers

Opcode	Instruction	Clocks	Description
61	POPA	9	Pop DI, SI, BP, BX, DX, CX, and AX
61	POPAD	9	Pop EDI, ESI, EBP, EDX, ECX, and EAX

Operation

```
IF OperandSize = 16 (* instruction = POPA *)
THEN
   DI ←Pop();
   SI ← Pop();
   BP ← Pop();
   throwaway ← Pop (); (* Skip SP *)
   BX ← Pop();
   DX ← Pop();
   CX ← Pop();
   AX ← Pop();
ELSE (* OperandSize = 32, instruction = POPAD *)
   EDI ← Pop();
   ESI ← Pop();
   EBP ← Pop();
   throwaway ← Pop (); (* Skip ESP *)
   EBX ← Pop();
   EDX ← Pop();
   ECX ← Pop();
   EAX ← Pop();
FI;
```

Description

The POPA instruction pops the eight 16-bit general registers. However, the SP value is discarded instead of loaded into the SP register. The POPA instruction reverses a previous PUSHA instruction, restoring the general registers to their values before the PUSHA instruction was executed. The first register popped is the DI register.

The POPAD instruction pops the eight 32-bit general registers. The ESP value is discarded instead of loaded into the ESP register. The POPAD instruction reverses the previous PUSHAD instruction, restoring the general registers to their values before the PUSHAD instruction was executed. The first register popped is the EDI register.

Flags Affected

None

Protected Mode Exceptions

#SS(0) if the starting or ending stack address is not within the stack segment; #PF(fault-code) for a page fault

Real Address Mode Exceptions

Interrupt 13 if any part of the operand would lie outside of the effective address space from 0 to 0FFFFH

Virtual 8086 Mode Exceptions

Same exceptions as in real-address mode; #PF(fault-code) for a page fault

POPF/POPFD — Pop Stack into FLAGS or EFLAGS Register

Opcode	Instruction	Clocks	Description
9D	POPF	9,*pm*=6	Pop top of stack FLAGS
9D	POPFD	9,*pm*=6	Pop top of stack into EFLAGS

Operation

Flags ← Pop();

Description

The POPF and POPFD instructions pop the word or doubleword on the top of the stack and store the value in the flags register. If the operand-size attribute of the instruction is 16 bits, then a word is popped and the value is stored in the FLAGS register. If the operand-size attribute is 32 bits, then a doubleword is popped and the value is stored in the EFLAGS register.

Refer to Chapter 2 and Chapter 4 for information about the FLAGS and EFLAGS registers. Note that bits 16 and 17 of the EFLAGS register, called the VM and RF flags, respectively, are not affected by the POPF or POPFD instruction.

The I/O privilege level is altered only when executing at privilege level 0. The interrupt flag is altered only when executing at a level at least as privileged as the I/O privilege level. (Real-address mode is equivalent to privilege level 0.) If a POPF instruction is executed with insufficient privilege, an exception does not occur, but the privileged bits do not change.

Flags Affected

All flags except the VM and RF flags

Protected Mode Exceptions

#SS(0) if the top of stack is not within the stack segment

Real Address Mode Exceptions

Interrupt 13 if any part of the operand would lie outside of the effective address space from 0 to 0FFFFH

Virtual 8086 Mode Exceptions

#GP(0) fault if the I/O privilege level is less than 3, to permit emulation

PUSH — Push Operand onto the Stack

Opcode	Instruction	Clocks	Description
FF /6	PUSH *m16*	4	Push memory word
FF /6	PUSH *m32*	4	Push memory dword
50+ /r	PUSH *r16*	1	Push register word
50+ /r	PUSH *r32*	1	Push register dword
6A	PUSH *imm8*	1	Push immediate byte
68	PUSH *imm16*	1	Push immediate word
68	PUSH *imm32*	1	Push immediate dword
0E	PUSH CS	3	Push CS
16	PUSH SS	3	Push SS
1E	PUSH DS	3	Push DS
06	PUSH ES	3	Push ES
0F A0	PUSH FS	3	Push FS
0F A8	PUSH GS	3	Push GS

Operation

```
IF StackAddrSize = 16
THEN
  IF OperandSize = 16 THEN
    SP ← SP − 2;
    (SS:SP) ← (SOURCE); (* word assignment *)
  ELSE
    SP ← SP − 4;
    (SS:SP) ← (SOURCE); (* dword assignment *)
  FI;
ELSE (* StackAddrSize = 32 *)
  IF OperandSize = 16
  THEN
    ESP ← ESP − 2;
    (SS:ESP) ← (SOURCE); (* word assignment *)
  ELSE
    ESP ← ESP − 4;
    (SS:ESP) ← (SOURCE); (* dword assignment *)
  FI;
FI;
```

Description

The PUSH instruction decrements the stack pointer by 2 if the operand-size attribute of the instruction is 16 bits; otherwise, it decrements the stack pointer by 4. The PUSH instruction then places the operand on the new top of stack, which is pointed to by the stack pointer.

The PUSH ESP instruction pushes the value of the ESP register as it existed before the instruction. This differs from the 8086, where the PUSH SP instruction pushes the new value (decremented by 2).

Flags Affected

None

Protected Mode Exceptions

#SS(0) if the new value of the SP or ESP register is outside the stack segment limit; #GP(0) for an illegal memory operand effective address in the CS, DS, ES, FS, or GS segments; #SS(0) for an illegal address in the SS segment; #PF(fault-code) for a page fault; #AC for unaligned memory reference if the current privilege level is 3

Real Address Mode Exceptions

None; if the SP or ESP register is 1, the processor shuts down due to a lack of stack space

Virtual 8086 Mode Exceptions

Same exceptions as in real-address mode; #PF(fault-code) for a page fault; #AC for unaligned memory reference if the current privilege level is 3

Notes

When used with an operand in memory, the PUSH instruction takes longer to execute than a two-instruction sequence which moves the operand through a register.

Back-to-back PUSH/POP instruction sequences are allowed without incurring an additional clock.

PUSHA/PUSHAD—Push all General Registers

Opcode	Instruction	Clocks	Description
60	PUSHA	11	Push AX, CX, DX, BX, original SP, BP, SI, and DI
60	PUSHAD	11	Push EAX, ECX, EDX, EBX, original ESP, EBP, ESI, and EDI

Operation

```
IF OperandSize = 16 (* PUSHA instruction *)
THEN
   Temp ← (SP);
   Push(AX);
   Push(CX);
   Push(DX);
   Push(BX);
   Push(Temp);
   Push(BP);
   Push(SI);
   Push(DI);
ELSE (* OperandSize = 32, PUSHAD instruction *)
   Temp ← (ESP);
   Push(EAX);
   Push(ECX);
   Push(EDX);
   Push(EBX);
   Push(Temp);
   Push(EBP);
   Push(ESI);
   Push(EDI);
FI;
```

Description

The PUSHA and PUSHAD instructions save the 16-bit or 32-bit general registers, respectively, on the i486 processor stack. The PUSHA instruction decrements the stack pointer (SP) by 16 to hold the eight word values. The PUSHAD instruction decrements the stack pointer (ESP) by 32 to hold the eight doubleword values. Because the registers are pushed onto the stack in the order in which they were given, they appear in the 16 or 32 new stack bytes in reverse order. The last register pushed is the DI or EDI register.

Flags Affected

None

Protected Mode Exceptions

#SS(0) if the starting or ending stack address is outside the stack segment limit; #PF(fault-code) for a page fault

Real Address Mode Exceptions

Before executing the PUSHA or PUSHAD instruction, the 386 DX processor shuts down if the SP or ESP register equals 1, 3, or 5; if the SP or ESP register equals 7, 9, 11, 13, or 15, exception 13 occurs

Virtual 8086 Mode Exceptions

Same exceptions as in real-address mode; #PF(fault-code) for a page fault

PUSHF/PUSHFD—Push Flags Register onto the Stack

Opcode	Instruction	Clocks	Description
9C	PUSHF	4,*pm*=3	Push FLAGS
9C	PUSHFD	4,*pm*=3	Push EFLAGS

Operation

```
IF OperandSize = 32
THEN push(EFLAGS);
ELSE push(FLAGS);
FI;
```

Description

The PUSHF instruction decrements the stack pointer by 2 and copies the FLAGS register to the new top of stack; the PUSHFD instruction decrements the stack pointer by 4, and the EFLAGS register is copied to the new top of stack which is pointed to by SS:ESP. Refer to Chapter 2 and to Chapter 4 for information on the EFLAGS register.

Flags Affected

None

Protected Mode Exceptions

#SS(0) if the new value of the ESP register is outside the stack segment boundaries

Real Address Mode Exceptions

None; the i486 processor shuts down due to a lack of stack space

Virtual 8086 Mode Exceptions

#GP(0) fault if the I/O privilege level is less than 3, to permit emulation

RCL/RCR/ROL/ROR-—Rotate

Opcode	Instruction	Clocks	Description
D0 /2	RCL *r/m8*,1	3/4	Rotate 9 bits (CF,*r/m* byte) left once
D2 /2	RCL *r/m8*,CL	8-30/9-31	Rotate 9 bits (CF,*r/m* byte) left CL times
C0 /2 *ib*	RCL *r/m8,imm8*	8-30/9-31	Rotate 9 bits (CF,*r/m* byte) left *imm8* times
D1 /2	RCL *r/m16*,1	3/4	Rotate 17 bits (CF,*r/m* word) left once
D3 /2	RCL *r/m16*,CL	8-30/9-31	Rotate 17 bits (CF,*r/m* word) left CL times
C1 /2 *ib*	RCL *r/m16,imm8*	8-30/9-31	Rotate 17 bits (CF,*r/m* word) left *imm8* times
D1 /2	RCL *r/m32*,1	3/4	Rotate 33 bits (CF,*r/m* dword) left once
D3 /2	RCL *r/m32*,CL	8-30/9-31	Rotate 33 bits (CF,*r/m* dword) left CL times
C1 /2 *ib*	RCL *r/m32,imm8*	8-30/9-31	Rotate 33 bits (CF,*r/m* dword) left *imm8* times
D0 /3	RCR *r/m8*,1	3/4	Rotate 9 bits (CF,*r/m* byte) right once
D2 /3	RCR *r/m8*,CL	8-30/9-31	Rotate 9 bits (CF,*r/m* byte) right CL times
C0 /3 *ib*	RCR *r/m8,imm8*	8-30/9-31	Rotate 9 bits (CF,*r/m* byte) right *imm8* times
D1 /3	RCR *r/m16*,1	3/4	Rotate 17 bits (CF,*r/m* word) right once
D3 /3	RCR *r/m16*,CL	8-30/9-31	Rotate 17 bits (CF,*r/m* word) right CL times
C1 /3 *ib*	RCR *r/m16,imm8*	8-30/9-31	Rotate 17 bits (CF,*r/m* word) right *imm8* times
D1 /3	RCR *r/m32*,1	3/4	Rotate 33 bits (CF,*r/m* dword) right once
D3 /3	RCR *r/m32*,CL	8-30/9-31	Rotate 33 bits (CF,*r/m* dword) right CL times
C1 /3 *ib*	RCR *r/m32,imm8*	8-30/9-31	Rotate 33 bits (CF,*r/m* dword) right *imm8* times
D0 /0	ROL *r/m8*,1	3/4	Rotate 8 bits *r/m* byte left once
D2 /0	ROL *r/m8*,CL	3/4	Rotate 8 bits *r/m* byte left CL times
C0 /0 *ib*	ROL *r/m8,imm8*	2/4	Rotate 8 bits *r/m* byte left *imm8* times
D1 /0	ROL *r/m16*,1	3/4	Rotate 16 bits *r/m* word left once
D3 /0	ROL *r/m16*,CL	3/4	Rotate 16 bits *r/m* word left CL times
C1 /0 *ib*	ROL *r/m16,imm8*	2/4	Rotate 16 bits *r/m* word left *imm8* times
D1 /0	ROL *r/m32*,1	3/4	Rotate 32 bits *r/m* dword left once
D3 /0	ROL *r/m32*,CL	3/4	Rotate 32 bits *r/m* dword left CL times
C1 /0 *ib*	ROL *r/m32,imm8*	2/4	Rotate 32 bits *r/m* dword left *imm8* times
D0 /1	ROR *r/m8*,1	3/4	Rotate 8 bits *r/m* byte right once
D2 /1	ROR *r/m8*,CL	3/4	Rotate 8 bits *r/m* byte right CL times
C0 /1 *ib*	ROR *r/m8,imm8*	2/4	Rotate 8 bits *r/m* word right *imm8* times
D1 /1	ROR *r/m16*,1	3/4	Rotate 16 bits *r/m* word right once
D3 /1	ROR *r/m16*,CL	3/4	Rotate 16 bits *r/m* word right CL times
C1 /1 *ib*	ROR *r/m16,imm8*	2/4	Rotate 16 bits *r/m* word right *imm8* times
D1 /1	ROR *r/m32*,1	3/4	Rotate 32 bits *r/m* dword right once
D3 /1	ROR *r/m32*,CL	3/4	Rotate 32 bits *r/m* dword right CL times
C1 /1 *ib*	ROR *r/m32,imm8*	2/4	Rotate 32 bits *r/m* dword right *imm8* times

Operation

```
(* ROL - Rotate Left *)
temp ← COUNT;
WHILE (temp < > 0)
DO
   tmpcf ← high-order bit of (r/m);
   r/m ← r/m * 2 + (tmpcf);
   temp ← temp − 1;
OD;
IF COUNT = 1
THEN
   IF high-order bit of r/m < > CF
   THEN OF ← 1;
   ELSE OF ← 0;
   FI;
ELSE OF ← undefined;
FI;
```

```
(* ROR - Rotate Right *)
temp ← COUNT;
WHILE (temp < > 0 )
DO
  tmpcf ← low-order bit of (r/m);
  r/m ← r/m / 2 + (tmpcf * 2^width(r/m));
  temp ← temp − 1;
DO;
IF COUNT = 1
THEN
  IF (high-order bit of r/m) < > (bit next to high-order bit of r/m)
  THEN OF ← 1;
  ELSE OF ← 0;
  FI;
ELSE OF ← undefined;
FI;
```

Description

Each rotate instruction shifts the bits of the register or memory operand given. The left rotate instructions shift all the bits upward, except for the top bit, which is returned to the bottom. The right rotate instructions do the reverse: the bits shift downward until the bottom bit arrives at the top.

For the RCL and RCR instructions, the CF flag is part of the rotated quantity. The RCL instruction shifts the CF flag into the bottom bit and shifts the top bit into the CF flag; the RCR instruction shifts the CF flag into the top bit and shifts the bottom bit into the CF flag. For the ROL and ROR instructions, the original value of the CF flag is not a part of the result, but the CF flag receives a copy of the bit that was shifted from one end to the other.

The rotate is repeated the number of times indicated by the second operand, which is either an immediate number or the contents of the CL register. To reduce the maximum instruction execution time, the i486 processor does not allow rotation counts greater than 31. If a rotation count greater than 31 is attempted, only the bottom five bits of the rotation are used. The 8086 does not mask rotation counts. The i486 processor in Virtual 8086 Mode does mask rotation counts.

The OF flag is defined only for the single-rotate forms of the instructions (second operand is a 1). It is undefined in all other cases. For left shifts/rotates, the CF bit after the shift is XORed with the high-order result bit. For right shifts/rotates, the high-order two bits of the result are XORed to get the OF flag.

Flags Affected

The OF flag is affected only for single-bit rotates; the OF flag is undefined for multi-bit rotates; the CF flag contains the value of the bit shifted into it; the SF, ZF, AF, and PF flags are not affected

Protected Mode Exceptions

#GP(0) if the result is in a nonwritable segment; #GP(0) for an illegal memory operand effective address in the CS, DS, ES, FS, or GS segments; #SS(0) for an illegal address in the SS segment; #PF(fault-code) for a page fault; #AC for unaligned memory reference if the current privilege level is 3

Real Address Mode Exceptions

Interrupt 13 if any part of the operand would lie outside of the effective address space from 0 to 0FFFFH

Virtual 8086 Mode Exceptions

Same exceptions as in Real Address Mode; #PF(fault-code) for a page fault; #AC for unaligned memory reference if the current privilege level is 3

REP/REPE/REPZ/REPNE/REPNZ—Repeat Following String Operation

Opcode	Instruction	Clocks	Description
F3 6C	REP INS *r/m8*, DX	16+8(E)CX, *pm*=10+8(E)CX*1/ 30+8(E)CX*2, VM=29+8(E)CX	Input (E)CX bytes from port DX into ES:[(E)DI]
F3 6D	REP INS *r/m16*,DX	16+8(E)CX, *pm*=10+8(E)CX*1/ 30+8(E)CX*2, VM=29+8(E)CX	Input (E)CX words from port DX into ES:[(E)DI]
F3 6D	REP INS *r/m32*,DX	16+8(E)CX, *pm*=10+8(E)CX*1/ 30+8(E)CX*2, VM=29+8(E)CX	Input (E)CX dwords from pot DX into ES:[(E)DI]
F3 A4	REP MOVS *m8,m8*	5*3,13*4,12+3(E)CX*5	Move (E)CX bytes from [(E)SI] to ES:[(E)DI]
F3 A5	REP MOVS *m16,m16*	5*3,13*4,12+3(E)CX*5	Move (E)CX words from [(E)SI] to ES:[(E)DI]
F3 A5	REP MOVS *m32,m32*	5*3,13*4,12+3(E)CX*5	Move (E)CX dwords from [(E)SI] to ES:[(E)DI]
F3 6E	REP OUTS DX,*r/m8*	17+5(E)CX, *pm*=11+5(E)CX*1/ 31+5(E)CX*2 vm=30+5(E)CX	Output (E)CX bytes from [(E)SI] to port DX
F3 6F	REP OUTS DX,*r/m16*	17+5(E)CX, *pm*=11+5(E)CX*1/ 31+5(E)CX*2 vm=30+5(E)CX	Output (E)CX words from [(E)SI] to port DX
F3 6F	REP OUTS DX,*r/m32*	17+5(E)CX, *pm*=11+5(E)CX*1/ 31+5(E)CX*2 vm=30+5(E)CX	Output (E)CX dwords from [(E)SI] to port DX
F2 AC	REP LODS *m8*	5*3,7+4(E)CX*6	Load (E)CX bytes from [(E)SI] to AL
F2 AD	REP LODS *m16*	5*3,7+4(E)CX*6	Load (E)CX words from [(E)SI] to AX
F2 AD	REP LODS *m32*	5*3,7+4(E)CX*6	Load (E)CX dwords from [(E)SI] to EAX
F3 AA	REP STOS *m8*	5*3,7+4(E)CX*6	Fill (E)CX bytes at ES:[(E)DI] with AL
F3 AB	REP STOS *m16*	5*3,7+4(E)CX*6	Fill (E)CX words at ES:[(E)DI] with AX
F3 AB	REP STOS *m32*	5*3,7+4(E)CX*6	Fill (E)CX dwords at ES:[(E)DI] with EAX
F3 A6	REPE CMPS *m8,m8*	5*3,7+7(E)CX*6	Find nonmatching bytes in ES:[(E)DI] and [(E)SI]
F3 A7	REPE CMPS *m16,m16*	5*3,7+7(E)CX*6	Find nonmatching words in ES:[(E)DI] and [(E)SI]
F3 A7	REPE CMPS *m32,m32*	5*3,7+7(E)CX*6	Find nonmatching dwords in ES:[(E)DI] and [(E)SI]
F3 AE	REPE SCAS *m8*	5*3,7+5(E)CX*6	Find non-AL byte starting at ES:[(E)DI]
F3 AF	REPE SCAS *m16*	5*3,7+5(E)CX*6	Find non-AX word starting at ES:[(E)DI]
F3 AF	REPE SCAS *m32*	5*3,7+5(E)CX*6	Find non-EAX dword starting at ES:[(E)DI]
F2 A6	REPNE CMPS *m8,m8*	5*3,7+7(E)CX*6	Find matching bytes in ES:[(E)DI] and [(E)SI]
F2 A7	REPNE CMPS *m16,m16*	5*3,7+7(E)CX*6	Find matching words in ES:[(E)DI] and [(E)SI]
F2 A7	REPNE CMPS *m32,m32*	5*3,7+7(E)CX*6	Find matching dwords in ES:[(E)DI] and [(E)SI]
F2 AE	REPNE SCAS *m8*	5*3,7+5(E)CX*6	Find AL, starting at ES:[(E)DI]
F2 AF	REPNE SCAS *m16*	5*3,7+5(E)CX*6	Find AX, starting at ES:[(E)DI]
F2 AF	REPNE SCAS *m32*	5*3,7+5(E)CX*6	Find EAX, starting at ES:[(E)DI]

NOTES: *1 If CPL ≤ IOPL
*2 If CPL > IOPL
*3 (E) CX=0
*4 (E) CX =1
*5 (E) CX > 1
*6 (E) CX > 0

Operation

```
IF AddressSize = 16
THEN use CX for CountReg;
ELSE (* AddressSize = 32 *) use ECX for CountReg;
FI;
```

```
WHILE CountReg < > 0
DO
   service pending interrupts (if any);
   perform primitive string instruction;
   CountReg ← CountReg − 1;
   IF primitive operation is CMPB, CMPW, SCAB, or SCAW
   THEN
      IF (instruction is REP/REPE/REPZ) AND (ZF=1)
      THEN exit WHILE loop
      ELSE
         IF (instruction is REPNZ or REPNE) AND (ZF=0)
         THEN exit WHILE loop;
         FI;
      FI;
   FI;
OD;
```

Description

The REP, REPE (repeat while equal), and REPNE (repeat while not equal) prefixes are applied to string operation. Each prefix causes the string instruction that follows to be repeated the number of times indicated in the count register or (for the REPE and REPNE prefixes) until the indicated condition in the ZF flag is no longer met.

Synonymous forms of the REPE and REPNE prefixes are the REPZ and REPNZ prefixes, respectively.

The REP prefixes apply only to one string instruction at a time. To repeat a block of instructions, use the LOOP instruction or another looping construct.

The precise action for each iteration is as follows:

1. If the address-size attribute is 16 bits, use the CX register for the count register; if the address-size attribute is 32 bits, use the ECX register for the count register.
2. Check the CX register. If it is zero, exit the iteration, and move to the next instruction.
3. Acknowledge any pending interrupts.
4. Perform the string operation once.
5. Decrement the CX or ECX register by one; no flags are modified.
6. Check the ZF flag if the string operation is a SCAS or CMPS instruction. If the repeat condition does not hold, exit the iteration and move to the next instruction. Exit the iteration if the prefix is REPE and the ZF flag is 0 (the last comparison was not equal), or if the prefix is REPNE and the ZF flag is one (the last comparison was equal).
7. Return to step 1 for the next iteration.

Repeated CMPS and SCAS instructions can be exited if the count is exhausted or if the ZF flag fails the repeat condition. These two cases can be distinguished by using either the JCXZ instruction, or by using the conditional jumps that test the ZF flag (the JZ, JNZ, and JNE instructions).

Flags Affected

The ZF flag is affected by the REP CMPS and REP SCAS as described above

Protected Mode Exceptions

None

Real Address Mode Exceptions

None

Virtual 8086 Mode Exceptions

None

Notes

Not all I/O ports can handle the rate at which the REP INS and REP OUTS instructions execute.

The repeat prefix is ignored when it is used with a non-string instruction.

RET — Return from Procedure

Opcode	Instruction	Clocks	Description
C3	RET	5	Return (near) to caller
CB	RET	13,*pm*=18	Return (far) to caller, same privilege
CB	RET	13,*pm*=33	Return (far), lesser privilege, switch stacks
C2 *iw*	RET *imm16*	5	Return (near), pop *imm16* bytes of parameters
CA *iw*	RET *imm16*	14,*pm*=17	Return (far), same privilege, pop *imm16* bytes
CA *iw*	RET *imm16*	14,*pm*=33	Return (far), lesser privilege, pop *imm16* bytes

Operation

```
IF instruction = near RET
THEN;
   IF OperandSize = 16
   THEN
      IP ← Pop();
      EIP ← EIP AND 0000FFFFH;
   ELSE (* OperandSize = 32 *)
      EIP ← Pop();
   FI;
   IF instruction has immediate operand THEN eSP ← eSP + imm16; FI;
FI;

IF (PE = 0 OR (PE = 1 AND VM = 1))
   (* real mode or virtual 8086 mode *)
   AND instruction = far RET
THEN;
   IF OperandSize = 16
   THEN
      IP ← Pop();
      EIP ← EIP AND 0000FFFFH;
      CS ← Pop(); (* 16-bit pop *)
   ELSE (* OperandSize = 32 *)
      EIP ← Pop();
      CS ← Pop(); (* 32-bit pop, high-order 16-bits discarded *)
   FI;
   IF instruction has immediate operand THEN eSP ← eSP + imm16; FI;
FI;

IF (PE = 1 AND VM = 0) (* Protected mode, not V86 mode *)
   AND instruction = far RET
THEN
   IF OperandSize=32
   THEN Third word on stack must be within stack limits else #SS(0);
   ELSE Second word on stack must be within stack limits else #SS(0);
   FI;
   Return selector RPL must be ≥ CPL ELSE #GP(return selector)
   IF return selector RPL = CPL
```

```
   THEN GOTO SAME-LEVEL;
   ELSE GOTO OUTER-PRIVILEGE-LEVEL;
   FI;
FI;

SAME-LEVEL:
   Return selector must be non-null ELSE #GP(0)
   Selector index must be within its descriptor table limits ELSE
      #GP(selector)
   Descriptor AR byte must indicate code segment ELSE #GP(selector)
   IF non-conforming
   THEN code segment DPL must equal CPL;
   ELSE #GP(selector);
   FI;
   IF conforming
   THEN code segment DPL must be ≤ CPL;
   ELSE #GP(selector);
   FI;
   Code segment must be present ELSE #NP(selector);
   Top word on stack must be within stack limits ELSE #SS(0);
   IP must be in code segment limit ELSE #GP(0);
   IF OperandSize=32
   THEN
      Load CS:EIP from stack
      Load CS register with descriptor
      Increment eSP by 8 plus the immediate offset if it exists
   ELSE (* OperandSize=16 *)
      Load CS:IP from stack
      Load CS register with descriptor
      Increment eSP by 4 plus the immediate offset if it exists
   FI;

OUTER-PRIVILEGE-LEVEL:
   IF OperandSize=32
   THEN Top (16+immediate) bytes on stack must be within stack limits
      ELSE #SS(0);
   ELSE Top (8+immediate) bytes on stack must be within stack limits ELSE
      #SS(0);
   FI;
   Examine return CS selector and associated descriptor:
      Selector must be non-null ELSE #GP(0);
      Selector index must be within its descriptor table limits ELSE
         #GP(selector)
      Descriptor AR byte must indicate code segment ELSE #GP(selector);
      IF non-conforming
      THEN code segment DPL must equal return selector RPL
      ELSE #GP(selector);
      FI;
      IF conforming
```

```
    THEN code segment DPL must be ≤ return selector RPL;
    ELSE #GP(selector);
    FI;
    Segment must be present ELSE #NP(selector)
  Examine return SS selector and associated descriptor:
    Selector must be non-null ELSE #GP(0);
    Selector index must be within its descriptor table limits
      ELSE #GP(selector);
    Selector RPL must equal the RPL of the return CS selector ELSE
      #GP(selector);
    Descriptor AR byte must indicate a writable data segment ELSE
      #GP(selector);
    Descriptor DPL must equal the RPL of the return CS selector ELSE
      #GP(selector);
    Segment must be present ELSE #NP(selector);
  IP must be in code segment limit ELSE #GP(0);
  Set CPL to the RPL of the return CS selector;
  IF OperandMode=32
  THEN
    Load CS:EIP from stack;
    Set CS RPL to CPL;
    Increment eSP by 8 plus the immediate offset if it exists;
    Load SS:eSP from stack;
  ELSE (* OperandMode=16 *)
    Load CS:IP from stack;
    Set CS RPL to CPL;
    Increment eSP by 4 plus the immediate offset if it exists;
    Load SS:eSP from stack;
  FI;
  Load the CS register with the return CS descriptor;
  Load the SS register with the return SS descriptor;
  For each of ES, FS, GS, and DS
  DO
    IF the current register setting is not valid for the outer level,
      set the register to null (selector ← AR ← 0);
    To be valid, the register setting must satisfy the following properties:
      Selector index must be within descriptor table limits;
      Descriptor AR byte must indicate data or readable code segment;
      IF segment is data or non-conforming code, THEN
        DPL must be ≥ CPL, or DPL must be ≥ RPL;
      FI;
  OD;
```

Description

The RET instruction transfers control to a return address located on the stack. The address is usually placed on the stack by a CALL instruction, and the return is made to the instruction that follows the CALL instruction.

The optional numeric parameter to the RET instruction gives the number of stack bytes (OperandMode = 16) or words (OperandMode = 32) to be released after the return address is popped. These items are typically used as input parameters to the procedure called.

For the intrasegment (near) return, the address on the stack is a segment offset, which is popped into the instruction pointer. The CS register is unchanged. For the intersegment (far) return, the address on the stack is a long pointer. The offset is popped first, followed by the selector.

In real mode, the CS and IP registers are loaded directly. In Protected Mode, an intersegment return causes the processor to check the descriptor addressed by the return selector. The AR byte of the descriptor must indicate a code segment of equal or lesser privilege (or greater or equal numeric value) than the current privilege level. Returns to a lesser privilege level cause the stack to be reloaded from the value saved beyond the parameter block.

The DS, ES, FS, and GS segment registers can be cleared by the RET instruction during an interlevel transfer. If these registers refer to segments that cannot be used by the new privilege level, they are cleared to prevent unauthorized access from the new privilege level.

Flags Affected

None

Protected Mode Exceptions

#GP, #NP, or #SS, as described under "Operation" above; #PF(fault-code) for a page fault

Real Address Mode Exceptions

Interrupt 13 if any part of the operand would be outside the effective address space from 0 to 0FFFFH

Virtual 8086 Mode Exceptions

Same exceptions as in Real Address Mode; #PF(fault-code) for a page fault

SAHF—Store AH into Flags

Opcode	Instruction	Clocks	Description
9E	SAHF	2	Store AH into flags SF ZF xx AF xx PF xx CF

Operation

SF:ZF:xx:AF:xx:PF:xx:CF ← AH;

Description

The SAHF instruction loads the SF, ZF, AF, PF, and CF flags with values from the AH register, from bits 7, 6, 4, 2, and 0, respectively.

Flags Affected

The SF, ZF, AF, PF, and CF flags are loaded with values form the AH register

Protected Mode Exceptions

None

Real Address Mode Exceptions

None

Virtual 8086 Mode Exceptions

None

SAL/SAR/SHL/SHR – Shift Instructions

Opcode	Instruction	Clocks	Description
D0 /4	SAL *r/m8*,1	3/4	Multiply *r/m* byte by 2, once
D2 /4	SAL *r/m8*,CL	3/4	Multiply *r/m* byte by 2, CL times
C0 /4 *ib*	SAL *r/m8*,*imm8*	2/4	Multiply *r/m* byte by 2, *imm8* times
D1 /4	SAL *r/m16*,1	3/4	Multiply *r/m* word by 2, once
D3 /4	SAL *r/m16*,CL	3/4	Multiply *r/m* word by 2, CL times
C1 /4 *ib*	SAL *r/m16*,*imm8*	2/4	Multiply *r/m* word by 2, *imm8* times
D1 /4	SAL *r/m32*,1	3/4	Multiply *r/m* dword by 2, once
D3 /4	SAL *r/m32*,CL	3/4	Multiply *r/m* dword by 2, CL times
C1 /4 *ib*	SAL *r/m32*,*imm8*	2/4	Multiply *r/m* dword by 2, *imm8* times
D0 /7	SAR *r/m8*,1	3/4	Signed divide[1] *r/m* byte by 2, once
D2 /7	SAR *r/m8*,CL	3/4	Signed divide[1] *r/m* byte by 2, CL times
C0 /7 *ib*	SAR *r/m8*,*imm8*	2/4	Signed divide[1] *r/m* byte by 2, *imm8* times
D1 /7	SAR *r/m16*,1	3/4	Signed divide[1] *r/m* word by 2, once
D3 /7	SAR *r/m16*,CL	3/4	Signed divide[1] *r/m* word by 2, CL times
C1 /7 *ib*	SAR *r/m16*,*imm8*	2/4	Signed divide[1] *r/m* word by 2, *imm8* times
D1 /7	SAR *r/m32*,1	3/4	Signed divide[1] *r/m* dword by 2, once
D3 /7	SAR *r/m32*,CL	3/4	Signed divide[1] *r/m* dword by 2, CL times
C1 /7 *ib*	SAR *r/m32*,*imm8*	2/4	Signed divide[1] *r/m* dword by 2, *imm8* times
D0 /4	SHL *r/m8*,1	3/4	Multiply *r/m* byte by 2, once
D2 /4	SHL *r/m8*,CL	3/4	Multiply *r/m* byte by 2, CL times
C0 /4 *ib*	SHL *r/m8*,*imm8*	2/4	Multiply *r/m* byte by 2, *imm8* times
D1 /4	SHL *r/m16*,1	3/4	Multiply *r/m* word by 2, once
D3 /4	SHL *r/m16*,CL	3/4	Multiply *r/m* word by 2, CL times
C1 /4 *ib*	SHL *r/m16*,*imm8*	2/4	Multiply *r/m* word by 2, *imm8* times
D1 /4	SHL *r/m32*,1	3/4	Multiply *r/m* dword by 2, once
D3 /4	SHL *r/m32*,CL	3/4	Multiply *r/m* dword by 2, CL times
C1 /4 *ib*	SHL *r/m32*,*imm8*	2/4	Multiply *r/m* dword by 2, *imm8* times
D0 /5	SHR *r/m8*,1	3/4	Unsigned divide *r/m* byte by 2, once
D2 /5	SHR *r/m8*,CL	3/4	Unsigned divide *r/m* byte by 2, CL times
C0 /5 *ib*	SHR *r/m8*,*imm8*	2/4	Unsigned divide *r/m* byte by 2, *imm8* times
D1 /5	SHR *r/m16*,1	3/4	Unsigned divide *r/m* word by 2, once
D3 /5	SHR *r/m16*,CL	3/4	Unsigned divide *r/m* word by 2, CL times
C1 /5 *ib*	SHR *r/m16*,*imm8*	2/4	Unsigned divide *r/m* word by 2, *imm8* times
D1 /5	SHR *r/m32*,1	3/4	Unsigned divide *r/m* dword by 2, once
D3 /5	SHR *r/m32*,CL	3/4	Unsigned divide *r/m* dword by 2, CL times
C1 /5 *ib*	SHR *r/m32*,*imm8*	2/4	Unsigned divide *r/m* dword by 2, *imm8* times

Not the same division as IDIV; rounding is toward negative infinity.

Operation

```
(* COUNT is the second parameter *)
(temp) ← COUNT;
WHILE (temp < > 0)
DO
   IF instruction is SAL or SHL
   THEN CF ← high-order bit of r/m;
   FI;
   IF instruction is SAR or SHR
   THEN CF ← low-order bit of r/m;
   FI;
   IF instruction = SAL or SHL
   THEN r/m ← r/m * 2;
   FI;
   IF instruction = SAR
   THEN r/m ← r/m /2 (*Signed divide, rounding toward negative infinity*);
```

```
    FI;
    IF instruction = SHR
    THEN r/m ← r/m / 2; (* Unsigned divide *);
    FI;
    temp ← temp − 1;
OD;
(* Determine overflow for the various instructions *)
IF COUNT = 1
THEN
    IF instruction is SAL or SHL
    THEN OF ← high-order bit of r/m < > (CF);
    FI;
    IF instruction is SAR
    THEN OF ← 0;
    FI;
    IF instruction is SHR
    THEN OF ← high-order bit of operand;
    FI;
ELSE OF ← undefined;
FI;
```

Description

The SAL instruction (or its synonym, SHL) shifts the bits of the operand upward. The high-order bit is shifted into the CF flag, and the low-order bit is cleared.

The SAR and SHR instructions shift the bits of the operand downward. The low-order bit is shifted into the CF flag. The effect is to divide the operand by two. The SAR instruction performs a signed divide with rounding toward negative infinity (not the same as the IDIV instruction); the high-order bit remains the same. The SHR instruction performs an unsigned divide; the high-order bit is cleared.

The shift is repeated the number of times indicated by the second operand, which is either an immediate number or the contents of the CL register. To reduce the maximum execution time, the i486 processor does not allow shift counts greater than 31. If a shift count greater than 31 is attempted, only the bottom five bits of the shift count are used. (The 8086 uses all eight bits of the shift count.)

The OF flag is affected only if the single-shift forms of the instructions are used. For left shifts, the OF flag is cleared if the high bit of the answer is the same as the result of the CF flag (i.e., the top two bits of the original operand were the same); the OF flag is set if they are different. For the SAR instruction, the OF flag is cleared for all single shifts. For the SHR instruction, the OF flag is set to the high-order bit of the original operand.

Flags Affected

The OF flag is affected for single shifts; the OF flag is undefined for multiple shifts; the CF, ZF, PF, and SF flags are set according to the result

Protected Mode Exceptions

#GP(0) if the result is in a nonwritable segment; #GP(0) for an illegal memory operand effective address in the CS, DS, ES, FS, or GS segments; #SS(0) for an illegal address in the SS segment; #PF(fault-code) for a page fault; #AC for unaligned memory reference if the current privilege level is 3

Real Address Mode Exceptions

Interrupt 13 if any part of the operand would lie outside of the effective address space from 0 to 0FFFFH

Virtual 8086 Mode Exceptions

Same exceptions as in Real Address Mode; #PF(fault-code) for a page fault; #AC for unaligned memory reference if the current privilege level is 3

SBB—Integer Subtraction with Borrow

Opcode	Instruction	Clocks	Description
1C *ib*	SBB AL,*imm8*	1	Subtract with borrow immediate byte from AL
1D *iw*	SBB AX,*imm16*	1	Subtract with borrow immediate word from AX
1D *id*	SBB EAX,*imm32*	1	Subtract with borrow immediate dword from EAX
80 /3 *ib*	SBB *r/m8,imm8*	1/3	Subtract with borrow immediate byte from *r/m* byte
81 /3 *iw*	SBB *r/m16,imm16*	1/3	Subtract with borrow immediate word from *r/m* word
81 /3 *id*	SBB *r/m32,imm32*	1/3	Subtract with borrow immediate dword from *r/m* dword
83 /3 *ib*	SBB *r/m16,imm8*	1/3	Subtract with borrow sign-extended immediate byte from *r/m* word
83 /3 *ib*	SBB *r/m32,imm8*	1/3	Subtract with borrow sign-extended immediate byte from *r/m* dword
18 /*r*	SBB *r/m8,r8*	1/3	Subtract with borrow byte register from *r/m* byte
19 /*r*	SBB *r/m16,r16*	1/3	Subtract with borrow word register from *r/m* word
19 /*r*	SBB *r/m32,r32*	1/3	Subtract with borrow dword register from *r/m* dword
1A /*r*	SBB *r8,r/m8*	1/2	Subtract with borrow byte register from *r/m* byte
1B /*r*	SBB *r16,r/m16*	1/2	Subtract with borrow word register from *r/m* word
1B /*r*	SBB *r32,r/m32*	1/2	Subtract with borrow dword register from *r/m* dword

Operation

IF SRC is a byte and DEST is a word or dword
THEN DEST = DEST − (SignExtend(SRC) + CF)
ELSE DEST ← DEST − (SRC + CF);

Description

The SBB instruction adds the second operand (SRC) to the CF flag and subtracts the result from the first operand (DEST). The result of the subtraction is assigned to the first operand (DEST), and the flags are set accordingly.

When an immediate byte value is subtracted from a word operand, the immediate value is first sign-extended.

Flags Affected

The OF, SF, ZF, AF, PF, and CF flags are set according to the result

Protected Mode Exceptions

#GP(0) if the result is in a nonwritable segment; #GP(0) for an illegal memory operand effective address in the CS, DS, ES, FS, or GS segments; #SS(0) for an illegal address in the SS segment; #PF(fault-code) for a page fault; #AC for unaligned memory reference if the current privilege level is 3

Real Address Mode Exceptions

Interrupt 13 if any part of the operand would lie outside of the effective address space from 0 to 0FFFFH

Virtual 8086 Mode Exceptions

Same exceptions as in Real Address Mode; #PF(fault-code) for a page fault; #AC for unaligned memory reference if the current privilege level is 3

SCAS/SCASB/SCASW/SCASD – Compare String Data

Opcode	Instruction	Clocks	Description
AE	SCAS *m8*	6	Compare bytes AL-ES:[DI], update (E)DI
AF	SCAS *m16*	6	Compare words AX-ES:[DI], update (E)DI
AF	SCAS *m32*	6	Compare dwords EAX-ES:[DI], update (E)DI
AE	SCASB	6	Compare bytes AL-ES:[DI], update (E)DI
AF	SCASW	6	Compare words AX-ES:[DI], update (E)DI
AF	SCASD	6	Compare dwords EAX-ES:[DI], update (E)DI

Operation

```
IF AddressSize = 16
THEN use DI for dest-index;
ELSE (* AddressSize = 32 *) use EDI for dest-index;
FI;
IF byte type of instruction
THEN
   AL – [dest-index]; (* Compare byte in AL and dest *)
   IF DF = 0 THEN IndDec ← 1 ELSE IncDec ← –1; FI;
ELSE
   IF OperandSize = 16
   THEN
      AX – [dest-index]; (* compare word in AL and dest *)
      IF DF = 0 THEN IncDec ← 2 ELSE IncDec ← –2; FI;
   ELSE (* OperandSize = 32 *)
      EAX – [dest-index];(* compare dword in EAX & dest *)
      IF DF = 0 THEN IncDec ← 4 ELSE IncDec ← –4; FI;
   FI;
FI;
dest-index = dest-index + IncDec
```

Description

The SCAS instruction subtracts the memory byte or word at the destination register from the AL, AX or EAX register. The result is discarded; only the flags are set. The operand must be addressable from the ES segment; no segment override is possible.

If the address-size attribute for this instruction is 16 bits, the DI register is used as the destination register; otherwise, the address-size attribute is 32 bits and the EDI register is used.

The address of the memory data being compared is determined solely by the contents of the destination register, not by the operand to the SCAS instruction. The operand validates ES segment addressability and determines the data type. Load the correct index value into the DI or EDI register before executing the SCAS instruction.

After the comparison is made, the destination register is automatically updated. If the direction flag is 0 (the CLD instruction was executed), the destination register is incremented; if the direction flag is 1 (the STD instruction was executed), it is decremented. The increments or decrements are by 1 if bytes are compared, by 2 if words are compared, or by 4 if doublewords are compared.

The SCASB, SCASW, and SCASD instructions are synonyms for the byte, word and doubleword SCAS instructions that don't require operands. They are simpler to code, but provide no type or segment checking.

The SCAS instruction can be preceded by the REPE or REPNE prefix for a block search of CX or ECX bytes or words. Refer to the REP instruction for further details.

Flags Affected

The OF, SF, ZF, AF, PF, and CF flags are set according to the result

Protected Mode Exceptions

#GP(0) for an illegal memory operand effective address in the CS, DS, ES, FS, or GS segments; #SS(0) for an illegal address in the SS segment; #PF(fault-code) for a page fault; #AC for unaligned memory reference if the current privilege level is 3

Real Address Mode Exceptions

Interrupt 13 if any part of the operand would lie outside of the effective address space from 0 to 0FFFFH

Virtual 8086 Mode Exceptions

Same exceptions as in Real Address Mode; #PF(fault-code) for a page fault; #AC for unaligned memory reference if the current privilege level is 3

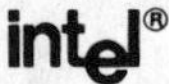

SETcc—Byte Set on Condition

Opcode	Instruction	Clocks	Description
0F 97	SETA *r/m8*	4/3	Set byte if above (CF=0 and ZF=0)
0F 93	SETAE *r/m8*	4/3	Set byte if above or equal (CF=0)
0F 92	SETB *r/m8*	4/3	Set byte if below (CF=1)
0F 96	SETBE *r/m8*	4/3	Set byte if below or equal (CF=1 or (ZF=1)
0F 92	SETC *r/m8*	4/3	Set if carry (CF=1)
0F 94	SETE *r/m8*	4/3	Set byte if equal (ZF=1)
0F 9F	SETG *r/m8*	4/3	Set byte if greater (ZF=0 or SF=OF)
0F 9D	SETGE *r/m8*	4/3	Set byte if greater or equal (SF=OF)
0F 9C	SETL *r/m8*	4/3	Set byte if less (SF< >OF)
0F 9E	SETLE *r/m8*	4/3	Set byte if less or equal (ZF=1 or SF< >OF)
0F 96	SETNA *r/m8*	4/3	Set byte if not above (CF=1)
0F 92	SETNAE *r/m8*	4/3	Set byte if not above or equal (CF=1)
0F 93	SETNB *r/m8*	4/3	Set byte if not below (CF=0)
0F 97	SETNBE *r/m8*	4/3	Set byte if not below or equal (CF=0 and ZF=0)
0F 93	SETNC *r/m8*	4/3	Set byte if not carry (CF=0)
0F 95	SETNE *r/m8*	4/3	Set byte if not equal (ZF=0)
0F 9E	SETNG *r/m8*	4/3	Set byte if not greater (ZF=1 or SF< >OF)
0F 9C	SETNGE *r/m8*	4/3	Set if not greater or equal (SF< >OF)
0F 9D	SETNL *r/m8*	4/3	Set byte if not less (SF=OF)
0F 9F	SETNLE *r/m8*	4/3	Set byte if not less or equal (ZF=0 and SF=OF)
0F 91	SETNO *r/m8*	4/3	Set byte if not overflow (OF=0)
0F 9B	SETNP *r/m8*	4/3	Set byte if not parity (PF=0)
0F 99	SETNS *r/m8*	4/3	Set byte if not sign (SF=0)
0F 95	SETNZ *r/m8*	4/3	Set byte if not zero (ZF=0)
0F 90	SETO *r/m8*	4/3	Set byte if overflow (OF=1)
0F 9A	SETP *r/m8*	4/3	Set byte if parity (PF=1)
0F 9A	SETPE *r/m8*	4/3	Set byte if parity even (PF=1)
0F 9B	SETPO *r/m8*	4/3	Set byte if parity odd (PF=0)
0F 98	SETS *r/m8*	4/3	Set byte if sign (SF=1)
0F 94	SETZ *r/m8*	4/3	Set byte if zero (ZF=1)

Operation

IF condition THEN *r/m8* ← 1 ELSE *r/m8* ← 0; FI;

Description

The SETcc instruction stores a byte at the destination specified by the effective address or register if the condition is met, or a 0 byte if the condition is not met.

Flags Affected

None

Protected Mode Exceptions

#GP(0) if the result is in a non-writable segment; #GP(0) for an illegal memory operand effective address in the CS, DS, ES, FS, or GS segments; #SS(0) for an illegal address in the SS segment; #PF(fault-code) for a page fault; #AC for unaligned memory reference if the current privilege level is 3

Real Address Mode Exceptions

Interrupt 13 if any part of the operand would lie outside of the effective address space from 0 to 0FFFFH

Virtual 8086 Mode Exceptions

Same exceptions as in Real Address Mode; #PF(fault-code) for a page fault; #AC for unaligned memory reference if the current privilege level is 3

SGDT/SIDT—Store Global/Interrupt Descriptor Table Register

Opcode	Instruction	Clocks	Description
0F 01 /0	SGDT *m*	10	Store GDTR to *m*
0F 01 /1	SIDT *m*	10	Store IDTR to *m*

Operation

DEST ← 48-bit BASE/LIMIT register contents;

Description

The SGDT and SIDT instructions copy the contents of the descriptor table register to the six bytes of memory indicated by the operand. The LIMIT field of the register is assigned to the first word at the effective address. If the operand-size attribute is 32 bits, the next three bytes are assigned the BASE field of the register, and the fourth byte is written with zero. The last byte is undefined. Otherwise, if the operand-size attribute is 16 bits, the next four bytes are assigned the 32-bit BASE field of the register.

The SGDT and SIDT instructions are used only in operating system software; they are not used in application programs.

Flags Affected

None

Protected Mode Exceptions

Interrupt 6 if the destination operand is a register; #GP(0) if the destination is in a nonwritable segment; #GP(0) for an illegal memory operand effective address in the CS, DS, ES, FS, or GS segments; #SS(0) for an illegal address in the SS segment; #PF(fault-code) for a page fault; #AC for unaligned memory reference if the current privilege level is 3

Real Address Mode Exceptions

Interrupt 6 if the destination operand is a register; Interrupt 13 if any part of the operand would lie outside of the effective address space from 0 to 0FFFFH

Virtual 8086 Mode Exceptions

Same exceptions as in Real Address Mode; #PF(fault-code) for a page fault; #AC for unaligned memory reference if the current privilege level is 3

Compatibility Note

The 16-bit forms of the SGDT and SIDT instructions are compatible with the 80286 processor, if the value in the upper eight bits is not referenced. The 80286 processor stores 1's in these upper bits, whereas the 386 DX and i486 processors store 0's if the operand-size attribute is 16 bits. These bits were specified as undefined by the SGDT and SIDT instructions in the *iAPX 286 Programmer's Reference Manual*.

SHLD—Double Precision Shift Left

Opcode	Instruction	Clocks	Description
0F A4	SHLD *r/m16,r16,imm8*	2/3	*r/m16* gets SHL of *r/m16* concatenated with *r16*
0F A4	SHLD *r/m32,r32,imm8*	2/3	*r/m32* gets SHL of *r/m32* concatenated with *r32*
0F A5	SHLD *r/m16,r16*,CL	3/4	*r/m16* gets SHL of *r/m16* concatenated with *r16*
0F A5	SHLD *r/m32,r32*,CL	3/4	*r/m32* gets SHL of *r/m32* concatenated with *r32*

Operation

```
(* count is an unsigned integer corresponding to the last operand of the instruction, either an
immediate byte or the byte in register CL *)
ShiftAmt ← count MOD 32;
inBits ← register; (* Allow overlapped operands *)
IF ShiftAmt = 0
THEN no operation
ELSE
  IF ShiftAmt ≥ OperandSize
  THEN (* Bad parameters *)
    r/m ← UNDEFINED;
    CF, OF, SF, ZF, AF, PF ← UNDEFINED;
  ELSE (* Perform the shift *)
    CF ← BIT[Base, OperandSize – ShiftAmt];
      (* Last bit shifted out on exit *)
    FOR i ← OperandSize – 1 DOWNTO ShiftAmt
    DO
      BIT[Base, i] ← BIT[Base, i – ShiftAmt];
    OF;
    FOR i ← ShiftAmt – 1 DOWNTO 0
    DO
      BIT[Base, i] ← BIT[inBits, i – ShiftAmt + OperandSize];
    OD;
    Set SF, ZF, PF (r/m);
      (* SF, ZF, PF are set according to the value of the result *)
    AF ← UNDEFINED;
  FI;
FI;
```

Description

The SHLD instruction shifts the first operand provided by the *r/m* field to the left as many bits as specified by the count operand. The second operand (*r16* or *r32*) provides the bits to shift in from the right (starting with bit 0). The result is stored back into the *r/m* operand. The register remains unaltered.

The count operand is provided by either an immediate byte or the contents of the CL register. These operands are taken MODULO 32 to provide a number between 0 and 31 by which to shift. Because the bits to shift are provided by the specified registers, the operation is useful for multiprecision shifts (64 bits or more). The SF, ZF and PF flags are set according to the value of the result. The CF flag is set to the value of the last bit shifted out. The OF and AF flags are left undefined.

Flags Affected

The SF, ZF, and PF, flags are set according to the result; the CF flag is set to the value of the last bit shifted out; after a shift of one bit position, the OF flag is set if a sign change occurred, otherwise it is cleared; after a shift of more than one bit position, the OF flag is undefined; the AF flag is undefined, except for a shift count of zero, which does not affect any flags.

Protected Mode Exceptions

#GP(0) if the result is in a nonwritable segment; #GP(0) for an illegal memory operand effective address in the CS, DS, ES, FS, or GS segments; #SS(0) for an illegal address in the SS segment; #PF(fault-code) for a page fault; #AC for unaligned memory reference if the current privilege level is 3

Real Address Mode Exceptions

Interrupt 13 if any part of the operand would lie outside of the effective address space from 0 to 0FFFFH

Virtual 8086 Mode Exceptions

Same exceptions as in Real Address Mode; #PF(fault-code) for a page fault; #AC for unaligned memory reference if the current privilege level is 3

SHRD – Double Precision Shift Right

Opcode	Instruction	Clocks	Description
0F AC	SHRD *r/m16,r16,imm8*	2/3	*r/m16* gets SHR of *r/m16* concatenated with *r16*
0F AC	SHRD *r/m32,r32,imm8*	2/3	*r/m32* gets SHR of *r/m32* concatenated with *r32*
0F AD	SHRD *r/m16,r16*,CL	3/4	*r/m16* gets SHR of *r/m16* concatenated with *r16*
0F AD	SHRD *r/m32,r32*,CL	3/4	*r/m32* gets SHR of *r/m32* concatenated with *r32*

Operation

```
(* count is an unsigned integer corresponding to the last operand of the instruction, either an
   immediate byte or the byte in register CL *)
ShiftAmt ← count MOD 32;
inBits ← register; (* Allow overlapped operands *)
IF ShiftAmt = 0
THEN no operation
ELSE
  IF ShiftAmt ≥ OperandSize
  THEN (* Bad parameters *)
     r/m ← UNDEFINED;
     CF, OF, SF, ZF, AF, PF ← UNDEFINED;
  ELSE (* Perform the shift *)
     CF ← BIT[r/m, ShiftAmt – 1]; (* last bit shifted out on exit *)
     FOR i ← 0 TO OperandSize – 1 – ShiftAmt
     DO
        BIT[r/m, i] ← BIT[r/m, i – ShiftAmt];
     OD;
     FOR i ← OperandSize – ShiftAmt TO OperandSize – 1
     DO
        BIT[r/m,i] ← BIT[inBits,i + ShiftAmt – OperandSize];
     OD;
     Set SF, ZF, PF (r/m);
        (* SF, ZF, PF are set according to the value of the result *)
     Set SF, ZF, PF (r/m);
     AF ←UNDEFINED;
  FI;
FI;
```

Description

The SHRD instruction shifts the first operand provided by the *r/m* field to the right as many bits as specified by the count operand. The second operand (*r16* or *r32*) provides the bits to shift in from the left (starting with bit 31). The result is stored back into the *r/m* operand. The register remains unaltered.

The count operand is provided by either an immediate byte or the contents of the CL register. These operands are taken MODULO 32 to provide a number between 0 and 31 by which to shift. Because the bits to shift are provided by the specified register, the operation is useful for multi-precision shifts (64 bits or more). The SF, ZF and PF flags are set according to the value of the result. The CF flag is set to the value of the last bit shifted out. The OF and AF flags are left undefined.

Flags Affected

The SF, ZF, and PF flags are set according to the result; the CF flag is set to the value of the last bit shifted out; after a shift of one bit position, the OF flag is set if a sign change occurred, otherwise it is cleared; after a shift of more than one bit position, the OF flag is undefined; the AF flag is undefined, except for a shift count of zero, which does not affect any flags.

Protected Mode Exceptions

#GP(0) if the result is in a nonwritable segment; #GP(0) for an illegal memory operand effective address in the CS, DS, ES, FS, or GS segments; #SS(0) for an illegal address in the SS segment; #PF(fault-code) for a page fault; #AC for unaligned memory reference if the current privilege level is 3

Real Address Mode Exceptions

Interrupt 13 if any part of the operand would lie outside of the effective address space from 0 to 0FFFFH

Virtual 8086 Mode Exceptions

Same exceptions as in Real Address Mode; #PF(fault-code) for a page fault; #AC for unaligned memory reference if the current privilege level is 3

SLDT—Store Local Descriptor Table Register

Opcode	Instruction	Clocks	Description
0F 00 /0	SLDT *r/m16*	2/3	Store LDTR to EA word

Operation

r/m16 ← LDTR;

Description

The SLDT instruction stores the Local Descriptor Table Register (LDTR) in the two-byte register or memory location indicated by the effective address operand. This register is a selector that points into the Global Descriptor Table.

The SLDT instruction is used only in operating system software. It is not used in application programs.

Flags Affected

None

Protected Mode Exceptions

#GP(0) if the result is in a nonwritable segment; #GP(0) for an illegal memory operand effective address in the CS, DS, ES, FS, or GS segments; #SS(0) for an illegal address in the SS segment; #PF(fault-code) for a page fault; #AC for unaligned memory reference if the current privilege level is 3

Real Address Mode Exceptions

Interrupt 6; the SLDT instruction is not recognized in Real Address Mode

Virtual 8086 Mode Exceptions

Same exceptions as in Real Address Mode; #PF(fault-code) for a page fault; #AC for unaligned memory reference if the current privilege level is 3

Notes

The operand-size attribute has no effect on the operation of the instruction.

SMSW—Store Machine Status Word

Opcode	Instruction	Clocks	Description
0F 01 /4	SMSW *r/m16*	2/3	Store machine status word to EA word

Operation

r/m16 ← MSW;

Description

The SMSW instruction stores the machine status word (part of the CR0 register) in the two-byte register or memory location indicated by the effective address operand.

Flags Affected

None

Protected Mode Exceptions

#GP(0) if the result is in a nonwritable segment; #GP(0) for an illegal memory operand effective address in the CS, DS, ES, FS, or GS segments; #SS(0) for an illegal address in the SS segment; #PF(fault-code) for a page fault; #AC for unaligned memory reference if the current privilege level is 3

Real Address Mode Exceptions

Interrupt 13 if any part of the operand would lie outside of the effective address space from 0 to 0FFFFH

Virtual 8086 Mode Exceptions

Same exceptions as in Real Address Mode; #PF(fault-code) for a page fault; #AC for unaligned memory reference if the current privilege level is 3

Notes

This instruction is provided for compatibility with the 80286 processor; programs for the i486 processor should use the MOV ..., CR0 instruction.

STC — Set Carry Flag

Opcode	Instruction	Clocks	Description
F9	STC	2	Set carry flag

Operation

CF ← 1;

Description

The STC instruction sets the CF flag.

Flags Affected

The CF flag is set

Protected Mode Exceptions

None

Real Address Mode Exceptions

None

Virtual 8086 Mode Exceptions

None

STD—Set Direction Flag

Opcode	Instruction	Clocks	Description
FD	STD	2	Set direction flag so (E)SI and/or (E)DI decrement

Operation

DF ← 1;

Description

The STD instruction sets the direction flag, causing all subsequent string operations to decrement the index registers, (E)SI and/or (E)DI, on which they operate.

Flags Affected

The DF flag is set

Protected Mode Exceptions

None

Real Address Mode Exceptions

None

Virtual 8086 Mode Exceptions

None

STI — Set Interrupt Flag

Opcode	Instruction	Clocks	Description
F13	STI	5	Set interrupt flag; interrupts enabled at the end of the next instruction

Operation

IF ← 1

Description

The STI instruction sets the IF flag. The processor then responds to external interrupts after executing the next instruction if the next instruction allows the IF flag to remain enabled. If external interrupts are disabled and you code the STI instruction followed by the RET instruction (such as at the end of a subroutine), the RET instruction is allowed to execute before external interrupts are recognized. Also, if external interrupts are disabled and you code the STI instruction followed by the CLI instruction, then external interrupts are not recognized because the CLI instruction clears the IF flag during its execution.

Flags Affected

The IF flag is set

Protected Mode Exceptions

#GP(0) if the current privilege level is greater (has less privilege) than the I/O privilege level

Real Address Mode Exceptions

None

Virtual 8086 Mode Exceptions

None

STOS/STOSB/STOSW/STOSD — Store String Data

Opcode	Instruction	Clocks	Description
AA	STOS *m8*	5	Store AL in byte ES:[(E)DI], update (E)DI
AB	STOS *m16*	5	Store AX in word ES:[(E)DI], update (E)DI
AB	STOS *m32*	5	Store EAX in dword ES:[(E)DI], update (E)DI
AA	STOSB	5	Store AL in byte ES:[(E)DI], update (E)DI
AB	STOSW	5	Store AX in word ES:[(E)DI], update (E)DI
AB	STOSD	5	Store EAX in dword ES:[(E)DI], update (E)DI

Operation

```
IF AddressSize = 16
THEN use ES:DI for DestReg
ELSE (* AddressSize = 32 *) use ES:EDI for DestReg;
FI;
IF byte type of instruction
THEN
  (ES:DestReg) ← AL;
  IF DF = 0
  THEN DestReg ← DestReg + 1;
  ELSE DestReg ← DestReg − 1;
  FI;
ELSE IF OperandSize = 16
  THEN
    (ES:DestReg) ← AX;
    IF DF = 0
    THEN DestReg ← DestReg + 2;
    ELSE DestReg ← DestReg − 2;
    FI;
  ELSE (* OperandSize = 32 *)
    (ES:DestReg) ← EAX;
    IF DF = 0
    THEN DestReg ← DestReg + 4;
    ELSE DestReg ← DestReg − 4;
    FI;
  FI;
FI;
```

Description

The STOS instruction transfers the contents of the AL, AX, or EAX register to the memory byte or word given by the destination register relative to the ES segment. The destination register is the DI register for an address-size attribute of 16 bits or the EDI register for an address-size attribute of 32 bits.

The destination operand must be addressable from the ES register. A segment override is not possible.

The address of the destination is determined by the contents of the destination register, not by the explicit operand of the STOS instruction. This operand is used only to validate ES segment addressability and to determine the data type. Load the correct index value into the destination register before executing the STOS instruction.

After the transfer is made, the DI register is automatically updated. If the DF flag is 0 (the CLD instruction was executed), the DI register is incremented; if the DF flag is 1 (the STD instruction was executed), the DI register is decremented. The DI register is incremented or decremented by 1 if a byte is stored, by 2 if a word is stored, or by 4 if a doubleword is stored.

The STOSB, STOSW, and STOSD instructions are synonyms for the byte, word, and doubleword STOS instructions, that do not require an operand. They are simpler to use, but provide no type or segment checking.

The STOS instruction can be preceded by the REP prefix for a block fill of CX or ECX bytes, words, or doublewords. Refer to the REP instruction for further details.

Flags Affected

None

Protected Mode Exceptions

#GP(0) if the result is in a nonwritable segment; #GP(0) for an illegal memory operand effective address in the CS, DS, ES, FS, or GS segments; #SS(0) for an illegal address in the SS segment; #PF(fault-code) for a page fault; #AC for unaligned memory reference if the current privilege level is 3

Real Address Mode Exceptions

Interrupt 13 if any part of the operand would lie outside of the effective address space from 0 to 0FFFFH

Virtual 8086 Mode Exceptions

Same exceptions as in Real Address Mode; #PF(fault-code) for a page fault; #AC for unaligned memory reference if the current privilege level is 3

STR — Store Task Register

Opcode	Instruction	Clocks	Description
0F 00 /1	STR *r/m16*	2/3	Store task register to EA word

Operation

r/m ← task register;

Description

The contents of the task register are copied to the two-byte register or memory location indicated by the effective address operand.

The STR instruction is used only in operating system software. It is not used in application programs.

Flags Affected

None

Protected Mode Exceptions

#GP(0) if the result is in a nonwritable segment; #GP(0) for an illegal memory operand effective address in the CS, DS, ES, FS, or GS segments; #SS(0) for an illegal address in the SS segment; #PF(fault-code) for a page fault; #AC for unaligned memory reference if the current privilege level is 3

Real Address Mode Exceptions

Interrupt 6; the STR instruction is not recognized in Real Address Mode

Virtual 8086 Mode Exceptions

Same exceptions as in Real Address Mode

Notes

The operand-size attribute has no effect on this instruction.

SUB — Integer Subtraction

Opcode	Instruction	Clocks	Description
2C *ib*	SUB AL,*imm8*	1	Subtract immediate byte from AL
2D *iw*	SUB AX,*imm16*	1	Subtract immediate word from AX
2D *id*	SUB EAX,*imm32*	1	Subtract immediate dword from EAX
80 /5 *ib*	SUB *r/m8,imm8*	1/3	Subtract immediate byte from *r/m* byte
81 /5 *iw*	SUB *r/m16,imm16*	1/3	Subtract immediate word from *r/m* word
81 /5 *id*	SUB *r/m32,imm32*	1/3	Subtract immediate dword from *r/m* dword
83 /5 *ib*	SUB *r/m16,imm8*	1/3	Subtract sign-extended immediate byte from *r/m* word
83 /5 *ib*	SUB *r/m32,imm8*	1/3	Subtract sign-extended immediate byte from *r/m* dword
28 /*r*	SUB *r/m8,r8*	1/3	Subtract byte register from *r/m* byte
29 /*r*	SUB *r/m16,r16*	1/3	Subtract word register from *r/m* word
29 /*r*	SUB *r/m32,r32*	1/3	Subtract dword register from *r/m* dword
2A /*r*	SUB *r8,r/m8*	1/2	Subtract byte register from *r/m* byte
2B /*r*	SUB *r16,r/m16*	1/2	Subtract word register from *r/m* word
2B /*r*	SUB *r32,r/m32*	1/2	Subtract dword register from *r/m* dword

Operation

```
IF SRC is a byte and DEST is a word or dword
THEN DEST = DEST - SignExtend(SRC);
ELSE DEST ← DEST - SRC;
FI;
```

Description

The SUB instruction subtracts the second operand (SRC) from the first operand (DEST). The first operand is assigned the result of the subtraction, and the flags are set accordingly.

When an immediate byte value is subtracted from a word operand, the immediate value is first sign-extended to the size of the destination operand.

Flags Affected

The OF, SF, ZF, AF, PF, and CF flags are set according to the result

Protected Mode Exceptions

#GP(0) if the result is in a nonwritable segment; #GP(0) for an illegal memory operand effective address in the CS, DS, ES, FS, or GS segments; #SS(0) for an illegal address in the SS segment; #PF(fault-code) for a page fault; #AC for unaligned memory reference if the current privilege level is 3

Real Address Mode Exceptions

Interrupt 13 if any part of the operand would lie outside of the effective address space from 0 to 0FFFFH

Virtual 8086 Mode Exceptions

Same exceptions as in Real Address Mode; #PF(fault-code) for a page fault; #AC for unaligned memory reference if the current privilege level is 3

TEST — Logical Compare

Opcode	Instruction	Clocks	Description
A8 *ib*	TEST AL,*imm8*	1	AND immediate byte with AL
A9 *iw*	TEST AX,*imm16*	1	AND immediate word with AX
A9 *id*	TEST EAX,*imm32*	1	AND immediate dword with EAX
F6 /0 *ib*	TEST *r/m8,imm8*	1/2	AND immediate byte with *r/m* byte
F7 /0 *iw*	TEST *r/m16,imm16*	1/2	AND immediate word with *r/m* word
F7 /0 *id*	TEST *r/m32,imm32*	1/2	AND immediate dword with *r/m* dword
84 /r	TEST *r/m8,r8*	1/2	AND byte register with *r/m* byte
85 /r	TEST *r/m16,r16*	1/2	AND word register with *r/m* word
85 /r	TEST *r/m32,r32*	1/2	AND dword register with *r/m* dword

Operation

DEST : = LeftSRC AND RightSRC;
CF ← 0;
OF ← 0;

Description

The TEST instruction computes the bit-wise logical AND of its two operands. Each bit of the result is 1 if both of the corresponding bits of the operands are 1; otherwise, each bit is 0. The result of the operation is discarded and only the flags are modified.

Flags Affected

The OF and CF flags are cleared; the SF, ZF, and PF flags are set according to the result

Protected Mode Exceptions

#GP(0) for an illegal memory operand effective address in the CS, DS, ES, FS, or GS segments; #SS(0) for an illegal address in the SS segment; #PF(fault-code) for a page fault; #AC for unaligned memory reference if the current privilege level is 3

Real Address Mode Exceptions

Interrupt 13 if any part of the operand would lie outside of the effective address space from 0 to 0FFFFH

Virtual 8086 Mode Exceptions

Same exceptions as in Real Address Mode; #PF(fault-code) for a page fault; #AC for unaligned memory reference if the current privilege level is 3

VERR, VERW—Verify a Segment for Reading or Writing

Opcode	Instruction	Clocks	Description
0F 00 /4	VERR *r/m16*	11/11	Set ZF = 1 if segment can be read, selector in *r/m16*
0F 00 /5	VERW *r/m16*	11/11	Set ZF = 1 if segment can be written, selector in *r/m16*

Operation

```
IF segment with selector at (r/m) is accessible
   with current protection level
   AND ((segment is readable for VERR) OR
      (segment is writable for VERW))
THEN ZF ← 1;
ELSE ZF ← 0;
FI;
```

Description

The two-byte register or memory operand of the VERR and VERW instructions contains the value of a selector. The VERR and VERW instructions determine whether the segment denoted by the selector is reachable from the current privilege level and whether the segment is readable (VERR) or writable (VERW). If the segment is accessible, the ZF flag is set; if the segment is not accessible, the ZF flag is cleared. To set the ZF flag, the following conditions must be met:

- The selector must denote a descriptor within the bounds of the table (GDT or LDT); the selector must be "defined."
- The selector must denote the descriptor of a code or data segment (not that of a task state segment, LDT, or a gate).
- For the VERR instruction, the segment must be readable. For the VERW instruction, the segment must be a writable data segment.
- If the code segment is readable and conforming, the descriptor privilege level (DPL) can be any value for the VERR instruction. Otherwise, the DPL must be greater than or equal to (have less or the same privilege as) both the current privilege level and the selector's RPL.

The validation performed is the same as if the segment were loaded into the DS, ES, FS, or GS register, and the indicated access (read or write) were performed. The ZF flag receives the result of the validation. The selector's value cannot result in a protection exception, enabling the software to anticipate possible segment access problems.

Flags Affected

The ZF flag is set if the segment is accessible, cleared if it is not

Protected Mode Exceptions

Faults generated by illegal addressing of the memory operand that contains the selector; the selector is not loaded into any segment register, and no faults attributable to the selector operand are generated

#GP(0) for an illegal memory operand effective address in the CS, DS, ES, FS, or GS segments; #SS(0) for an illegal address in the SS segment; #PF(fault-code) for a page fault; #AC for unaligned memory reference if the current privilege level is 3

Real Address Mode Exceptions

Interrupt 6; the VERR and VERW instructions are not recognized in Real Address Mode

Virtual 8086 Mode Exceptions

Same exceptions as in Real Address Mode; #AC for unaligned memory reference if the current privilege level is 3

WAIT — Wait

Opcode	Instruction	Clocks	Description
9B	WAIT	1-3	Causes processor to check for numeric exceptions.

Description

WAIT causes the processor to check for pending unmasked numeric exceptions before proceding.

Flags Affected

None

Protected Mode Exceptions

#NM if both MP and TS in CR0 are set

Real Address Mode Exceptions

Interrupt 7 if both MP and TS in CR0 are set

Virtual 8086 Mode Exceptions

#NM if both MP and TS in CR0 are set

Notes

Coding WAIT after an ESC instruction ensures that any unmasked floating-point exceptions the instruction may cause are handled before the processor has a chance to modify the instruction's results.

FWAIT is an alternate mnemonic for WAIT.

Information about when to use WAIT (FWAIT) is given in Chapter 18, in the section on "Concurrent Processing."

WBINVD — Write-Back and Invalidate Cache

Opcode	Instruction	Clocks	Description
0F 09	WBINVD	5	Write-Back and Invalidate Entire Cache

Operation

FLUSH INTERNAL CACHE
SIGNAL EXTERNAL CACHE TO WRITE-BACK
SIGNAL EXTERNAL CACHE TO FLUSH

Description

The internal cache is flushed, and a special-function bus cycle is issued which indicates that external cache should write-back its contents to main memory. Another special-function bus cycle follows, directing the external cache to flush itself.

Flags Affected

None

Protected Mode Exceptions

None

Real Address Mode Exceptions

None

Virtual 8086 Mode Exceptions

None

Notes

This instruction is implementation-dependent; its function may be implemented differently on future Intel processors.

It is the responsibility of hardware to respond to the external cache write-back and flush indications.

This instruction is not supported on 386 processors. See Section 3.11 for information on using this instruction compatible with 386 processors. See Section 12.2 on disabling the cache.

XADD – Exchange and Add

Opcode	Instruction	Clocks	Description
0F C0/r	XADD *r/m8,r8*	3/4	Exchange byte register and r/m byte; load sum into r/m byte.
0F C1/r	XADD *r/m16,r16*	3/4	Exchange word register and r/m word; load sum into r/m word.
0F C1/r	XADD *r/m32,r32*	3/4	Exchange dword register and r/m dword; load sum into r/m dword.

Operation

TEMP ← DEST
DEST ← TEMP + SRC
SRC ← TEMP

Description

The XADD instruction loads DEST into SRC, and then loads the sum of DEST and the original value of SRC into DEST.

Flags Affected

The CF, PF, AF, SF, ZF, and OF flags are affected as if an ADD instruction had been executed.

Protected Mode Exceptions

#GP(0) if the result is in a nonwritable segment; #GP(0) for an illegal memory operand effective address in the CS, DS, ES, FS, or GS segments; #SS(0) for an illegal address in the SS segment; #PF(fault-code) for a page fault; #NM if either EM or TS in CR0 is set; #AC for unaligned memory reference if the current privilege level is 3

Real Address Mode Exceptions

Interrupt 13 if any part of the operand would lie outside the effective address space from 0 to 0FFFFH

Virtual 8086 Mode Exceptions

Same exceptions as in real-address mode; #PF(fault code) for a page fault; #AC for unaligned memory reference if the current privilege level is 3

Notes

This instruction can be used with a LOCK prefix. The 386 DX microprocessor does not implement this instruction. If this instruction is used, you should provide an equivalent code that runs on a 386 DX processor as well. See Section 3.11 for detecting an i486 processor at runtime.

XCHG—Exchange Register/Memory with Register

Opcode	Instruction	Clocks	Description
90+ *r*	XCHG AX,*r16*	3	Exchange word register with AX
90+ *r*	XCHG *r16*,AX	3	Exchange word register with AX
90+ *r*	XCHG EAX,*r32*	3	Exchange dword register with EAX
90+ *r*	XCHG *r32*,EAX	3	Exchange dword register with EAX
86 /*r*	XCHG *r/m8,r8*	3/5	Exchange byte register with EA byte
86 /*r*	XCHG *r8,r/m8*	3/5	Exchange byte register with EA byte
87 /*r*	XCHG *r/m16,r16*	3/5	Exchange word register with EA word
87 /*r*	XCHG *r16,r/m16*	3/5	Exchange word register with EA word
87 /*r*	XCHG *r/m32,r32*	3/5	Exchange dword register with EA dword
87 /*r*	XCHG *r32,r/m32*	3/5	Exchange dword register with EA dword

Operation

temp ← DEST
DEST ← SRC
SRC ← temp

Description

The XCHG instruction exchanges two operands. The operands can be in either order. If a memory operand is involved, the LOCK# signal is asserted for the duration of the exchange, regardless of the presence or absence of the LOCK prefix or of the value of the IOPL.

Flags Affected

None

Protected Mode Exceptions

#GP(0) if either operand is in a nonwritable segment; #GP(0) for an illegal memory operand effective address in the CS, DS, ES, FS, or GS segments; #SS(0) for an illegal address in the SS segment; #PF(fault-code) for a page fault; #AC for unaligned memory reference if the current privilege level is 3

Real Address Mode Exceptions

Interrupt 13 if any part of the operand would lie outside of the effective address space from 0 to 0FFFFH

Virtual 8086 Mode Exceptions

Same exceptions as in Real Address Mode; #PF(fault-code) for a page fault; #AC for unaligned memory reference if the current privilege level is 3

XLAT/XLATB — Table Look-up Translation

Opcode	Instruction	Clocks	Description
D7	XLAT *m8*	4	Set AL to memory byte DS:[(E)BX + unsigned AL]
D7	XLATB	4	Set AL to memory byte DS:[(E)BX + unsigned AL]

Operation

```
IF AddressSize = 16
THEN
   AL ← (BX + ZeroExtend(AL))
ELSE (* AddressSize = 32 *)
   AL ← (EBX + ZeroExtend(AL));
FI;
```

Description

The XLAT instruction changes the AL register from the table index to the table entry. The AL register should be the unsigned index into a table addressed by the DS:BX register pair (for an address-size attribute of 16 bits) or the DS:EBX register pair (for an address-size attribute of 32 bits).

The operand to the XLAT instruction allows for the possibility of a segment override. The XLAT instruction uses the contents of the BX register even if they differ from the offset of the operand. The offset of the operand should have been moved into the BX or EBX register with a previous instruction.

The no-operand form, the XLATB instruction, can be used if the BX or EBX table will always reside in the DS segment.

Flags Affected

None

Protected Mode Exceptions

#GP(0) for an illegal memory operand effective address in the CS, DS, ES, FS, or GS segments; #SS(0) for an illegal address in the SS segment; #PF(fault-code) for a page fault; #AC for unaligned memory reference if the current privilege level is 3

Real Address Mode Exceptions

Interrupt 13 if any part of the operand would lie outside of the effective address space from 0 to 0FFFFH

Virtual 8086 Mode Exceptions

Same exceptions as in Real Address Mode; #PF(fault-code) for a page fault; #AC for unaligned memory reference if the current privilege level is 3

XOR — Logical Exclusive OR

Opcode	Instruction	Clocks	Description
34 *ib*	XOR AL,*imm8*	1	Exclusive-OR immediate byte to AL
35 *iw*	XOR AX,*imm16*	1	Exclusive-OR immediate word to AX
35 *id*	XOR EAX,*imm32*	1	Exclusive-OR immediate dword to EAX
80 /6 *ib*	XOR *r/m8,imm8*	1/3	Exclusive-OR immediate byte to *r/m* byte
81 /6 *iw*	XOR *r/m16,imm16*	1/3	Exclusive-OR immediate word to *r/m* word
81 /6 *id*	XOR *r/m32,imm32*	1/3	Exclusive-OR immediate dword to *r/m* dword
83 /6 *ib*	XOR *r/m16,imm8*	1/3	XOR sign-extended immediate byte with *r/m* word
83 /6 *ib*	XOR *r/m32,imm8*	1/3	XOR sign-extended immediate byte with *r/m* dword
30 /*r*	XOR *r/m8,r8*	1/3	Exclusive-OR byte register to *r/m* byte
31 /*r*	XOR *r/m16,r16*	1/3	Exclusive-OR word register to *r/m* word
31 /*r*	XOR *r/m32,r32*	1/3	Exclusive-OR dword register to *r/m* dword
32 /*r*	XOR *r8,r/m8*	1/2	Exclusive-OR byte register to *r/m* byte
33 /*r*	XOR *r16,r/m16*	1/2	Exclusive-OR word register to *r/m* word
33 /*r*	XOR *r32,r/m32*	1/2	Exclusive-OR dword register to *r/m* dword

Operation

DEST ← LeftSRC XOR RightSRC
CF ← 0
OF ← 0

Description

The XOR instruction computes the exclusive OR of the two operands. Each bit of the result is 1 if the corresponding bits of the operands are different; each bit is 0 if the corresponding bits are the same. The answer replaces the first operand.

Flags Affected

The CF and OF flags are cleared; the SF, ZF, and PF flags are set according to the result; the AF flag is undefined

Protected Mode Exceptions

#GP(0) if the result is in a nonwritable segment; #GP(0) for an illegal memory operand effective address in the CS, DS, ES, FS, or GS segments; #SS(0) for an illegal address in the SS segment; #PF(fault-code) for a page fault; #AC for unaligned memory reference if the current privilege level is 3

Real Address Mode Exceptions

Interrupt 13 if any part of the operand would lie outside of the effective address space from 0 to 0FFFFH

Virtual 8086 Mode Exceptions

Same exceptions as in Real Address Mode; #PF(fault-code) for a page fault; #AC for unaligned memory reference if the current privilege level is 3

Appendices

Opcode Map

A

APPENDIX A
OPCODE MAP

The opcode tables that follow aid in interpreting i486™ processor object code. Use the high-order four bits of the opcode as an index to a row of the opcode table; use the low-order four bits as an index to a column of the table. If the opcode is 0FH, refer to the two-byte opcode table and use the second byte of the opcode to index the rows and columns of that table.

A.1 KEY TO ABBREVIATIONS

Operands are identified by a two-character code of the form Zz. The first character, an uppercase letter, specifies the addressing method; the second character, a lowercase letter, specifies the type of operand.

A.2 CODES FOR ADDRESSING METHOD

A Direct address; the instruction has no modR/M byte; the address of the operand is encoded in the instruction; no base register, index register, or scaling factor can be applied; e.g., far JMP (EA).

C The reg field of the modR/M byte selects a control register; e.g., MOV (0F20, 0F22).

D The reg field of the modR/M byte selects a debug register; e.g., MOV (0F21,0F23).

E A modR/M byte follows the opcode and specifies the operand. The operand is either a general register or a memory address. If it is a memory address, the address is computed from a segment register and any of the following values: a base register, an index register, a scaling factor, a displacement.

F Flags Register.

G The reg field of the modR/M byte selects a general register; e.g., ADD (00).

I Immediate data. The value of the operand is encoded in subsequent bytes of the instruction.

J The instruction contains a relative offset to be added to the instruction pointer register; e.g., JMP short, LOOP.

M The modR/M byte may refer only to memory; e.g., BOUND, LES, LDS, LSS, LFS, LGS.

O The instruction has no modR/M byte; the offset of the operand is coded as a word or double word (depending on address size attribute) in the instruction. No base register, index register, or scaling factor can be applied; e.g., MOV (A0–A3).

R The mod field of the modR/M byte may refer only to a general register; e.g., MOV (0F20–0F24, 0F26).

S The reg field of the modR/M byte selects a segment register; e.g., MOV (8C,8E).

T The reg field of the modR/M byte selects a test register; e.g., MOV (0F24,0F26).

X Memory addressed by the DS:SI register pair; e.g., MOVS, COMPS, OUTS, LODS, SCAS.

Y Memory addressed by the ES:DI register pair; e.g., MOVS, CMPS, INS, STOS.

A.3 CODES FOR OPERAND TYPE

a Two one-word operands in memory or two double-word operands in memory, depending on operand size attribute (used only by BOUND).

b Byte (regardless of operand size attribute)

c Byte or word, depending on operand size attribute.

d Double word (regardless of operand size attribute)

p Thirty-two bit or 48-bit pointer, depending on operand size attribute.

s Six-byte pseudo-descriptor

v Word or double word, depending on operand size attribute.

w Word (regardless of operand size attribute)

A.4 REGISTER CODES

When an operand is a specific register encoded in the opcode, the register is identified by its name; e.g., AX, CL, or ESI. The name of the register indicates whether the register is 32-, 16-, or 8-bits wide. A register identifier of the form eXX is used when the width of the register depends on the operand size attribute; for example, eAX indicates that the AX register is used when the operand size attribute is 16 and the EAX register is used when the operand size attribute is 32.

[THIS PAGE INTENTIONALLY LEFT BLANK]

One-Byte Opcode Map

	0	1	2	3	4	5	6	7
0	ADD						PUSH ES	POP ES
	Eb,Gb	Ev,Gv	Gb,Eb	Gv,Ev	AL,Ib	eAX,Iv		
1	ADC						PUSH SS	POP SS
	Eb,Gb	Ev,Gv	Gb,Eb	Gv,Ev	AL,Ib	eAX,Iv		
2	AND						SEG =ES	DAA
	Eb,Gb	Ev,Gv	Gb,Eb	Gv,Ev	AL,Ib	eAX,Iv		
3	XOR						SEG =SS	AAA
	Eb,Gb	Ev,Gv	Gb,Eb	Gb,Ev	AL,Ib	eAX,Iv		
4	INC general register							
	eAX	eCX	eDX	eBX	eSP	eBP	eSI	eDI
5	PUSH general register							
	eAX	eCX	eDX	eBX	eSP	eBP	eSI	eDI
6	PUSHA	POPA	BOUND Gv,Ma	ARPL Ew,Rw	SEG =FS	SEG =GS	Operand Size	Address Size
7	Short-displacement jump on condition (Jb)							
	JO	JNO	JB	JNB	JZ	JNZ	JBE	JNBE
8	Immediate Grpl		MOVB	Grpl Ev,Ib	TEST		XCHG	
	Eb,Ib	Ev,Iv	AL,imm8		Eb,Gb	Ev,Gv	Eb,Gb	Ev,Gv
9	NOP	XCHG word or double-word register with eAX						
		eCX	eDX	eBX	eSP	eBP	eSI	eDI
A	MOV				MOVSB Xb,Yb	MOVSW/D Xv,Yv	CMPSB Xb,Yb	CMPSW/D Xv,Yv
	AL,Ob	eAX,Ov	Ob,AL	Ov,eAX				
B	MOV immediate byte into byte register							
	AL	CL	DL	BL	AH	CH	DH	BH
C	Shift Grp2		RET near		LES Gv,Mp	LDS Gv,Mp	MOV	
	Eb,Ib	Ev,Ib	Iw				Eb,Ib	Ev,Iv
D	Shift Grp2				AAM	AAD		XLAT
	Eb,1	Ev,1	Eb,CL	Ev,CL				
E	LOOPNE Jb	LOOPE Jb	LOOP Jb	JCXZ Jb	IN		OUT	
					Al,Ib	eAX,Ib	Ib,AL	Ib,eAX
F	LOCK		REPNE	REP REPE	HLT	CMC	Unary Grp3	
							Eb	Ev

One-Byte Opcode Map

	8	9	A	B	C	D	E	F
0	OR						PUSH CS	2-byte escape
	Eb,Gb	Ev,Gv	Gb,Eb	Gv,Ev	AL,Ib	eAX,Iv		
1	SBB						PUSH DS	POP DS
	Eb,Gb	Ev,Gv	Gb,Eb	Gv,Ev	AL,Ib	eAX,Iv		
2	SUB						SEG =CS	DAS
	Eb,Gb	Ev,Gv	Gb,Eb	Gv,Ev	AL,Ib	eAX,Iv		
3	CMP						SEG =DS	AAS
	Eb,Gb	Ev,Gv	Gb,Eb	Gv,Ev	AL,Ib	eAX,Iv		
4	DEC general register							
	eAX	eCX	eDX	eBX	eSP	eBP	eSI	eDI
5	POP into general register							
	eAX	eCX	eDX	eBX	eSP	eBP	eSI	eDI
6	PUSH Iv	IMUL GvEvIv	PUSH Ib	IMUL GvEvIb	INSB Yb,DX	INSW/D Yv,DX	OUTSB DX,Xb	OUTSW/D DX,Xv
7	Short-displacement jump on condition (Jb)							
	JS	JNS	JP	JNP	JL	JNL	JLE	JNLE
8	MOV				MOV Ew,Sw	LEA Gv,M	MOV Sw,Ew	POP Ev
	Eb,Gb	Ev,Gv	Gb,Eb	Gv,Ev				
9	CBW	CWD	CALL Ap	WAIT	PUSHF Fv	POPF Fv	SAHF	LAHF
A	TEST		STOSB Yb,AL	STOSW/D Yv,eAX	LODSB AL,Xb	LODSW/D eAX,Xv	SCASB AL,Xb	SCASW/D eAX,Xv
	AL,Ib	eAX,Iv						
B	MOV immediate word or double into word or double register							
	eAX	eCX	eDX	eBX	eSP	eBP	eSI	eDI
C	ENTER Iw,iB	LEAVE	RET far		INT 3	INT Ib	INTO	IRET
			Iw					
D	ESC (Escape to coprocessor instruction set)							
E	CALL Jv	JMP			IN		OUT	
		JV	AP	Jb	AL,DX	eAX,DX	DX,AL	DX,eAX
F	CLC	STC	CLI	STI	CLD	STD	INC/DEC Grp4	INC/DEC Grp5

Two-Byte Opcode Map (first byte is 0FH)

	0	1	2	3	4	5	6	7
0	Grp6	Grp7	LAR Gv,Ew	LSL Gv,Ew			CLTS	
1								
2	MOV Cd,Rd	MOV Dd,Rd	MOV Rd,Cd	MOV Rd,Dd	MOV Td,Rd		MOV Rd,Td	
3								
4								
5								
6								
7								
8	Long-displacement jump on condition (Jv)							
	JO	JNO	JB	JNB	JZ	JNZ	JBE	JNBE
9	Byte Set on condition (Eb)							
	SETO	SETNO	SETB	SETNB	SETZ	SETNZ	SETBE	SETNBE
A	PUSH FS	POP FS		BT Ev,Gv	SHLD EvGvIb	SHLD EvGvCL	CMPXCHG Eb,Gb	CMPXCHG Ev,Gv
B			LSS Mp	BTR Ev,Gv	LFS Mp	LGS Mp	MOVZX	
							Gv,Eb	Gv,Ew
C	XADD Eb,Gb	XADD Ev,Gv						
D								
E								
F								

Two-Byte Opcode Map (first byte is 0FH)

	8	9	A	B	C	D	E	F
0	INVD	WBINVD						
1								
2								
3								
4								
5								
6								
7								
8	Long-displacement jump on condition (Jv)							
	JS	JNS	JP	JNP	JL	JNL	JLE	JNLE
9	SETS	SETNS	SETP	SETNP	SETL	SETNL	SETLE	SETNLE
A	PUSH GS	POP GS		BTS Ev,Gv	SHRD EvGvIb	SHRD EvGvCL		IMUL Gv,Ev
B			Grp-8 Ev,Ib	BTC Ev,Gv	BSF Gv,Ev	BSR Gv,Ev	MOVSX	
							Gv,Eb	Gv,Ew
C	BSWAP EAX	BSWAP ECX	BSWAP EDX	BSWAP EBX	BSWAP ESP	BSWAP EBP	BSWAP ESI	BSWAP EDI
D								
E								
F								

Opcodes determined by bits 5,4,3 of modR/M byte:

mod	nnn	R/M

	000	001	010	011	100	101	110	111
1	ADD	OR	ADC	SBB	AND	SUB	XOR	CMP
2	ROL	ROR	RCL	RCR	SHL	SHR	SHL	SAR
3	TEST Ib/Iv	TEST Ib/Iv	NOT	NEG	MUL AL/eAX	IMUL AL/eAX	DIV AL/eAX	IDIV AL/eAX
4	INC Eb	DEC Eb						
5	INC Ev	IDEC Ev	CALL Ev	CALL eP	JMP Ev	JMP Ep	PUSH Ev	

Opcodes determined by bits 5,4,3 of modR/M byte:

mod	nnn	R/M

	000	001	010	011	100	101	110	111
6	SLDT Ew	STR Ew	LLDT Ew	LTR Ew	VERR Ew	VERW Ew		
7	SGDT Ms	SIDT Ms	LGDT Ms	LIDT Ms	SMSW Ew		LMSW Ew	
8					BT	BTS	BTR	BTC

Flag Cross-Reference B

APPENDIX B
FLAG CROSS-REFERENCE

B.1 KEY TO CODES

T	=	instruction tests flag
M	=	instruction modifies flag (either sets or resets depending on operands)
0	=	instruction resets flag
1	=	instruction sets flag
—	=	instruction's effect on flag is undefined
R	=	instruction restores prior value of flag
blank	=	instruction does not affect flag

Instruction	OF	SF	ZF	AF	PF	CF	TF	IF	DF	NT	RF
AAA	—	—	—	TM	—	M					
AAD	—	M	M	—	M	—					
AAM	—	M	M	—	M	—					
AAS	—	—	—	TM	—	M					
ADC	M	M	M	M	M	TM					
ADD	M	M	M	M	M	M					
AND	0	M	M	—	M	0					
ARPL			M								
BOUND											
BSF/BSR	—	—	M	—	—	—					
BSWAP											
BT/BTS/BTR/BTC	—	—	—	—	—	M					
CALL											
CBW											
CLC						0					
CLD									0		
CLI								0			
CLTS											
CMC						M					
CMP	M	M	M	M	M	M					
CMPS	M	M	M	M	M	M			T		
CMPXCHG	M	M	M	M	M	M					
CWD											
DAA	—	M	M	TM	M	TM					
DAS	—	M	M	TM	M	TM					
DEC	M	M	M	M	M						
DIV	—	—	—	—	—	—					
ENTER											
ESC											
HLT											
IDIV	—	—	—	—	—	—					
IMUL	M	—	—	—	—	M					
IN											
INC	M	M	M	M	M						
INS									T		
INT							0			0	
INTO	T						0			0	
INVD											
INVLPG											

Instruction	OF	SF	ZF	AF	PF	CF	TF	IF	DF	NT	RF
IRET	R	R	R	R	R	R	R	R	R	T	
Jcond	T	T	T		T	T					
JCXZ											
JMP											
LAHF											
LAR			M								
LDS/LES/LSS/LFS/LGS											
LEA											
LEAVE											
LGDT/LIDT/LLDT/LMSW											
LOCK											
LODS									T		
LOOP											
LOOPE/LOOPNE			T								
LSL			M								
LTR											
MOV											
MOV control, debug	—	—	—	—	—	—					
MOVS									T		
MOVSX/MOVZX											
MUL	M	—	—	—	—	M					
NEG	M	M	M	M	M	M					
NOP											
NOT											
OR	0	M	M	—	M	0					
OUT											
OUTS									T		
POP/POPA											
POPF	R	R	R	R	R	R	R	R	R	R	
PUSH/PUSHA/PUSHF											
RCL/RCR 1	M					TM					
RCL/RCR count	—					TM					
REP/REPE/REPNE											
RET											
ROL/ROR 1	M					M					
ROL/ROR count	—					M					
SAHF		R	R	R	R	R					
SAL/SAR/SHL/SHR 1	M	M	M	—	M	M					
SAL/SAR/SHL/SHR count	—	M	M	—	M	M					
SBB	M	M	M	M	M	TM					
SCAS	M	M	M	M	M	M			T		
SET cond	T	T	T		T	T					
SGDT/SIDT/SLDT/SMSW											
SHLD/SHRD	—	M	M	—	M	M					
STC						1					
STD									1		
STI								1			
STOS									T		
STR											
SUB	M	M	M	M	M	M					
TEST	0	M	M	—	M	0					
VERR/VERRW			M								
WAIT											
WBINVD											
XADD	M	M	M	M	M	M					
XCHG											
XLAT											
XOR	0	M	M	—	M	0					

Status Flag Summary

C

APPENDIX C
STATUS FLAG SUMMARY

C.1 STATUS FLAGS' FUNCTIONS

Bit	Name	Function
0	CF	Carry Flag – Set on high-order bit carry or borrow; cleared otherwise.
2	PF	Parity Flag – Set if low-order eight bits of result contain an even number of 1 bits; cleared otherwise.
4	AF	Adjust Flag – Set on carry from or borrow to the low order four bits of AL; cleared otherwise. Used for decimal arithmetic.
6	ZF	Zero Flag – Set if result is zero; cleared otherwise.
7	SF	Sign Flag – Set equal to high-order bit of result (0 is positive, 1 if negative).
11	OF	Overflow Flag – Set if result is too large a positive number or too small a negative number (excluding sign-bit) to fit in destination operand; cleared otherwise.

C.2 KEY TO CODES

T	=	instruction tests flag
M	=	instruction modifies flag (either sets or resets depending on operands)
0	=	instruction resets flag
–	=	instruction's effect on flag is undefined
blank	=	instruction does not affect flag

Instruction	OF	SF	ZF	AF	PF	CF
AAA	–	–	–	TM	–	M
AAS	–	–	–	TM	–	M
AAD	–	M	M	–	M	–
AAM	–	M	M	–	M	–
DAA	–	M	M	TM	M	TM
DAS	–	M	M	TM	M	TM
ADC	M	M	M	M	M	TM
ADD	M	M	M	M	M	M
XADD	M	M	M	M	M	M
SBB	M	M	M	M	M	TM
SUB	M	M	M	M	M	M

Instruction	OF	SF	ZF	AF	PF	CF
CMP	M	M	M	M	M	M
CMPS	M	M	M	M	M	M
CMPXCHG	M	M	M	M	M	M
SCAS	M	M	M	M	M	M
NEG	M	M	M	M	M	M
DEC	M	M	M	M	M	
INC	M	M	M	M	M	
IMUL	M	—	—	—	—	M
MUL	M	—	—	—	—	M
RCL/RCR 1	M					TM
RCL/RCR count	—					TM
ROL/ROR 1	M					M
ROL/ROR count	—					M
SAL/SAR/SHL/SHR 1	M	M	M	—	M	M
SAL/SAR/SHL/SHR count	—	M	M	—	M	M
SHLD/SHRD	—	M	M	—	M	M
BSF/BSR	—	—	M	—	—	—
BT/BTS/BTR/BTC	—	—	—	—	—	M
AND	0	M	M	—	M	0
OR	0	M	M	—	M	0
TEST	0	M	M	—	M	0
XOR	0	M	M	—	M	0

Condition Codes D

APPENDIX D
CONDITION CODES

Note: The terms "above" and "below" refer to the relation between two unsigned values (neither the SF flag nor the OF flag is tested). The terms "greater" and "less" refer to the relation between two signed values (the SF and OF flags are tested).

D.1 DEFINITION OF CONDITIONS

(For conditional instructions Jcond, and SETcond)

Mnemonic	Meaning	Instruction Subcode	Condition Tested
O	Overflow	0000	OF = 1
NO	No overflow	0001	OF = 0
B NAE	Below Neither above nor equal	0010	CF = 1
NB AE	Not below Above or equal	0011	CF = 0
E Z	Equal Zero	0100	ZF = 1
NE NZ	Not equal Not zero	0101	ZF = 0
BE NA	Below or equal Not above	0110	(CF or ZF) = 1
NBE A	Neither below nor equal Above	0111	(CF or ZF) = 0
S	Sign	1000	SF = 1
NS	No sign	1001	SF = 0
P PE	Parity Parity even	1010	PF = 1
NP PO	No parity Parity odd	1011	PF = 0
L NGE	Less Neither greater nor equal	1100	(SF xor OF) = 1
NL GE	Not less Greater or equal	1101	(SF xor OF) = 0
LE NG	Less or equal Not greater	1110	((SF xor OF) or ZF) = 1
NLE G	Neither less nor equal Greater	1111	((SF xor OF) or ZF) = 0

Instruction Format and Timing

E

APPENDIX E
INSTRUCTION FORMAT AND TIMING

This appendix is an excerpt from the *i486™ Processor Data Sheet*.

10.1 i486™ Microprocessor Instruction Encoding and Clock Count Summary

To calculate elapsed time for an instruction, multiply the instruction clock count, as listed in Tables 10.1 through 10.3 by the processor clock period (e.g., 40 ns for a 25 MHz 486 microprocessor).

For more detailed information on the encodings of instructions, refer to Section 10.2 Instruction Encodings. Section 10.2 explains the general structure of instruction encodings, and defines exactly the encodings of all fields contained within the instruction.

INSTRUCTION CLOCK COUNT ASSUMPTIONS

The 486 microprocessor instruction clock count tables give clock counts assuming data and instruction accesses hit in the cache. A separate penalty column defines clocks to add if a data access misses in the cache. The combined instruction and data cache hit rate is over 90%.

A cache miss will force the 486 microprocessor to run an external bus cycle. The 486 microprocessor 32-bit burst bus is defined as r−b−w.

Where:

r = The number of clocks in the first cycle of a burst read or the number of clocks per data cycle in a non-burst read.

b = The number of clocks for the second and subsequent cycles in a burst read.

w = The number of clocks for a write.

The fastest bus the 486 microprocessor can support is 2−1−2 assuming 0 wait states. The clock counts in the cache miss penalty column assume a 2−1−2 bus. For slower busses add r−2 clocks to the cache miss penalty for the first dword accessed. Other factors also affect instruction clock counts.

Instruction Clock Count Assumptions

1. The external bus is available for reads or writes at all times. Else add clocks to reads until the bus is available.
2. Accesses are aligned. Add three clocks to each misaligned access.
3. Cache fills complete before subsequent accesses to the same line. If a read misses the cache during a cache fill due to a previous read or pre-fetch, the read must wait for the cache fill to complete. If a read or write accesses a cache line still being filled, it must wait for the fill to complete.
4. If an effective address is calculated, the base register is not the destination register of the preceding instruction. If the base register is the destination register of the preceding instruction add 1 to the clock counts shown. Back-to-back PUSH and POP instructions are not affected by this rule.
5. An effective address calculation uses one base register and does not use an index register. However, if the effective address calculation uses an index register, 1 clock **may** be added to the clock count shown.
6. The target of a jump is in the cache. If not, add r clocks for accessing the destination instruction of a jump. If the destination instruction is not completely contained in the first dword read, add a maximum of 3b clocks. If the destination instruction is not completely contained in the first 16 byte burst, add a maximum of another r+3b clocks.
7. If no write buffer delay, w clocks are added only in the case in which all write buffers are full. Typically, this case rarely occurs.
8. Displacement and immediate not used together. If displacement and immediate used together, 1 clock **may** be added to the clock count shown.
9. No invalidate cycles. Add a delay of 1 clock for each invalidate cycle if the invalidate cycle contends for the internal cache/external bus when the 486 CPU needs to use it.
10. Page translation hits in TLB. A TLB miss will add 13, 21 or 28 clocks to the instruction depending on whether the Accessed and/or Dirty bit in neither, one or both of the page entries needs to be set in memory. This assumes that neither page entry is in the data cache and a page fault does not occur on the address translation.
11. No exceptions are detected during instruction execution. Refer to Interrupt Clock Counts Table for extra clocks if an interrupt is detected.
12. Instructions that read multiple consecutive data items (i.e. task switch, POPA, etc.) and miss the cache are assumed to start the first access on a 16-byte boundary. If not, an extra cache line fill may be necessary which may add up to (r+3b) clocks to the cache miss penalty.

Table 10.1. i486™ Microprocessor Integer Clock Count Summary

INSTRUCTION	FORMAT	Cache Hit	Penalty if Cache Miss	Notes
INTEGER OPERATIONS				
MOV = Move:				
reg1 to reg2	1000100W | 11 reg1 reg2	1		
reg2 to reg1	1000101w | 11 reg1 reg2	1		
memory to reg	1000101w | mod reg r/m	1	2	
reg to memory	1000100w | mod reg r/m	1		
Immediate to reg	1100011w | 11000 reg | immediate data	1		
or	1011w reg | immediate data	1		
Immediate to Memory	1100011w | mod 000 r/m | displacement immediate	1		
Memory to Accumulator	1010000w | full displacement	1	2	
Accumulator to Memory	1010001w | full displacement	1		
MOVSX/MOVZX = Move with Sign/Zero Extension				
reg2 to reg1	00001111 | 1011z11w | 11 reg1 reg2	3		
memory to reg	00001111 | 1011z11w | mod reg r/m	3	2	
PUSH = Push				
reg	11111111 | 11 110 reg	4		
or	01010 reg	1		
memory	11111111 | mod 110 r/m	4	1	1
immediate	011010s0 | immediate data	1		
PUSHA = Push All	01100000	11		
POP = Pop				
reg	10001111 | 11 000 reg	4	1	
or	01011 reg	1	2	
memory	10001111 | mod 000 r/m	5	2	1
POPA = Pop All	01100001	9	7/15	16/32
XCHG = Exchange				
reg1 with reg2	1000011w | 11 reg1 reg2	3		2
Accumulator with reg	10010 reg	3		2
Memory with reg	1000011w | mod reg r/m	5		2
NOP = No Operation	10010000	1		
LEA = Load EA to Register	10001101 | mod reg r/m			
no index register		1		
with index register		2		

z	Instruction
0	MOVZX
1	MOVSX

Table 10.1. i486™ Microprocessor Integer Clock Count Summary (Continued)

INSTRUCTION	FORMAT			Cache Hit	Penalty If Cache Miss	Notes
INTEGER OPERATIONS (Continued)						
Instruction	**TTT**					
ADD = Add	000					
ADC = Add with Carry	010					
AND = Logical AND	100					
OR = Logical OR	001					
SUB = Subtract	101					
SBB = Subtract with Borrow	011					
XOR = Logical Exclusive OR	110					
reg1 to reg2	0 0 T T T 0 0 w	11 reg1 reg2		1		
reg2 to reg1	0 0 T T T 0 1 w	11 reg1 reg2		1		
memory to register	0 0 T T T 0 1 w	mod reg r/m		2	2	
register to memory	0 0 T T T 0 0 w	mod reg r/m		3	6/2	U/L
immediate to register	1 0 0 0 0 0 s w	11 TTT reg	immediate register	1		
immediate to accumulator	0 0 T T T 1 0 w	immediate data		1		
immediate to memory	1 0 0 0 0 0 s w	mod TTT r/m	immediate data	3	6/2	U/L
Instruction	**TTT**					
INC = Increment	000					
DEC = Decrement	001					
reg	1 1 1 1 1 1 1 w	11 TTT reg		1		
or	0 1 T T T reg			1		
memory	1 1 1 1 1 1 1 w	mod TTT r/m		3	6/2	U/L
Instruction	**TTT**					
NOT = Logical Complement	010					
NEG = Negate	011					
reg	1 1 1 1 0 1 1 w	11 TTT reg		1		
memory	1 1 1 1 0 1 1 w	mod TTT r/m		3	6/2	U/L
CMP = Compare						
reg1 with reg2	0 0 1 1 1 0 0 w	11 reg1 reg2		1		
reg2 with reg1	0 0 1 1 1 0 1 w	11 reg1 reg2		1		
memory with register	0 0 1 1 1 0 0 w	mod reg r/m		2	2	
register with memory	0 0 1 1 1 0 1 w	mod reg r/m		2	2	
immediate with register	1 0 0 0 0 0 s w	11 111 reg	immediate data	1		
immediate with acc.	0 0 1 1 1 1 0 w	immediate data		1		
immediate with memory	1 0 0 0 0 0 s w	mod 111 r/m	immediate data	2	2	
TEST = Logical Compare						
reg1 and reg2	1 0 0 0 0 1 0 w	11 reg1 reg2		1		
memory and register	1 0 0 0 0 1 0 w	mod reg r/m		2	2	
immediate and register	1 1 1 1 0 1 1 w	11 000 reg	immediate data	1		
immediate and acc.	1 0 1 0 1 0 0 w	immediate data		1		
immediate and memory	1 1 1 1 0 1 1 w	mod 000 r/m	immediate data	2	2	

Table 10.1. i486™ Microprocessor Integer Clock Count Summary (Continued)

INSTRUCTION	FORMAT				Cache Hit	Penalty if Cache Miss	Notes
INTEGER OPERATIONS (Continued)							
MUL = Multiply (unsigned)							
acc. with register	1111011w	11 100 reg					
Multiplier-Byte					13/18		MN/MX, 3
Word					13/26		MN/MX, 3
Dword					13/42		MN/MX, 3
acc. with memory	1111011w	mod 100 r/m					
Multiplier-Byte					13/18	1	MN/MX, 3
Word					13/26	1	MN/MX, 3
Dword					13/42	1	MN/MX, 3
IMUL = Integer Multiply (signed)							
acc. with register	1111011w	11 101 reg					
Multiplier-Byte					13/18		MN/MX, 3
Word					13/26		MN/MX, 3
Dword					13/42		MN/MX, 3
acc. with memory	1111011w	mod 101 r/m					
Multiplier-Byte					13/18		MN/MX, 3
Word					13/26		MN/MX, 3
Dword					13/42		MN/MX, 3
reg1 with reg2	00001111	10101111	11 reg1 reg2				
Multiplier-Byte					13/18		MN/MX, 3
Word					13/26		MN/MX, 3
Dword					13/42		MN/MX, 3
register with memory	00001111	10101111	mod reg r/m				
Multiplier-Byte					13/18	1	MN/MX, 3
Word					13/26	1	MN/MX, 3
Dword					13/42	1	MN/MX, 3
reg1 with imm. to reg2	011010s1	11 reg1 reg2	immediate data				
Multiplier-Byte					13/18		MN/MX, 3
Word					13/26		MN/MX, 3
Dword					13/42		MN/MX, 3
mem. with imm. to reg.	011010s1	mod reg r/m	immediate data				
Multiplier-Byte					13/18	2	MN/MX, 3
Word					13/26	2	MN/MX, 3
Dword					13/42	2	MN/MX, 3
DIV = Divide (unsigned)							
acc. by register	1111011w	11 110 reg					
Divisor-Byte					16		
Word					24		
Dword					40		
acc. by memory	1111011w	mod 110 r/m					
Divisor-Byte					16		
Word					24		
Dword					40		
IDIV = Integer Divide (signed)							
acc. by register	1111011w	11 111 reg					
Divisor-Byte					19		
Word					27		
Dword					43		

Table 10.1. i486™ Microprocessor Integer Clock Count Summary (Continued)

INSTRUCTION	FORMAT				Cache Hit	Penalty if Cache Miss	Notes
INTEGER OPERATIONS (Continued)							
acc. by memory	1111011w	mod 111 r/m					
Divisor-Byte					20		
Word					28		
Dword					44		
CBW = Convert Byte to Word	10011000				3		
CWD = Convert Word to Dword	10011001				3		
Instruction	TTT						
ROL = Rotate Left	000						
ROR = Rotate Right	001						
RCL = Rotate through Carry Left	010						
RCR = Rotate through Carry Right	011						
SHL/SAL = Shift Logical/Arithmetic Left	100						
SHR = Shift Logical Right	101						
SAR = Shift Arithmetic Right	111						
Not Through Carry (ROL, ROR, SAL, SAR, SHL, and SHR)							
reg by 1	1101000w	11 TTT reg			3		
memory by 1	1101000w	mod TTT r/m			4	6	
reg by CL	1101001w	11 TTT reg			3		
memory by CL	1101001w	mod TTT r/m			4	6	
reg by immediate count	1100000w	11 TTT reg	immediate 8-bit data		2		
mem by immediate count	1100000w	mod TTT r/m	immediate 8-bit data		4	6	
Through Carry (RCL and RCR)							
reg by 1	1101000w	11 TTT reg			3		
memory by 1	1101000w	mod TTT r/m			4	6	
reg by CL	1101001w	11 TTT reg			8/30		MN/MX, 4
memory by CL	1101001w	mod TTT r/m			9/31		MN/MX, 5
reg by immediate count	1100000w	11 TTT reg	immediate 8-bit data		8/30		MN/MX, 4
mem by immediate count	1100000w	mod TTT r/m	immediate 8-bit data		9/31		MN/MX, 5
Instruction	TTT						
SHLD = Shift Left Double	100						
SHRD = Shift Right Double	101						
register with immediate	00001111	10TTT100	11 reg2 reg1	imm 8-bit data	2		
memory by immediate	00001111	10TTT100	mod reg r/m	imm 8-bit data	3	6	
register by CL	00001111	10TTT101	11 reg2 reg1		3		
memory by CL	00001111	10TTT101	mod reg r/m		4	5	
BSWAP = Byte Swap	00001111	11001 reg			1		
XADD = Exchange and Add							
reg1, reg2	00001111	1100000w	11 reg2 reg1		3		
memory, reg	00001111	1100000w	mod reg r/m		4	6/2	U/L
CMPXCHG = Compare and Exchange							
reg1, reg2	00001111	1011000w	11 reg2 reg1		6		
memory, reg	00001111	1011000w	mod reg r/m		7/10	2	6

Table 10.1. i486™ Microprocessor Integer Clock Count Summary (Continued)

INSTRUCTION	FORMAT				Cache Hit	Penalty if Cache Miss	Notes
CONTROL TRANSFER (within segment)							
NOTE: Times are jump taken/not taken							
Jccc = Jump on ccc							
8-bit displacement	0111tttn	8-bit disp.			3/1		T/NT, 23
full displacement	00001111	1000tttn	full displacement		3/1		T/NT, 23
NOTE: Times are jump taken/not taken							
SETcccc = Set Byte on cccc (Times are cccc true/false)							
reg	00001111	1001tttn	11 000 reg		4/3		
memory	00001111	1001tttn	mod 000 r/m		3/4		

Mnemonic cccc	Condition	tttn
O	Overflow	0000
NO	No Overflow	0001
B/NAE	Below/Not Above or Equal	0010
NB/AE	Not Below/Above or Equal	0011
E/Z	Equal/Zero	0100
NE/NZ	Not Equal/Not Zero	0101
BE/NA	Below or Equal/Not Above	0110
NBE/A	Not Below or Equal/Above	0111
S	Sign	1000
NS	Not Sign	1001
P/PE	Parity/Parity Even	1010
NP/PO	Not Parity/Parity Odd	1011
L/NGE	Less Than/Not Greater or Equal	1100
NL/GE	Not Less Than/Greater or Equal	1101
LE/NG	Less Than or Equal/Greater Than	1110
NLE/G	Not Less Than or Equal/Greater Than	1111

INSTRUCTION	FORMAT		Cache Hit	Penalty if Cache Miss	Notes
LOOP = LOOP CX Times	11100010	8-bit disp.	7/6		L/NL, 23
LOOPZ/LOOPE = Loop with Zero/Equal	11100001	8-bit disp.	9/6		L/NL, 23
LOOPNZ/LOOPNE = Loop while Not Zero	11100000	8-bit disp.	9/6		L/NL, 23
JCXZ = Jump on CX Zero	11100011	8-bit disp.	8/5		T/NT, 23
JECXZ = Jump on ECX Zero	11100011	8-bit disp.	8/5		T/NT, 23
(Address Size Prefix Differentiates JCXZ for JECXZ)					
JMP = Unconditional Jump (within segment)					
Short	11101011	8-bit disp.	3		7, 23
Direct	11101001	full displacement	3		7, 23
Register Indirect	11111111	11 100 reg	5		7, 23
Memory Indirect	11111111	mod 100 r/m	5	5	7
CALL = Call (within segment)					
Direct	11101000	full displacement	3		7, 23
Register Indirect	11111111	11 010 reg	5		7, 23
Memory Indirect	11111111	mod 010 r/m	5	5	7
RET = Return from CALL (within segment)					
	11000011		5	5	
Adding Immediate to SP	11000010	16-bit disp.	5	5	

Table 10.1. i486™ Microprocessor Integer Clock Count Summary (Continued)

INSTRUCTION	FORMAT	Cache Hit	Penalty if Cache Miss	Notes
CONTROL TRANSFER (within segment) (Continued)				
ENTER = Enter Procedure	11001000 | 16-bit disp., 8-bit level			
Level = 0		14		
Level = 1		17		
Level (L) > 1		17+3L		8
LEAVE = Leave Procedure	11001001	5	1	
MULTIPLE-SEGMENT INSTRUCTIONS				
MOV = Move				
reg. to segment reg.	10001110 | 11 sreg3 reg	3/9	0/3	RV/P, 9
memory to segment reg.	10001110 | mod sreg3 r/m	3/9	2/5	RV/P, 9
segment reg. to reg.	10001100 | 11 sreg3 reg	3		
segment reg. to memory	10001100 | mod sreg3 r/m	3		
PUSH = Push				
segment reg. (ES, CS, SS, or DS)	000 sreg2 110	3		
segment reg. (FS or GS)	00001111 | 10 sreg3 000	3		
POP = Pop				
segment reg. (ES, SS, or DS)	000 sreg2 111	3/9	2/5	RV/P, 9
segment reg. (FS or GS)	00001111 | 10 sreg3 001	3/9	2/5	RV/P, 9
LDS = Load Pointer to DS	11000101 | mod reg r/m	6/12	7/10	RV/P, 9
LES = Load Pointer to ES	11000100 | mod reg r/m	6/12	7/10	RV/P, 9
LFS = Load Pointer to FS	00001111 | 10110100 | mod reg r/m	6/12	7/10	RV/P, 9
LGS = Load Pointer to GS	00001111 | 10110101 | mod reg r/m	6/12	7/10	RV/P, 9
LSS = Load Pointer to SS	00001111 | 10110010 | mod reg r/m	6/12	7/10	RV/P, 9
CALL = Call				
Direct intersegment	10011010 | unsigned full offset, selector	18	2	R, 7, 22
to same level		20	3	P, 9
thru Gate to same level		35	6	P, 9
to inner level, no parameters		69	17	P, 9
to inner level, x parameter (d) words		77+4X	17+n	P, 11, 9
to TSS		37+TS	3	P, 10, 9
thru Task Gate		38+TS	3	P, 10, 9
Indirect intersegment	11111111 | mod 011 r/m	17	8	R, 7
to same level		20	10	P, 9
thru Gate to same level		35	13	P, 9
to inner level, no parameters		69	24	P, 9
to inner level, x parameter (d) words		77+4X	24+n	P, 11, 9
to TSS		37+TS	10	P, 10, 9
thru Task Gate		38+TS	10	P, 10, 9
RET = Return from CALL				
intersegment	11001011	13	8	R, 7
to same level		17	9	P, 9
to outer level		35	12	P, 9
intersegment adding imm. to SP	11001010 | 16-bit disp.	14	8	R, 7
to same level		18	9	P, 9
to outer level		36	12	P, 9

Table 10.1. i486™ Microprocessor Integer Clock Count Summary (Continued)

INSTRUCTION	FORMAT				Cache Hit	Penalty if Cache Miss	Notes
MULTIPLE-SEGMENT INSTRUCTIONS (Continued)							
JMP = Unconditional Jump							
Direct intersegment	11101010	unsigned full offset, selector			17	2	R, 7, 22
to same level					19	3	P, 9
thru Call Gate to same level					32	6	P, 9
thru TSS					42+TS	3	P, 10, 9
thru Task Gate					43+TS	3	P, 10, 9
Indirect intersegment	11111111	mod 101 r/m			13	9	R, 7, 9
to same level					18	10	P, 9
thru Call Gate to same level					31	13	P, 9
thru TSS					41+TS	10	P, 10, 9
thru Task Gate					42+TS	10	P, 10, 9
BIT MANIPULATION							
BT = Test bit							
register, immediate	00001111	10111010	11 100 reg	imm. 8-bit data	3		
memory, immediate	00001111	10111010	mod 100 r/m	imm. 8-bit data	3	1	
reg1, reg2	00001111	10100011	11 reg2 reg1		3		
memory, reg	00001111	10100011	mod reg r/m		8	2	
Instruction	**TTT**						
BTS = Test Bit and Set	101						
BTR = Test Bit and Reset	110						
BTC = Test Bit and Compliment	111						
register, immediate	00001111	10111010	11 TTT reg	imm. 8-bit data	6		
memory, immediate	00001111	10111010	mod TTT r/m	imm. 8-bit data	8	2/0	U/L
reg1, reg2	00001111	10TTT011	11 reg2 reg1		6		
memory, reg	00001111	10TTT011	mod reg r/m		13	3/1	U/L
BSF = Scan Bit Forward							
reg1, reg2	00001111	10111100	11 reg2 reg1		6/42		MN/MX, 12
memory, reg	00001111	10111100	mod reg r/m		7/43	2	MN/MX, 13
BSR = Scan Bit Reverse							
reg1, reg2	00001111	10111101	11 reg2 reg1		6/103		MN/MX, 14
memory, reg	00001111	10111101	mod reg r/m		7/104	1	MN/MX, 15
STRING INSTRUCTIONS							
CMPS = Compare Byte Word	1010011w				8	6	16
LODS = Load Byte/Word to AL/AX/EAX	1010110w				5	2	
MOVS = Move Byte/Word	1010010w				7	2	16
SCAS = Scan Byte/Word	1010111w				6	2	
STOS = Store Byte/Word from AL/AX/EX	1010101w				5		
XLAT = Translate String	11010111				4	2	

Table 10.1. i486™ Microprocessor Integer Clock Count Summary (Continued)

INSTRUCTION	FORMAT		Cache Hit	Penalty if Cache Miss	Notes
REPEATED STRING INSTRUCTIONS					
Repeated by Count in CX or ECX (C = Count in CX or ECX)					
REPE CMPS = Compare String	11110011	1010011w			
(Find Non-Match)					
C = 0			5		
C > 0			7+7c		16, 17
REPNE CMPS = Compare String	11110010	1010011w			
(Find Match)					
C = 0			5		
C > 0			7+7c		16, 17
REP LODS = Load String	11110010	1010110w			
C = 0			5		
C > 0			7+4c		16, 18
REP MOVS = Move String	11110010	1010010w			
C = 0			5		
C = 1			13	1	16
C > 1			12+3c		16, 19
REPE SCAS = Scan String	11110011	1010111w			
(Find Non-AL/AX/EAX)					
C = 0			5		
C > 0			7+5c		20
REPNE SCAS = Scan String	11110010	1010111w			
(Find AL/AX/EAX)					
C = 0			5		
C > 0			7+5c		20
REP STOS = Store String	11110010	1010101w			
C = 0			5		
C > 0			7+4c		
FLAG CONTROL					
CLC = Clear Carry Flag	11111000		2		
STC = Set Carry Flag	11111001		2		
CMC = Complement Carry Flag	11110101		2		
CLD = Clear Direction Flag	11111100		2		
STD = Set Direction Flag	11111101		2		
CLI = Clear Interrupt Enable Flag	11111010		5		
STI = Set Interrupt Enable Flag	11111011		5		
LAHF = Load AH into Flag	10011111		3		
SAHF = Store AH into Flags	10011110		2		
PUSHF = Push Flags	10011100		4/3		RV/P
POPF = Pop Flags	10011101		9/6		RV/P
DECIMAL ARITHMETIC					
AAA = ASCII Adjust for Add	00110111		3		
AAS = ASCII Adjust for Subtract	00111111		3		
AAM = ASCII Adjust for Multiply	11010100	00001010	15		

Table 10.1. i486™ Microprocessor Integer Clock Count Summary (Continued)

INSTRUCTION	FORMAT	Cache Hit	Penalty if Cache Miss	Notes
DECIMAL ARITHMETIC (Continued)				
AAD = ASCII Adjust for Divide	11010101 | 00001010	14		
DAA = Decimal Adjust for Add	00100111	2		
DAS = Decimal Adjust for Subtract	00101111	2		
PROCESSOR CONTROL INSTRUCTIONS				
HLT = Halt	11110100	4		
MOV = Move To and From Control/Debug/Test Registers				
CR0 from register	00001111 | 00100010 | 11 000 reg	17	2	
CR2/CR3 from register	00001111 | 00100010 | 11 eee reg	4		
Reg from CR0–3	00001111 | 00100000 | 11 eee reg	4		
DR0–3 from register	00001111 | 00100011 | 11 eee reg	10		
DR6–7 from register	00001111 | 00100011 | 11 eee reg	10		
Register from DR6–7	00001111 | 00100001 | 11 eee reg	9		
Register from DR0–3	00001111 | 00100001 | 11 eee reg	9		
TR3 from register	00001111 | 00100110 | 11 011 reg	4		
TR4–7 from register	00001111 | 00100110 | 11 eee reg	4		
Register from TR3	00001111 | 00100100 | 11 011 reg	3		
Register from TR4–7	00001111 | 00100100 | 11 eee reg	4		
CLTS = Clear Task Switched Flag	00001111 | 00000110	7	2	
INVD = Invalidate Data Cache	00001111 | 00001000	4		
WBINVD = Write-Back and Invalidate Data Cache	00001111 | 00001001	5		
INVLPG = Invalidate TLB Entry				
INVLPG memory	00001111 | 00000001 | mod 111 r/m	12/11		H/NH
PREFIX BYTES				
Address Size Prefix	01100111	1		
LOCK = Bus Lock Prefix	11110000	1		
Operand Size Prefix	01100110	1		
Segment Override Prefix				
CS:	00101110	1		
DS:	00111110	1		
ES:	00100110	1		
FS:	01100100	1		
GS:	01100101	1		
SS:	00110110	1		

Table 10.1. i486™ Microprocessor Integer Clock Count Summary (Continued)

INSTRUCTION	FORMAT			Cache Hit	Penalty if Cache Miss	Notes
PROTECTION CONTROL						
ARPL = Adjust Requested Privilege Level						
From register	01100011	11 reg1 reg2		9		
From memory	01100011	mod reg r/m		9		
LAR = Load Access Rights						
From register	00001111	00000010	11 reg1 reg2	11	3	
From memory	00001111	00000010	mod reg r/m	11	5	
LGDT = Load Global Descriptor						
Table register	00001111	00000001	mod 010 r/m	12	5	
LIDT = Load Interrupt Descriptor						
Table register	00001111	00000001	mod 011 r/m	12	5	
LLDT = Load Local Descriptor						
Table register from reg.	00001111	00000000	11 010 reg	11	3	
Table register from mem.	00001111	00000000	mod 010 r/m	11	6	
LMSW = Load Machine Status Word						
From register	00001111	00000001	11 110 reg	13		
From memory	00001111	00000001	mod 110 r/m	13	1	
LSL = Load Segment Limit						
From register	00001111	00000011	11 reg1 reg2	10	3	
From memory	00001111	00000011	mod reg r/m	10	6	
LTR = Load Task Register						
From Register	00001111	00000000	11 001 reg	20		
From Memory	00001111	00000000	mod 001 r/m	20		
SGDT = Store Global Descriptor Table						
	00001111	00000001	mod 000 r/m	10		
SIDT = Store Interrupt Descriptor Table						
	00001111	00000001	mod 001 r/m	10		
SLDT = Store Local Descriptor Table						
To register	00001111	00000000	11 000 reg	2		
To memory	00001111	00000000	mod 000 r/m	3		
SMSW = Store Machine Status Word						
To register	00001111	00000001	11 100 reg	2		
To memory	00001111	00000001	mod 100 r/m	3		
STR = Store Task Register						
To register	00001111	00000000	11 001 reg	2		
To memory	00001111	00000000	mod 001 r/m	3		
VERR = Verify Read Access						
Register	00001111	00000000	11 100 r/m	11	3	
Memory	00001111	00000000	mod 100 r/m	11	7	
VERW = Verify Write Access						
To register	00001111	00000000	11 101 reg	11	3	
To memory	00001111	00000000	mod 101 r/m	11	7	

Table 10.1. i486™ Microprocessor Integer Clock Count Summary (Continued)

INSTRUCTION	FORMAT		Cache Hit	Penalty if Cache Miss	Notes
INTERRUPT INSTRUCTIONS					
INT n = Interrupt Type n	1 1 0 0 1 1 0 1	type	INT+4/0		RV/P, 21
INT 3 = Interrupt Type 3	1 1 0 0 1 1 0 0		INT+0		21
INTO = Interrupt 4 if Overflow Flag Set	1 1 0 0 1 1 1 0				
Taken			INT+2		21
Not Taken			3		21
BOUND = Interrupt 5 if Detect Value Out Range	0 1 1 0 0 0 1 0	mod reg r/m			
If in range			7	7	21
If out of range			INT+24	7	21
IRET = Interrupt Return	1 1 0 0 1 1 1 1				
Real Mode/Virtual Mode			15	8	
Protected Mode					
To same level			20	11	9
To outer level			36	19	9
To nested task (EFLAGS.NT = 1)			TS+32	4	9, 10
External Interrupt			INT+11		21
NMI = Non-Maskable Interrupt			INT+3		21
Page Fault			INT+24		21
VM86 Exceptions					
CLI			INT+8		21
STI			INT+8		21
INT n			INT+9		
PUSHF			INT+9		21
POPF			INT+8		21
IRET			INT+9		
IN					
Fixed Port			INT+50		21
Variable Port			INT+51		21
OUT					
Fixed Port			INT+50		21
Variable Port			INT+51		21
INS			INT+50		21
OUTS			INT+50		21
REP INS			INT+51		21
REP OUTS			INT+51		21

Task Switch Clock Counts Table

Method	Value for TS	
	Cache Hit	Miss Penalty
VM/486 CPU/286 TSS To 486 CPU TSS	162	55
VM/486 CPU/286 TSS To 286 TSS	143	31
VM/486 CPU/286 TSS To VM TSS	140	37

Interrupt Clock Counts Table

Method	Value for INT		
	Cache Hit	**Miss Penalty**	**Notes**
Real Mode	26	2	
Protected Mode			
Interrupt/Trap gate, same level	44	6	9
Interrupt/Trap gate, different level	71	17	9
Task Gate	37 + TS	3	9, 10
Virtual Mode			
Interrupt/Trap gate, different level	82	17	
Task gate	37 + TS	3	10

Abbreviations	Definition
16/32	16/32 bit modes
U/L	unlocked/locked
MN/MX	minimum/maximum
L/NL	loop/no loop
RV/P	real and virtual mode/protected mode
R	real mode
P	protected mode
T/NT	taken/not taken
H/NH	hit/no hit

NOTES:

1. Assuming that the operand address and stack address fall in different cache sets.
2. Always locked, no cache hit case.
3. Clocks = 10 + $\max(\log_2(|m|),n)$
   m = multiplier value (min clocks for m=0)
   n = 3/5 for ±m
4. Clocks = {quotient(count/operand length)}*7+9
   = 8 if count ≤ operand length (8/16/32)
5. Clocks = {quotient(count/operand length)}*7+9
   = 9 if count ≤ operand length (8/16/32)
6. Equal/not equal cases (penalty is the same regardless of lock).
7. Assuming that addresses for memory read (for indirection), stack push/pop, and branch fall in different cache sets.
8. Penalty for cache miss: add 6 clocks for every 16 bytes copied to new stack frame.
9. Add 11 clocks for each unaccessed descriptor load.
10. Refer to task switch clock counts table for value of TS.
11. Add 4 extra clocks to the cache miss penalty for each 16 bytes.

For notes 12–13: (b = 0–3, non-zero byte number);
(i = 0–1, non-zero nibble number);
(n = 0–3, non bit number in nibble);

12. Clocks = 8+4 (b+1) + 3(i+1) + 3(n+1)
    = 6 if second operand = 0
13. Clocks = 9+4(b+1) + 3(i+1) + 3(n+1)
    = 7 if second operand = 0

For notes 14–15: (n = bit position 0–31)

14. Clocks = 7 + 3(32−n)
    6 if second operand = 0
15. Clocks = 8 + 3(32−n)
    7 if second operand = 0
16. Assuming that the two string addresses fall in different cache sets.
17. Cache miss penalty: add 6 clocks for every 16 bytes compared. Entire penalty on first compare.
18. Cache miss penalty: add 2 clocks for every 16 bytes of data. Entire penalty on first load.
19. Cache miss penalty: add 4 clocks for every 16 bytes moved.
    (1 clock for the first operation and 3 for the second)
20. Cache miss penalty: add 4 clocks for every 16 bytes scanned.
    (2 clocks each for first and second operations)
21. Refer to interrupt clock counts table for value of INT
22. Clock count includes one clock for using both displacement and immediate.
23. Refer to assumption 6 in the case of a cache miss.

Table 10.2. i486™ Microprocessor I/O Instructions Clock Count Summary

INSTRUCTION	FORMAT		Real Mode	Protected Mode (CPL≤IOPL)	Protected Mode (CPL>IOPL)	Virtual 86 Mode	Notes
I/O INSTRUCTIONS							
IN = Input from:							
Fixed Port	1110010w	port number	14	9	29	27	
Variable Port	1110110w		14	8	28	27	
OUT = Output to:							
Fixed Port	1110011w	port number	16	11	31	29	
Variable Port	1110111w		16	10	30	29	
INS = Input Byte/Word from DX Port	0110110w		17	10	32	30	
OUTS = Output Byte/Word to DX Port	0110111w		17	10	32	30	1
REP INS = Input String	11110010	0110110w	16+8c	10+8c	30+8c	29+8c	2
REP OUTS = Output String	11110010	0110111w	17+5c	11+5c	31+5c	30+5c	3

NOTES:
1. Two clock cache miss penalty in all cases.
2. c = count in CX or ECX.
3. Cache miss penalty in all modes: Add 2 clocks for every 16 bytes. Entire penalty on second operation.

Table 10.3. i486™ Microprocessor Floating Point Clock Count Summary

INSTRUCTION	FORMAT			Cache Hit	Penalty if Cache Miss	Concurrent Execution	Notes
				Avg (Lower Range . . . Upper Range)		Avg (Lower Range . . . Upper Range)	
DATA TRANSFER							
FLD = Real Load to ST(0)							
32-bit memory	11011 001	mod 000 r/m	s-i-b/disp.	3	2		
64-bit memory	11011 101	mod 000 r/m	s-i-b/disp.	3	3		
80-bit memory	11011 011	mod 101 r/m	s-i-b/disp.	6	4		
ST(i)	11011 001	11000 ST(i)		4			
FILD = Integer Load to ST(0)							
16-bit memory	11011 111	mod 000 r/m	s-i-b/disp.	14.5(13–16)	2	4	
32-bit memory	11011 011	mod 000 r/m	s-i-b/disp.	11.5(9–12)	2	4(2–4)	
64-bit memory	11011 111	mod 101 r/m	s-i-b/disp.	16.8(10–18)	3	7.8(2–8)	
FBLD = BCD Load to ST(0)	11011 111	mod 100 r/m	s-i-b/disp.	75(70–103)	4	7.7(2–8)	
FST = Store Real from ST(0)							
32-bit memory	11011 001	mod 010 r/m	s-i-b/disp.	7			1
64-bit memory	11011 101	mod 010 r/m	s-i-b/disp.	8			2
ST(i)	11011 101	11010 ST(i)		3			
FSTP = Store Real from ST(0) and Pop							
32-bit memory	11011 011	mod 011 r/m	s-i-b/disp.	7			1
64-bit memory	11011 101	mod 011 r/m	s-i-b/disp.	8			2
80-bit memory	11011 011	mod 111 r/m	s-i-b/disp.	6			
ST(i)	11011 101	11001 ST(i)		3			
FIST = Store Integer from ST(0)							
16-bit memory	11011 111	mod 010 r/m	s-i-b/disp.	33.4(29–34)			
32-bit memory	11011 011	mod 010 r/m	s-i-b/disp.	32.4(28–34)			
FISTP = Store Integer from ST(0) and Pop							
16-bit memory	11011 111	mod 011 r/m	s-i-b/disp.	33.4(29–34)			
32-bit memory	11011 011	mod 011 r/m	s-i-b/disp.	33.4(29–34)			
64-bit memory	11011 111	mod 111 r/m	s-i-b/disp.	33.4(29–34)			
FBSTP = Store BCD from ST(0) and Pop	11011 111	mod 110 r/m	s-i-b/disp.	175(172–176)			
FXCH = Exchange ST(0) and ST(i)	11011 001	11001 ST(i)		4			
COMPARISON INSTRUCTIONS							
FCOM = Compare ST(0) with Real							
32-bit memory	11011 000	mod 010 r/m	s-i-b/disp.	4	2	1	
64-bit memory	11011 100	mod 010 r/m	s-i-b/disp.	4	3	1	
ST(i)	11011 000	11010 ST(i)		4		1	
FCOMP = Compare ST(0) with Real and Pop							
32-bit memory	11011 000	mod 011 r/m	s-i-b/disp.	4	2	1	
64-bit memory	11011 100	mod 011 r/m	s-i-b/disp.	4	3	1	
ST(i)	11011 000	11011 ST(i)		4		1	

Table 10.3. i486™ Microprocessor Floating Point Clock Count Summary (Continued)

INSTRUCTION	FORMAT			Cache Hit Avg (Lower Range . . . Upper Range)	Penalty if Cache Miss	Concurrent Execution Avg (Lower Range . . . Upper Range)	Notes
COMPARISON INSTRUCTIONS (Continued)							
FCOMPP = Compare ST(0) with ST(1) and Pop Twice	11011 110	1101 1001		5		1	
FICOM = Compare ST(0) with Integer							
16-bit memory	11011 110	mod 010 r/m	s-i-b/disp.	18(16–20)	2	1	
32-bit memory	11011 010	mod 010 r/m	s-i-b/disp.	16.5(15–17)	2	1	
FICOMP = Compare ST(0) with Integer							
16-bit memory	11011 110	mod 011 r/m	s-i-b/disp.	18(16–20)	2	1	
32-bit memory	11011 010	mod 011 r/m	s-i-b/disp.	16.5(15–17)	2	1	
FTST = Compare ST(0) with 0.0	11011 001	1110 0100		4		1	
FUCOM = Unordered compare ST(0) with ST(i)	11011 101	11100 ST(i)		4		1	
FUCOMP = Unordered compare ST(0) with ST(i) and Pop	11011 101	11101 ST(i)		4		1	
FUCOMPP = Unordered compare ST(0) with ST(i) and Pop Twice	11011 101	11101 1001		5		1	
FXAM = Examine ST(0)	11011 001	1110 0101		8			
CONSTANTS							
FLDZ = Load +0.0 into ST(0)	11011 001	1110 1110		4			
FLD1 = Load +1.0 into ST(0)	11011 001	1110 1000		4			
FLDPI = Load π into ST(0)	11011 001	1110 1011		8		2	
FLDL2T = Load $\log_2(10)$ into ST(0)	11011 001	1110 1001		8		2	
FLDL2E = Load $\log_2(e)$ into ST(0)	11011 001	1110 1010		8		2	
FLDLG2 = Load $\log_{10}(2)$ into ST(0)	11011 001	1110 1100		8		2	
FLDLN2 = Load $\log_e(2)$ into ST(0)	11011 001	1110 1101		8		2	
ARITHMETIC							
FADD = Add Real with ST(0)							
ST(0) ← ST(0) + 32-bit memory	11011 000	mod 000 r/m	s-i-b/disp.	10(8–20)	2	7(5–17)	
ST(0) ← ST(0) + 64-bit memory	11011 100	mod 000 r/m	s-i-b/disp.	10(8–20)	3	7(5–17)	
ST(d) ← ST(0) + ST(i)	11011 d00	11000 ST(i)		10(8–20)		7(5–17)	
FADDP = Add real with ST(0) and Pop (ST(i) ← ST(0) + ST(i))	11011 110	11000 ST(i)		10(8–20)		7(5–17)	
FSUB = Subtract real from ST(0)							
ST(0) ← ST(0) − 32-bit memory	11011 000	mod 100 r/m	s-i-b/disp.	10(8–20)	2	7(5–17)	
ST(0) ← ST(0) − 64-bit memory	11011 100	mod 100 r/m	s-i-b/disp.	10(8-20)	3	7(5–17)	
ST(d) ← ST(0) − ST(i)	11011 d00	11101 ST(i)		10(8–20)		7(5–17)	
FSUBP = Subtract real from ST(0) and Pop (ST(i) ← ST(0) − ST(i))	11011 110	11101 ST(i)		10(8–20)		7(5–17)	

Table 10.3. i486™ Microprocessor Floating Point Clock Count Summary (Continued)

INSTRUCTION	FORMAT					Cache Hit Avg (Lower Range... Upper Range)	Penalty if Cache Miss	Concurrent Execution Avg (Lower Range... Upper Range)	Notes
ARITHMETIC (Continued)									
FSUBR = Subtract real reversed (Subtract ST(0) from real)									
ST(0) ← 32-bit memory − ST(0)	11011 000	mod 101	r/m	s-i-b/disp.		10(8–20)	2	7(5–17)	
ST(0) ← 64-bit memory − ST(0)	11011 100	mod 101	r/m	s-i-b/disp.		10(8–20)	3	7(5–17)	
ST(d) ← ST(i) − ST(0)	11011 d00	11100	ST(i)			10(8–20)		7(5–17)	
FSUBRP = Subtract real reversed and Pop (ST(i) ← ST(i) − ST(0))	11011 110	11100	ST(i)			10(8–20)		7(5–17)	
FMUL = Multiply real with ST(0)									
ST(0) ← ST(0) × 32-bit memory	11011 000	mod 001	r/m	s-i-b/disp.		11	2	8	
ST(0) ← ST(0) × 64-bit memory	11011 100	mod 001	r/m	s-i-b/disp.		14	3	11	
ST(d) ← ST(0) × ST(i)	11011 d00	11001	ST(i)			16		13	
FMULP = Multiply ST(0) with ST(i) and Pop (ST(i) ← ST(0) × ST(i))	11011 110	11001	ST(i)			16		13	
FDIV = Divide ST(0) by Real									
ST(0) ← ST(0)/32-bit memory	11011 000	mod 110	r/m	s-i-b/disp.		73	2	70	3
ST(0) ← ST(0)/64-bit memory	11011 100	mod 100	r/m	s-i-b/disp.		73	3	70	3
ST(d) ← ST(0)/ST(i)	11011 d00	11111	ST(i)			73		70	3
FDIVP = Divide ST(0) by ST(i) and Pop (ST(i) ← ST(0)/ST(i))	11011 110	11111	ST(i)			73		70	3
FDIVR = Divide real reversed (Real/ST(0))									
ST(0) ← 32-bit memory/ST(0)	11011 000	mod 111	r/m	s-i-b/disp.		73	2	70	3
ST(0) ← 64-bit memory/ST(0)	11011 100	mod 111	r/m	s-i-b/disp.		73	3	70	3
ST(d) ← ST(i)/ST(0)	11011 d00	11110	ST(i)			73		70	3
FDIVRP = Divide real reversed and Pop (ST(i) ← ST(i)/ST(0))	11011 110	11110	ST(i)			73		70	3
FIADD = Add Integer to ST(0)									
ST(0) ← ST(0) + 16-bit memory	11011 110	mod 000	r/m	s-i-b/disp.		24(20–35)	2	7(5–17)	
ST(0) ← ST(0) + 32-bit memory	11011 010	mod 000	r/m	s-i-b/disp.		22.5(19–32)	2	7(5–17)	
FISUB = Subtract Integer from ST(0)									
ST(0) ← ST(0) − 16-bit memory	11011 110	mod 100	r/m	s-i-b/disp.		24(20–35)	2	7(5–17)	
ST(0) ← ST(0) − 32-bit memory	11011 010	mod 100	r/m	s-i-b/disp.		22.5(19–32)	2	7(5–17)	
FISUBR = Integer Subtract Reversed									
ST(0) ← 16-bit memory − ST(0)	11011 110	mod 101	r/m	s-i-b/disp.		24(20–35)	2	7(5–17)	
ST(0) ← 32-bit memory − ST(0)	11011 010	mod 101	r/m	s-i-b/disp.		22.5(19–32)	2	7(5–17)	
FIMUL = Multiply Integer with ST(0)									
ST(0) ← ST(0) × 16-bit memory	11011 110	mod 001	r/m	s-i-b/disp.		25(23–27)	2	8	
ST(0) ← ST(0) × 32-bit memory	11011 010	mod 001	r/m	s-i-b/disp.		23.5(22–24)	2	8	
FIDIV = Integer Divide									
ST(0) ← ST(0)/16-bit memory	11011 110	mod 110	r/m	s-i-b/disp.		87(85–89)	2	70	3
ST(0) ← ST(0)/32-bit memory	11011 010	mod 110	r/m	s-i-b/disp.		85.5(84–86)	2	70	3

Table 10.3. i486™ Microprocessor Floating Point Clock Count Summary (Continued)

INSTRUCTION	FORMAT			Cache Hit Avg (Lower Range... Upper Range)	Penalty if Cache Miss	Concurrent Execution Avg (Lower Range... Upper Range)	Notes
ARITHMETIC (Continued)							
FIDIVR = Integer Divide Reversed							
ST(0) ← 16-bit memory/ST(0)	11011 110	mod 111 r/m	s-i-b/disp.	87(85–89)	2	70	3
ST(0) ← 32-bit memory/ST(0)	11011 010	mod 111 r/m	s-i-b/disp.	85.5(84–86)	2	70	3
FSQRT = Square Root	11011 001	1111 1010		85.5(83–87)		70	
FSCALE = Scale ST(0) by ST(1)	11011 001	1111 1101		31(30–32)		2	
FXTRACT = Extract components of ST(0)	11011 001	1111 0100		19(16–20)		4(2–4)	
FPREM = Partial Reminder	11011 001	1111 1000		84(70–138)		2(2–8)	
FPREM1 = Partial Reminder (IEEE)	11011 001	1111 0101		94.5(72–167)		5.5(2–18)	
FRNDINT = Round ST(0) to integer	11011 001	1111 1100		29.1(21–30)		7.4(2–8)	
FABS = Absolute value of ST(0)	11011 001	1110 0001		3			
FCHS = Change sign of ST(0)	11011 001	1110 0000		6			
TRANSCENDENTAL							
FCOS = Cosine of ST(0)	11011 001	1111 1111		241(193–279)		2	6, 7
FPTAN = Partial tangent of ST(0)	11011 001	1111 0010		244(200–273)		70	6, 7
FPATAN = Partial arctangent	11011 001	1111 0011		289(218–303)		5(2–17)	6
FSIN = Sine of ST(0)	11011 001	1111 1110		241(193–279)		2	6, 7
FSINCOS = Sine and cosine of ST(0)	11011 001	1111 1011		291(243–329)		2	6, 7
F2XM1 = $2^{ST(0)} - 1$	11011 001	1111 0000		242(140–279)		2	6
FYL2X = ST(1) × log_2(ST(0))	11011 001	1111 0001		311(196–329)		13	6
FYL2XP1 = ST(1) × log_2(ST(0) + 1.0)	11011 001	1111 1001		313(171–326)		13	6
PROCESSOR CONTROL							
FINIT = Initialize FPU	11011 011	1110 0011		17			4
FSTSW AX = Store status word into AX	11011 111	1110 0000		3			5
FSTSW = Store status word into memory	11011 101	mod 111 r/m	s-i-b/disp.	3			5
FLDCW = Load control word	11011 001	mod 101 r/m	s-i-b/disp.	4	2		
FSTCW = Store control word	11011 001	mod 111 r/m	s-i-b/disp.	3			5
FCLEX = Clear exceptions	11011 011	1110 0010		7			4
FSTENV = Store environment	11011 001	mod 110 r/m	s-i-b/disp.				
Real and Virtual modes 16-bit Address				67			4
Real and Virtual modes 32-bit Address				67			4
Protected mode 16-bit Address				56			4
Protected mode 32-bit Address				56			4
FLDENV = Load environment	11011 001	mod 100 r/m	s-i-b/disp.				
Real and Virtual modes 16-bit Address				44	2		
Real and Virtual modes 32-bit Address				44	2		
Protected mode 16-bit Address				34	2		
Protected mode 32-bit Address				34	2		

Table 10.3. i486™ Microprocessor Floating Point Clock Count Summary (Continued)

INSTRUCTION	FORMAT	Cache Hit Avg (Lower Range... Upper Range)	Penalty If Cache Miss	Concurrent Execution Avg (Lower Range... Upper Range)	Notes
PROCESSOR CONTROL (Continued)					
FSAVE = Save state	11011 101 | mod 110 r/m | s-i-b/disp.				
Real and Virtual modes 16-bit Address		154			4
Real and Virtual modes 32-bit Address		154			4
Protected mode 16-bit Address		143			4
Protected mode 32-bit Address		143			4
FRSTOR = Restore state	11011 101 | mod 100 r/m | s-i-b/				
Real and Virtual modes 16-bit Address		131	23		
Real and Virtual modes 32-bit Address		131	27		
Protected mode 16-bit Address		120	23		
Protected mode 32-bit Address		120	27		
FINCSTP = Increment Stack Pointer	11011 001 | 1111 0111	3			
FDECSTP = Decrement Stack Pointer	11011 001 | 1111 0110	3			
FFREE = Free ST(i)	11011 101 | 11000 ST(i)	3			
FNOP = No operations	11011 001 | 1101 0000	3			
WAIT = Wait until FPU ready (Minimum/Maximum)	10011011	1/3			

NOTES:
1. If operand is 0 clock counts = 27.
2. If operand is 0 clock counts = 28.
3. If CW.PC indicates 24 bit precision then subtract 38 clocks.
   If CW.PC indicates 53 bit precision then subtract 11 clocks.
4. If there is a numeric error pending from a previous instruction add 17 clocks.
5. If there is a numeric error pending from a previous instruction add 18 clocks.
6. The INT pin is polled several times while this instruction is executing to assure short interrupt latency.
7. If ABS(operand) is greater than $\pi/4$ then add n clocks. Where n = (operand/($\pi/4$)).

10.2 Instruction Encoding

10.2.1 OVERVIEW

All instruction encodings are subsets of the general instruction format shown in Figure 10.1. Instructions consist of one or two primary opcode bytes, possibly an address specifier consisting of the "mod r/m" byte and "scaled index" byte, a displacement if required, and an immediate data field if required.

Within the primary opcode or opcodes, smaller encoding fields may be defined. These fields vary according to the class of operation. The fields define such information as direction of the operation, size of the displacements, register encoding, or sign extension.

Almost all instructions referring to an operand in memory have an addressing mode byte following the primary opcode byte(s). This byte, the mod r/m byte, specifies the address mode to be used. Certain encodings of the mod r/m byte indicate a second addressing byte, the scale-index-base byte, follows the mod r/m byte to fully specify the addressing mode.

Addressing modes can include a displacement immediately following the mod r/m byte, or scaled index byte. If a displacement is present, the possible sizes are 8, 16 or 32 bits.

If the instruction specifies an immediate operand, the immediate operand follows any displacement bytes. The immediate operand, if specified, is always the last field of the instruction.

Figure 10.1 illustrates several of the fields that can appear in an instruction, such as the mod field and the r/m field, but the Figure does not show all fields. Several smaller fields also appear in certain instructions, sometimes within the opcode bytes themselves. Table 10.4 is a complete list of all fields appearing in the 486 Microprocessor instruction set. Further ahead, following Table 10.4, are detailed tables for each field.

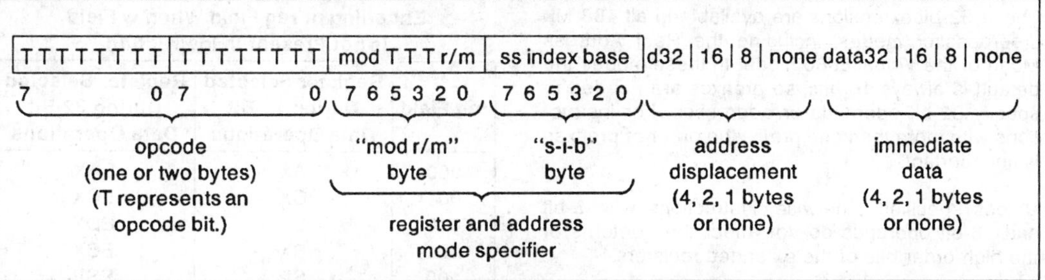

Figure 10.1. General Instruction Format

Table 10.4. Fields within i486™ Microprocessor Instructions

Field Name	Description	Number of Bits
w	Specifies if Data is Byte or Full Size (Full Size is either 16 or 32 Bits	1
d	Specifies Direction of Data Operation	1
s	Specifies if an Immediate Data Field Must be Sign-Extended	1
reg	General Register Specifier	3
mod r/m	Address Mode Specifier (Effective Address can be a General Register)	2 for mod; 3 for r/m
ss	Scale Factor for Scaled Index Address Mode	2
index	General Register to be used as Index Register	3
base	General Register to be used as Base Register	3
sreg2	Segment Register Specifier for CS, SS, DS, ES	2
sreg3	Segment Register Specifier for CS, SS, DS, ES, FS, GS	3
tttn	For Conditional Instructions, Specifies a Condition Asserted or a Condition Negated	4

NOTE:
Tables 10.1–10.3 show encoding of individual instructions.

10.2.2 32-BIT EXTENSIONS OF THE INSTRUCTION SET

With the 486 Microprocessor, the 8086/80186/80286 instruction set is extended in two orthogonal directions: 32-bit forms of all 16-bit instructions are added to support the 32-bit data types, and 32-bit addressing modes are made available for all instructions referencing memory. This orthogonal instruction set extension is accomplished having a Default (D) bit in the code segment descriptor, and by having 2 prefixes to the instruction set.

Whether the instruction defaults to operations of 16 bits or 32 bits depends on the setting of the D bit in the code segment descriptor, which gives the default length (either 32 bits or 16 bits) for both operands and effective addresses when executing that code segment. In the Real Address Mode or Virtual 8086 Mode, no code segment descriptors are used, but a D value of 0 is assumed internally by the 486 Microprocessor when operating in those modes (for 16-bit default sizes compatible with the 8086/80186/80286).

Two prefixes, the Operand Size Prefix and the Effective Address Size Prefix, allow overriding individually the Default selection of operand size and effective address size. These prefixes may precede any opcode bytes and affect only the instruction they precede. If necessary, one or both of the prefixes may be placed before the opcode bytes. The presence of the Operand Size Prefix and the Effective Address Prefix will toggle the operand size or the effective address size, respectively, to the value "opposite" from the Default setting. For example, if the default operand size is for 32-bit data operations, then presence of the Operand Size Prefix toggles the instruction to 16-bit data operation. As another example, if the default effective address size is 16 bits, presence of the Effective Address Size prefix toggles the instruction to use 32-bit effective address computations.

These 32-bit extensions are available in all 486 Microprocessor modes, including the Real Address Mode or the Virtual 8086 Mode. In these modes the default is always 16 bits, so prefixes are needed to specify 32-bit operands or addresses. For instructions with more than one prefix, the order of prefixes is unimportant.

Unless specified otherwise, instructions with 8-bit and 16-bit operands do not affect the contents of the high-order bits of the extended registers.

10.2.3 ENCODING OF INTEGER INSTRUCTION FIELDS

Within the instruction are several fields indicating register selection, addressing mode and so on. The exact encodings of these fields are defined immediately ahead.

10.2.3.1 Encoding of Operand Length (w) Field

For any given instruction performing a data operation, the instruction is executing as a 32-bit operation or a 16-bit operation. Within the constraints of the operation size, the w field encodes the operand size as either one byte or the full operation size, as shown in the table below.

w Field	Operand Size During 16-Bit Data Operations	Operand Size During 32-Bit Data Operations
0	8 Bits	8 Bits
1	16 Bits	32 Bits

10.2.3.2 Encoding of the General Register (reg) Field

The general register is specified by the reg field, which may appear in the primary opcode bytes, or as the reg field of the "mod r/m" byte, or as the r/m field of the "mod r/m" byte.

Encoding of reg Field When w Field is not Present in Instruction

reg Field	Register Selected During 16-Bit Data Operations	Register Selected During 32-Bit Data Operations
000	AX	EAX
001	CX	ECX
010	DX	EDX
011	BX	EBX
100	SP	ESP
101	BP	EBP
110	SI	ESI
111	DI	EDI

Encoding of reg Field When w Field is Present in Instruction

Register Specified by reg Field During 16-Bit Data Operations:

reg	Function of w Field (when w = 0)	Function of w Field (when w = 1)
000	AL	AX
001	CL	CX
010	DL	DX
011	BL	BX
100	AH	SP
101	CH	BP
110	DH	SI
111	BH	DI

Register Specified by reg Field During 32-Bit Data Operations

reg	Function of w Field (when w = 0)	Function of w Field (when w = 1)
000	AL	EAX
001	CL	ECX
010	DL	EDX
011	BL	EBX
100	AH	ESP
101	CH	EBP
110	DH	ESI
111	BH	EDI

10.2.3.3 Encoding of the Segment Register (sreg) Field

The sreg field in certain instructions is a 2-bit field allowing one of the four 80286 segment registers to be specified. The sreg field in other instructions is a 3-bit field, allowing the 486 Microprocessor FS and GS segment registers to be specified.

2-Bit sreg2 Field

2-Bit sreg2 Field	Segment Register Selected
00	ES
01	CS
10	SS
11	DS

3-Bit sreg3 Field

3-Bit sreg3 Field	Segment Register Selected
000	ES
001	CS
010	SS
011	DS
100	FS
101	GS
110	do not use
111	do not use

10.2.3.4 Encoding of Address Mode

Except for special instructions, such as PUSH or POP, where the addressing mode is pre-determined, the addressing mode for the current instruction is specified by addressing bytes following the primary opcode. The primary addressing byte is the "mod r/m" byte, and a second byte of addressing information, the "s-i-b" (scale-index-base) byte, can be specified.

The s-i-b byte (scale-index-base byte) is specified when using 32-bit addressing mode and the "mod r/m" byte has r/m = 100 and mod = 00, 01 or 10. When the sib byte is present, the 32-bit addressing mode is a function of the mod, ss, index, and base fields.

The primary addressing byte, the "mod r/m" byte, also contains three bits (shown as TTT in Figure 10.1) sometimes used as an extension of the primary opcode. The three bits, however, may also be used as a register field (reg).

When calculating an effective address, either 16-bit addressing or 32-bit addressing is used. 16-bit addressing uses 16-bit address components to calculate the effective address while 32-bit addressing uses 32-bit address components to calculate the effective address. When 16-bit addressing is used, the "mod r/m" byte is interpreted as a 16-bit addressing mode specifier. When 32-bit addressing is used, the "mod r/m" byte is interpreted as a 32-bit addressing mode specifier.

Tables on the following three pages define all encodings of all 16-bit addressing modes and 32-bit addressing modes.

Encoding of 16-bit Address Mode with "mod r/m" Byte

mod r/m	Effective Address
00 000	DS:[BX+SI]
00 001	DS:[BX+DI]
00 010	SS:[BP+SI]
00 011	SS:[BP+DI]
00 100	DS:[SI]
00 101	DS:[DI]
00 110	DS:d16
00 111	DS:[BX]
01 000	DS:[BX+SI+d8]
01 001	DS:[BX+DI+d8]
01 010	SS:[BP+SI+d8]
01 011	SS:[BP+DI+d8]
01 100	DS:[SI+d8]
01 101	DS:[DI+d8]
01 110	SS:[BP+d8]
01 111	DS:[BX+d8]

mod r/m	Effective Address
10 000	DS:[BX+SI+d16]
10 001	DS:[BX+DI+d16]
10 010	SS:[BP+SI+d16]
10 011	SS:[BP+DI+d16]
10 100	DS:[SI+d16]
10 101	DS:[DI+d16]
10 110	SS:[BP+d16]
10 111	DS:[BX+d16]
11 000	register—see below
11 001	register—see below
11 010	register—see below
11 011	register—see below
11 100	register—see below
11 101	register—see below
11 110	register—see below
11 111	register—see below

Register Specified by r/m During 16-Bit Data Operations

mod r/m	Function of w Field (when w=0)	Function of w Field (when w=1)
11 000	AL	AX
11 001	CL	CX
11 010	DL	DX
11 011	BL	BX
11 100	AH	SP
11 101	CH	BP
11 110	DH	SI
11 111	BH	DI

Register Specified by r/m During 32-Bit Data Operations

mod r/m	Function of w Field (when w=0)	Function of w Field (when w=1)
11 000	AL	EAX
11 001	CL	ECX
11 010	DL	EDX
11 011	BL	EBX
11 100	AH	ESP
11 101	CH	EBP
11 110	DH	ESI
11 111	BH	EDI

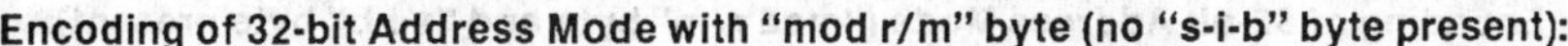

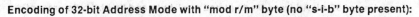

Encoding of 32-bit Address Mode with "mod r/m" byte (no "s-i-b" byte present):

mod r/m	Effective Address
00 000	DS:[EAX]
00 001	DS:[ECX]
00 010	DS:[EDX]
00 011	DS:[EBX]
00 100	s-i-b is present
00 101	DS:d32
00 110	DS:[ESI]
00 111	DS:[EDI]
01 000	DS:[EAX+d8]
01 001	DS:[ECX+d8]
01 010	DS:[EDX+d8]
01 011	DS:[EBX+d8]
01 100	s-i-b is present
01 101	SS:[EBP+d8]
01 110	DS:[ESI+d8]
01 111	DS:[EDI+d8]

mod r/m	Effective Address
10 000	DS:[EAX+d32]
10 001	DS:[ECX+d32]
10 010	DS:[EDX+d32]
10 011	DS:[EBX+d32]
10 100	s-i-b is present
10 101	SS:[EBP+d32]
10 110	DS:[ESI+d32]
10 111	DS:[EDI+d32]
11 000	register—see below
11 001	register—see below
11 010	register—see below
11 011	register—see below
11 100	register—see below
11 101	register—see below
11 110	register—see below
11 111	register—see below

Register Specified by reg or r/m during 16-Bit Data Operations:

mod r/m	Function of w field	
	(when w=0)	(when w=1)
11 000	AL	AX
11 001	CL	CX
11 010	DL	DX
11 011	BL	BX
11 100	AH	SP
11 101	CH	BP
11 110	DH	SI
11 111	BH	DI

Register Specified by reg or r/m during 32-Bit Data Operations:

mod r/m	Function of w field	
	(when w=0)	(when w=1)
11 000	AL	EAX
11 001	CL	ECX
11 010	DL	EDX
11 011	BL	EBX
11 100	AH	ESP
11 101	CH	EBP
11 110	DH	ESI
11 111	BH	EDI

Encoding of 32-bit Address Mode ("mod r/m" byte and "s-i-b" byte present):

mod base	Effective Address
00 000	DS:[EAX+(scaled index)]
00 001	DS:[ECX+(scaled index)]
00 010	DS:[EDX+(scaled index)]
00 011	DS:[EBX+(scaled index)]
00 100	SS:[ESP+(scaled index)]
00 101	DS:[d32+(scaled index)]
00 110	DS:[ESI+(scaled index)]
00 111	DS:[EDI+(scaled index)]
01 000	DS:[EAX+(scaled index)+d8]
01 001	DS:[ECX+(scaled index)+d8]
01 010	DS:[EDX+(scaled index)+d8]
01 011	DS:[EBX+(scaled index)+d8]
01 100	SS:[ESP+(scaled index)+d8]
01 101	SS:[EBP+(scaled index)+d8]
01 110	DS:[ESI+(scaled index)+d8]
01 111	DS:[EDI+(scaled index)+d8]
10 000	DS:[EAX+(scaled index)+d32]
10 001	DS:[ECX+(scaled index)+d32]
10 010	DS:[EDX+(scaled index)+d32]
10 011	DS:[EBX+(scaled index)+d32]
10 100	SS:[ESP+(scaled index)+d32]
10 101	SS:[EBP+(scaled index)+d32]
10 110	DS:[ESI+(scaled index)+d32]
10 111	DS:[EDI+(scaled index)+d32]

NOTE:
Mod field in "mod r/m" byte; ss, index, base fields in "s-i-b" byte.

ss	Scale Factor
00	x1
01	x2
10	x4
11	x8

index	Index Register
000	EAX
001	ECX
010	EDX
011	EBX
100	no index reg**
101	EBP
110	ESI
111	EDI

****IMPORTANT NOTE:**
When index field is 100, indicating "no index register," then ss field MUST equal 00. If index is 100 and ss does not equal 00, the effective address is undefined.

10.2.3.5 Encoding of Operation Direction (d) Field

In many two-operand instructions the d field is present to indicate which operand is considered the source and which is the destination.

d	Direction of Operation
0	Register/Memory <- - Register "reg" Field Indicates Source Operand; "mod r/m" or "mod ss index base" Indicates Destination Operand
1	Register <- - Register/Memory "reg" Field Indicates Destination Operand; "mod r/m" or "mod ss index base" Indicates Source Operand

10.2.3.6 Encoding of Sign-Extend (s) Field

The s field occurs primarily to instructions with immediate data fields. The s field has an effect only if the size of the immediate data is 8 bits and is being placed in a 16-bit or 32-bit destination.

s	Effect on Immediate Data8	Effect on Immediate Data 16|32
0	None	None
1	Sign-Extend Data8 to Fill 16-Bit or 32-Bit Destination	None

10.2.3.7 Encoding of Conditional Test (tttn) Field

For the conditional instructions (conditional jumps and set on condition), tttn is encoded with n indicating to use the condition (n=0) or its negation (n=1), and ttt giving the condition to test.

Mnemonic	Condition	tttn
O	Overflow	0000
NO	No Overflow	0001
B/NAE	Below/Not Above or Equal	0010
NB/AE	Not Below/Above or Equal	0011
E/Z	Equal/Zero	0100
NE/NZ	Not Equal/Not Zero	0101
BE/NA	Below or Equal/Not Above	0110
NBE/A	Not Below or Equal/Above	0111
S	Sign	1000
NS	Not Sign	1001
P/PE	Parity/Parity Even	1010
NP/PO	Not Parity/Parity Odd	1011
L/NGE	Less Than/Not Greater or Equal	1100
NL/GE	Not Less Than/Greater or Equal	1101
LE/NG	Less Than or Equal/Greater Than	1110
NLE/G	Not Less or Equal/Greater Than	1111

10.2.3.8 Encoding of Control or Debug or Test Register (eee) Field

For the loading and storing of the Control, Debug and Test registers.

When Interpreted as Control Register Field

eee Code	Reg Name
000	CR0
010	CR2
011	CR3
Do not use any other encoding	

When Interpreted as Debug Register Field

eee Code	Reg Name
000	DR0
001	DR1
010	DR2
011	DR3
110	DR6
111	DR7
Do not use any other encoding	

When Interpreted as Test Register Field

eee Code	Reg Name
011	TR3
100	TR4
101	TR5
110	TR6
111	TR7
Do not use any other encoding	

<table>
<tr><th colspan="5"></th><th colspan="6">Instruction</th><th colspan="2" rowspan="2">Optional Fields</th></tr>
<tr><th colspan="5">First Byte</th><th colspan="6">Second Byte</th></tr>
<tr><td>1</td><td>11011</td><td colspan="2">OPA</td><td>1</td><td colspan="2">mod</td><td>1</td><td>OPB</td><td colspan="2">r/m</td><td>s-i-b</td><td>disp</td></tr>
<tr><td>2</td><td>11011</td><td colspan="2">MF</td><td>OPA</td><td colspan="2">mod</td><td colspan="2">OPB</td><td colspan="2">r/m</td><td>s-i-b</td><td>disp</td></tr>
<tr><td>3</td><td>11011</td><td>d</td><td>P</td><td>OPA</td><td>1</td><td>1</td><td colspan="2">OPB</td><td colspan="2">ST(i)</td><td colspan="2"></td></tr>
<tr><td>4</td><td>11011</td><td>0</td><td>0</td><td>1</td><td>1</td><td>1</td><td>1</td><td colspan="3">OP</td><td colspan="2"></td></tr>
<tr><td>5</td><td>11011</td><td>0</td><td>1</td><td>1</td><td>1</td><td>1</td><td>1</td><td colspan="3">OP</td><td colspan="2"></td></tr>
<tr><td></td><td>15–11</td><td>10</td><td>9</td><td>8</td><td>7</td><td>6</td><td>5</td><td>4 3</td><td>2</td><td>1 0</td><td colspan="2"></td></tr>
</table>

10.2.4 ENCODING OF FLOATING POINT INSTRUCTION FIELDS

Instructions for the FPU assume one of the five forms shown in the following table. In all cases, instructions are at least two bytes long and begin with the bit pattern 11011B.

OP = Instruction opcode, possible split into two fields OPA and OPB

MF = Memory Format
- 00—32-bit real
- 01—32-bit integer
- 10—64-bit real
- 11—16-bit integer

P = Pop
- 0—Do not pop stack
- 1—Pop stack after operation

d = Destination
- 0—Destination is ST(0)
- 1—Destination is ST(i)

R XOR d = 0—Destination (op) Source
R XOR d = 1—Source (op) Destination

ST(i) = Register stack element *i*
- 000 = Stack top
- 001 = Second stack element
- •
- •
- •
- 111 = Eighth stack element

mod (Mode field) and r/m (Register/Memory specifier) have the same interpretation as the corresponding fields of the integer instructions.

s-i-b (Scale Index Base) byte and disp (displacement) are optionally present in instructions that have mod and r/m fields. Their presence depends on the values of mod and r/m, as for integer instructions.

Numeric Exception Summary F

APPENDIX F
NUMERIC EXCEPTION SUMMARY

The following table lists the instruction mnemonics in alphabetical order. For each mnemonic, it summarizes the exceptions that the instruction may cause. When writing numeric programs that may be used in an environment that employs numerics exception handlers, assembly-language programmers should be aware of the possible exceptions for each instruction in order to determine the need for exception synchronization. Chapter 18 explains the need for exception synchronization.

Mnemonic	Instruction	IS	I	D	Z	O	U	P
F2XM1	$2^X - 1$	Y	Y	Y			Y	Y
FABS	Absolute value	Y						
FADD(P)	Add real	Y	Y	Y		Y	Y	Y
FBLD	BCD load	Y						
FBSTP	BCD store and pop	Y	Y					Y
FCHS	Change sign	Y						
FCLEX	Clear exceptions							
FCOM(P)(P)	Compare real	Y	Y	Y				
FCOS	Cosine	Y	Y	Y			Y	Y
FDECSTP	Decrement stack pointer							
FDIV(R)(P)	Divide real	Y	Y	Y	Y	Y	Y	Y
FFREE	Free register							
FIADD	Integer add	Y	Y	Y		Y	Y	Y
FICOM(P)	Integer compare	Y	Y	Y				
FIDIV	Integer divide	Y	Y	Y	Y		Y	Y
FIDIVR	Integer divide reversed	Y	Y	Y	Y	Y	Y	Y
FILD	Integer load	Y						
FIMUL	Integer multiply	Y	Y	Y		Y	Y	Y
FINCSTP	Increment stack pointer							
FINIT	Initialize processor							
FIST(P)	Integer store	Y	Y					Y
FISUB(R)	Integer subtract	Y	Y	Y		Y	Y	Y
FLD extended or stack	Load real	Y						
FLD single or double	Load real	Y	Y	Y				
FLD1	Load + 1.0	Y						
FLDCW	Load Control word	Y	Y	Y	Y	Y	Y	Y
FLDENV	Load environment	Y	Y	Y	Y	Y	Y	Y
FLDL2E	Load $\log_2 e$	Y						
FLDL2T	Load $\log_2 10$	Y						
FLDLG2	Load $\log_{10} 2$	Y						
FLDLN2	Load $\log_e 2$	Y						
FLDPI	Load π	Y						
FLDZ	Load + 0.0	Y						
FMUL(P)	Multiply real	Y	Y	Y		Y	Y	Y
FNOP	No operation							
FPATAN	Partial arctangent	Y	Y	Y			Y	Y
FPREM	Partial remainder	Y	Y	Y			Y	
FPREM1	IEEE partial remainder	Y	Y	Y			Y	
FPTAN	Partial tangent	Y	Y	Y			Y	Y
FRNDINT	Round to integer	Y	Y	Y				Y
FRSTOR	Restore state	Y	Y	Y	Y	Y	Y	Y
FSAVE	Save state							
FSCALE	Scale	Y	Y	Y		Y	Y	Y

Mnemonic	Instruction	IS	I	D	Z	O	U	P
FSIN	Sine	Y	Y	Y			Y	Y
FSINCOS	Sine and cosine	Y	Y	Y			Y	Y
FSQRT	Square root	Y	Y	Y				Y
FST(P) stack or extended	Store real	Y						
FST(P) single or double	Store real	Y	Y	Y		Y	Y	Y
FSTCW	Store control word							
FSTENV	Store environment							
FSTSW (AX)	Store status word							
FSUB(R)(P)	Subtract real	Y	Y	Y		Y	Y	Y
FTST	Test	Y	Y	Y				
FUCOM(P)(P)	Unordered compare real	Y	Y	Y				
FWAIT	CPU Wait							
FXAM	Examine							
FXCH	Exchange registers	Y						
FXTRACT	Extract	Y	Y	Y	Y			
FYL2X	$Y \cdot \log_2 X$	Y	Y	Y	Y	Y	Y	Y
FYL2XP1	$Y \cdot \log_2(X + 1)$	Y	Y	Y			Y	Y

IS – Invalid operand due to stack overflow/underflow
I – Invalid operand due to other cause
D – Denormal operand
Z – Zero-divide
O – Overflow
U – Underflow
P – Inexact result (precision)

Code Optimization G

APPENDIX G
CODE OPTIMIZATION

The i486™ processor is binary-compatible with the 386™ DX and SX processors. Only three new application-level instructions have been added, which are useful in special situations. Any existing 8086/8088, 80286 and 386 processor applications will be able to execute on the i486 processor immediately without any modification or recompilation. Any compiler that currently generates code for the 386 processor family will also generate code that will run on the i486 processor without any modifications.

However, there are certain code-optimization techniques which will make applications execute faster on the i486 processor with only minor or no change to their performance on the 386 DX or SX processor, except possibly for code size differences. These techniques have to do with instruction sequence selection and instruction scheduling to take advantage of the internal pipelined execution units of the i486 processor and the large on-chip cache.

G.1 ADDRESSING MODES

Like the 386 processors, the i486 processor needs an additional clock cycle to generate an effective address when an index register is used. Therefore, if only one indexing component is used (i.e., not both a base register and an index register), and scaling is not necessary, then it is faster to use the register as a base rather than an index. For example:

```
mov eax,  [esi]    ; use esi as base
mov eax,  [esi*]   ; use esi as index, 1 clock penalty
```

If both base and index are used, or if scale indexing is necessary, then it is faster to use the combined addressing mode, even though it will take an additional clock cycle to execute.

When a register is used as the base component, an additional clock cycle is used if that register is the destination of the immediately preceding instruction (assuming all instructions are already in the prefetch queue). So to get the best performance, the two instructions should be separated by at least one other instruction. For example:

```
add  esi, eax     ; esi is destination register
mov  eax, [esi]   ; esi is base, 1 clock penalty
```

There are other hidden or implicit usages of destination and base registers, primarily the stack pointer register ESP. The ESP register is the implicit base of all PUSH/POP/RET instructions and it is the implicit destination for the CALL/ENTER/LEAVE/RET/PUSH/POP instruction. Therefore a LEAVE instruction followed immediately by a RET instruction will use one additional clock. But if the LEAVE and RET are rearranged so that they are separated by another instruction, then no such penalty is entailed. (See other recommendations regarding the LEAVE instruction.)

It is not necessary to separate back-to-back PUSH/POP instructions. The i486 processor will allow this sequence without incurring an additional clock.

All such instruction rearrangements of the instructions will not affect the performance of 386 processors.

The i486 processor will also take an additional clock to execute an instruction that has both an immediate data field and a memory offset field. For example:

```
mov dword ptr foo, 1234h    ; both immediate and memory offset
mov dword ptr baz, 1234h
mov [ebp-200],      1234h
```

When it is necessary to use constants, it would still be more efficient to use immediate data instead of loading the constant into a register first. But if the same immediate data is used more than once, then it would be faster to load the constant in a register and then use the register multiple times. This optimization will not affect the performance of 386 processors. The following sequence is faster than the one above, if all instructions are in the prefetch queue, and because the instructions are shorter, it will actually make it easier to prefetch:

```
mov eax, 1234h
mov dword ptr foo, eax
mov dword ptr baz, eax
mov [ebp-200], eax
```

G.2 PREFETCH UNIT

The i486 processor prefetch unit will access the on-chip cache to fill the prefetch queue whenever the cache is idle, and there is enough room in the queue for another cache line (16 bytes). If the prefetch queue becomes empty, it can take up to three additional clocks to start the next instruction. The prefetch queue is 32 bytes in size (2 cache lines).

Because data accesses always have priority over prefetch requests, keeping the cache busy with data access can lock out the prefetch unit.

Therefore it is important to arrange the instructions so that the memory bus is not used continuously by a series of memory reference instructions. The instructions should be rearranged so that there is a non-memory referencing instruction (such as a register/

register instruction) at least two clocks before the prefetch queue becomes exhausted. This will allow the prefetch unit to transfer a cache line into the queue. For example:

Instruction	Length
mov mem, 1234567h	10 bytes
mov mem, 1234567h	10 bytes
mov mem, 1234567h	10 bytes
mov mem, 1234567h	10 bytes
mov mem, 1234567h	10 bytes
add reg, reg	2 bytes

If the prefetch queue started out full, then by the third MOV instruction, there is enough room for another cache line in the queue, but because the memory bus is continuously being used, there is no time for the transfer from the cache to the prefetch queue. If a non-memory instruction is not inserted before or after the third MOV instruction, the queue will be exhausted by the fourth MOV instruction. In this case, the instructions should be rearranged so the ADD instruction is before or after the third MOV instruction, to allow the cache to transfer another instruction line to the prefetch unit.

No such rearrangements of the instructions will affect the performance of the 386 DX processor.

G.3 CACHE AND CODE ALIGNMENT

On the 386 DX processor, the destination of any JUMP/CALL/RET instructions should be aligned on a 0-mod-4 address, this helps the instruction prefetch unit in filling the prefetch queue as quickly as possible, since fetches are done 4-bytes at a time on aligned boundaries. On the i486 processor, because of the on-chip cache, any instruction fetch will fetch 16 bytes to fill a cache line. Therefore better performance can be obtained by aligning JUMP/CALL/RET destinations at 0-mod-16 addresses.

However, aligning at 0-mod-16 will cause the code to grow bigger, and the tradeoff between execution speed and code size is important.

Therefore, it is recommended that only the function entry address (i.e., destination of CALL instructions) be aligned on a 0-mod-16 address; while all labels (i.e., destination of JUMP instructions) will continue to be aligned on 0-mod-4 addresses.

On the i486 processor, it takes up to five additional clocks to start execution of an instruction if it is split across two 16-byte cache lines. For example, if a CALL instruction ends at address 0x0000000E and the next instruction is a multiple-byte instruction, then upon return from the CALL, the processor must take five additional clocks to fill the prefetch queue if the target instruction is not already in the cache. Even if the target instruction is already in the cache, it will take an additional 2 clocks to transfer it into the prefetch unit.

So if the compiler knows the alignment of the destination, then it will be faster to insert a filler instruction so that the multiple-byte instruction starts on an aligned address. This can be done either by rearranging the instructions or actually inserting a NOP instruction.

Such instruction alignments will also improve the performance on the 386 processors.

G.4 NOP INSTRUCTIONS

Sometimes programs need filler between instructions to align them. On the 386 and i486 processors, there is a one-byte NOP instruction which is really an exchange EAX with EAX.

Other lengths can be executed in a single clock. The table below lists some.

```
1-byte    inc   reg           ; will modify register and flags
2-bytes   mov   reg, reg      ; true NOP
3-bytes   lea   reg, 0[reg]   ; true NOP, use 8-bit displacement
5-bytes   mov   eax, 0        ; will modify eax register
5-bytes   add   eax, 0        ; will modify flags
6-bytes   lea   reg, 0[eax]   ; true NOP, use 32-bit displacement
```

Additionally, many of the 386/i486 processor instructions have several forms and lengths, using different-sized immediate data or different-sized memory offsets. Also some instructions have shorter forms if the destination register is EAX/AX/AL.

Not all instructions with different forms will execute in the same clocks. An example where different forms will execute in different clocks is the PUSH/POP REG instructions, if they are coded in the one-byte form, they will execute in one clock, but if coded in the 2-byte form, they will execute in 4 clocks.

The NOP replacement instructions will also execute faster than the XCHG instruction on 386 processors. Using different forms of the same instruction will not affect performance on the 386 processor.

G.5 INTEGER INSTRUCTIONS

The i486 processor can execute most of the frequently-used instructions (such as register load/store, register ALU operations, etc.) in one clock. However, unlike the 386 processor, some of the memory operations now take more clocks than the corresponding register instructions. For example, the PUSH MEM instruction:

Instruction	386™ DX CPU Clocks	i486™ CPU Clocks
mov reg, mem	4	1
push reg	2	1
push mem	5	4

So for the i486 processor, loading a value from memory into a register first and then pushing that register will result in a net saving of 2 clocks; but for the 386 DX processor, the same instruction sequence will result in a net loss of one clock. However, in order to load the value into a register on the i486 processor, an empty register must be found; if the action of loading the value will destroy a value in a register that may be re-used later, then the saving may be negated by the loss of the re-usable value.

Another example is the LEAVE instruction:

Instruction	386™ DX CPU Clocks	i486™ CPU Clocks
mov esp, ebp	2	1
pop ebp	4	1+1 (esp. penalty)
leave	4	5

Again, for the i486 processor, doing the MOV/POP sequence will result in a net saving of 2 clocks over the LEAVE instruction; while on the 386 DX processor, the LEAVE instruction is both faster and shorter. However, because the first MOV instruction uses ESP as the destination register, and the POP instruction also implicitly uses the ESP register as a base (as mentioned above), this sequence will result in a one clock penalty unless the two instructions are separated by another instruction. If it is possible to rearrange the instructions so the MOV/POP instructions are separated by a useful instruction, then the net savings over a LEAVE instruction is 3 clocks on the i486 processor.

Because the i486 processor can operate with operands in registers faster than out of memory (just like most other architectures), it is important to have good register allocation and value tracking optimizations in any compiler. On the other hand, there is no savings in loading up every value before using it, as in a RISC architecture. The i486 processor can perform *reg, mem* type ALU operations as fast as *load/op/store* sequences. For example, for the assignment

```
mem1 = mem1 + mem2
```

the following instruction sequences could be used, with varying total clock counts on the 386 DX and SX processor, but identical clock counts on the i486 processor:

Instruction	386™ DX CPU Clocks	i486™ CPU Clocks
mov eax, mem1	4	1
mov ebx, mem2	4	1
add eax, ebx	2	1
mov mem1, eax	2	1
mov eax, mem1	4	1
add eax, mem2	6	2
mov mem1, eax	2	1
mov eax, mem1	4	1
add mem2, eax	7	3

The MOVZX is another example where the i486 processor can execute faster using simple instructions, if the destination is a register that is also byte addressable. For example, loading a byte value:

Instruction	386™ DX CPU Clocks	i486™ CPU Clocks
movzx eax, mem1	6	3 + 1 (0Fh prefix)
xor eax, eax	2	1
movb al, mem1	4	1

So for the i486 processor, clearing the register first and then loading the byte value may result in a net saving of two clocks (depending on whether the prefix decode clock can be overlapped with the previous instruction, see Section G.8 on Prefix opcodes), while there is no difference in performance on the 386 DX processor.

G.6 CONDITION CODES

In some high level languages, it is sometimes necessary to convert the result of a boolean condition (e.g., equality, greater-than or less-than, etc.) into a true or false (i.e., 0/1) value. The 386 and i486 processors normally maintain the results of comparisons in the flags register, so in order to convert the result of a comparison into a true/false value, it is necessary to convert the flags settings into an integer value.

The 386 and i486 processors have a set of SETcc instructions which will do such conversions, however, the SETcc instructions take 3 or 4 clocks to execute on the i486 processor depending on whether the condition being tested for is true or false. Specifically while comparing unsigned values for greater-than or less-than, there is an optional sequence to use. For example, if "x" and "y" are both unsigned values, and "x" is loaded into register eax and "y" is loaded in register ecx, then the code for "(x < y)" could be generated in several ways:

Instruction	386™ DX CPU Clocks	i486™ CPU Clocks
cmp eax, ecx	2	1
mov eax, 0	2	1
jnb L1	7+m/3	3/1
mov eax, 1	2	1
L1:		
cmp eax, ecx	2	1
setb al	4/5	4/3
movsx eax, al	3	3
cmp eax, ecx	2	1
sbb eax, eax	2	1
neg eax	2	1

So using the SBB instruction to capture the flags setting of an unsigned compare gives the fastest performance, without breaking the prefetch pipeline because there are no jumps involved. Note that although this is specific for the "(x < y)" condition, it is possible to transform other tests to this form by either negating the condition or by exchanging the operands.

Such condition code instruction replacements will also improve the performance on the 386 CPUs.

G.7 STRING INSTRUCTIONS

Like the 386 DX processor, the i486 processor executes string instructions slower than the load/store instructions. For example, the LODS instruction:

Instruction	386™ DX CPU Clocks	i486™ CPU Clocks
mov eax, [esi]	4	1
add esi, 4	2	1
lods	5	4

The LODS instruction does more than the individual MOV instruction, it also updates the ESI register. However, if it is not necessary to have the register updated, then the MOV instruction will result in a net saving of 3 clocks on both the 386 DX and the i486 processors. The minor tradeoff is that the LODS instruction is shorter than the MOV instruction.

Also in a non-REPeated usage, individual MOV instructions will always be faster than the string MOVS instruction. And even in a REPeated loop, if the loop is small enough, it will be faster to use individual load/store instructions than to set up for a REPeated MOVS. The tradeoff again is speed vs. code space, with the REP MOVS loop being shorter but slower. However, as discussed above, a long sequence of load/store instructions will prevent the prefetch unit from filling the prefetch queue and slow the processor, so the recommendation is not to move more than 16 bytes with load/store instructions before a non-memory instruction to allow the prefetch unit to access the cache.

Similar optimizations can also be made for the STOS and other string instructions. Such string instruction replacements will also improve the performance on the 386 processor.

G.8 FLOATING-POINT INSTRUCTIONS

As with the 386 processor/387 math coprocessor combination, the floating point unit of the processor is a separate execution unit and it operates in parallel with the integer unit, even though they are physically, on the same chip. Therefore any instruction sequence that allows the two independent units to execute in parallel will be faster.

Floating point instructions should not be placed one immediately after another. The instructions should be rearranged so that two floating point instructions are separated by other non-floating point instructions so the two units can execute in parallel. Pay particular attention to the clock counts of the floating point instruction, so sufficient number of integer instructions could be executed without causing the floating point unit to wait before the next floating point instruction is issued. Such rearrangements of the instructions will also improve the performance on the 386 processor/387 math coprocessor, however, the clock counts used by the processor is much lower than the clock counts used by the 387 math coprocessor for the same floating point instructions.

As a reminder, any simple arrangements or movement of floating point values should not be done via the floating point unit, but rather through the integer unit with integer instructions. Also FWAIT's are never required around simple floating point instructions.

G.9 PREFIX OPCODES

On either processor, all prefix opcodes, including 0Fh, segment override, operand size/addressing, bus-lock, repeat, etc. require an additional clock to decode. This clock can be overlapped with the execution of the previous instruction if it takes more than one clock to execute.

Therefore it will be faster to expand 16-bit operands to a full 32-bits and then operate on the 32-bit value instead of using the 66h prefix to operate on 16-bit operands.

If prefix opcodes must be used, try to rearrange the instructions so that the instruction with the prefix is after an instruction that takes multiple clocks to execute.

An additional reason for not using 16-bit operands is that if the destination of one instruction is a 16-bit register, and the immediately following instruction uses that register as a 32-bit operand, then there is a one clock penalty. Again, the two instructions should be separated by another instruction to avoid the penalty.

G.10 OVERLAPPED CLOCKS

As mentioned above, there are several situations where an instruction will take an extra clock to execute, but some of these extra clock penalties can overlap with one another. So an instruction that uses multiple features mentioned above will not necessarily have a total penalty that is the sum of the individual penalties.

In particular, the following combinations will overlap:

- Having an index register and an immediate field with a memory offset field will only cost a one clock penalty.
- Having a prefix opcode and using the result register of the previous instruction as a base will only cost a one clock penalty.
- Having a prefix opcode after a multi-clock instruction will not cost any additional clock penalty.

G.11 MISCELLANEOUS USAGE GUIDELINES

The instruction set of the 386 processors was designed with certain programming practices in mind. Many of these practices remain relevant in assembly-language programming for the i486 processor, and may be of interest in compiler design as well.

- Use the EAX register when possible. Many instructions are one byte shorter when the EAX register is used, such as loads and stores to memory when absolute addresses are used, transfers to other registers using the XCHG instruction, and operations using immediate operands.
- Use the D-data segment when possible. Instructions which deal with the D-space are one byte shorter than instructions which use the other data segments, because of the lack of a segment-override prefix.
- Emphasize short one-, two-, and three-byte instructions. Because instructions for the i486 processor begin and end on byte boundaries, it has been possible to provide many instruction encodings which are more compact than those for processors with word-aligned instruction sets. An instruction in a word-aligned instruction set must be either two or four bytes long (or longer). Byte alignment reduces code size and increases execution speed.
- Access 16-bit data with the MOVSX and MOVZX instructions. These instructions sign-extend and zero-extend word operands to doubleword length. This eliminates the need for an extra instruction to initialize the high word.
- For faster interrupt response, use the NMI interrupt when possible.

- In place of using an ENTER instruction at lexical level 0, use a code sequence like:

```
PUSH EBP
MOV EBP, ESP
SUB ESP, BYTE_COUNT
```

  This executes in seven clock cycles, rather than ten.

The following techniques may be applied as optimizations to enhance the speed of a system after its basic functions have been implemented:

- The jump instructions come in two forms: one form has an eight-bit immediate for relative jumps in the range from 128 bytes back to 127 bytes forward, the other form has a full 32-bit displacement. Many assemblers use the long form in situations where the short form can be used. When it is clear that the short form may be used, explicitly specify the destination operand as being byte length. This tells the assembler to use the short form. If the assembler does not support this function, it will generate an error. Note that some assemblers perform this optimization automatically.
- Use the ESP register to reference the stack in the deepest level of subroutines. Don't bother setting up the EBP register and stack frame.
- For fastest task switching, perform task switching in software. This allows a smaller processor state to be saved and restored. See Chapter 7 for a discussion of multitasking.
- Use the LEA instruction for adding registers together. When a base register and index register are used with the LEA instruction, the destination is loaded with their sum. The contents of the index register may be scaled by 2, 4, or 8.
- Use the LEA instruction for adding a constant to a register. When a base register and a displacement are used with the LEA instruction, the destination is loaded with their sum. The LEA instruction can be used with a base register, index register, scale factor, and displacement.
- Use integer move instructions to transfer floating-point data.
- Use the form of the RET instruction which takes an immediate value for byte-count, rather than an ADD ESP instruction. It saves one clock cycle and three bytes on every subroutine call.
- When several references are made to a variable addressed with a displacement, load the displacement into a register.
- The PUSH and POP instructions, when used with an operand in memory, take two more clock cycles to execute than an equivalent two-instruction sequence which moves the operand through a general register before pushing it on the stack.
- The LOOP instruction takes two more clock cycles to execute than the equivalent decrement and conditional jump instructions.
- The JECXZ instruction takes one more clock cycle to execute than the equivalent compare and conditional jump instructions.

Glossary

GLOSSARY

Abort—An exception which is completely unrecoverable, such as stack exception during an attempt to invoke an exception handler.

Address—See *Logical Address, Linear Address,* and *Physical Address.*

Address Space—The range of memory locations which may be accessed by an address.

Address-Size Prefix—An instruction prefix which selects the size of address offsets. Offsets may be 16- or 32-bit. The default address size is specified by the D bit in the code segment for the instruction. Use of the address-size prefix selects the non-default size.

Address Translation—The process of mapping addresses from one address space to another. Segmentation and paging both perform address translation.

Base Address—The address of the beginning of a data structure, such as a segment, descriptor table, page, or page table.

Base Register—A register used for addressing an operand relative to an address held in the register.

Base—(1) A term used in logarithms and exponentials. In both contexts, it is a number that is being raised to a power. The two equations (y=log base b of x) and (by=x) are the same. (2) A number that defines the representation being used for a string of digits. Base 2 is the binary representation; base 10 is the decimal representation; base 16 is the hexadecimal representation. In each case, the base is the factor of increased significance for each succeeding digit (working up from the bottom). (3) See *Base Address.*

BCD—Binary Coded Decimal; a format for representing numbers in base 10. One byte is used for each digit of the number, with bit positions 0 to 3 specifying the value for the digit. The auxiliary carry flag isused to perform BCD arithmetic. The FPU supports a packed form of BCD, in which 18 digits and a sign bit are contained in an 80-bit operand.

Bias—A constant that is added to the true exponent of a real number to obtain the exponent field of that number's floating-point representation in the FPU. To obtain the true exponent, you must subtract the bias from the given exponent. For example, the single real format has a bias of 127 whenever the given exponent is nonzero. If the 8-bit exponent field contains 10000011 (binary), which is 131 (decimal), the true exponent is 131−127, or +4. Also known as an excess representation, in this case excess −127.

Biased Exponent—The exponent as it appears in a floating-point representation of a number. The biased exponent is interpreted as an unsigned, positive number. In the above example, 131 is the biased exponent.

Binary Coded Decimal—A method of storing numbers that retains a base 10 representation. Each decimal digit occupies 4 full bits (one hexdecimal digit). The hexadecimal values A through F (1010 to 1111) are not used. The i486™ processor supports a packed decimal format that consists of 9 bytes of binary coded decimal (18 decimal digits) and one sign byte.

Binary Point—An entity just like a decimal point, except that it exists in floating-point binary numbers. Each binary digit to the right of the binary point is multiplied by an increasing negative power of two.

Bit Field—A sequence of up to 32 bits which may start at any bit position of any byte address. The i486 processor has instructions for efficient operations on bit fields.

Bit String—A sequence of up to $2^{32}-1$ bits which may start at any bit position of any byte address. The i486 processor has instructions for efficient operations on bit strings.

Breakpoint—An aid to program debugging in which the programmer specifies forms of memory access which generate exceptions. The exceptions invoke debugging software. The i486 processor supports software and hardware breakpoints. A software breakpoint is an instruction inserted into the program being debugged. When the INT 3 instruction is executed, a breakpoint occurs. A hardware breakpoint is set up by programming the debugging registers. The contents of the debugging registers specify the address, size, and type of reference for as many as four breakpoints. Unlike software breakpoints, hardware breakpoints can be applied to data.

Byte—An 8-bit quantity of memory; the smallest unit of memory referenced by an address.

C3–C0—The four "condition code" bits of the FPU status word. These bits are set to certain values by the compare, test, examine, and remainder functions of the FPU.

Cache—A small, fast memory which holds the active parts of a larger, slower memory.

Cache Flush—An operation which marks all cache lines as invalid. The i486 processor has instructions for flushing internal and external caches.

Cache Line—The smallest unit of storage which can be allocated in a cache. The internal cache of the i486 processor has a line size of 128 bits.

Cache Line Fill—An operation which loads an entire cache line using multiple read cycles to main memory.

Cache Miss—A request for access to memory which requires actually reading main memory.

Call Gate—A gate descriptor for invoking a procedure with a CALL or JUMP instruction.

Characteristic—A term used for some non-Intel® computers, meaning the exponent field of a floating-point number.

Chop—In the FPU, to set one or more low-order bits of a real number to zero, yielding the nearest representable number in the direction of zero.

Code Segment—An address space which contains instructions; an executable segment. An instruction-fetch cycle must address a code segment. The type of information held in a segment is specified in its segment descriptor.

Condition Code—The four bits of the FPU status word that indicates the results of the compare, test, examine, and remainder functions of the FPU.

Conforming Segment—A code segment which executes with the RPL of the segment selector or the CPL of the calling program, whichever is less privileged.

Context Switch—See *Task Switch*.

Control Word—A 16-bit FPU register that the user can set, to determine the modes of computation the FPU will use and the exception interrupts that will be enabled.

Coprocessor—An extension to the base architecture and instruction set of a processor. The 387™ numerics coprocessor is used to add floating-point arithmetic instructions and registers to the 386™ processor. Coprocessors allow present-day systems to enjoy the architectural enhancements which will be available in future processor chips.

CPL—See *Current Privilege Level.*

CPU—Central Processor Unit. *See Processor.*

Current Privilege Level (CPL)—The privilege level of the program which is executing. Normally, the privilege level is loaded from a code segment descriptor. It is loaded into the CS segment register, where it is visible to software as the two lowest bits of the register. When execution is transferred to a conforming code segment, the privilege level does not change. In this case, the CPL may be different from the privilege level specified in the descriptor (DPL).

Data Segment—An address space which contains data. As many as four data segments may be in use without reloading the segment registers. The type of information held in a segment is specified in its segment descriptor.

Data Structure—An area of memory defined for a particular use by hardware or software, such as a page table or task state segment (TSS).

Debug Registers—A set of registers used to specify as many as four hardware breakpoints. Unlike breakpoint instructions, which only can be used for code breakpoints, the debug registers can specify breakpoints in either code or data.

Denormal—A special form of floating-point number. On the FPU, a denormal is defined as a number that has a biased exponent of zero. By providing a significand with leading zeros, the range of possible negative exponents can be extended by the number of bits in the significand. Each leading zero is a bit of lost accuracy, so the extended exponent range is obtained by reducing significance.

Descriptor Privilege Level (DPL)—The privilege level applied to a segment. The DPL is a field in the segment descriptor.

Descriptor Table—An array of segment descriptors. There are two kinds of descriptor tables: the Global Descriptor Table (GDT) and an arbitrary number of Local Descriptor Tables (LDTs).

Device Driver—A procedure or task used to manage a peripheral device, such as a disk drive.

Displacement—A constant used in calculating effective addresses. A displacement modifies the address independently of any scaled indexing. A displacement often is used to access operands which have a fixed relation to some other address, such as a field of a record in an array.

Double Extended—IEEE Std 754 term for the FPU's extended format, with more exponent and significand bits than the double format and an explicit integer bit in the significand.

Double Format—A floating-point format supported by the FPU that consists of a sign, an 11-bit biased exponent, an implicit integer bit, and a 52-bit significand, a total of 64 explicit bits.

Doubleword—A 32-bit quantity of memory. The i486 processor allows 32-bit doublewords to begin at any byte address, but a performance penalty is taken when a doubleword crosses the boundary between two doublewords in physical memory.

DPL—See *Descriptor Privilege Level.*

Effective Address—The address produced from addressing-mode calculations. A base register, scaled index, and displacement may be used in the calculations.

Environment—The 14 or 28 (depending on addressing mode) bytes of FPU registers affected by the FSTENV and FLDENV instructions. It encompasses the entire state of the FPU, except for the 8 registers of the FPU stack. Included are the control word, status word, tag word, and the instruction, opcode, and operand information provided by interrupts.

ESC Instruction—An instruction encoding used for coprocessor instructions.

Exception—A forced call to a procedure or a task which is generated when the processor fails to interpret an instruction or when an INT *n* instruction is executed. Causes of exceptions include division by zero, stack overflow, undefined opcodes, and memory-protection violations. Exceptions are faults, traps, aborts, and software-initiated interrupts.

Exception Pointers—In the FPU, the indication used by exception handlers to identify the cause of an exception. This data consists of a pointer to the most recently executed ESC instruction and a pointer to the memory operand of this instruction, if it had a memory operand of this instruction, if it had a memory operand. An exception handler can use the FSTENV and FSAVE instructions to access these pointers.

Expand-Down Segment—A type of data segment in which the meaning of the segment limit is reversed. All other segments accept legal offsets from the base address to the base address plus the segment limit. An expand-down segment accepts legal addresses in two ranges: from 0 to one byte below the base address, and from one byte past the segment limit to the top of the address space.

Exponent—(1) Any number that indicates the power to which another number is raised. (2) The field of a floating-point number that indicates the magnitude of the number. This would fall under the above more general definition (I), except that a bias sometimes needs to be subtracted to obtain the correct power.

Extended Format—The FPU's implementation of the double extended format of IEEE Std 754. Extended format is the main floating-point format used by the FPU. It consists of a sign, a 15-bit biased exponent, and a significand with an explicit integer bit and 63 fractional-part bits.

External Cache—A cache memory provided outside of the processor chip. External caches can be added to any kind of processor which has external main memory. The i486 processor has instructions and page-table entry bits which are used to control external caches from software.

Far Pointer—A reference to memory which includes both a segment selector and an offset. Used to access memory when the segment selector has not been loaded into the processor, for example when making a procedure call from one segment to another.

Fault—An exception which is reported at the instruction boundary immediately before the instruction which generated the exception. When a fault is generated, enough of the state of the processor is restored to permit another attempt to execute the instruction which generated the fault. The fault handler is called with a return address which points to the faulting instruction, rather than the instruction which follows the faulting instruction. After the handler fixes the source of the exception, such as a segment or page which is not present in memory, the program is restarted.

Flat Model—A memory organization in which all segments are mapped to the same range of linear addresses. This organization removes segmentation from the environment of application programs to the greatest degree possible.

Floating-Point Operand – A representation for a number expressed as a base, a sign, a significand, and a signed exponent. The value of the number is the signed product of its significand and the base raised to the power of the exponent. Floating-point representations are more versatile than integer representations in two ways. First, they include fractions. Second, their exponent parts allow a much wider range of magnitude than possible with fixed-length integer representations.

Floating-Point Unit (FPU) – The part of the i486 processor which contains the floating-point registers and performs the operations required by floating-point instructions.

FPU – See *Floating-Point Unit.*

Flush – See *Cache Flush.*

Gate Descriptor – A segment descriptor which can be the destination of a call or jump. A gate descriptor can be used to invoke a procedure or task in another privilege level. There are four types of gate descriptors: call gates, trap gates, interrupt gates, and task gates.

GDT – See *Global Descriptor Table.*

Global Descriptor Table (GDT) – An array of segment descriptors for all programs in a system. There is only one GDT in a system.

Gradual Underflow – A method of handling the floating-point underflow error condition that minimizes the loss of accuracy in the result. If there is a denormal number that represents the correct result, the denormal is returned. Thus, digits are lost only to the extent of denormalization. Most computers return zero when underflow occurs, losing all signficant digits.

Handler – A procedure or task which is called as a result of an exception or interrupt.

Hit – See *Cache Hit.*

IDT – See *Interrupt Descriptor Table.*

IEEE Standard 754 – A set of formats and operations which apply to floating-point numbers. The formats cover 32-, 64-, and 80-bit operand sizes. The standard was developed by the Institute for Electrical and Electronics Engineeers (IEEE). The FPU supports all operand sizes covered by the standard.

Immediate Operand – Data encoded in an instruction.

Implicit Integer Bit – A part of the significand in the single real and double real floating-point formats that is not explicitly given. In these formats, the entire given significand is considered to be the right of the binary point. A single implicit integer bit to the left of the binary point is always one, except in one case. When the exponent is the minimum (biased exponent is zero), the implicit integer bit is zero.

Indefinite—A special value that is returned by floating-point functions when the inputs are such that no other sensible answer is possible. For each floating-point format these exits one quiet NaN that is designated as the indefinite value. For binary integer formats, the negative number furthest from zero is often considered the indefinite value. For the FPU packed decimal format, the indefinite value contains all 1's in the sign byte and the uppermost digits byte.

Index—A number used to access a table. An index is scaled (multiplied by shifting left) to account for the size of the operand. The scaled index is added to the base address of the table to get the address of the table entry.

Inexact—IEEE Std 754 term for the FPU's precision exception.

Infinity—A floating-point result that has greater magnitude than any integer or any real number. It is often useful to consider infinity as another number, subject to special rules of arithmetic. All three Intel floating-point formats provide representations for +infinity and −infinity.

Initialization—The process of setting up the programming environment following reset. The processor begins execution in real-address mode. A few processor registers have defined states following reset, which permit execution to begin. Initial states of the segment registers allow memory to be accessed, even though no segment selectors have been loaded. The DR7 register (debug control register) is clear, so no breakpoint will occur during initialization. The real mode program can set up data structures such as descriptor tables and page tables, then transfer execution to a program running in protected mode.

Instruction Prefetch—Reading instructions into the processor from sequentially higher addresses in advance of execution; a technique for overlapping the execution of instructions.

Instruction Restart—An ability to make a second attempt to execute an instruction which generates an exception. Instruction restart is necessary for supporting virtual memory. When an application makes reference to a segment or page which is not present in memory, the application must be suspended in a way which allows restarting after the operating system has brought the segment or page into physical memory. Instruction restart restores enough of the processor state to allow the exception handler to be called with a return address pointing to the instruction which generated the exception, rather than the instruction following it.

Integer—A number (positive, negative, or zero) that is finite and has no fractional part. Integer can also mean the computer representation for such a number: a sequence of data bytes interpreted in a standard way. It is perfectly reasonable for integers to be represented in a floating-point format; this is what the FPU does whenever an integer is pushed onto the FPU stack.

Integer Bit—A part of the significand in floating-point formats. In these formats, the integer bit is the only part of the significand considered to be to the left of the binary point. The integer bit is always one, except in one case: when the exponent is the minimum (biased exponent is zero), the integer bit is zero. In the extended format the integer bit is explicit; in the single format and double format the integer bit is implicit; i.e., is not actually stored in memory.

Internal Cache—A cache memory on the processor chip. The i486 processor has 8K bytes of internal cache memory.

Interrupt—A forced transfer of program control caused by a hardware signal or execution of the INT *n* instruction. Interrupt handlers called by software are processed like exceptions.

Interrupt Descriptor Table (IDT)—An array of gate descriptors for invoking the handlers associated with exceptions and interrupts. A handler may be invoked by a task gate, interrupt gate, or trap gate.

Interrupt Gate—A gate descriptor used to invoke an interrupt handler. An interrupt gate is different from a trap gate only in its effect on the IF flag. An interrupt gate clears the flag (disables interrupts) for the duration of the handler.

Invalid—Unallocated. Invalid cache lines do not cause cache hits. Valid cache lines have been loaded with data and may cause cache hits.

Invalid Operation—The exception condition for the FPU that covers all cases not covered by other exceptions. Included are FPU stack overflow and underflow, NaN inputs, illegal infinite inputs, out-of-range inputs, and inputs in unsupported formats.

Label—An identifier used to name places in the source code of a program, so that statements can refer to those places. Places named by labels include procedure entry points, beginning of blocks of data, and base addresses for descriptor tables.

LDT—See *Local Descriptor Table.*

Linear Address—A 32-bit address into a large, unsegmented address space. If paging is enabled, it translates the linear address into a physical address. If paging is not enabled, the linear address is used as the physical address.

Local Descriptor Table (LDT)—An array of segment descriptors for one program. Each program may have its own LDT, a program may share its LDT with another program, or a program may have no LDT, in which case, it uses the global descriptor table (GDT).

Locked Instructions—Instructions which read and write a destination in memory without allowing other devices to become bus masters between the read cycle and the write cycle. This mechanism is necessary for supporting reliable communications among multiprocessors. The mechanism is invoked using the LOCK instruction prefix. Only certain instructions may be locked, and only when they have destination operands in memory (other uses of the LOCK prefix generate an invalid-opcode exception).

Logical Address – The number used by application programs to reference virtual memory. This number consists of two parts: a segment selector (16 bits) and an offset (32 bits). The segment selector is used to specify an independent, protected address space (segment). The offset is used as an address within that segment. Segmentation translates the logical address into a linear address.

Long Integer – An integer format supported by the FPU that consists of a 64-bit two's complement quantity.

Long Real – An older term for the FPU's 64-bit double format.

Main Memory – The large memory, external to the processor, used for holding most instruction code and data. Generally built from cost-effective DRAM memory chips. May be used with the internal cache of the processor and an optional external cache.

Mantissa – A term used with some non-Intel computers for the significand of a floating-point number.

Masked – A term that can apply to each of the six FPU exceptions I, D, A, O U, P. An exception is masked if a corresponding bit in the FPU control word is set to one. If an exception is masked, the FPU will not generate an interrupt when the exception condition occurs; it will instead provide its own exception recovery.

Memory Management – Support for simplified models of memory; a process consisting of address translation and protection checks. There are two forms of memory management, segmentation and paging. Segmentation provides protected, independent address spaces (segments). Paging provides access to data structures larger than the available memory space by keeping them partly in memory and partly on disk.

Microprocessor – See *Processor.*

Miss – See *Cache Miss.*

Mode – (1) One of the FPU status word fields "rounding control" and "precision control" which programs can set, sense, save, and restore to control the execution of subsequent arithmetic operations. (2) See *Real-Address Mode, Protected Mode, Virtual-8086 Mode, Supervisor Mode, User Mode.*

ModR/M Byte – A byte following an instruction opcode which is used to specify instruction operands.

MPU – Micro-Processor Unit. See *Processor.*

Multiprocessing – Using more than one processor in a system. The i486 processor supports two kinds of multiprocessing: coprocessors, which are special-purpose performance-enhancing extensions to the architecture and instruction set, and multiple general-purpose processors, such as additional i486 processors.

Multisegmented Model—A memory organization in which different segments are mapped to different ranges of linear addresses. This organization uses segmentation to protect data structures from damage caused by program errors. For example, the stack can be kept from growing into memory occupied by instruction code.

Multitasking—Timesharing a processor among several programs, executing some number of instructions from each. The i486 processor has instructions and data structures which support multitasking.

NaN—An abbreviation for "Not a Number"; a floating-point quantity that does not represent any numeric or infinite quantity. NaN's should be returned by functions that encounter serious errors. If created during a sequence of calculations, they are transmitted to the final answer and can contain information about where the error occurred.

Near Pointer—A reference to memory without a segment selector; an offset. Used to access memory when the segment selector has already been loaded into the processor, for example when one procedure calls another within the same segment.

Normal—The representation of a number in a floating-point format in which the significand has an integer bit one (either explicit or implicit).

Normalize—Convert a denormal floating-point representation of a number to a normal representation.

Offset—A 16- or 32-bit number which specifies a memory location relative to the base address of a segment. A program's code segment descriptor specifies whether 16- or 32-bit offsets are the default. An address-size prefix specifies use of the non-default size.

Operand—Data in a register or in memory which an instruction reads or writes (or both).

Operand-Size Prefix—An instruction prefix which selects the sizes of integer operands. Operands may be 8- and 16-bit, or they may be 8- and 32-bit. The default operand size is specified by the D bit in the descriptor for the code segment which contains the instruction. Use of the operand-size prefix selects the non-default size.

Overflow—A floating-point exception condition in which the correct answer is finite, but has magnitude too great to be represented in the destination format. This kind of overflow (also called numeric overflow) is not to be confused with stack overflow.

Packed BCD—Packed Binary Coded Decimal; a format for representing numbers in base 10. One byte is used for each two digits of the number, with bit positions 0 to 3 specifying the value for the less significant digit and bit positions 4 to 7 specifying the value for the more significant digit. Packed BCD is one of the data types supported by the FPU.

Packed Decimal—An integer format supported by the FPU. A packed decimal number is a 10-byte quantity, with nine bytes of 18 binary coded decimal digits and one byte for the sign.

Page Directory—The first-level page table. The paging hardware of the i486 processor uses two levels of page tables, where the physical address produced by the first-level page table is the base address of the second-level page table. The use of two levels allows the second-level tables to be paged to disk.

Page Directory Base Register (PDBR)—A processor register which holds the base address of the page directory; same as the CR3 register. Because the contents of the PDBR register are loaded from the task state segment (TSS) during a task switch, each task can have its own page directory, so each can have a different mapping of virtual pages to physical pages.

Page—A 4K-byte block of neighboring memory locations; the unit of memory used by paging hardware.

Page Table—A table which maps part of a linear address to a physical address. The paging hardware of the i486 processor uses two levels of page tables, where the physical address produced by the first-level page table is the base address of the second-level page table. The use of two levels allows the second-level tables to be paged to disk.

Page Table Entry—A 32-bit data structure in memory used for paging. It includes the physical address for a page and the page's protection information. It is set up by operating system software and accessed by paging hardware.

Paging—A form of memory management used to simulate a large, unsegmented address space using a small, fragmented address space and some disk storage. Paging provides access to data structures larger than the available memory space by keeping them partly in memory and partly on disk.

PDBR—See *Page Directory Base Register.*

Physical Address—The address which appears on the local bus. The i486 processor has a 32-bit physical address, which may be used to address as much as 4 gigabytes of memory.

Physical Memory—The address space on the local bus; the hardware implementation of memory. Memory is addressed as 8-bit bytes, but it is implemented as 32-bit doublewords which start at addresses which are multiples of four (addresses which are clear in their two least significant bits). The i486 processor may have up to 4 gigabytes of physical memory.

Precision—The effective number of bits in the significand of the floating-point representation of a number.

Precision Control—An option, programmed through the FPU control word, that allows all FPU arithmetic to be performed with reduced precision. Because no speed advantage results from this option, its only use is for strict compatibility with IEEE Std 754 and with other computer systems.

Precision Exception—An FPU exception condition that results when a calculation does not return an exact answer. This exception is usually masked and ignored; it is used only in extremely critical applications, when the user must know if the results are exact. The precision exceptions is called inexact in IEEE Std 754.

Privilege Level—A protection parameter applied to segments and segment selectors. There are four privilege levels, ranging from 0 (most privileged) to 3 (least privileged). Level 0 is used for critical system software, such as the operating system. Level 3 is used for application programs. Some system software, such as device drivers, may be put in intermediate levels 1 and 2.

Processor—The part of a computer system which executes instructions; also called microprocessor, CPU, or MPU.

Protected Mode—An execution mode in which the full 32-bit architecture of the processor is available.

Protection—A mechanism which can be used to protect the operating system and applications from programming errors in applications. Protection can be used to define the address spaces accessible to a program, the kind of memory references which may be made to those address spaces, and the privilege level required for access. Any violation of these protections generates a general-protection exception. Protection can be applied to segments or pages.

Pseudo-Descriptor—A 48-bit memory operand accessed when a descriptor table base register is loaded or stored.

Pseudozero—One of a set of special values of the extended real format. The set consists of numbers with a zero significand and an exponent that is neither all zeros nor all ones. Pseudozeros are not created by the FPU but are handled correctly when encountered as operands.

Quadword—A 64-bit operand. The CDQ instruction can be used to convert a doubleword to a quadword. A quadword held in the EDX and EAX registers may be the dividend used with a doubleword divisor.

Quiet NaN—A floating-point NaN in which the most significant bit of the fractional part of the significand is one. By convention, these NaN's can undergo certain operations without causing an exception.

Re-entrant—Allowing a program to call itself; recursive. For certain kinds of problems, such as operations performed on hierarchical data structures, procedures which call themselves are simple and efficient solutions. On the i486 processor, procedures may be re-entrant, however tasks are not. A task may not call itself because it has only one task state segment (TSS) for storing the processor state. Procedures store the processor state on the stack, so they may be re-entrant to an arbitrary number of levels.

Real-Address Mode – An execution mode which provides an emulation of the architecture of an 8086 processor; also called "real mode." In this mode the i486 processor appears as a fast 8086 processor. The architectural extensions for protection and multitasking are not available in this mode. Following reset initialization, the i486 processor begins execution in real mode.

Real – Any finite value (negative, positive, or zero) that can be represented by a (possibly infinite) decimal expansion. Reals can be represented as the points of a line marked off like a ruler. The term can also refer to a floating-point number that represents a real value.

Requested Privilege Level (RPL) – The privilege level applied to a segment selector. If the RPL is less privileged than the current privilege level (CPL), access to a segment takes place at the RPL level. This keeps privileged software from being used by an application to interfere with the operating system or other applications. For example, a privileged program which loads memory from disk should not be permitted to overwrite the operating system as a result of a call from an application. With RPL, the attempt to access the memory space of the operating system takes place with the privleges of the application.

Reset – See *Initialization.*

RPL – See *Requested Privilege Level.*

Segment – An independent, protected address space. A program may have as many as 16,383 segments, each of which can be up to 4 gigabytes in size.

Segment Descriptor – A 64-bit data structure in memory used for segmentation. It includes the base address for a segment, its size (limit), its type, and protection information. It is set up by operating system software and accessed by segmentation hardware.

Segment-Override Prefix – An instruction prefix which overrides the default segment selection. There are six segment-override prefixes, one each for the CS, SS, DS, ES, FS, and GS segments.

Segment Selector – A 16-bit number used to specify an address space (segment). Bit position 3 to 15 are used as an index into a descriptor table. Bit position 2 specifies whether the global descriptor table (GDT) or local descriptor table (LDT) is used. Bit positions 0 and 1 are the requested privilege level (RPL), which may lower the priority of access, as an additional protection check.

Segmentation – A form of memory management used to provide multiple independent, protected address spaces. Segmentation aids program debugging by reporting programming errors when they first occur, rather than when their effects become apparent. Segmentation makes programs provided to the end-user more reliable by limiting the damage which can be caused by undetected errors. Segmentation increases the address space available to a program by providing up to 16,383 segments, each of which can be up to 4 gigabytes in size.

Set-Associative—A form of cache organization in which the location of a data block in main memory constrains, but does not completely determine, its location in the cache. Set-associative organization is a compromise between direct-mapped organization, in which data from a given address in main memory has only one possible cache location, and fully-associative organization, in which data from anywhere in main memory can be put anywhere in the cache. An "n-way set-associative" cache allows data from a given address in main memory to be cached in any of n locations. Both the Translation Lookaside Buffer (TLB) and the integral cache of the i486 processor have a four-way set-associative organization.

Short Integer—An integer format supported by the FPU that consists of a 32-bit two's complement quantity. Short integer is not the shortest FPU integer format—the 16-bit word integer is.

Short Real—An older term for the FPU's 32-bit single format.

SIB Byte—A byte following an instruction opcode and modR/M bytes which is used to specify a scale factor, index, and base register.

Sign Extension—Conversion of data to a larger format, where empty bit positions are filled with the value of the sign. This form of conversion preserves the value of signed integers. See *Zero Extension.*

Signaling NaN—A floating-point NaN that causes an invalid-operation exception whenever it enters into a calculation or comparison, even an unordered comparison.

Significand—The part of a floating-point number that consists of the most significant nonzero bits of the number, if the number were written out in an unlimited binary format. The significand is composed of an integer bit and a fraction. The integer bit is implicit in the single format and double format. The significand is considered to have a binary point after the integer bit; the binary point is then moved according to the value of the exponent.

Single Extended—A floating-point format, required by the IEEE Std 754, that provides greater precision than single; it also provides an explicit integer bit in the significand. The FPU's extended format meets the single extended requirement as well as the double extended requirement.

Single Format—A floating-point format supported by the FPU, which consists of a sign, an 8-bit biased exponent, an implicit integer bit, and a 23-bit significand—a total of 32 explicit bits.

Stack Fault—A special case of the invalid-operation exception which is indicated by a one in the SF bit of the status word. This condition usually results from stack underflow or overflow in the FPU.

Stack Frame—The space used on the stack by a procedure. The stack frame includes parameters, return addresses, saved registers, temporary storage, and any other stack space the procedure uses.

Stack Segment—A data segment which is used to hold a stack. A stack segment may be expand-down, which allows the segment to be resized toward lower address. The type of information held in a segment is specified in its segment descriptor.

Status Word—A 16-bit FPU register that can be manually set, but which is usually controlled by side effects to FPU instructions. It contains condition codes, the FPU stack pointer, busy and interrupt bits, and exception flags.

String—A sequence of bytes, word, or doublewords which may start at any byte address in memory. The i486 processor has instructions for efficient operations on strings.

Supervisor Mode—The privilege level applied to operating system pages. Paging only recognizes two privilege levels: supervisor mode and user mode. A program executing from a segment at privilege level 0, 1, 2 is in supervisor mode.

Table—An array of records in memory having equal size.

Tag Word—A 16-bit FPU register that it automatically maintained by the FPU. For each space in the FPU stack, it tells if the space is occupied by a number; if so, it gives information about what kind of number.

Tag Word—A 16-bit FPU register that it automatically maintained by the FPU. For each space in the FPU stack, it tells if the space is occupied by a number; if so, it gives information about what kind of number.

Tag—The part of a cache line which holds the address information used to determine if a memory operation is a hit or a miss on that cache line.

Task Register—A register which holds a segment selector for the current task. The selector references a task state segment (TSS). Like the segment registers, the TR register has a visible part and an invisible part. The visible part holds the segment selector, and the invisible part holds information cached from the segment descriptor for the TSS.

Task State Segment (TSS)—A segment used to store the processor state during a task switch. If a separate I/O address space is used, the TSS holds permission bits which control access to the I/O space. Operating systems may define additional structures which exist in the TSS.

Task Switch—A transfer of execution between tasks; a context switch. Unlike the procedure calls, which save only the contents of the general registers, a task switch saves most of the processor state. For example, the registers used for address translation are reloaded, so that each task can have a different logical-to-physical address mapping.

Task—A program running, or waiting to run, in a multitasking system.

Temporary Real—An older term for the FPU's 80-bit extended format.

Tiny—Of or pertaining to a floating-point number that is so close to zero that its exponent is smaller than smallest exponent that can be represented in the destination format.

TLB – See *Translation Lookaside Buffer.*

Top – The three-bit field of the status word that indicates which FPU register is the current top of stack.

Transcendental – One of a class of functions for which polynomial formulas are always appropriate, never exact for more than isolated values. The FPU supports trigonometric, exponential, and logarithmic functions; all are transcendental.

Translation Lookaside Buffer (TLB) – The on-chip cache for page table entries. In typical systems, about 99% of the references to page table entries can be satisfied by information in the TLB.

Trap – An exception which is reported at the instruction boundary immediately following the instruction which generated the exception.

Trap Gate – A gate descriptor used to invoke an exception handler. A trap gate is different from an interrupt gate only in its effect on the IF flag. Unlike an interrupt gate, which clears the flag (disables interrupts) for the duration of the handler, a trap gate leaves the flag unchanged.

TSS – See *Task State Segment.*

Two's Complement – A method of representing integers. If the uppermost bit is zero, the number is considered positive, with the value given by the rest of the bits. If the uppermost bit is one, the number is negative, with the value obtained by subtracting ($2^{\text{bit count}}$) from all the given bits. For example, the 8-bit number 11111100 is −4, obtained by subtracting 2^8 from 252.

Unbiased Exponent – The true value that tells how far and in which direction to move the binary point of the significand of a floating-point number. For example, if a single-format exponent is 131, we subtract the Bias 127 to obtain the unbiased exponent +4. Thus, the real number being represented is the significand with the binary point shifted 4 bits to the right.

Underflow – An exception condition in which the correct answer is nonzero, but has a magnitude too small to be represented as a normal number in the destination floating-point format. IEEE Std 754 specifies that an attempt be made to represent the number as a denormal. This denormalization may result in a loss of significant bits from the significand. This kind of underflow (also called numeric overflow) is not be confused with stack overflow.

Unmasked – A term that can apply to each of the six FPU exceptions: I, D, Z, O, U, P. An exception is unmasked if a corresponding bit in the FPU control word is set to zero. If an exception is unmasked, the FPU will generate an interrupt whent he exception condition occurs. You can provide an interrupt routine that customizes your exception recovery.

Unnormal—An extended real representation in which the explicit integer bit of the significand is zero and the exponent is nonzero. Unnormal values are not supported by the FPU. This includes several formats that are recognized by the 8087 and 287 coprocessors; they cause the invalid-operation exception when encountered as operands.

Unsupported Format—Any number representation that is not recognized by the FPU. This includes several formats that are recognized by the 8087 and 287 coprocessors; namely: pseudo-NaN, pseudoinfinity, and unnormal.

USE16—An assembly language directive for specifying 16-bit code and data segments.

USE32—An assembly language directive for specifying 32-bit code and data segments.

User Mode—The privilege level applied to application pages. Paging only recognizes two privilege levels: supervisor mode and user mode. A program executing from a segment at privilege level 3 is in user mode.

V86 Mode—See *Virtual-8086 Mode.*

Valid—Allocated. Valid cache lines have been loaded with data and may cause cache hits. Invalid cache lines do not cause cache hits.

Vector—A number used to identify the source of an exception or interrupt. A vector is used to index into the IDT table for a gate descriptor. The gate descriptor is used to call the handler for the exception or interrupt.

Virtual Memory—The memory model for application programs; a simplified organization for memory supported by memory management hardware and operating system software. On the i486 processor, virtual memory is supported by segmentation and paging. Segmentation is a mechanism for providing multiple independent, protected address spaces. Paging is a mechanism for providing access to data structures larger than physical memory by keeping them partly in memory and partly on disk.

Virtual-8086 Mode—An execution mode which provides an emulation of the architecture of an 8086 processor. Unlike real-address mode, virtual-8086 mode is compatible with multitasking; a protected mode operating system may be used to run a mix of protected mode and virtual-8086 mode tasks.

Word—A 16-bit quantity of memory. The i486 processor allows 16-bit words to begin at any byte address, but a performance penalty is taken when a word crosses the boundary between two doublewords in physical memory.

Word Integer—An integer format supported by the i486 processor that consists of a 16-bit two's complement quantity.

Write-Back—A form of caching in which memory writes load only the cache memory. Data propagates to main memory when a write-back operation is invoked.

Write-Through – A form of caching in which memory writes load both the cache memory and main memory.

Zero Divide – An exception condition in which floating-point inputs are finite, but the correct answer, even with an unlimited exponent, has infinite magnitude.

Zero Extension – Conversion of data to a larger format, where empty bit positions are filled with zero. This form of conversion preserves the value of unsigned integers. See *Sign Extension*.

Index

INDEX